U.S. SUBMARINES SINCE 1945

U.S. SUBMARINES SINCE 1945

AN ILLUSTRATED DESIGN HISTORY

By Norman Friedman

Ship Plans by Jim Christley and Norman Friedman

Naval Institute Press
Annapolis, Maryland

© 1994
by the U.S. Naval Institute
Annapolis, Maryland

All photographs are official U.S. Navy

Library of Congress Cataloging in Publication Data
Friedman, Norman, 1946–
    U.S. submarines since 1945 : an illustrated design history/by
  Norman Friedman ; ship plans by Jim Christley and Norman Friedman.
      p. cm.
    Includes bibliographical references and index.
    ISBN 1-55750-260-9 (alk. paper)
    1. Submarine boats—United States—History—20th century.
I. Title. II. Title: United States submarines since 1945.
III. Title: US submarines since 1945.
V858.F75   1994
623.8′257′0973—dc20   93-42132
                                              CIP

Printed in the United States of America on acid-free paper ⊗

9 8 7 6 5 4 3 2

First printing

CONTENTS

TABLES

PREFACE

Intense debate is currently focused on the future of U.S. submarines. This book is intended partly as a contribution to that debate, in the belief that an understanding of the past is necessary to make wise decisions about the future. Clearly, any account of the evolution of the present U.S. submarine force must arouse questions of security. Submarines are valuable because they are stealthy; it is natural to feel that technical revelations must compromise stealth. Although similar considerations apply to many ships and weapons, security seems particularly important in undersea warfare where the margin between survival and disaster is quite narrow. For example, many people believe that, early in World War II (WW II), a reporter's offhand comment about the Japanese setting depth charges too shallow led them to correct their settings and thus kill American submariners.[1]

Security rules are indeed tight, and the reader should not construe this book as a relaxation of the rules. I was able to write the book only because much of the relevant data has leaked out over time. I avoid references to concepts and systems that have not been revealed elsewhere. It is possible to lay out the main lines of development, as well as the essential logic, of the submarine force. Also, it is possible to describe many of the different alternatives to the ships actually built that were discarded along the way. The variety attests to the continuing vigor and creativity of the submarine community.

This book does not represent a change in U.S. Navy security policy. Speeds above 20 kts, diving depths below 400 ft, and nuclear horsepowers are all classified. Many significant figures have appeared in unclassified or declassified publications or in unofficial publications whose content is clearly plausible. I have used those data. I do not reveal figures thus far unpublished, nor have such figures been released in order to be part of this book.[2] Often, I rely on standard published (and therefore unofficial) sources and tend to use figures common to the major handbooks.

One important point emerged as I was writing the book. The Soviets were able to penetrate U.S. security to a remarkable extent. Examples of parallels to U.S. projects include the Nobska automated submarine (Alfa), the turboelectric design concept for *Thresher* (again, Alfa), and the Subroc/BQQ-2 combination (SS-N-15 and Victor-class bow sonar). We were not alone in being penetrated. There is now good evidence, for example, that the Soviets obtained the combat direction system designed in Norway for the *Ula* and German Type 212 submarine classes and retrofitted it into some Victor III–class submarines. Other evidence indicates that many Soviet sonars were copies of British and French types. As we learn more of Soviet submarine developments, this book might provide some insight into how well we kept our undersea warfare secrets through the Cold War.

Other books in this series are based almost exclusively on the internal papers of the Navy Department, generally including designers' notebooks. Given the natural reticence of the submarine community, this book is based in larger part, though by no means entirely, on interviews. Unfortunately, memory is often selective, and feelings, particularly about the late Adm. Hyman G. Rickover, often run high. Generally, I have had no problem tracking down what was actually done: what submarines were ordered, what weapons and propulsion systems they had, how they performed, and what sonars and combat systems were developed. The murkier element is the record of contemporary, as opposed to remembered, concerns and motivations, particularly for the period after 1962.

Among those who helped me were C. H. Allen, A. J. Baciocco, Jr., A. D. Baker III, E. L. (Ned) Beach, K. M. Carr, J. L. Christley, Dan Curran, Charles E. Haberlein, Jack Fagan, Sue Fili, Harry Jackson, Robert Y. Kaufman, Don Kern, R. B. Laning, Malcolm Mackinnon, Will O'Neill, Robin Pirie, Don Ulmer, Bruce Vandermark, Mark Wertheimer, and C. C. Wright. I am much indebted, as always, to the staff of the Naval Historical Center, particularly its Operational Archives.

Although all of their contributions are greatly appreciated, I alone am responsible for the content of this book. I hope that I present an accurate picture and properly serve those kind enough to help me. I could not have written this book without the loving support and encouragement of my wife, Rhea.

ABBREVIATIONS

AAW	antiair warfare
ABM	antiballistic missile
AC	alternating current
ACM	advanced cruise missile
ACNO	Assistant Chief of Naval Operations
ACSAS	advanced conformal array sonar system
A/D	analog-to-digital
ADC	acoustic device, countermeasure
ADCAP	advanced capability (version of a Mk 48 torpedo)
Adm.	Admiral
ADO	advanced development objective
ADSCS	Autonetics aided display submarine control system
AEC	Atomic Energy Commission
AFSR	advanced fleet submarine reactor
AIAA	American Institute of Aeronautics and Astronautics
AIGS	acoustic intelligence gathering systems
AIP	air-independent propulsion
AMC	automatic maneuvering control
APHNAS	advanced performance high-speed nuclear attack submarine
ARDC	Air Research and Development Command
A/S	antisubmarine
ASORG	ASW Operational Research Group
ASUW	antisurface warfare
ASW	antisubmarine warfare
ATF	automatic target follower
AUTOTAB	automatic trim and ballast
BDI	bearing deviation indication
BHP	brake horsepower
BMC	Ballistic Missile Committee
BRASS	bottom-reflection active sonar system
BSAWS	basic submarine acoustic warfare system
BT	bathythermograph
BTR	bearing-time recorder
BuAer	Bureau of Aeronautics (Navy)
BuEng	Bureau of Engineering
BuOrd	Bureau of Ordinance
BuShips	Bureau of Ships

Capt.	Captain
CCS	combat control system
CEP	circular error (probable)
CF	concept formulation
CF/CD	concept formulation/concept definition
CIA	Central Intelligence Agency
CIC	combat information center
CinCLant	Commander in Chief, Atlantic
CinCPac	Commander in Chief, Pacific
CIP	class improvement plan
CLAMS	countermeasure launcher acoustic module system
CM	countermeasure (usually acoustic)
CNO	Chief of Naval Operations
CO	commanding officer
CO_2	carbon dioxide
COEA	cost and operational effectiveness analysis
Comdr.	Commander
Cominch	Commander-in-Chief, U.S. Fleet (also Office of)
ComSubPac	Commander, Submarines, Pacific (World War II)
CONALOG	contact analog
CONFORM	concept formulation
C&R	Bureau of Construction and Repair
CRT	cathode-ray tube
CUW	Committee on Undersea Warfare (National Academy of Sciences)
CW	continuous wave
dB	decibel
DC	direct current
DCDI	depth charge direction indicator
DCNO	Deputy Chief of Naval Operations
DCP	decision coordinating paper
DCRE	depth charge range estimator
DDR&E	Director of Defense Research and Engineering
DDS	dry deck shelter
DE	destroyer escort
D/E	depression/elevation
DEER	directional explosive echo-ranging

DEMON	demodulated noise
DesLant	Atlantic Fleet Destroyer Command
DEXTOR	deep external torpedo
DIFAR	directional Lofar
DIMUS	digital multi-beam steering
DoD	Department of Defense
DPM	draft presidential memorandum
DRT	dead reckoning tracer
DSRV	deep-submergence rescue vehicle
DTIC	Defense Technical Information Center
EDM	engineering development model
EDO	engineering duty officer
EER	explosive echo-ranging
EHP	effective horsepower
EKB	even keel ballast maneuvering
EKPM	even keel planes maneuvering
ELF	extremely low frequency
ESGN	electrically suspended gyro navigator
ESM	electronic support measures
EXPO	expanded Poseidon
F/A	fleet attack
FCS	fire-control system
FLIR	forward-looking infrared (sensor)
FLIT	frequency-line integration tracking
FM	frequency modulated
FRAM	fleet rehabilitation and modernization
FRISVO	fast-reaction submarine control
ft	foot/feet
FY	fiscal year
gal	gallon(s)
GE	General Electric
geosit	geographical situation
GHG	Gruppen Horch Geraeten (German listening array)
GM	General Motors
GOR	general operational requirement
GPVC	general-purpose underwater voice communications
HF	high frequency
HP	horsepower
HPR	high-powered reactor
hr	hour(s)
HSNAS	high-speed nuclear attack submarine
HTS	high-tensile steel
Hz	Hertz (one cycle per second)
IACS	integrated acoustic communications system
ICBM	intercontinental ballistic missile
ICDC	improved control-display console
IFF	identification friend or foe

in	inch(es)
IR	intermediate range
IRBM	intermediate-range ballistic missile
JATO	jet-assisted takeoff
JCAE	Joint Committee on Atomic Energy
JCS	Joint Chiefs of Staff
JSTPS	Joint Strategic Target Planning System
kHz	kiloHertz (one thousand cycles per second)
kt	knot(s)
kT	kiloton (of TNT equivalent)
kw	kilowatt(s)
kwh	kilowatt-hour(s)
kyd	kiloyard(s) (one thousand yards)
lb	pound(s)
LBP	length between perpendiculars
LF	low frequency
LFS	amphibious fire support ship
LOA	length overall
LP	low pressure
LRO	long-range objective
LS	light ship
LSD	landing ship dock
LSR	large ship reactor
LSST	landing submarine tank
LSV	large-scale vehicle
Lt.	Lieutenant
Lt. Comdr.	Lieutenant Commander
m	meter(s)
MATE	manual adaptive TMA (target motion analyses) evaluation
MF	medium frequency
mi	mile(s)
microsec	microsecond(s)
min	minute(s)
MIRV	maneuvering independently—targetable reentry vehicle
MIT	Massachusetts Institute of Technology
Mk	mark (number-ordnance designation)
mm	millimeter(s)
MMD	mobile multifunction decoy
mo	month(s)
MOSS	mobile submarine simulator
MRO	medium-range objective
MS	mild steel
MT	megaton
NAS	National Academy of Sciences
NATO	North Atlantic Treaty Organization
NAVSEA	Naval Sea Systems Command

NCR	natural circulation reactor
NECPA	national emergency command post afloat
NELC	Naval Electronic Laboratory Center
nm	nautical mile(s) (2 kiloyards equal about 1 nautical mile)
NOL	Naval Ordnance Laboratory
NOSC	Naval Ocean Systems Center (formerly NELC)
NOTS	Naval Ordnance Test Station (China Lake)
NPN	normal plane maneuvering
NSC	National Security Council
NSIA	National Security Industrial Association
NTDS	naval tactical data system
NUSC	Naval Undersea Systems Center (formerly NUSL)
NUSL	Naval Underwater Sound Laboratory
OASD	Office of the Assistant Secretary of Defense
OASD(SA)	Office of the Assistant Secretary of Defense for System Analysis
OEG	Operational Evaluation Group
ONI	Office of Naval Intelligence
ONR	Office of Naval Research
OpNav	Office of the Chief of Naval Operations
Op-O2	Deputy Chief of Naval Operations
Op-O5	Deputy Chief of Naval Operations for Air
OSD	Office of the Secretary of Defense
OTH-T	over the horizon targeting
PCP	program change proposal
PK	probability of kill
PMS	program manager for (naval) sea systems command
POMCUS	prepositioned army materiel (Europe)
PPI	plan-position indicator
PRESCAN	predictive scanning
psi	pounds per square inch
PTA	proposed technical approach
PUFFS	passive underwater fire control feasibility
RAFOS	inverse version of SOFAR (sound fixing and ranging)
RAP	reliable acoustic path
RAPLOC	rapid localization
R&D	research and development
RDT&E	research and development, test and engineering
RETORC	research torpedo configuration

RPN	revolutions per minute
RV	rescue vehicle
SAC	Strategic Air Command
SADS	submarine active detection system
SAR	submarine advanced reactor
SAWS	submarine acoustic warfare system
SBM	small ballistic missile
SBP	shipbuilding program
SCAD	subsonic cruise armed decoy
SCAM	subsonic cruise armed missile
SCB	Ship Characteristics Board
SCS	sea control ship
SCUD	subsonic cruise unarmed decoy
SDAP	Systems Development Analysis Program
SDO	specific development objective
SDV	swimmer delivery vehicle
SEAL	Sea-Air-Land Team
sec	second(s)
SEER	submarine explosive echo-ranging
SESCO	secure submarine communications
SFR	submarine fleet reactor
SHAB	steerable hull arrray beamformer
SHP	shaft horsepower
SINS	ships inertial navigation system
SIOP	single integrated operational plan
SIR	submarine intermediate reactor
SISS	submarine improved sonar system
SITTAR	submarine integrated tactical towed array
SLAM	supersonic low-altitude missile
SMTD	submarine torpedo defense
SOFAR	sound fixing and ranging
SOR	Specific Operational Requirement
SORG	Submarine Operational Research Group
SOSUS	sound surveillance system
SOW	standoff weapon
SPO	Special Projects Office
SPR	small power reactor
SPUME	short pulse message
SQUIRE	submarine quickened response
SRS	submarine reactor, small
SS	submarine
SSBN	ballistic missile submarine (nuclear)
SSG	cruise missile submarine
SSK	ASW (antisubmarine warfare) submarine
SSN	nuclear attack submarine
SSR	submarine radar picket
STAM	submarine tactical missile
STASS	submarine tactical array sonar system
STR	submarine thermal reactor
SUBACS	submarine advanced combat system
SUBAJAD	submarine acoustic jamming and deception

SubDevGru	Submarine Development Group
SubDiv	Submarine Division
SUBIC	submarine integrated control
SubLant	Submarine Commander Atlantic
SubPAC	Submarine Commander Pacific
TACAN	tactical air navigation
TARP	towed array range processor
TBM	tactical ballistic missile
TDC	torpedo data computer
TEDS	turboelectric drive submarine
TFCS	torpedo fire control system
TMA	target motion analyses
TROUNCE	tactical radar omnidirectional underwater navigational control equipment

UDT	undersea long-range missile system
UUV	unmanned underwater vehicle
V	speed (used in tables)
VCNO	Vice Chief of Naval Operations
VLF	very low frequency
VLS	vertical launching system
WAA	wide aperture array
WCC	weapon control console
wk	week(s)
WSEG	Weapon System Evaluation Group
WW I	World War I
WW II	World War II
yd	yard(s)
yr	year(s)

U.S. SUBMARINES SINCE 1945

1

Introduction

AT THE END of World War II, the submarine force of the United States was obsolete—not only technically but strategically. It had been designed for a world that ceased to exist with the defeat of the seaborne Japanese Empire. Almost half a century later, the new world for which later submarines were designed also seems to have ended with the collapse of the land-based (and submarine-rich) Soviet Empire. As this book shows, the U.S. submarine force survived and prospered after 1945 because submarines offered the nation far more than the roles of strategic scouting and attacks on shipping, for which they had been designed. Although it took time, their potential was eventually realized.

After 1945, as now, submarines offered the ability to operate covertly off another country's coast. That eventually translated into two new vital missions, forward-based anti-submarine warfare and strategic deterrence. Strategic deterrence was so important that it raised the submarine from its former subsidiary role to the center of national power. Each new mission could be traced back to a minor one of the past. It seems likely that the central post–Cold War missions will echo the secondary submarine missions of the Cold War described in chapter 5.

The missions we now identify with the Cold War were not obviously the most important in 1945–46. The submariners of that day knew that Russia was not Japan and that they would have to change, but they were not quite sure how to proceed. For a time, the most important submarine mission was to simulate the potential of enemy submarines, so that anti-submarine technology could be developed to cope with them. It justified submarine modernization and new construction because existing submarines could not match the performance of the German submarines that the Soviets had just captured and surely would copy.

Many new missions were suggested and tried before the key missions were found about a decade after the end of the war. So long afterward, it is easy to forget the earlier uncertainty, much like what we are now experiencing. Examination of the history of U.S. submarines before 1945 shows similar trauma at the end of World War I, when the U.S. focus shifted from the Atlantic to the Pacific.

Then, as after WW II, the submarine had to be, in effect, reinvented. The first stage of reinvention is denial: everyone wants to continue as before, as though the wrench had not occurred. Couched in the language of the past, arguments often fail because they seem so artificial. Then comes confusion: many possible missions are proposed. Much of what is suggested later seems silly or self-serving. It is not; it is an honest attempt to reach a viable policy. Finally, the new primary missions are recognized. Their seeds can always be found in the first stage, simply because the history of the submarine force encompasses so many different missions.

One vital lesson of the past seems to be that large submarines offer a vital flexibility in this process. The United States was extremely fortunate in that the submarines retained after WW II were so large. Their size was mainly due to the prewar requirement to operate across the Pacific without relying on foreign bases (the prewar United States eschewed alliances). During the Cold War, it was sometimes argued that submarines could be made much smaller, hence cheaper, by relying on forward bases. With the end of the Cold War comes not only the end of the potential bases but also of the particular roles, primarily forward anti-submarine warfare (ASW), for which those bases would have been appropriate.

It is also most unlikely that the roles developed during the Cold War will vanish. Nuclear deterrence will continue to be important and perhaps even more important as nuclear weapons proliferate. Similarly, it would be foolish to abandon the submarines' ASW role, given the number of submarines in the Third World and the possibility that Russian design experience, or perhaps even hulls (maybe

Submarines offer the nation an unequalled combination of stealth and mobility. Here, the ballistic missile submarine *Sam Houston* returns to the Holy Loch in Scotland on 9 July 1963, after the first Polaris patrol in the Mediterranean. Merely by operating in the Mediterranean, U.S. missile submarines could enormously complicate any Soviet attempts to defend against U.S. missile attack, and thus much improve the chances of other U.S. weapons, which had to come from the north. U.S. submarines are no longer based at the Holy Loch. The big sonar dome forward conceals an upward-looking under-ice sonar (carried by many SSBNs to detect polynyas), through which the submarine might surface to fire her missiles. It was superseded by the mast-mounted Top Hat (BQR-19).

with Russians to operate them), will migrate there. Nor can a prudent American be sure that the collapsing remains of the Soviet Empire will not turn to anti-American policy and a revived Cold War. History has hardly ended. After all, we now know that the most recent Soviet submarines were quite sophisticated and those planned for production were easily equal to those now in U.S. service.

That submarine roles will change again in the long history of these craft is hardly cause for a cry of doom. The U.S. submarine force will celebrate, not mourn, its centennial in the year 2000.

New roles have not always entailed new submarine construction. After 1945, both the submarine fleet and the surface fleet had to adapt to a radically new environment, as well as new technology, but with very different consequences. Each fleet had large inventories of new hulls left over from WW II, and Congress was reluctant to buy new ones. Surface ships could be adapted; massive new construction was not needed until they wore out in the 1960s. Then, large numbers of new surface combatants, such as the *Spruances*, had to be built over short periods. They will encounter their own block obsolescence later on.

Submarines were different. Although the fleet boats could be modernized, existing hulls could not be adapted to nuclear power. Nuclear submarines were too expensive to build in a block (to replace WW II submarines as they wore out). Instead, beginning in the late 1950s, steady production was maintained over a period of many years.

The production rate fell gradually, largely because submarines, like other warships, became far more expensive. The size of the force was maintained by making the submarines last longer. Now, with the end of the Cold War, the force is being reduced. Steady annual submarine production may therefore cease, with the resulting dissolution of much of the submarine industrial base. The cost of re-creating this base may preclude new production start-up. Quite aside from money, the skills involved in designing and building submarines could be extremely difficult to resurrect.

The situation is not the same as producing surface ships. Even though particular types of surface warships are built in blocks, some sort of surface warship is always under construction. Design and production skills are not allowed to lapse. Submarine design and production differ enough from surface ships that surface ship expertise does not generally translate into submarine expertise.

A steady rate of production ensures that designers will gain experience over their careers and that succeeding designs will incorporate experience at sea. The advantages of steady production were so obvious that in the 1980s the U.S. surface warship community decided to follow the submarine model. It justified its new construction program on the ground that existing ships could not be modified to incorporate an essential and revolutionary new technology, the Aegis missile control system.

Submarine design is radically different from its surface counterpart, largely because a submarine's weight is equal

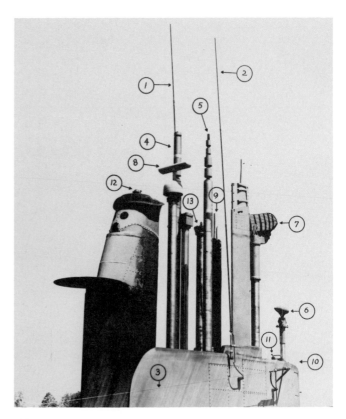

Tang, the first submarine designed post–WW II, shows her ferrite-core loop antenna, At-274/BRR (6). The great distinguishing feature of post–WW II submarines was their ability to operate submerged almost continuously. They had to be able to receive radio messages while submerged. Before WW II, it was discovered that wire loops (intended for radio direction finding) could receive VLF signals at periscope depth. Postwar, NRL developed the much smaller ferrite-core loop, which could be wrapped in a small streamlined body. It was first tested in 1948. Unlike the old air-core loop, it was omnidirectional (two loops were wrapped at right angles). Other antennas visible in the photo are: (1) retractable MF/HF whip (NT 66053), (2) fixed MF/HF whip (NT 66053), (3) emergency wire antenna, (4) VHF/IFF antenna (AS-524/BPX), (5) AEW (airborne early warning) link and beacon and UHF antenna (AS-493/U), (7) SV-3 radar, (8) BPS-1 air search radar, (9) ST-1 range-only radar on the periscope, (10) SPR-1 ESM antenna, (11) AS-371/S antenna, (12) AS-373/BLR ESM antenna, and (13) position of a planned ECM direction-finding antenna. The AEW link allowed the submarine to work with a patrol airplane equipped with an AEW radar (APS-20), which was often used to detect periscopes and snorkels.

to her displacement (i.e., to her volume). A surface ship designer compensates for minor changes in equipment weight or volume by adding more deck space or by changing displacement (allowing for a bit more or less draft). In a submarine, everything must fit within the envelope of the pressure hull. That is why a submarine is inherently very cramped; it has about one third of the internal volume of a surface ship of the same tonnage.

Modern surface ship design begins with computer runs to estimate the displacement required to support given sets of weapons and other parts. The computer can work in gross terms because it is relatively easy to estimate the effect on overall ship size of changing, say, the number of missiles on board. A typical computer run may provide hundreds of rough design alternatives from which policy makers can choose.

A submarine is another proposition. A modern U.S. submarine design begins with a general arrangement drawing that, in effect, wraps a hull around the desired components, even down to individual bunks. Hull volume (displacement) is then calculated, as well as component weights, including the weight of pressure hull structure. This first design stage is already far more detailed than relatively advanced stages of a surface ship design. Gross submarine size can be estimated from parametric curves reflecting past practice, but this is not considered acceptable. A parametric approach makes it impossible to answer the most common design question, which is to estimate the effect of minor alternatives to a given design (e.g., six torpedo tubes rather than four or slightly larger or smaller living spaces). Probably, the parametric approach also implicitly locks in earlier design practice in a way which cannot be easily extracted.

The arrangement sketch must reflect a variety of technical factors. For example, the arrangement of the bow depends in large part on the size of the sonar sphere filling it. If the submarine has the usual angled torpedo tubes, sufficient length must be provided for the torpedo's run

The step beyond the loop on a mast was a towed buoy, which might contain both a loop and a surface-piercing whip. This type of buoy (12) is shown on board *Hardhead,* at Philadelphia, 29 May 1961. Modern submarines use trailing-wire antennas, which can include surface-piercing elements for UHF reception. Floating very close to the surface, such wires also can be used for short-range submarine-to-submarine communication.

out of the shutters. The torpedo room must be long enough to allow for a transfer tray to swing out to the angle of the tube. Much of the length abaft the torpedo room will be filled with machinery, the size and design of which is already more or less fixed.

Once the arrangement is complete, weight and volume can be compared. They are unlikely to match. If the submarine is too light, lead must be added to make up the difference. This situation is common in ballistic missile submarines, in which a relatively light payload must be spread over a considerable space. For example, missile tubes cannot be allowed to penetrate the pressure hull too close together. Attack submarines tend to be slightly light (i.e., they require some lead). In each case, the lead represents the gross margin available for further growth, as equipment weight displaces it. The catch, however, is that weight distribution must be even fore and aft; trim lead maintains the distribution. Thus, a given additional weight, far less than the total amount of lead in the design, could be unacceptable because of its effect on trim. On the other hand, adding a bit of weight in the right place might actually solve a trim problem. An example is the *Los Angeles* class. As built, it had substantial trim lead forward to balance a heavy power plant aft. It was relatively easy to install vertical launch tubes for cruise missiles forward. Adding a similar weight aft would have required much more trim lead forward, possibly approaching the submarine's total weight margin.

If the submarine is heavy, she may have to be enlarged to gain buoyancy. That is most common in very deep-diving craft, which have extremely heavy pressure hulls.

Performance can be estimated at this stage. For the hull designer, machinery is a given. The design of a nuclear power plant is so complicated that it cannot be easily changed (e.g., to add a few horsepower for slightly higher speed). Nor can its arrangement or volume or center of gravity be easily altered. The situation with diesels was not too much better because the companies providing engines could not readily change them.

After the basic arrangement of the submarine has been developed, the detailed design is done by a building yard, which is often said to have ''designed'' the submarine. For example, the design contract for *Thresher* went to Portsmouth Naval Shipyard; the *Los Angeles* contract went to Newport News. Generally, machinery spaces are separately designed by a building yard, so Code 1500 or SEA 08 often referred to a yard that had ''designed'' the submarine, meaning only its power plant and the plant's shipboard installation. In some cases, the design yard makes considerable changes, although the end result is always a recognizable version of the original sketch design.

Then, exactly who designs a submarine? The naval architect is responsible for the arrangement sketch, the first recognizable approach to the design. The marine engineer develops the power plant. At least in the case of nuclear power, this takes far longer than the hull. In a few cases, a new sonar or weapons system so dominates the design that the sonar developer deserves almost equal billing.

Each has a different outlook. A naval architect generally tries to achieve high performance through hull form and propeller design, as in *Albacore*. Historically, marine engineers have distrusted this approach; they prefer to add horsepower. U.S. wartime experience seemed to prove their point—new destroyers failed to meet their design speeds. Ever since, designers have rated their ships a knot or two below the estimated full speed. Sonar developers are most interested in flow conditions and self-noise.

Until 1940, engineers and naval architects inhabited separate organizations—Bureau of Engineering (BuEng) and Bureau of Construction and Repair (C&R), respectively. They then merged into a single Bureau of Ships (BuShips). Many engineers saw the merger as the submergence of their bureau in punishment for weight problems in new destroyers powered by the bureau's new high-pressure steam machinery. Some, like the last bureau chief, Adm. H. G. Bowen, argued that the real culprit, the Bureau of Ordnance (BuOrd), had escaped punishment because it had so many highly placed friends. BuOrd's turn came in 1966, when it merged with BuShips in a new Naval Sea Systems Command (NAVSEA). Even then it was largely independent of the two ship design organizations. A peculiarity of naval organization was that sonar (and radar) design came under BuShips, whereas weapons and fire control came under BuOrd.

Admiral Rickover was a survivor of BuEng. He shared the outlook of his predecessors. For example, in the CONFORM (concept formulation) versus *Los Angeles* fight in 1968 (see chapter 10), Rickover clearly doubted that the naval architects' solution would work as promised. His fights with the naval architects recall earlier battles between chief engineers and chief constructors (i.e., C&R chiefs). Modern readers are struck by the engineers' (and Admiral Rickover's) standard phrase for having designed a ship's machinery: "I designed that ship."

That phrase was shorthand, not arrogance. It was little appreciated before the advent of nuclear power plants, simply because ship power plants generally did not have individual designations or well-known histories apart from the ships they powered. To anyone outside the ship design community, design was equated with hull form and arrangement. In fact, power plants were separate BuEng projects, and the naval architect had to choose from BuEng's menu. The individual designations accorded nuclear power plants emphasize their separate histories.

When BuShips was formed, BuEng survivors feared that their new masters, initially naval architects, would not be willing to expend sufficient effort to ensure that new power plants were safe and reliable. Admiral Rickover apparently resolved that nuclear power would be different; in effect, a separate nuclear version of BuEng would be hived off from BuShips. He argued that many post-BuEng machinery developments, such as the 1,200-lb steam plant, lightweight gears, and "pancake" diesels, had gone disastrously wrong just because BuShips had relegated machinery design to a secondary position.

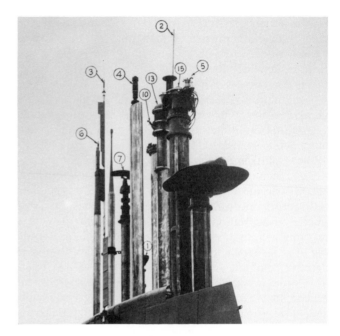

Hardhead, a Guppy, shows her sail antennas in this 29 May 1961 photo. Many of the antennas were used for ESM: (1) to warn of an approaching hostile airplane (so that the submarine could crash dive), and (2) to assist in her electronic reconnaissance role, a most important application of her inherent stealth. Thus, the ECM whip (6, AT-822/BLR) atop the search periscope is surely for radar warning, but there is a separate ECM (actually ESM) mast (topped by 13, the AS-944/BLR array of the WLR-1 ELINT system). The short dipole (10, AS-371/S) on the mast is part of a monopulse direction-finder. The mast also carries AT-693/BLR (11). Antenna 3 is a communications whip, with special fairings to reduce the wake it can make, and mast 4 carries IFF and UHF antennas. The fat mast abaft the ECM mast (topped by antennas 5 [AT-497/URC] and 15) is the snorkel induction, with the unmarked snorkel exhaust abaft it, fitting down atop the sail when it is retracted. The loop (1) barely shows. The search periscope also carries an ST range-only radar (9) with a UHF (submarine-to-air) antenna (AT-849/ARR, item 8) above it; neither shows clearly here. Items 2 and 7 are, respectively, AT-818/BRC (a radio whip antenna) and the SS-2 search radar antenna. The buoy antenna (12), carried on deck well abaft the sail, is not visible.

Rickover earned a master's degree in electrical engineering at Columbia University and became an engineering duty officer (EDO). He spent most of WW II in the BuEng (later BuShips) electrical section. He had grown up in a bureau that was extremely proud of developing turboelectric power for battleships and diesel-electric drive for submarines. Rickover found that civilian contractors could not always meet his wartime requirements quickly enough and he needed to maintain considerable design expertise within the electrical section of the bureau. He also argued that without his own designers he could not hope to monitor outside design and production practices.

Because Rickover was responsible for the national allocation of scarce electrical conductors, such as copper, perhaps he became aware of the wartime nuclear program through its heavy use of such conductors (e.g., for electromagnetic separation of uranium isotopes). He was also deeply involved in wartime submarine silencing, partly through developing direct-drive motors.

As it happened, quirks in the atomic energy law made it quite practical for Rickover to form a separate agency, initially designated Code 1500 (within BuShips) and then SEA 08 (within the Naval Sea Systems Command), that was nominally within but effectively outside BuShips and its successor. When he achieved flag rank, Rickover became the equivalent of a full bureau chief.

At this remove, Rickover's thinking cannot be precisely reconstructed. He must have learned quite early just how complex a nuclear plant could be and how difficult it would be to develop one suited to submarines. Given the high degree of classification then accorded anything nuclear, much of the preliminary work had to be done within BuShips. Rickover's leadership skills and his ability to obtain very high priority for his project—and thus to call on some of the navy's best engineering officers—made the original nuclear reactor project a success. Moreover, Rickover could point to failures in three important cases in which his organization, with its conservative engineering approach, had not been involved: the initial U.S. commercial reactor at Shippingport, Pennsylvania; the nuclear-powered merchant ship *Savannah;* and the nuclear-powered airplane. Rickover's view was that typical commercial engineering practice was far too slipshod in a field as unforgiving as nuclear power. Further, a failure that would merely shut down a commercial power reactor might well doom a submarine operating far below the surface of the sea. The demand for excellence at any cost was somewhat overstated, of course, but the navy's fiscal constraints were far less pressing than those common in the commercial world. Rickover was also well aware that the best conceivable is the deadly enemy of what is quite good enough.

Rickover had another important trait. Like other naval officers of his time, he believed that it was far better to make a quick, firm decision than to dither, even if dithering ultimately produced a better choice. He collided directly with an evolving bureaucratic culture that much preferred studies to action. This new culture also favored elaborate management schemes. Rickover had an engineer's instinctive hatred for both protracted studies and schemes. Probably his most important—and most courageous—decision was made in 1948: enough reactor design studies had been made; it was time to design and build real reactors. Rickover was not pigheaded. He ordered two competing types of reactor and changed his order of preference while they were being tested. He also knew that his resources were limited. Once he had opted for pressurized water, he quickly abandoned the alternative of liquid metal. Experience suggests that he made the right choice; the alternatives tried by others have been found wanting.

The record shows that it was far from easy for Rickover to produce a functioning plant in time to take *Nautilus* to sea in 1955, despite his willingness to make an early decision. In 1945, ironically, the navy officially estimated that it would take about a decade to build the first nuclear submarine (by 1948, no one was that sanguine). Perhaps more importantly, the first operational reactor was technically mature enough to be safe and quite reliable. This was a surprise. Dr. Edward Teller, a prominent physicist, had suggested that nuclear submarines were so dangerous that they should be moored at offshore artificial islands. Those who have followed the sad history of the Soviet nuclear submarine force can see the wisdom of this advice. Rickover felt that exceptionally careful training of the nuclear operators would prevent any problems. As captain, he personally guaranteed the safety of the reactors as long as he could select and train the operators and commanding officers. Presumably, he felt that an untrained commanding officer might order his engineer to carry out unsafe practices because he would not appreciate the consequences.

Rickover's demand had a significant unintended consequence. Because command depended on prowess in nuclear plant operation, tactical prowess often seemed less important. A former submariner suggested that progress toward a U.S. digital integrated submarine combat system, an important development, was much slower than necessary because there was no clear path to submarine command or seniority through a tour in ordnance. Moreover, because he was able to veto candidates for command, Rickover could enforce some of his views not directly related to power plants, such as his distrust of computers.

Rickover's position was not altogether anomalous. Before the creation of the position of Deputy Chief of Naval Operations for Air (Op-05) in 1943, the Bureau of Aeronautics had selected both materiel and air personnel. The old BuEng had been responsible for machinery operators, as BuOrd had been for gunners (who had the favored path to command before WW II). Surely, Rickover's bureau of nuclear engineering deserved much the same power over its very dangerous products. His claims were viable only because Rickover had built up a powerful outside political following. His successors inherited Rickover's separate bureau but not its political power base.

Like his predecessors in BuEng, Rickover considered that a quantum leap in propulsion could be as important tactically as a new sonar, torpedo, or airplane. He naturally sought to emphasize three ship traits within a design: speed, endurance, and reliability. The other bureaus had their own contributions; BuOrd, for example, favored sensors and firepower. This natural rivalry was always deliberately encouraged on the theory that it would bring out the best in each ship. How to achieve the best possible compromise among competing bureaus has been one of the great dilemmas of 20th-century U.S. naval administration.

In 1945, the Navy had begun a long-term attempt to achieve such a compromise. The General Board was being replaced by the Ship Characteristics Board (SCB), a new organization within the Office of the Chief of Naval Operations (OpNav). The General Board, consisting of senior officers independent of both the technical bureaus and

OpNav, had been created to force the bureaus to produce designs in accord with naval needs, particularly those revealed by war planning. The SCB was quite different. Its members represented the bureaus, and it reached decisions by vote. On the other hand, its location within OpNav was supposed to ensure that the SCB's ideas reflected operational experience. Both the SCB and the General Board produced design requirements, called characteristics, for new ships. SCB characteristics were given numbers, sometimes called shipbuilding program (SBP) numbers. For example, the *Nautilus* design was SCB 64. The SCB also issued design policy papers, such as one reflecting its decision to increase operating depth in 1955.

The SCB was concerned with relatively short-term policy. For about 15 years after WW II, however, the navy's real problem was how to adjust to a radically different world situation. The General Board tried to turn into a long-range planning agency, but it was abolished in 1951. By that time, interest had focused on the Korean War and the distinct possibility that it might lead to World War III. In 1954, a Standing Committee on the Long-Term Shipbuilding Program, with a direct connection to the SCB, was appointed. The committee needed broader guidance; in 1955, Chief of Naval Operations (CNO) Adm. Robert Carney created a new Long Range Objectives (LRO) group (Op-93G), which tried to look far enough ahead (10 to 15 years) in order to affect ship and submarine choices. The LRO lasted until 1970, but it seems to have achieved its greatest influence under Adm. Arleigh Burke, who published a sanitized version of its study, "The Navy of the 1965–75 Era." The LRO probably was responsible for the decision to merge the ASW and attack submarine development lines that produced *Thresher*.

The importance of long-range planning within the navy declined with the rise of the central Office of the Secretary of Defense (OSD) under Secretary Robert S. McNamara. Although the Department of Defense (DOD) had been established in 1947, during most of its pre-McNamara life it was concerned mainly with allocating gross resources among the services, who spent their money largely as they saw fit. McNamara rejected any such view on the ground that many missions were spread among the services and it was better to examine budgetary choices in far greater detail. Within OSD, the director of defense research and engineering (DDR&E) was responsible for approving new programs. OSD and DDR&E were key to the hotly debated 1968 choice to build the *Los Angeles*-class submarine. They also were much involved in the strategic submarine program, particularly in the Poseidon and Trident decisions.

Following *Los Angeles*, submarine characteristics generally were developed by ad hoc groups organized either by the CNO or by the secretary of defense. A special Group Tango produced the design requirements for the current *Seawolf*. The group was chaired by Adm. Nils Thunman, who was then Op-02, (deputy chief of naval operations [DCNO] for undersea warfare), and included Adm. Kinnaird McKee (SEA 08), Admiral Rickover's successor.

Submarines were so special that the submarine community itself much influenced their characteristics, largely through the OpNav submarine branch (OP-313) established within the OpNav ASW Division (Op-31). In 1959, Adm. Lawson P. Ramage, a submariner, became director of Op-31, which he transformed into the Anti-Submarine/Submarine Division effective 1 January 1960. Op-31 became the Submarine Warfare Branch in 1964 and was elevated to DCNO (vice admiral) status as Op-02 in 1972. The creation of Op-02 removed submarines from the aegis of the SCB, which now came under the DCNO for surface ships, Op-03. A reorganization ordered in 1992 moved sponsorship of the submarine community from Op-02 (now redesignated N87) to Submarine Commander Atlantic (SubLant), although N87 is probably still responsible for characteristics. Since 1955, the strategic submarines have had their own Special Projects Office (SPO) cutting across the bureau structure.

A Submarine Officers Conference was established in 1926 specifically to provide the Washington bureaucracy with submariners' views. The conference was also used to transmit information to the officer community. It was sufficiently successful for OpNav to establish parallel ASW and destroyer conferences in 1946. Their resolutions helped shape early postwar policy, including that relating to ASW submarines.

Two nongovernmental bodies that have influenced submarine design are the National Academy of Sciences (NAS) and the National Security Industrial Association (NSIA). The NAS was founded during the Civil War to provide the government, particularly the military, with the fruits of academic research. Its Committee on Undersea Warfare (CUW) may have been responsible for the construction of *Albacore*. Admiral Burke, much impressed by the performance of *Nautilus*, asked the CUW in 1955 to study the impact of nuclear power on ASW. After a study at Nobska, Massachusetts, that summer, CUW recommended several new programs. It is not clear to what extent Nobska initiated programs and to what extent it alerted the navy to approaches not yet taken. NSIA was an outgrowth of the old Ordnance Association of major manufacturers. Its 1964 study of ASW seems to have begun the submarine towed array program.

Submarine stealth can serve many purposes. *Grayback* began life as an attack submarine, but she was completed as a strategic cruise missile carrier. Later (as shown here in 1969), she transported SEAL teams in her former missile hangar. Her attack submarine sail proved too short (it was about the same height as her missile hangar) and had to be raised considerably, as seen above.

2

The Postwar Attack Submarine

THE SNORKEL WAS the prerequisite for the new post–WW II submarine. No longer was there need to surface to run at speed for a protracted period or to charge batteries for underwater operation.[1] The Germans proved that the snorkel could change undersea warfare, but their design serviced 4-cycle diesels and was not directly adaptable to U.S. practice. The U.S. 2-cycle engine needed much more air to scavenge each cylinder (i.e., to blow out exhaust). It also required a steadier air supply because each cylinder drew in fresh air twice as often; the supply was interrupted when a wave passed over the snorkel intake. U.S. submarines also presented the special problem of drawing their air deeper into the water, simply because of their sheer size. Moreover, the only successful German snorkel was a tube, hinged to the submarine deck, that was raised for use. Hence, it was unsuitable for streamlined submarine. (A German attempt to design a telescoping snorkel for the fast Type XXI had failed.)

These problems were solved by the David Taylor Model Basin and Portsmouth Navy Yard. A prototype snorkel was installed in the otherwise unconverted *Irex*. It consisted of two parallel 15-in tubes joined by a yoke, the forward one carrying air. The first Guppy snorkels could supply air to either of the two forward engines. BuShips soon extended the snorkel to serve any two of the four engines.

There was one major surprise: a snorkeling submarine was considerably louder than a surfaced submarine because all, rather than part, of her engine noise went into the water around her. That was quite aside from the usual propeller noises that resulted mainly from cavitation. Existing homing torpedoes, designed to listen for surface ship noise, were thus quite suitable for attacks on snorkeling submarines. In neither case did the torpedo have to steer in depth. Similarly, a passive sonar capable of detecting and tracking a surface ship could easily deal with either a surfaced or a snorkeling submarine. These discoveries were the basis of early postwar work on submarine-based ASW. U.S. submarines could lurk off Soviet bases

and catch their targets on the way out. The Soviet submarines would have to run on diesels (surfaced or submerged), simply to make good time to their target areas.

A submerged submarine running on batteries was a different proposition. She was inherently far quieter. Once she reached her patrol area, a submarine could run on batteries most of the time and snorkel only intermittently. To home on such a target, a torpedo had to ping actively. Pinging was ineffective near the surface (i.e., against a snorkeler) because the pings reflected off the surface.

In 1945, U.S. submariners still thought mainly in terms of attacking surface ships, but even then German-style fully submerged operation demanded a new emphasis on sonar. Wartime U.S. submarines often patrolled on the surface and dived only when relatively close to a target. The initial search was conducted by lookouts or through radar or electronic surveillance. During the approach and attack, the submarine might well track the target by sonar. Her fire control device, the torpedo data computer (TDC), projected ahead the target's position in order to aim torpedoes. That estimate was often checked by a single ranging ping and the TDC setting revised to match. However, the TDC was designed to start on the basis of a target course and range estimated by periscope. The range could be determined optically by stadimeter or by a range-only radar on the periscope.

U.S. sonars matched these tactics. They were designed primarily to track targets, not to search wide arcs. Tracking required a relatively narrow sonar beam. For a given array size, the higher the frequency and the narrower the beam. For a given frequency, the larger the array, the higher the gain and thus the better the chance of detecting a relatively weak signal. The simplest sonar was the searchlight, a single transducer producing a single beam, hence the name. The U.S. Navy chose a frequency of about 25–30 kHz, for a range of 3,000–4,000 yd and a typical beam width of 15 degrees. The major wartime advance was automatic target tracking by comparing echoes in two slightly separated beams, referred to as bearing deviation

The *Tang*s were the first U.S. postwar-designed attack submarines. *Trigger* is shown in May 1967, with a somewhat modified sail but without PUFFS. Only *Gudgeon*, *Harder*, and *Wahoo* were refitted with PUFFS passive ranging sonar (as was the very similar *Darter*).

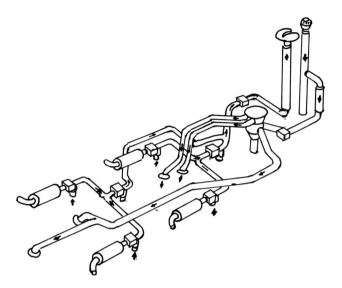

A typical snorkel arrangement for a Guppy or fleet snorkel submarine. It was the key to sustained submerged operation. The two vertical masts are the 15-in induction and the 15-in exhaust. The induction masts lead into a moisture separator and then, via a 22-in pipe, into the main induction valve. Dual 15-in pipes lead air into each engine room. The engine room acts as a plenum, feeding the two diesel engines, which keep running even if the snorkel head closes temporarily as a wave sweeps over. By way of contrast, each engine exhaust leads directly into an uptake, exiting either through a car-type muffler or via the snorkel exhaust trunk. Most of this piping was led under the superstructure abaft the submarine's sail. Later submarines had their induction and exhaust pipes combined into a single mast. U.S. snorkels used electrodes to sense water sweeping over the snorkel head.

* Unless otherwise noted, all line drawings are done by the author.

indication (BDI). In 1945, the main U.S. submarine sonar was WFA, an active pinger with an instrumented range (i.e., usual expected range) of 3,750 yd.

It was well known that greater ranges could be achieved at lower frequencies, but then large arrays were needed. U.S. submarines had a 5-ft low-frequency (110 Hz to 15 kHz) line hydrophone, JT, which was still small enough to train toward a target.[2] Like WFA, it had BDI. WFA could listen at JT frequencies, but it could not track targets very effectively. As an interim measure, the postwar U.S. Navy improved both sonars to produce the active BQS-3 and passive BQR-3 (essentially JT in a sonar dome so that it could function above its usual limit of 7 kt).[3]

The Germans' approach was quite different. Lacking effective radar, they emphasized low-frequency passive sound for search as well as for attack.[4] Long range required too large an array to train physically. A beam in a given direction could be formed by applying an appropriate delay (phase) to each element of the array. In the German passive array, called Gruppen Horch Geraeten (GHG), fixed delay lines made the horseshoe-shaped array equivalent to a straight-line array. Turning a commutator within the contacts of the delay lines turned the beam. As in all passive sonars of this era, further processing was very limited. The listener had only a rectifier for emphasizing propeller beats and similar sounds. There was no means of bringing high-frequency signals down to the audible range.

The Allies first encountered a GHG when the British captured U-570 in 1941. She had 48 spot hydrophones, flush mounted in the outer bow plating, that formed a circle 8 ft in diameter. In good conditions, the U-570 array could detect targets at distances up to 10 nm, far beyond anything the later WFA or JT could do. The Germans' next step, in 1943, was to mount the hydrophones on a

Tiru, a Guppy II, is shown off Mare Island, 10 February 1949. Note that her sail bulges out at its top. The radio direction-finding loop, which was used mainly to receive VLF radio messages while submerged, was soon replaced by a smaller streamlined loop. The sonar dome forward housed one transducer of a WFA single-ping searchlight (the other projected from below the hull); the passive trainable JT abaft it retracted into the deck.

cylinder, 2 m (6 ft 6 in) in diameter, below the bow, called a Balkon (balcony). It solved a problem of alignment between the two halves of the U-570 array, which precluded good tracking of a target more or less dead ahead. A surfaced U-boat making 7–9 kt could expect to hear a single medium-sized target at 5,000 (about 5,550 yd). The German fast submarine U-2513, taken over by the U.S. Navy, managed to detect targets out to 10,000 yd while running at high submerged speed. Her GHG, installed on board the Guppy II submarine *Cochino* in 1949, became the basis for postwar U.S. passive submarine sonars. GHG was also taken over by the French and Soviets and was revived by the Germans when they resumed submarine construction.

At the end of the war, the Germans were planning a more elaborate device, a teardrop bow 1.5 m in diameter and 1.0 m high (5 ft × 3 ft 3 in), with four rows of 12 parallel connected receivers, for a total of 48. They hoped to cut background noise by giving the array some vertical directivity. Larger arrays could do more. The heavy cruiser *Prinz Eugen* reportedly detected a British cruiser at about 33,000 yd while making 30 kt. This performance was achieved with relatively primitive microphones and mechanical installations.

The U.S. Navy independently developed another type of array to replace its active searchlight sonars. As in a GHG, a beam was formed by adding up the outputs of different elements with different phases. In the U.S. array, the sonar transducer was a cylinder of separate staves. Each stave was wired to a corresponding element on what amounted to a scale model of the array. The appropriate phases were supplied by a commutator rotating around the model, connecting a few at a time to the receiver. For an active sonar, the great advantage of such scanning operation was much better search performance. A searchlight operator had to ping in a given direction, then wait for an echo before looking elsewhere. The greater the effective range of the set, the longer was the wait and the

less useful the search. Such considerations did not, of course, affect single-ping ranging or target tracking.

The first operational U.S. scanning sonar, QHB, operated at the usual high frequency. It put out a ping in all directions. The commutator spun at 300 RPM, thus, in effect, sampling all directions to seek echoes. Some range was lost because the commutator could never pick up more than a fraction of the full echo from any given direction, but that was accepted. Many sonars had an additional commutator, embodying BDI, specifically for target tracking. Later scanning sonars used additional commutators to put out directional beams for greater range. Even then, the sonar operator did not have to wait for a ping to come back from any given direction because the transmission and reception beams were no longer connected.

Scanning operation went with a type of display new to sonar, a radar-style plan-position indicator (PPI), that symbolized the new search role. Although QHB was designed for surface ships, it was an attractive WFA replacement. Two QHB-1s were mounted, top and keel, aboard *Clamagore* in July 1948. Later, many modernized fleet submarines had QHB or one of its successors, BQS-2, SQS-10, or SQS-11, mounted on the keel and, in some cases, on deck.[5] Many submarines of the early 1950s also had a separate single-ping searchlight sonar, either WFA or BQS-3. These units vanished when directional-ping commutators were added to the scanning sonars.

Unlike the searchlights, scanning sonar transducers could be fixed in place. Because they no longer had to train, the hull itself was the only real limit on size, hence on reducing their frequency. By the early 1950s, the U.S. Navy was experimenting with SQS-4, essentially QHB operating at half the frequency (ultimately 8–14 kHz) and achieving twice the range (nominally 5,000 yd for a surface ship, far more for a submarine). Lower frequency brought even greater range. While testing a 5- to 10-kHz searchlight sonar off Key West in 1951, *Guavina* detected the submarine *Seacat* and the tug *Salinas* at 16,000 to 18,000 yd under

Newly completed, *Trout* shows her original Guppy-like sail (the raised forward part helped to protect the periscopes when they were raised at speed). The open bridge was soon raised to the level of the top of the sail and the raised portion cut down. The sonar dome on deck covers a QHB-1 transducer. A retractable keel dome covered another QHB-1 transducer and a QXB-1 "sonaramic" passive torpedo-detection set. Abaft the deck dome is the trainable array of the JT passive attack sonar.

conditions in which QHB would have managed 2,500. By the end of the decade, BQS-6 was operating at 3.5 kHz (see chapter 4).

BQR-2, the U.S. version of GHG, had 48 vertical staves, each 3 ft long, in a 6-ft circle within a 5-ft–high dome; the array operated at 150 Hz to 15 kHz.[6] The Germans used GHG like a searchlight: it was turned in a direction for listening before it was turned again. The U.S. version added a commutator, operating at 5 to 9 kHz, that scanned either continuously (at 4 RPM) or tracked by BDI. The later BQR-2B added a second scanning commutator, working at 700 Hz to 1.4 kHz, that fed a bearing-time recorder (BTR). A paper rolled down past the BTR stylus, which moved horizontally. Each pass of the stylus was equivalent to a full commutator scan. Whenever the received signal exceeded a set level, the stylus marked the paper. As time passed, the BTR provided a crude record of the target's motion that was useful, among other things, to estimate target position. The BTR beam could be driven at 1 or 10 RPM, the higher speed being used for a stronger target signal. The BTR, a variation on the wartime chemical recorder, was first tested about 1952 by the Naval Underwater Sound Laboratory (NUSL) at New London, which later became the Naval Undersea Systems Center (NUSC). BQR-2C (1959) added a third mode. The entire passive array could be used as the receiver for an active sonar, BQS-4 (seven transducers, stacked on a stave inside the BQR-2 array, pinging at 7 kHz). Many BQR-2Bs were combined with BQS-4s.[7]

A larger version, BQR-4, was designed specifically for ASW submarines. Each of its 58 staves was 10 ft tall (overall dimensions of 10 × 20 × 10 ft) and operated at 150 Hz to 5 kHz. Originally, BQR-4 was limited to audio listening, but later a BTR was added for the 700-Hz to 1.4-kHz range. The array could be scanned at 1 or 4 RPM. In early tests, BQR-4 often tracked targets within 5 degrees. It held contact on surfaced submarines at 10–50 nm, and on snorkelers at 20–50 nm. Because it had no means of automatic tracking, it was generally supplemented by BQR-3, an improved JT in a sonar dome, so that it could operate at high speed.

NUSC tested the next step up, 20 × 40 × 8 ft—wrapped around the bridge fairwater of *Flying Fish*. This device, sensitive down to 30 Hz, was never adopted.

The ultimate development of the GHG idea was BQR-7, a triple line of 52 groups of hydrophones (roughly 21 × 45 ft) wrapped around a submarine's bow, which was the quietest part of the submarine in terms of flow noise. Originally operating between 150 Hz and 5 kHz, BQR-7 provided both detection and automatic target tracking. Later, it was extended down in frequency to 50 Hz to feed a Lofar analyzer (see chapter 4). In the integrated sonar (BQQ-1) introduced in the late 1950s, BQR-7 was wrapped around a spherical active sonar, BQS-6.

All of the commutators, active and passive, missed some signals because they pointed their beams in only one direction at a time. As computer technology matured,

Portsmouth's *Gudgeon* runs off Block Island, 25 May 1953. Her snorkel induction and ECM (ESM) masts are raised. The big fairing on the starboard side (abaft the sonar dome) supports her trainable BQR-3 attack sonar.

The *Tang*s introduced the first postwar long-range passive sonar, BQR-2, in a chin dome. This BQR-2B dome is on board the missile submarine *Grayback*, December 1977.

an alternative became practical. The outputs of all the staves or all the transducers could be fed into a computer memory in digital form. The commutator could be replaced by a fast computer, a beamformer, which applied phases to the outputs to form the equivalents of the old beam outputs. Unlike a commutator, a beamformer could form all the beams simultaneously (because it embodied all the appropriate phases all the time, it was called a beam preformer). This type of operation is also called DIMUS (digital multi-beam steering). It was first demonstrated in 1963 aboard *Hardhead* (SS 365). The DIMUS version of BQR-2 was BQR-2E, later superseded by BQR-21. DIMUS was also applied to the receivers of active sonars.[8]

The digital equivalent of the BTR is a waterfall display. The outputs of all the beams are displayed across the screen of a cathode-ray tube (CRT). As in the BTR, time is indicated vertically. A target appears as a more or less vertical line, its maneuvers showing as turns in that line.

With several targets showing, the display looks like a waterfall; hence the name.

None of the passive sonars could measure range. The U.S. Navy tried three approaches. Target motion analysis (TMA) became extremely important as attention turned to ASW.[9] As a target moves past a submarine, its bearing changes; the rate of change depends on both the range and the target's speed, which can be estimated from the target's audible propeller blade rate). Similarly, if a submarine maneuvers, the way target bearing changes depends on target range.

TMA was invented in 1942 by Lt. Frank Lynch to be used against surface ships. Work continued after the war; in 1953, Comdr. Fred Spiess developed the first bearings-only means of solving for target position. In 1958, Lt. (later Rear Adm.) John J. Ekelund developed a technique based on the way that the bearing rate changes as a submarine runs back and forth across the line of sight to

Caiman is shown on 31 July 1958 after a San Francisco overhaul. The large dome enclosed BQR-3, a modernized JT, permitting it to function at higher underwater speeds. The smaller dome housed a single-ping searchlight sonar, BQS-3, successor to the wartime WFA.

a distant target. If the target is far enough away, it can be considered stationary. Ekelund's technique was embodied in the Mk 113 fire control systems of many ballistic missile submarines, which have to determine the range of a very distant target. Such submarines do not move fast enough to get much information from the change of bearing as they proceed along a more or less straight line. Many other TMA techniques were developed, hence, the importance of the BTRs. A ruler laid along the series of dots could measure the rate at which the target bearing changed. TMA in itself did not offer precise ranges, but it could tell a submarine commander that a target was close enough to be worth a single ranging ping for torpedo firing.

Vertical triangulation is a related technique. As a submarine changes depth, the target's elevation angle changes; the rate of change gives the slant range to the target. A sonar based on this idea, BQR-6, proved unsuccessful, but the idea was revived in the late 1950s. The technique's main drawback was that vertical angles cannot always be measured accurately because sound waves bend up and down in the ocean.

A third technique, adapted to relatively short range, was triangulation using the length of the submarine as the baseline. The first approach was JX, a pair of JTs near either end of a submarine, that was tested in 1951 aboard the submarine *Corsair*. JX automatically measured ranges out to 5,000 yd, but it was not adopted. Dr. Herman E. Ellingson and Dr. John C. Munson of the Naval Ordnance Laboratory (NOL), White Oak, Maryland, however, developed a successful alternative called PUFFS (passive underwater fire control feasibility study). Using hand calculations, the two scientists analyzed thousands of sonar runs to show that a pair of hydrophones could precisely measure the direction of an incoming sound wave by matching (correlating) their inputs. A pair of such pairs could trian-

gulate. At ranges too great for triangulation, the three-hydrophone array could precisely measure the target bearing for a TMA solution.

The feasibility study was conducted in March 1953 and an operational requirement issued in July 1954. Tests to prove the PUFFS concept were completed in 1956. The first contract was let in April 1957; the first engineering development model was tested on board *Blenny* in November 1960, and the first set operationally evaluated in May 1961. On board *Blenny*, PUFFS tracked a snorkeler out to 20,000 yd, continuously measuring range to within 5 percent and bearing to within 0.1 degree. It could track two targets simultaneously. Guppy IIIs and some postwar diesel-electric submarines were eventually equipped with a mature form of PUFFs, BQG-4, using three big vertical hydrophones (six hydrophones per array using beam-forming techniques to limit self-noise). Typically, range on a snorkeler at 7,000–9,000 yd (within 30 degrees of the beam) was accurate to within 200 yd.

Initially, however, installation on board nuclear submarines seemed far more urgent. Two BQG-1 prototypes were authorized in March 1958 for the new *Tullibee* and *Thresher*, and two more in June 1959 for two ballistic missile submarines (SSBN 608 and SSBN 609). *Thresher* presented particular problems because she was highly streamlined. Four single hydrophones were mounted in a parallelogram: two top, two bottom. This version failed; the hydrophones had so little gain that even in her quietest mode *Thresher* could track the noisiest targets out to only 4,000 or 5,000 yd. The next step (BQG-2A) was to use six 10-hydrophone arrays, three on each side in free-flooding tanks. The forward two arrays were in the BQR-7 area, the midships pair in recesses in the midships ballast tanks, and the after two in fairings at the tips of the horizontal stabilizers. The subarrays beamformed and were electrically steered. It turned out that the two aft arrays could

A standard early postwar sonar space is shown on *Trout* (SS 566) at the Philadelphia Naval Shipyard, 1993. This submarine was sold to the Shah of Iran in 1979, but she was sequestered after the Iranian Revolution and preserved while the United States negotiated with Iran. With the elimination of the conning tower, the eyepieces of the periscopes were brought down into the former control room, which was split into a diving station (to port, with ballast and plane controls) and an attack center (to starboard), with a raised periscope stand between them. The sonar space, shown here, was on a low platform (extending out from the periscope stand) on the forward starboard side of the control room, next to the helm. The Mk 101 fire-control system was arranged along the starboard side of the hull abaft the sonar station, with other electronics (BPS-12 radar, WLR-1, WLR-3, WLR-10 radar warner, and BRD-6) across from it abaft the periscopes. Submarines in this class varied; some had their two periscopes side by side; others (e.g., *Trout*) had them in tandem, to narrow the periscope stand. The consoles here are for BQR-2B (center) and BQS-4C (background). The handwheel turns the BQR-2B listening beam (its orientation shows on the big dial); the window above covers the paper output of a bearing-time recorder used to plot target course. BQS-4C has only a PPI display. These consoles are arranged athwartships. The vertical cylinder on the right is the recorder of the depth-sound speed measuring device, BQH-1A, which used pairs of the sound heads in the keel and on the sail. The active element of the pair that was used transmitted a sound pulse received by the other; thus, sound velocity was measured directly. Typically, the lower pair was used while diving and the upper pair while ascending, so that radiated heat washed away from the submarine and did not affect readings. (Author)

measure bearings on targets within 10 degrees of the stern, an unexpected bonus. Fortunately, the system was removed from *Thresher* before her loss and installed on board *Barb*. PUFFS figured in submarine characteristics through the 1960s, but it was never adopted as standard.[10] The wide aperture array, described in chapter 10, is a lineal successor.

The first post–WW II submarines, the *Tang*s, were completed with QHB active sonars (in deck and keel domes), BQR-2 passive search sonars in 16-ft chin sonar domes, and JT or BQR-3 passive trackers. Ultimately, the separate active sonars were replaced by a BQS-4 pinger within the BQR-2 array, and the passive tracker was removed. *Darter* seems to have been unique in having a separate BQS-2 transducer behind a separate sonar window above her BQR-2 sonar dome. She never had any deck sonar domes. The early nuclear attack submarines (*Skate* and *Skipjack* classes) and the *Barbel*s had a more elaborate sonar suite: an SQS-4 active sonar and the BQR-2/BQS-4 combination.

Early Guppy conversions retained their wartime combination of WFA and JT; both were largely unusable at high speed. Many later had QHB or equivalent sonars, such as BQS-2, in deck and keel sonar domes, plus BQR-3 track-

Off Mare Island on 30 March 1953, *Ronquil* shows a new 100-in sonar dome on deck forward to accommodate a WFA-1 transducer (but designed for the BQS-2 that replaced it). Note also the sleeve, surrounding her raised periscope, that was designed to permit vibration-free operation at higher speeds. The sleeve is now standard in U.S. submarines.

ers on deck. Guppy IIAs were all fitted with BQR-2 passive sonars, BQS-2 (or equivalent) active sonars in deck and keel domes, and JT or BQR-3 passive trackers in deck domes, as in the *Tang*s. All Guppies were later so fitted. By the late 1950s, the passive trackers were gone, leaving BQS-2s in a pair of domes (upper deck and keel) and a chin dome for BQR-2B. When the latter was fitted with the BQS-4 active pinger, the two smaller domes were eliminated. That left only the chin dome (BQR-2B plus BQS-4). Many submarines had a small deck radome for a UQC-1 or WQC-1 underwater telephone.

By the 1960s, the Guppies' sonar was quite obsolescent; an operational requirement for a replacement was issued on 16 December 1965 but canceled in July 1967. It would have used the DIMUS version of BQR-2, as well as a new preformed-beam vertical triangulation sonar (using elevation/depression beams between + 15 and − 75 degrees). The new sonar would detect a noisy nuclear submarine, such as *Nautilus,* at 10,000 yd after listening for 10 min (at an own-ship speed of 5 kt) or a 10-kt snorkeler at 40,000 yd.

Work continued on the other main sensors, with three new periscope types: 5, 6, and 7. Type 5, tested in the fall of 1948, was primarily for photoreconnaissance. It carried integral still and movie cameras. Type 6 carried a German-type ''any-height'' fixed eyepiece. Bought for the *Tang* class and other early postwar attack submarines, it provided too massive a radar target and was abandoned. (U.S. submarines still carry advanced versions of the old Type 2.) Type 7 was a 9-inch modification of the wartime Type 4 radar periscope. It carried a range-only ST radar suitable for snorkel operation at 14 kt and was fitted with an infrared direction finder. Type 7 was soon supplanted by Type 8, which is still in use. Replacements for wartime electronic surveillance devices also were developed.

The new sensors developed during WW II inspired development of a new submarine fire control system, a Mk 101. Automatic target tracking (e.g., by JT) and accurate ranging by radar or single ping could be used to develop good initial estimates of target course, speed, and range. The data were fed into a position keeper, such as the TDC,

in place of the earlier method of quick guesses. This made for a quicker and smoother path to a target solution, as the estimated target position was compared with later measurements. A Mk 101 had a pair of analyzers to make initial estimates. One used passive bearings only. Each could be fed with three sets of observations.[11] Unlike the TDC, a Mk 101's position keeper could assume that the target would follow a curved path, that is, take an evasive turn (the operator set the target's tactical diameter). As in the TDC, the position keeper fed automatically into a ballistic section, the angle solver, that automatically aimed the torpedoes by adjusting their gyros and changing settings as the target moved or the calculation progressed. Without an analyzer, a plotting party could develop initial estimates for a TDC, but automation greatly simplified the job and was well adapted to the new sonars.

A Mk 101 was too expensive to be installed in all existing and modernized submarines. A simplified Mk 106 was built around the existing Mk 4 TDC. Most versions incorporated a single analyzer. Unlike a Mk 101, a Mk 106 lacked automatic sonar inputs.

It was soon obvious that a Mk 101 would be so much more massive than the TDC that it would not fit a submarine's conning tower. Even the existing conning tower made for a large submarine bridge fairwater (later called a sail) and thus for considerable drag. Once sonar became the main submarine sensor, moreover, much of the logic of the conning tower, that it placed the TDC near the periscopes (the main sensors), no longer held. High underwater speed demanded that the conning tower be abolished altogether. A price was paid. The conning tower carried the periscope eyepieces well clear of the submarine's main pressure hull, so that the submarine rode deeper at periscope depth.

Unfortunately, the radar ranging periscope (Type 4) carried its radar electronics below the eyepiece section, so it could not retract as far into the periscope well. That limited its travel to about 8 ft. To use it, a submarine without a conning tower had to approach the surface too closely and risk broaching. Small conning towers, therefore, were revived in some submarine classes during the

Parts of a standard postwar analog submarine fire-control system are shown aboard USS *Trout* at the Philadelphia Naval Shipyard in 1993. The backs of the consoles curve to fit the inside of the pressure hull. The closest panel is for the Mk 18 angle solver. The drawing of the torpedo on the panel shows relative torpedo course; the operator used the big knob directly below it to steer a single wire-guided Mk 37. Although the angle solver was designed to handle the nuclear Mk 45 (it has dials showing, for example, "run to burst"), the ship could fire only the non-nuclear Mk 37. To the left is the panel of the Mk 101 position-keeper, with its dials showing own and target courses. (Author)

1950s but were far too small to accommodate a Mk 101. A submarine commander found himself separated from the evolving tactical picture, as displayed on the Mk 101 console, if he wanted to use the periscopes. That was less than satisfactory. In all classes, a Mk 101 occupied a new space, an attack center (a term proposed in December 1946 by the Submarine Officers Conference) on one side of the control room. That made for crowding; in response to a January 1951 Submarine Development Group 2 (SubDevGru 2) proposal, the sonar consoles were moved into a separate space.

A Mk 101 controlled long-range offensive torpedoes. The prewar-type straight runners, steam Mk 14 and a Mk 23 and the quieter electric MK 18, were set only for range,

speed, and gyro angle. The Germans added pattern running—the torpedo ran back and forth through a formation until it hit something. This was embodied in the new hydrogen peroxide Mk 16 (it needed more energy to go farther while running its pattern).

During WW II, the U.S. Navy developed a Mk 28, a passive offensive homing torpedo that was electrically powered (to limit self-noise to an acceptable level). A Mk 28 required far more elaborate settings than a straight runner. They could be applied at the torpedo tube, but, ideally, the submarine fire control system would automatically make all settings responsive to last-minute tactical decisions. The U.S. Navy had relied on spindles, which turned to set its torpedoes, but they were no longer satisfactory. Postwar, electric cables were substituted, and many existing torpedoes were modified for their use. Many Mk 106 systems could set only some tubes electrically; the others were reserved for spindle-set weapons.

During WW II, a new kind of torpedo, a Mk 27, had been introduced as a defensive weapon. A fleeing submarine fired a Mk 27 back at escorts tormenting her. Evasion precluded any sort of fire control setup; a Mk 27 circled and awaited a noisy target. Existing pneumatic torpedo tubes could not eject torpedoes at any great depth, but a Mk 27 had to be launchable as the submarine dove to escape. As the torpedo swam out of the tube, water flowed back over it. To allow for this flow, the torpedo had to be smaller than the tube.

In mid-1945, BuOrd planned to continue development of both species. The near-term offensive torpedo would make 65 kt out to at least 10,000 yd; in September the bureau suggested a longer-term goal of 100 kt.[12] That proved excessive. By 1950, the goal was 20,000 yd at 60 kt, the torpedo to be adaptable to wire guidance. At least one version of a Mk 36 would have incorporated wake-following guidance.[13] A Mk 36 never entered service. The 1945 defensive torpedo goal was 20 kt to 3,000 yd, with a warhead as large (500 lb) as that of the offensive torpedo and launchable at maximum submarine depth. (The goal for depth was then increasing.) The torpedoes would be short and stowed two per rack.

The ASW mission then became dominant. The new main offensive torpedo, designated a Mk 35 by 1950, would be used to attack submarines near enemy bases.[14] The companion defensive torpedo, which became a Mk 37, would protect the submarine mainly from any small ASW craft prowling its operating area. It could make do with a small warhead, initially 100 lb, but it also had to engage much quieter targets. By this time, U.S. submarines were being designed to dive to 700 ft, and it was generally assumed that they would soon operate at 1,000 ft. The latter became the standard operating depth and, in the case of a Mk 37, the launch depth. Characteristics for both torpedoes were developed by the Countermeasures Group of the Submarine Officers Conference.

The offensive torpedo was intended to deal with Type XXI, the German's best diesel-electric submarine (and presumably the prototype of any Soviet boats). The submarine officers wanted a Mk 35 to be so quiet and so fast that it would give its quarry no more than a 10-sec warning. It would home either passively (at 1,000 yd against a snorkeler) or actively (at 1,500 yd), and it would have a range of 20,000 yd. The warhead would be equivalent to at least 300 lb of the new HBX explosive. Because the new torpedo had a passive homing mode, it could attack surface ships; it was the natural successor to the wartime Mk 28 long-range anti-ship homing weapon. A Mk 35 was a full-diameter (21 × 162 in, 1,560 lb) electric torpedo. The first two preproduction prototypes were completed in 1947, and six were ready by 1950. About 400 torpedoes were made in 1949–52; a Mk 35 was not withdrawn from service until 1960.

The new defensive swim-out torpedo had to be able to home on a 100-ton, 6-kt patrol boat from 750 yd. It would circle at 5 kt for up to 45 min, then run at 30 kt for up to 5 min in its attack. Alternatively, it might be used as a lure, repeating sonar pings to attract an ASW craft.

A Mk 37 soon displaced the original offensive weapon. It was designed to run out to 10,000 yd at 15 kt, turn on its sonar (either pinging or listening) at a preset enabling range, and search in a sine curve around its gyro course. Once it found a target, it would chase at 25 kt. It was soon redesigned as a two-speed torpedo (10,000 yd at 26.0 kt or 23,500 yd at 17.5 kt), with an enabling range of 300–10,000 yd. From January to April 1956, tests at Key West showed that it was quite effective against both shallow and deep-running submarines but, ironically, not against escorts. A Mk 37 was too slow to attack fast surface ships, so submarines generally also carried straight-running Mks 14 and 16.

Neither a Mk 35 nor a Mk 37 was available soon enough; a Mk 27 was modified (as Mod 4) as an interim ASW weapon. It was given a gyro, so that it could be fired along a course to at least safe distance before turning on its seeker, and a new power plant (7,000 yd at 18 kt). Unlike a Mk 37, it could not run below 400 ft, the test depth of the wartime fleet submarines for which it had been designed. The first production models appeared in the winter of 1951; about 3,000 torpedoes were made in 1946–54. A Mk 27 Mod 4 was replaced by a Mk 37 in 1960.

None of the homing torpedoes could detect a target at maximum running range. Each had to be fired on a gyro course into the predicted vicinity of the target; in effect, the torpedo seeker made the target larger and hence easier to hit. Homing torpedoes had to be slow (otherwise self-noise would overwhelm their seekers), however, and targets might well move outside the hitting zone while they approached. Therefore, BuOrd picked up the German concept of wire guidance. After firing, the fire control system continued to command the torpedo, a technique called corrected intercept. A torpedo director dead reckoned torpedo position on the basis of telemetered torpedo speed and the steering commands it sent. It also converted relative target bearing to true target bearing, so that the torpedo could be steered without reference to the submarine's maneuvers. Dead-reckoned true torpedo bearing

and true target bearing were displayed on concentric dials. In the first such device, the Mk 37 torpedo director, the operator literally steered the torpedo by matching bearings using the "steer" knob on the director. Commands went simultaneously to the torpedo and to the torpedo position keeper in the director. This system sent the torpedo along a pursuit curve, which was inefficient. The next step, taken with the Mk 37 Mod 1 torpedo, was to steer the torpedo toward a calculated collision, aiming at a point ahead of the target. By 1949, BuOrd had managed to control a wire-guided weapon out to 4,000 yd.

The first U.S. wire-guided torpedo was a Mk 39 Mod 1 (originally Ex-4), a modified Mk 27. It carried 10,000 yd of wire, and the launcher carried another 3,000 yd. Listening as it ran, the torpedo switched from external to internal guidance when it heard a sufficiently strong signal or when its wire ran out. A Mk 39 was tried on board *Medregal* in 1955, and 60 prototypes were delivered in 1956. Although at one time 24 submarines (15 Atlantic, 9 Pacific) were to have been converted to fire a Mk 39, few must actually have been fitted because a Mk 39 was always considered an interim weapon.

For the longer term, there were more exotic concepts, including a rocket anti-escort torpedo (range 1,000 yd) and an atomic warhead that could be attached to a torpedo body and launched from a standard torpedo tube to neutralize an enemy harbor. Later, rocket torpedoes would be proposed as anti-submarine weapons to be fired by midget submarine interceptors. The atomic torpedo eventually entered service as an anti-submarine weapon, a Mk 45 (Astor; see chapter 7). Reportedly, the Russians actually deployed nuclear torpedoes intended to attack harbors.

Mks 35 and 37 were fast enough to deal with the near-term threat, Type XXI. They were practical because they were not so fast that flow noise blinded them. The far-term fast submarine, nuclear or closed cycle, typified by Type XXVI, was a more difficult proposition. In theory, a homing torpedo had to be about 50 percent faster than its target. That meant a speed of 37.5 kt for a 25-kt submarine, compared with 22.5 kt for a 15-kt Type XXI. BuOrd outlined its new torpedo program at the May 1951 Undersea Symposium. Type I was a short-range, medium-speed homer with a small warhead for air or surface craft. It became a Mk 44. Type II was a faster equivalent to a Mk 37 for submarines, surface ships, and aircraft that could tolerate some weight. Type III was a Mk 36, soon to be abandoned. Types I and II were to have countered the 25-kt threat; however, by about 1955, it was generally accepted that 30 kt (corresponding to a 20-kt target) was a practical upper limit on torpedo speed.

These torpedoes could be quite dangerous to the submarine carrying them. After *Scorpion* (SSN 589) sank on 22 May 1968, a navy court of inquiry found that she was most likely lost after jettisoning a Mk 37 torpedo, which had accidentally been set off by stray voltage in its tube. Standard procedure was to flood the tube (to cool the torpedo), then turn before jettisoning the torpedo, so that its anticircular run device would shut it down (after a turn of 170 degrees or more). Then the torpedo would be taken from the tube, its propeller locked, and it would be jettisoned. In theory, a Mk 37 would not enable before it reached a range of 300 yds, but stray voltage might set it randomly. The court of inquiry suggested that a torpedoman, perhaps influenced by successful ejection of a hot-running MK 37 exercise torpedo in December 1967, released the weapon, which became fully armed and homed on *Scorpion*, hitting her roughly amidships.[15]

The torpedo tubes themselves were unsatisfactory, partly because they were noisy and produced air bubbles when firing. By 1944, BuOrd was working on a new hydraulic tube that was inherently bubble free. It had the added advantage, not yet important, of firing at any depth.[16] In 1948, Electric Boat suggested an air-actuated piston pump to replace BuOrd's motor-driven centrifugal unit. This type was adopted for the new fast submarines, with one pump for each bank of three tubes (one tube fired per pump stroke).

The development of defensive sensors and devices ran parallel to the work on offensive weapons. In 1945, U.S. submarines were equipped with depth charge direction indicators (DCDIs) and depth charge range estimators (DCREs) as aids to evasion. As a submarine evaded, she could release decoys through her 3-in signal ejector. (A larger-diameter self-propelled decoy could be fired from a torpedo tube to simulate a moving submarine.) Early postwar efforts produced an abortive BQR-1 (combined DCDI and DCRE) and QXB, a passive scanning sonar to detect the noise strobes of approaching torpedoes. QXB was less than successful; in July 1954, it was eliminated from the list of sonars for ASW submarines.[17] Prototypes may have been installed on board the *Tang*s, but they did not last. As yet, there were no sonar intercept receivers, perhaps because existing U.S. sonars operated at the same high frequencies as possible enemy units, hence could hear them.

Systematic postwar work on submarine countermeasures seems to date from the mid-1950s. A September 1954 feasibility study led to the design of the WLR-2 intercept receiver. The contract was let in April 1956, and the unit was operationally evaluated beginning in July 1961. WLR-2 was a very ambitious attempt to detect signals automatically over the full range of sonars and torpedo pingers (5–120 kHz); they would be indicated aurally or visually. The program also included a hull-mounted BLQ-1 jammer, for which a feasibility study was conducted in December 1955, an operational requirement issued in June 1956, and a contract award in April 1957; operational evaluation began in December 1961. There were also expendable decoys. Controlled from within a submarine, BLQ-1 was expected to jam three ship or torpedo sonars simultaneously (5 to 100 kHz). The first unit was delivered in December 1960 and the second in April 1961. About 1961, the submarine acoustic warfare system became known as SUBAJAD (SUBmarine Acoustic Jamming and Deception).

Neither WLR-2 nor BLQ-1 passed operational evaluation. The navy's need for an intercept receiver was so urgent that it bought the French Velox (DUUG-1) pending development of a new acoustic intercept receiver, WLR-5. Velox worked over a far narrower frequency band (5–40 kHz), provided no signal analysis (to identify a threat), and gave only rough bearing data (within about 20 degrees). It was fitted to all of the diesel submarines and many nuclear submarines through the early *Sturgeon*s. WLR-5 promised broader coverage (about 1–70 kHz), signal analysis, and twice the angular accuracy of Velox; it used directional receivers instead of spot hydrophones spread around the submarine's sail. No replacement jammer was immediately available.

Expendable jammers became a slightly happier story. Although BLQ-2, the self-propelled submarine simulator, failed its operational evaluation, it was superseded by a better BLQ-9 and eventually by the current MOSS (MObile Submarine Simulator) a Mk 57.[18] The accompanying unpowered 3-in decoys dealt with the sonar (7–30 kHz) and torpedo seeker (30–70 kHz) frequency ranges: BLQ-3 and BLQ-5 were anti-sonar spot (noise) and deception (echo

Electric Boat's *Wahoo* is pictured about 1955; her cockpit has been raised to the top of her sail. The white objects are messenger buoys.

repeater) jammers; BLQ-4 and BLQ-6 were the corresponding higher-frequency decoys. The current equivalents are ADCs (acoustic devices, countermeasures).

WLR-5 was no more successful than its predecessor, but the later WLR-9 was adopted. Typically, it was installed in a small separate dome forward of the sail in *Skipjack* class and later submarines (replacing DUUG-1 in many). It was later replaced by WLR-12, which had a wider frequency range (sonars plus torpedoes, rather than sonars alone). WLR-17, a modified version for *Ohio*-class missile submarines, provides a remote tactical situation display in the control room to make evasion easier; the same display also provides details of the received ping (identified with the aid of an enlarged receiver/processor). WLR-9 was part of an integrated basic submarine acoustic warfare system (BSAWS) analogous to a surface ship's countermeasures system. The signal processor was WLR-14; the whole system was designated BLR-14/14A.

SAWS was the later standard system: SAWS I for *Sturgeon* class; SAWS II for *Los Angeles* class and earlier submarines refitted with the digital BQQ-5 sonar. More sophisticated processing in SAWS II was expected to cut alert processing time by about five sixths. Each version incorporated dedicated 3-in CLAMS (countermeasure launcher acoustic module system)—one in *Sturgeon*, two in *Los Angeles*—mounted in the hull abaft the sail and firing vertically. During the design of *Los Angeles*, a proposal to fit a special 10-in launcher for MOSS was rejected for fear that such a choice would limit future mobile decoys. Without a special large-diameter launcher, MOSS must be launched from a torpedo tube. Because a submarine generally must be able to fire a MOSS at any time, one tube is always kept empty. Thus, although in theory *Los Angeles* can carry 26 weapons (4 in the tubes, 22 reloads), she will generally carry only 25 (3 in the tubes). A 5-in decoy fired from a 6-in tube was also developed. Although the *Los Angeles* program envisaged ultimate installation of a 6-in external launcher during the mid-1970s, this device (CSA Mk 1) appeared only on board ballistic missile submarines.

SAWS and BSAWS also employ a hull-mounted jammer, GNATS (generalized noise and tonal system)/NAU, typically mounted right aft. The current projected replacement for BSAWS/SAWS utilizes a new sonar intercept system (WLY-1) that feeds a new consolidated command and control system. It controls a new generation of decoys: ADC Mk 4, a new mobile multifunction decoy (MMD), and a special-purpose countermeasure (NLQ-1); and a hard-kill countermeasure: active submarine torpedo defense (SMTD) device.

The new weapons and sensors were intended for a postwar generation of submarines designed primarily for submerged operations. Thus, they were much faster underwater than their predecessors. They were inspired mainly by two German WW II submarines, Type XXI (diesel-electric) and Type XXVI (Walter, or hydrogen peroxide). The Germans developed the closed-cycle Walter turbine, which promised several hours at speeds as high as 25 kt, first. Hydrogen peroxide oxidizer was stowed in

a second pressure hull suspended below the main hull, the two forming a figure eight in cross section.

Unknown to the Allies, the Germans encountered so many problems that they had to defer the Walter boat. As an interim step, the lower hull (designed for peroxide stowage) was filled with batteries and the boat provided with a powerful electric motor, allowing it to run for some hours at 15 kt, about twice the underwater speed of a conventional U-boat. That was also about the maximum smooth-water speed of many existing ASW craft. In theory, the resulting Type XXI could outrun a corvette. The submarine skipper no longer would be furtive. He could run in at will, fire long-range homing or pattern-running torpedoes, and then retire without serious pursuit. These were terrifying possibilities. In the 1945 distribution of German submarines, the Soviets received four Type XXIs that supplemented partly completed hulls they had already captured. The prewar Soviet navy had the world's largest submarine force. There was no reason to imagine that it would not soon place Type XXI in production.

By mid-1944, the Allies were uncomfortably aware of what these new submarines were expected to do, though not aware of the problems of the Walter power plant.[19] Type XXI was clearly so imminent a threat that fast submarine targets were urgently needed to teach ASW forces to deal with it. With its modern submarines fully committed in the Pacific, the U.S. Navy could not provide those targets. But the British could and did.

Beginning in mid-1944, the British converted seven S-class submarines by cutting down conning towers and fairing over torpedo tubes and hull flooding openings. There was no time for fitting snorkels. The submarines could neither fight nor dive quickly, but they could make 12.5 kt underwater. Operating at Bermuda, the converted S-boats were available to both navies.[20]

What followed was ironic. The conversions convinced the British that no streamlined battery submarine could achieve much of a performance. Because they already had the conversions and planned a more elaborate one (HMS *Scotsman*), the British saw little point in placing Type XXI U-boats in service after the war. Instead, they concentrated their limited resources on recovering what they assumed was a fully developed German closed-cycle technology. About three years passed before they discovered that the Walter power plant was hardly ready for service and that it would be well worthwhile to develop the "interim" submarine, the fast battery type. Only the small Type XVII, with a 2,500-SHP engine, had been built. The 7,500-SHP engine of Type XXVI had been designed but not built (or debugged).

With the end of the war, the United States lost access to S-boat conversions and had to rely on captured enemy submarines. The U.S. Navy placed in service the two Type XXIs, U-2513 and U-3008, that it received. The Pacific Fleet considered activating several fast Japanese submarines, in effect the Japanese version of Type XXI, but soon abandoned the idea as far too dangerous. Britain was also allocated two Type XIIs. Happy with their S-boats, the

British lent their only operable Type XXI to France. They retained a cannibalized boat but never placed it in service.

Type XXI was a revelation. Because S-boats were so noisy, a wartime tactical note had suggested that Type XXI might best be countered by passive sonar. In reality, it was far quieter than a fleet submarine, both at high and low speeds. It had a special low-speed quiet "creep" motor. Running noise at 6 kt (creep speed) was roughly that of a fleet boat at minimum speed (2 kt). It was much faster than an S-boat. On postwar U.S. trials, for example, U-2513 made 16 kt submerged for 1 hr 12 min. Because she had been designed for high underwater speed, her diesels were far less powerful than her electric motors. She made 13.5 kt on diesels and 18 kt on electric motors when surfaced. There was no vibration at maximum submerged speed and no noticeable increase in noise at high speed, except when accelerating or decelerating. U-2513 was a very quick diver (18 sec). Although it was believed that she had gone below 600 ft while in service, her designed operating depth was only 120 m (394 ft); BuShips set maximum operating depth at 440 ft.[21]

Unlike the slower U.S. fleet submarines, Type XXI relied mainly on dynamic forces for control. The alternative, pumping, would have been far too slow to maintain trim at high speed. Actually, its high speed made control easier for a skilled planesman. It also helped that Type XXI was relatively stiff in the vertical plane (the fleet boat had only 65 percent as much turning moment). The Germans considered the lack of bow planes no problem, but postwar U.S. analysis suggested that they might have been quite useful for maintaining depth control at periscope depth, an important consideration in attacking surface ships. Partly because she was shorter, Type XXI turned more tightly, both surfaced and submerged, than a U.S.-type fleet boat.

As the only available representatives of the new kind of submarine, the two U.S. Type XXIs were worked very hard. In 1947, for example, a list of planned operational tests totaled 204 operating days (87 for two boats, 30 for one), against a total of 150 available per year (187 between 15-month overhauls). Spares sufficient for three years were shipped from Bremerhaven on 4 February 1946. It was clear from the beginning that replacements would be needed within a few years, because neither U-boat could be expected to last very long.[22] The effective lifetime was set by the need for frequent refits and, ultimately, by the life of the existing main storage battery; cells had been salvaged from Type IX U-boats, but the supply was exhausted. There were no more Type XXIs, and new submarines would take too long to build. The only near-term solution was to convert existing U.S. fleet submarines to simulate Type XXIs. Although conceived as replacement targets rather than operational submarines, these units became the core of the first postwar generation of U.S. submarines, the Guppies.

U-3008, the worse of the two Type XXIs, was decommissioned first.[23] Her sister, the U-2513, was decommissioned 8 July 1949 after running out of battery life. At first, both were preserved for possible recommissioning because they had some features the new Guppies lacked, but on 7 November 1950 OpNav formally certified that they were no longer needed.[24] Both were used for weapons trials.[25]

Clearly, Type XXI was one possible prototype for future U.S. submarines, but she was not the only one. The only existing U.S. design was the "General Board" submarine, an enlarged fleet boat conceived late in 1944. Rumors, many of them incorrect, about German developments strongly suggested that this design was obsolete. As in Britain, no one knew the status of what seemed to be the next generation of technology, the Walter engine.[26] In particular, no one yet knew that the Germans had not solved the fundamental hydrodynamic and control issues that a very fast submarine raised; it was by no means clear that Type XXVI could have operated at her design speed. The atomic bomb was another new factor, but details were not yet available. In 1945, optimists within the U.S. submarine force imagined that both closed-cycle (Walter) and nuclear power plants could be made operational within two or three years.

Another great question was whether special types of submarines should be developed for new missions. Unlike the United States, which adopted a single standard type, Germany had developed a wide range of designs, though not all had been built.[27] Early in September 1945, the Submarine Operations Research Group (SORG) was asked to consider such alternative roles as radar picket (conversions for this had already been ordered) and missile guidance and defense.

On 30 August 1945, Adm. E. J. King, CNO and commander in chief of the U.S. Fleet, ordered a series of evaluations of Pacific combat experience, including one of ship and aircraft characteristics. The submarine portion of the study was conducted by Commodore Merrill Comstock, chief Pacific submarine training officer. An early draft of the study was circulated at the Submarine Officers Conferences in Washington during the fall of 1945.

Comstock also circulated a questionnaire among Pacific submariners. He wanted views on future submarine speed and design depth, future power plants, effect of the atomic bomb, and atomic energy for submarine weapons and propulsion. Operating depth was a particularly sore point; in developing the General Board submarine, BuShips had rejected the submariners' demands for much greater depth in order to evade depth charges. Few Pacific submariners accepted that.

Typically, Capt. L. S. Parks of Submarine Squadron 2 called for a depth of 1,500 feet (the fleet boat was limited to 400). He wanted high speed, probably because so many wartime submarine attacks on fast Japanese warships had been frustrated. That meant 35 kt on the surface to gain an attack position in the brief time that air patrols might allow and 25 kt submerged, in case surface operation was altogether impossible. Such performance, entirely impractical, seemed possible in view of muddled reports about the potential of the gas turbine for surface running and the

Walter engine, both of which Parks thought were already operational.

The first postwar Submarine Officers Conference, in September, rejected the General Board design as outmoded. It conceded, however, that the boat might have to be built in small numbers to keep the two main submarine yards, Electric Boat and Portsmouth, alive while they developed a successor. BuShips was ordered to develop a U.S. snorkel.

At the next meeting on 12 October, BuShips announced that the Walter power plant, far from being nearly ready, could not yet be built and might never be affordable. Only the General Board submarine could be built at once, although plans for an experimental fast diesel-electric submarine, in effect a U.S. equivalent of Type XXI, might be completed sometime in 1946. It might be designed for later conversion to a Walter power plant. The conference suggested that such a submarine should have submerged speed of better than 20 kt and surface speed of 14 kt, test depth of 800–1,000 ft, and six bow torpedo tubes plus waist tubes, rather than stern tubes, for better streamlining. As for hydrogen peroxide, some conference members suggested that a less expensive closed-cycle plant, or perhaps a less expensive peacetime alternative to hydrogen peroxide in a Walter plant, be sought.

The SORG study of alternative submarine roles became a joint study by SORG (led by Dr. W. J. Horvath) and ASORG (ASW Operations Research Group led by Dr. W. E. Albertson) of the future U.S. submarine force. It also became the agenda of the Submarine Officers Conference. This must have been one of the first explicit statements that war against the Soviet Union would be much like the Battle of the Atlantic, with the Soviets providing the threat, rather than the target, at sea. Submarines would still be valuable but only in new roles exploiting their inherent

stealth and surprise, and some special designs might be required.

The main new roles, mostly presaged by wartime experience, were transport of cargo and troops (200 to 300), for surprise landings, reconnaissance of both beaches and enemy electronics, and missile bombardment against industrial targets inaccessible to aircraft.

SORG/ASORG saw an Americanized Type XXVI as the ideal future attack submarine. She would make 25 kt for at least 6 hr, as in Type XXVI, 15 kt for 15 hr, and 3 kt on silent motor for 30 hr. Diving depth would be 500 ft, which BuShips had fixed as a practical limit in 1944. A German-type array sonar would detect a 9-kt merchant ship at 15 nm or a convoy at 20 nm, with the Germans' 3-degree precision. The submarine would be armed with long-range homing or pattern-running torpedoes (20,000 yd at 40 kt) and with underwater rockets (about 1,500 yd at 120 kt). Although the new submarine might have no more torpedo tubes than existing types, they could be designed for fast reloading. The submarine would have antiradar coating on her snorkel and antisonar coating on her hull, both of which the Germans had tried. She would displace 800–1,600 tons.

The study also suggested developing several types of fast midget submarines, to be carried to their objectives by submarine or surface ship. Some would have torpedo tubes and others (like the British X-craft), detachable charges for harbor attack.[28]

Having heard the SORG/ASORG report, the next Submarine Officers Conference (23 October) proposed a first postwar building program. It reluctantly accepted the BuShips proposal to build two General Board submarines to keep the yards alive, as long as the two that followed them were the fast diesel-electric type (15 kt for 3 hr, six bow tubes and four to six waist tubes, test depth of

Halfbeak (as well as *Amberjack* and *Cobbler*) had a topside rudder aft for better underwater maneuverability. Newly converted by Electric Boat, *Halfbeak* is pictured on 22 April 1948. Her snorkel induction (intake) and exhaust masts are raised.

800–1,000 ft). This was accepted by 41 percent of the participants as an interim measure pending development of closed-cycle engines, not only Walter but also pure oxygen, which seemed superior. The latter were to be installed in an existing hull as soon as possible.

With little hope of modifying existing fleet submarines for high underwater performance, the conference suggested minor improvements—a snorkel and better underwater maneuverability to be achieved by adding either rudder flaps or a topside rudder. Ongoing improvement programs, such as direct drive for quieter underwater operation, would be continued because the large force of 199 fleet boats was still a valuable asset. Comstock would later suggest that new fleet boats, if they were built to keep the yards going, should have snorkels, combat information centers (CICs) in their forward torpedo rooms or under their conning towers (to accommodate torpedo and gun control, fighter direction, and lifeguard equipment), improved mine-detection gear, automatic remote control for 40-mm and lighter guns, remote-control bombardment rockets loaded from within the hull, and fire-control radar with overhead coverage.

The one real prospect for greater underwater performance was a new type of battery cell, two thirds the weight of a Sargo battery but with 75 percent more capacity. Its life was reduced by 75 percent, from 6 yr to 18 mo. Installing such batteries in the General Board submarine would buy 2 kt of underwater speed. The new battery became the Guppy type used in several later classes.[29]

Members feared that it would take too long to develop the many new types of submarines suggested by SORG/ASORG, but Comdr. A. R. Callisher suggested that some existing fleet boats might be converted. The conference suggested conversions for bombardment and troop transport, with others (radar picket, reconnaissance, fighter director) to be considered later. Comstock supported "sea cows" to replenish fleet submarines at sea, but that idea was specifically rejected by the conference. The conference conversion program, including development and installation of snorkels, was formalized by the General Board and approved by CNO Adm. Chester Nimitz. It is described in chapter 5.

Because it seemed impossible to match Type XXI (let alone XXVI) performance in a modified fleet submarine, new construction became urgent, justified in part by the need to train ASW forces. The next conference (6 November 1945) proposed the characteristics listed in Table 2–1. They were formally embodied in General Board characteristics in February 1946 and became the basis of the *Tang* class, the first postwar U.S. design.

As the conference had proposed, the new submarine would be adaptable to a future closed-cycle power plant. This, in turn, defined the envelope into which the follow-on power plant would have to fit in order to achieve the required 25 kt: 15,000 SHP on two shafts; down to 700 ft, or perhaps 1,000 ft because a new hull steel surely would be available soon; within an 18-ft cylinder (see chapter 3).

Table 2–1. Submarine Characteristics Proposed by Submarine Officers Conference, November 1945

	Closed-Cycle	Fast Battery	General Board
Displacement (tons)	1,200	1,600	1,400–1,600
Diameter (ft)	17		
Depth (ft)	600*	600–800+	800
SHP	7,500†		
V Submerged (kt)	20 (40–150 ft)	15	15
Endurance (hr)	12	3	>1‡
Creep speed (nm)	4		
Endurance (hr)	30		
V Surfaced (kt)	14§	15	15
Endurance (nm)	10,000	15,000/6‖	15,000/6‖
Torpedo Tubes	6 (bow only)		6 (bow only)#
Reloads	2 (per tube)		2

* 800, if possible.
† Power of the German Type XXVI, an 850-ton submarine.
‡ 2 hr, if possible.
§ On two 960-BHP diesels.
‖ Submerged, on snorkel; 10,000/15 on surface.
Add two stern tubes, if possible, without reduction in 15-kt submerged speed.

Work on the new design, designated Study 19 in the series developed for the General Board craft, began in October. Preliminary designers at BuShips used the known design of the fleet submarine as a basis, although they had no hope of actually modifying existing submarines. The British S-boat experience did suggest that something short of a completely new design might achieve higher underwater performance. Capt. L. A. Kniskern, chief of preliminary design, suggested that the after torpedo tubes and deck guns be eliminated. The bridge would be cut down, the conning tower would remain. Underwater power would be increased by replacing the forward and auxiliary engines with batteries. The new high-capacity batteries possibly could be installed to deliver the roughly 5,000 SHP needed to make the required 15 kt.

By November, estimates showed that such a craft, shorn of all unnecessary fittings, could make 12 kt submerged with the existing type of battery but containing 403 cells, rather than the usual 252, for 4,360 SHP at the 1-hr rate. With 642 cells of the new type (6,400 SHP at the 1-hr rate), she could make 14.5 kt submerged, very nearly the required figure. A highly streamlined bridge fairwater was designed, and some work was done on a better hull shape.

No modified fleet submarine could meet the new demand for deep diving. The submariners already believed that greater depth could guarantee survival against depth charges; many were alive mainly because their boats could dive to 600 ft. Too, many wartime submariners hid beneath the isothermal layer. In the winter Atlantic, the layer might lie as deep as 600 ft. Finally, it would soon be discovered that a fast submarine could be directionally unstable; she could easily dive through her designed operating depth. BuShips argued that deeper diving would entail a more cramped submarine. Type XXI, already far too cramped by U.S. standards, was not the sort of deep diver the submariners wanted.

The submariners were adamant. Standard operating depth was increased from the wartime 400 ft to 700 ft. BuShips found that the wartime high-tensile steel, with a yield of 42,000 psi, solved the problem. A new 75,000-psi steel, then under development, promised a 1,000-ft operating depth, although it seems unlikely that hull penetrations and vital auxiliaries were designed for the greater depth. About a decade later, HY-80, which is somewhat stronger (80,000 psi), allowed a further advance in diving depth.

For high underwater speed, the designers sought minimum length (for minimum wetted area). To improve streamlining, they eliminated the conning tower in favor of an attack center. That crowded the control room, a problem alleviated only in the later *Barbels*. The change, however, was well worthwhile. January 1947 model tests showed that the bridge structure of a fleet submarine contributed 51 percent of total resistance at 15 kt. All appendages, except the essentials (rudder, shafts, struts, and bilge keels), contributed 60 percent. In contrast, a streamlined Guppy experienced 58 percent of the total resistance of her fleet submarine predecessor. The bridge accounted for only 28 percent of that (16 percent of the total of the original fleet boat). The smaller fairwater of the new submarine was even better, particularly when the bridge was covered. Model tests showed the new design to be more efficient than a Type XXI; the appendages contributed only 16 percent to overall resistance, compared with 37 percent for a Type XXI.

For all their high underwater speed, *Tang*s used much the same sort of handwheel controls (for bow and stern planes) as their WW II predecessors. *Tang*'s diving station shows the usual plane angle indicators, depth gauge, and ''bubble'' (in the curved tube) that indicates the angle of the boat. *Nautilus* had similar controls for her planesmen, with a separate wheel for steering. In effect, this arrangement clearly separated steering in the vertical and horizontal (rudder) planes. Traditionally arranged submarines, such as *Nautilus*, made a tremendous impression by their ability to jump in and out of sonar beams, but they could not coordinate such maneuvers with violent turns.

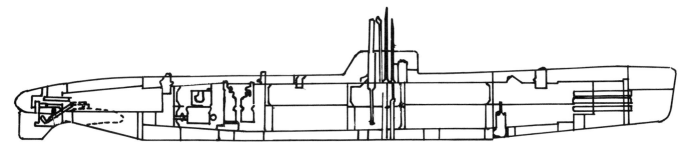

Tang, as conceived, 1947. The single engine room (containing four vertical "pancake" diesels) was combined with her motor room (but still with a separate maneuvering room above the motor), to reduce length and to provide space for the large battery (two 126-cell units, fore and aft, under the officers' quarters forward of the control room and the crew's quarters abaft it). The pipe extending up from the fore end of the motor/engine room is the snorkel exhaust (the pipe in the sail is the snorkel induction); the exhaust would soon be led up into the sail, to reduce back pressure. The large object in the bottom of the torpedo room is a retractable sonar transducer. At this stage of the design the ship still had separate escape hatches distinct from her torpedo loading hatch (forward); as *Tang* was completed, the two functions were combined (for the forward torpedo room), again to save length. At this stage of the design the ship still had only a small-diameter countermeasures tube aft (she was completed with a full-diameter swim-out tube there). Dimensions: 252×25 ft, 1,550 tons (standard). Estimated performance: 4,000 SHP = 15.3 kt surfaced and 4,700 SHP = 17.5 kt (1-hr rate) submerged. She would have carried six bow tubes and 22 torpedoes.

Two hull forms were tried: a 261-ft circular section and a 243-ft German-style figure eight. The circular section hull, formally proposed in November 1946, was selected. Possibly, it was chosen, in part, because it provided much more usable internal volume. It also minimized wetted surface for a given length and beam. The submarine was double-hulled amidships with single-hull ends (for fineness, surface performance, and access to structure). BuShips argued that such a design offered better surface stability and propulsion than a longer single-hull alternative. The pressure hull was 166 ft long and 18 ft in diameter, compared with 266 ft long and 16 ft in diameter for a fleet submarine.

Model tests showed that the shorter hull of the new submarine would have better underwater performance than the longer hull of a Guppy (see below), with easier depth changing (e.g., to evade attack) and better depth keeping (e.g., for snorkeling). A shorter submarine might also find it easier to correct a dive before reaching test depth.

The ideal length for underwater speed would have been even shorter; by late 1946, model basin tests had shown that the ideal length-to-diameter ratio was 5:1. Such dimensions were unacceptable because a submarine with a single internal deck had to be long enough to accommodate torpedo tubes, attack center/control room, engines, and motors. A very short hull also would impose too much resistance on the surface; the designers hoped that the longer hull would not add too much underwater resistance.

To keep length as short as possible, the new submarine was powered by a new compact General Motors (GM) "pancake" diesel. The cylinders were arranged radially (in layers, hence the name) around a vertical shaft, with the generator at the bottom. To minimize radiated noise, each engine-generator set was mounted on a rubber pad. The diesels were concentrated in a single engine room

(the fleet submarine had two). With less than half the space and weight per horsepower of a conventional diesel, 4,000 BHP could fit within 22 ft, compared with 6,400 BHP in 53 ft in a fleet boat or a Guppy. Unfortunately, although smaller pancakes had been successfully used in wartime small surface craft, the submarine diesels proved extremely unreliable, largely because of their high speed, 1,400–1,500 RPM, chosen to achieve compactness.

The submarine had no special silencing features, as such. It seemed likely, however, that the large, slow-turning propellers would be quieter than those of fleet submarines.

The new design incorporated the six-tube bow nest and 16 bow reloads of the earlier fleet boats. The characteristics required power loading (2 min to load the entire nest), but that feature apparently did not survive.

BuShips wanted to omit stern torpedo tubes in order to save weight and maintain sufficient reserve buoyancy. When the Submarine Officers Conference objected, BuShips argued that any revision to the design would cost three or four months and thus jeopardize early construction of so essential a type. In December 1946, the conference resolved to ask for an astern-firing countermeasures tube in any future design. A submarine panel, formed to assist the SCB, proposed a compromise, a single 12×120-inch decoy-firing tube aft. The CNO approved. The ships were built with pairs of swim-out tubes for defensive torpedoes (always described as countermeasures tubes). One reload per tube was provided.

Table 2–2 compares the 1947 fast submarine design with both Type XXI and *Tang,* the submarine that was actually built.

The size of the program was set by two quite different considerations: (1) the industrial importance of keeping both specialist yards open, and (2) the argument that existing submarines were so clearly obsolete that new ones would be required to fill out the authorized strength of

Table 2–2.   The 1947 Attack Submarine

	Type XXI	1947	*Tang*
Displacement (tons)	1,600	1,550	1,617
Length × beam (ft)	251.5 × 21.5	262 × 25	268 × 25
Submerged resistance, relative	100%	85%*	
Test depth (ft)	393	700	700
Collapse	800 SHP	1,100 SHP	1,100 SHP
Power, surface	4,000 SHP	4,000 SHP	4,000 SHP
Power, submerged, 15 kt	5,000 SHP	4,700 SHP	4,700 SHP
Speed, surface (kt)	15.6	15.5	15.5
Speed, submerged (kt)	16.0	17.5	17.5
Torpedo tubes	6	6	8
Torpedoes	20	22	26†
Complement	57	62	61

* Resistance of the 1947 submarine is 33 percent of that of fleet type.
† The torpedo load-out is sometimes given as 22, with the four weapons aft being classed merely as countermeasures.

80. Submarines were expected to last 15 yr; theoretically, the 80-submarine force demanded an annual rate of 5 to 6 boats, but money was far too tight. The FY 47 program included only two new boats, one for each main yard: *Tang* at Electric Boat, *Trigger* at Portsmouth. The design was designated SCB 2 in the new series of SCB projects.

Even so, the new submarines had a high priority, second only to the special ASW cruiser *Norfolk* and ahead of the carrier *United States*, because of their importance to the national ASW program. They were considered live targets and testers of tactics, however, and not prototype ASW platforms. The secretary of the navy approved construction on 5 March 1946, as part of an immediate experimental program, but contracts were not actually awarded until FY 48.

A draft version of the FY 48 program, proposed by Adm. Forrest Sherman (then deputy CNO for operations, Op-03), included four types of closed-cycle submarines and two atomic submarine prototypes, as well as an arctic submarine and a midget. The Bureau of the Budget was willing to contemplate only one prototype of each; the navy argued for one atomic and two closed-cycle boats, plus an arctic picket and a midget. Advanced propulsion soon had to be relegated to the future. In December 1947, the Submarine Officers Conference suggested that the FY 48 submarines duplicate the FY 47 type, with the addition only of improvements immediately available. Three submarines were approved, but one was changed to an SSK (see chapter 4).

Early proposals for the FY 49 program included four attack submarines; OpNav rejected the six-boat replacement level on the ground that submarine design was still changing too rapidly. Hopefully, the design would offer some improvement over the FY 47–48 type. In the end, a third pair of *Tang*s was included in the FY 49 program. Electric Boat and Portsmouth each built three boats.

In 1957, the FY 47–48 quartet (SS 563–566) had to be lengthened by 9 ft so that lightweight Fairbanks-Morse diesels (1,600-BHP 10-cylinder 38D8-1/8s) could replace the unreliable pancakes. They offered 25 percent more power per cylinder than their wartime predecessors, albeit at a higher price and with reduced reliability; however, they were used in all later U.S. diesel-electric attack submarines. The two FY 49 boats (SS 567, 568) were completed with Fairbanks-Morse engines. Boats fitted with PUFFS (SS 563, 565, 567, 568, 574) received a 15-ft hull plug around 1967.

Defense funding soon collapsed. As drawn up in 1948, the FY 50 program included no submarines at all; they lacked sufficient priority to survive the cutting process. Similarly, as drafted in 1949, the FY 51 program included only small combatants. By 1950, the atomic and closed-cycle power plants were so far advanced that their proponents could argue for prototypes in the FY 52 budget. Money was still tight, but then war broke out in Korea.

The FY 52 budget provided the nuclear prototype *Nautilus* and two new radar pickets (SSRs) that were needed to support carrier strike operations. The budget did not stretch to include any additional *Tang*s. That omission was not altogether irrational; aside from its ability to dive deeper, *Tang* was not much better than a Guppy (see below). Likely, OpNav was willing to accept drastic limits on new attack submarine construction precisely because the Guppies were such satisfactory alternatives. Something smaller and cheaper surely could be built.[30]

The FY 53 program included a single new attack submarine, *Grayback*. *Darter* followed in FY 54. They would have been sister ships, but *Grayback* was completed as a missile submarine. Two more such attack submarines were included in the draft FY 55 program on the ground that the superior nuclear and closed-cycle submarines could never be built in sufficient numbers. They were cut to one hull, *Growler*, which was completed as a missile submarine (see chapter 9). The FY 55 program also included the first production of nuclear submarines (the *Skate*s) intended as direct replacements for diesel craft.

To the submariners, these thin programs delayed the important work of mass replacement of existing craft. A June 1954 draft of the FY 56 program included no fewer than seven improved *Tang*s (i.e., *Darter*s) plus one nuclear attack submarine and one diesel missile submarine. The diesel attack craft had low priority, and they were squeezed out in favor of nuclear attack submarines. By early 1955, the program showed four diesel and two nuclear submarines; in May 1955, the CNO asked for a third nuclear submarine in place of one of the diesels. For a time, the program showed only two diesel attack submarines. Three eventually were built (as well as three SSNs). They were the last U.S. diesel-electric submarines, the *Barbel* class (initially to have been built to an SCB 124 design but ultimately to the more radical SCB 150 design).

By 1952, the *Tang* design was six years old. The first proposal for the FY 53 submarines was a redesign, SCB 2A (see Table 2–3 for the state of the design in November 1952). The long-range passive sonar was relocated to the ideal position, the bridge fairwater. The noisy machinery normally below the bridge was relocated aft, with one generator and drain pump left in the former location to be used if the main units aft fail. A small conning tower was added, to put the pressure hull farther below the surface at periscope depth (a similar conning tower was provided in the nuclear submarine *Seawolf* designed at this time).[31] The battery was enlarged and diesel fuel added. Crew berths were moved from the stern to amidships, and the sonar space relocated from the passage at the fore end of the control room to a more enclosed space at the after end of the attack center across from the radio room. The resulting submarine would have been slightly larger than the *Tang*s, with somewhat more efficient control surfaces and without the drag-inducing shaft line stabilizers of earlier types.

OpNav rejected SCB 2A as too large and too complex. With the advent of nuclear submarines, the diesel boats were the low end of a high-low mix; they had to be more affordable. Table 2–4 lists a series of alternatives presented in December 1953. Schemes 1 and 2 show that nothing could be saved through a reduction in pressure hull weight, by substituting HY-80 for high-tensile steel or by reducing diving depth, unless internal volume were cut (e.g., by accepting a simplified power plant). In scheme 4, the conning tower was eliminated. Scheme 5 shows the effect of reducing the strength of internal bulkheads. Other schemes indicate the effects of detail changes: full-length stern tubes (or none at all, as in scheme 11), pneumatic versus hydraulic torpedo ejection, and substitution of two Fairbanks-Morse 38D8-1/8s for three 8-38A6-3/4s.

By this time, *Albacore* had been built, and some interest in an attack submarine version emerged. That possibility was represented by scheme 12, a single-screw submarine

Table 2–3.   Comparison of SCB 2A and SS 563, 1952

	563	SCB 2A
Dimensions (ft)	268 × 27-4 × 18-0 (diameter)	295 × 30-5 × 19-6 (diameter)
Surface N	1,821	2,480
Surface M	2,047	2,732
Submerged M	2,270	3,150
Standard	1,610	2,160
Reserve buoyancy M	10.7%	15.0%
GM(N)	16	16
Lead at axis	——	88
Lead 2 ft above BL	78	50 T
Diesel	4 GM	4 GM
Battery	504 Guppy	504 Sargo II
SHP surfaced	3,400	3,400
SHP snorkel	3,400	3,400
SHP submerged (1 hr)	4,700	5,800
V surface (kt)	15.0	15.2
V snorkel (kt)	11.3	12.1
V (1 hr submerged) (kt)	15.4	16.1
Surface (endurance at 10 kt)	11,500	13,700
Snorkel (endurance at 7 kt)	10,100	11,500
Submerged 3 (hr)	43	64

Note: Condition N, normal fuel load in surface trim.
   Condition M, maximum fuel load, including fuel ballast tanks.

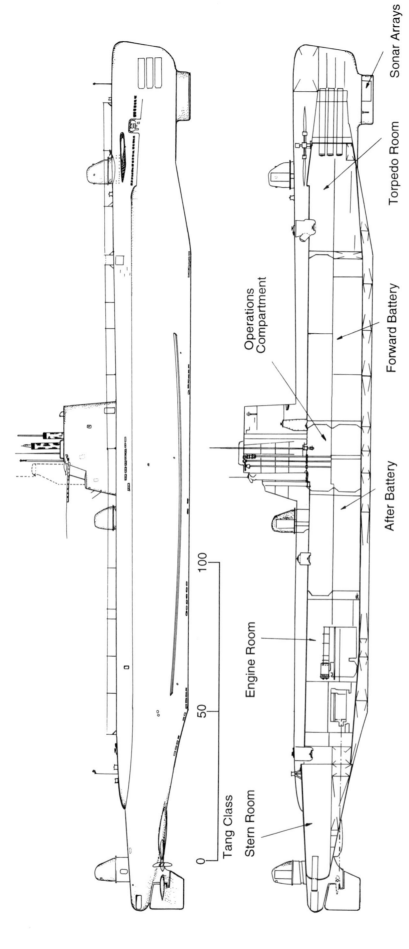

Tang Class

Stern Room

Engine Room

Operations Compartment

After Battery

Forward Battery

Torpedo Room

Sonar Arrays

0 50 100

Tang in her final configuration, with three PUFFS (BQG-4) passive-ranging arrays along her upper deck and Fairbanks-Morse diesels. She has been lengthened partly to provide additional plotting space to control Mk 45 torpedoes. (Jim Christley)

Table 2–4. Alternative Design Schemes—1953

	0	1	2	3	4	5	6	7	8	9	10	11	12	13
							Full-Length Stern Tubes							
	SBP 2A SS 574	HY-80	HY-80	High-Tensile Steel	No Conning Tower	Light Bulkheads	Two Pneumatic	Two Hydraulic	Four Pneumatic	Four Hydraulic	No CM Tubes	Two Engines	Single Screw	Sargo II
LS displacement (tons)	1,756	1,600	1,756	1,636	1,716	1,716	1,779	1,788	1,804	1,824	1,740	1,774	1,716	1,709
Submerged (tons)	2,600	2,380	2,600	2,400	2,530	2,535	2,640	2,650	2,690	2,710	2,580	2,630	2,440	2,535
Length (ft)	273	260	273	265	273	269	280	280	286	286	271	275	268	267
SHP surfaced	3,150	3,150	3,150	3,150	3,150	3,150	3,150	3,150	3,150	3,150	3,150	3,150	3,150	3,150
SHP snorkel	3,150	3,150	3,150	3,150	3,150	3,150	3,150	3,150	3,150	3,150	3,150	2,300	3,150	3,150
SHP submerged	4,700	4,700	4,700	4,700	4,700	4,700	4,700	4,700	4,700	4,700	4,700	4,700	4,700	3,400
V surface (kt)	15.5	15.5	15.5	15.5	15.5	15.5	15.5	15.5	15.5	15.5	15.5	15.5	16.0	15.5
V snork (kt)	12.0	12.2	12.0	12.2	12.5	12.1	12.0	12.0	11.9	11.9	12.0	10.7	13.2	12.1
V submerged (kt)	15.5	15.7	15.5	15.7	16.1	15.6	15.4	15.3	15.3	15.2	15.5	15.5	17.0	14.0
Endurance at 10 kt surfaced (nm)	13,500	13,500	13,500	13,500	13,500	13,500	13,500	13,500	13,500	13,500	13,500	13,500	13,500	13,500
Snorkel at 7 kt (nm)	11,500	11,500	11,500	11,500	11,500	11,500	11,500	11,500	11,500	11,500	11,500	11,500	11,500	11,500
Submerged at 3 kt (nm)	165	167	165	167	170	165	164	163	163	162	162	165	175	135

with better submerged performance, including higher cavitation speed. The single-screw design could not accommodate stern torpedo tubes; all torpedoes were concentrated forward. Auxiliary machinery was concentrated aft. BuShips also considered installing power torpedo loading. In scheme 13, the 504 Guppy cells were replaced by 252 Sargo II cells to save weight and volume.

The FY 54 submarine, SCB 116 (*Darter*), was built as a slightly enlarged *Tang*, so similar that she was usually classed with the six earlier boats. She was slightly larger (specified submerged displacement was 2,475 tons), and her formal characteristics called for special attention to silencing and shock. The preliminary designers found that they had to accept a reduced battery; a 504-cell battery would have increased submerged displacement to 3,100 tons. Even then, the submarine was somewhat too large at 2,600 tons, and the internal bulkheads had to be shaved. The diesels were the same lightweight units as in the last *Tang*s. The characteristics were modified in February 1955 to include a simple automatic steering system.

SCB 124, the version planned for FY 56, had an enlarged attack center to accommodate Regulus guidance equipment. The sail was enlarged to carry the corresponding guidance radar. This would have cost 6 ft of length. SCB 124 was 274 ft long; SCB 116, 268 ft.

This was less than exciting. In November 1954, BuShips presented OpNav with a series of FY 56 options (see Table 2–5). *Albacore* had clearly shown the value of a short, fat, single-screw hull. U.S. nuclear submarine designers had accepted multiple decks, which made more efficient use of available internal volume (displacement). Crew accommodation could be improved, and adding a deck level would eliminate through traffic in the control room and officers' country. BuShips objected to a single-screw design, probably because it was thought to be unreliable.

Reportedly, Rickover was an important voice for twin screws. The hydrodynamicists argued that no twin-screw submarine could approach single-screw efficiency.

Sometime in late 1953 or early 1954, Portsmouth Navy Yard formally proposed that it design an attack version of *Albacore*, which it had designed and built, for the FY 55 program. Portsmouth hoped to fit a *Tang* combat system in the *Albacore* hull, based on *Albacore* and *Tang* experience. BuShips in Washington normally would have prepared the preliminary design, but the yard received a formal request for one on 9 February 1954. It was by no means clear, at this time, that any such ship would be built. The preliminary design, dated 1 May 1954, showed a circular nest of five bow tubes, rather than the usual six; a chin sonar dome; a *Tang* sail; pancake diesels; and an HY-80 hull, which would save about 100 tons. Collapse depth was 1,000 ft (operating depth of 625 ft, with a safety factor of 1.6).

The key was to use the internal volume of the submarine more efficiently in order to gain the highest possible ratio of deck space to volume (.09 in the Portsmouth design, .07 in *Tang*) by providing three decks, rather than the usual one, amidships. Crewmen no longer had to pass through the attack center, control center, and officers' quarters merely to get from one end of the submarine to the other. They could now pass along the deck underneath these areas; some spaces were provided with dead-end passageways. The forward room could be devoted entirely to loading and firing torpedoes, and no one had to live aft of the engine room, as they did in earlier submarines. The batteries were concentrated under the amidships compartment, in place of their previous distribution fore and aft. Push-button ballast control, adopted from *Albacore*, saved valuable control room space, which had become particularly critical after the attack center was carved out

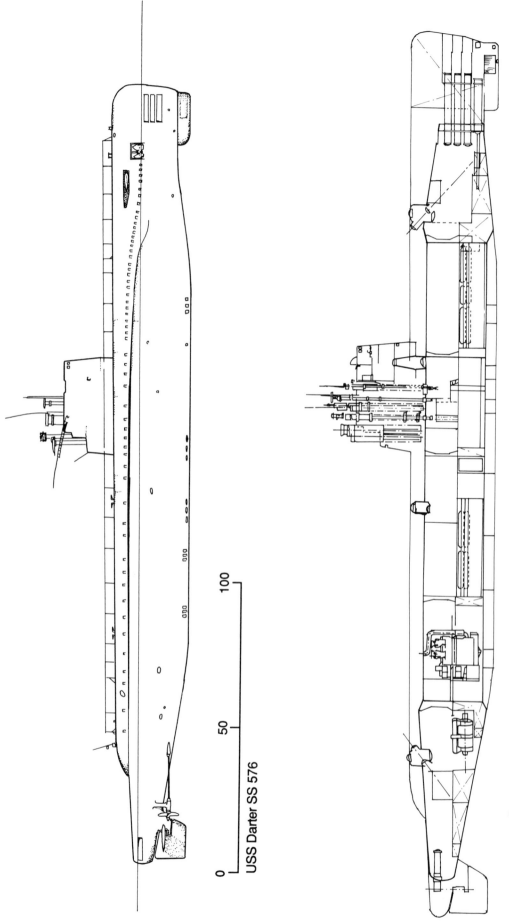

USS Darter SS 576

Darter inboard profile, as built (January 1957). The upper transducer in the bow is for BQS-2; the lower, for BQR-2, with a UQC-1 underwater telephone transducer in the fore end of the big sonar dome, and a UQN-1B (sounder) transducer in its bottom. The big tube under the nest of six bow tubes is the ejector pump (like the tubes, it had a shutter in the bow). Note that, unlike a fleet boat, Darter has a single engine room abaft her after crew spaces, containing three engines side by side (the centerline one is below the other two). Masts, fore to aft, are: Nos. 1 and 2 periscopes, side by side (Types 2A and 6, the latter carrying the ST range-only radar); a fixed whip (starboard side); the SS-2A radar mast (port); the UHF-IFF antenna; the retractable whip (port); the ECM/DF antenna (port) with VLF loop (starboard) alongside; and the snorkel induction and exhaust. (Darter introduced the type of snorkel mast used in all later U.S. submarines.) As in contemporary submarines, the ECM mast carries a series of stub dipoles along its length, with the dome of the direction-finder at the top. There was also a UQC-1 transducer on top of the sail, roughly alongside the UHF-IFF mast. The line of masts divides the space below the sail into a control room to port and an attack center to starboard, with separate radio room abaft the control room and sonar room abaft the attack center. Unlike a World War II submarine (or a Tang), Darter had her plane controls athwartships, on the forward bulkhead of the control room, alongside the helm. The air main controls, automatic depth control, and UQC were all against the side of the pressure hull. (Jim Christley)

Table 2–5. Submarine Options, Fiscal Year 1956

	SS 576 (SCB 116)	Twin-Screw	Single-Screw
		(Both Three-Level)	
LOA	268-7	208	205
Beam maximum (ft)	27-2	29	29
Diameter (ft)	18	22-6	22-6
LS displacement (tons)	1,609	1,589	1,579
Surface displacement (tons)	2,102	2,033	2,020
Submerged displacement (tons)	2,369	2,300	2,285
Torpedo tubes		Six full-length forward	
CM*	2 aft	2 aft	——
Surface speed (kt)	15.7	14.0	14.1
Submerged speed (1 hr) (kt)	16.3	17.4	18.6
Snorkel, maximum speed (kt)	11.8	13.3	14.2
Submerged endurance at 3 kt (relative)	1.0	1.07	1.1
Submerged endurance at 12 kt (relative)	1.0	1.34	1.69
Tactical diameter (relative)	1.0	0.6	0.5

* With CM torpedoes aft, the twin-screw would be able to carry more full-sized torpedoes forward.

of the control room. The only major change from the *Alba-core* hull was a much larger sail to accommodate the snorkel and electronic masts.

BuShips prepared an alternative twin-screw design, which it wanted built in FY 56. Table 2–6 shows why it was rejected in favor of a modified single-screw design, SCB 150 (*Barbel*, SS 580).

BuShips redesigned the Portsmouth submarine, fairing her two sonars (SQS-4 above, BQR-2/BQS-4 below) into the hull, with six torpedo tubes between them in two horizontal, rather than the usual two vertical, rows.

Three submarines were built as the *Barbel* class. After features of the design were disclosed to NATO officers at the Armed Forces Staff College in September 1959, Dutch and Japanese officers requested details.[32] Both navies built versions of *Barbel*. After *Thresher* was designed, *Barbel* was redesigned with an integrated sonar nose and a silver-zinc battery. This version did not enter production, partly because it provided insufficient power to the big sonar.

Modern Japanese submarines, however, are essentially *Barbel*s with their bows cleared to accommodate large (albeit not U.S.-style spherical) sonars. Their torpedo tubes are moved back, as in *Thresher*.

Overall, the new construction program produced only 10 new diesel attack submarines in 10 years (FY 47–56), compared with 60 wanted by the submariners. This figure was tolerable only because the fleet boats, contrary to expectation, could be modernized. One important reason was the diesel-electric propulsion system adopted by the United States before WW II. Each of four diesels drove a generator; all were entirely separate from the propeller shafts. The shafts were driven by motors, both on the surface (directly by the generators) and submerged (by the batteries). Electric motor power was set by the need for high surface speed. Because the old fleet submarines needed far less power submerged, they had dual motors, with only half of each motor used underwater. The obvious solution to high underwater speed was to use the

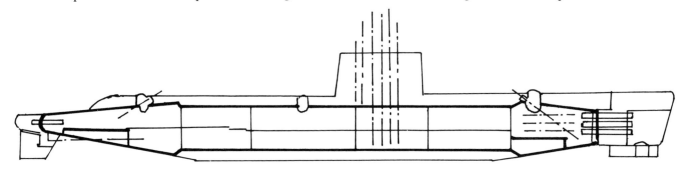

SS 577 design sketch, from the BuShips 1955 "dream book." She was converted on the slip to a missile submarine. Characteristics: 268×27 ft, 2,369 tons; submerged speed 16 kt (snorkel speed 11.8 kt, surfaced speed 15.7 kt). She would have had 504 Guppy battery cells. Weapons: 18 full-length torpedoes plus four "countermeasures" (Mk 37s). Estimated cost for the FY 57 program was $22 million, as of January 1955.

Table 2–6. The Selection of *Barbel*, 1956

	SS 580	Twin-Screw Equivalent
Length (ft)	219	245
Displacement (submerged) (tons)	2,600	3,050
Speed at 1-hr rate (kt)	18.6	18.6
SHP	4,700	6,900
Battery cells	504	744
Endurance (submerged) at 3 kt (hr)	93	114
V snorkel (kt)	14.2	12.5
Tactical diameter	140	220
Reliability		Better

entire motor when submerged and double battery capacity so that high-speed underwater endurance did not suffer.[33] Diesel-electric power was by no means universal; it weighed more than the simpler direct-drive arrangements adopted by other navies. The system had been chosen for its flexibility; batteries were easily charged while the boat ran at speed on the surface. Also, a major diesel problem of unacceptable vibration at certain critical engine speeds was avoided. The diesels could always run at optimal speeds because they were not connected directly to the shafts.

Presumably encouraged by the early *Tang* class studies, BuShips formally began work on a high-speed fleet submarine conversion around mid-June 1946. The bureau first sought a fast target. Streamlining would require removal of the conning tower. It seemed that 342 new battery cells would have to be installed in the forward torpedo and engine rooms, to supplement 198 cells in each of the existing tanks for a total of 738. Total battery capacity would more than double. At this stage, the designers assumed that new 3,900-SHP electric motors would be used. They estimated underwater speed at 14–15 kt at the 1-hr rate. At the ½-hr rate, the batteries would give 10,200 SHP (15.5–16.0 kt). The price included reduction to only two torpedo tubes.

This study suggested that something more conservative was possible. The fleet boat might actually retain her combatant qualities by fitting new cells only in the existing

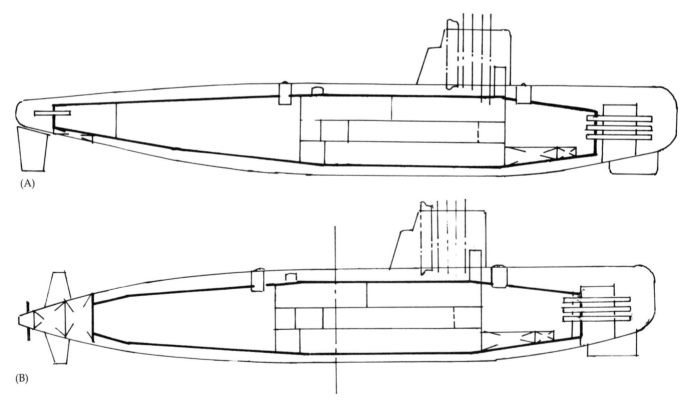

(A)

(B)

Three-deck attack submarines for the FY 57 program, as sketched by BuShips in 1955. (A) is the conventional twin-screw version, 214×29 ft (2,330 tons; 1,589 tons light), capable of 17 kt, carrying 18 full-length torpedoes and four "countermeasures" (Mk 37s). She would have cost $21.9 million. (B) is the equivalent single-screw submarine bought under the FY 56 program, *Barbel*. At this stage her sonar had not yet been faired into her bow, but she had six torpedo tubes rather than the five proposed by Portsmouth Naval Shipyard. Dimensions: 204×29 ft, displacement 1,579 tons light (2,260 submerged). Calculated speed was 18.6 kt. The single torpedo room, forward, would have accommodated as many weapons as the forward room and after countermeasure room of the twin-screw design. Estimated cost was $21.5 million. In each case, the three-deck arrangement was quite different from earlier submarines. Instead of being divided fore and aft, the batteries were concentrated amidships, under the crew's living space (which in turn was under the control room [to port] opposite the attack center [to starboard]). Abaft these spaces were the sonar and radio rooms and, further aft, the wardroom and officers' country.

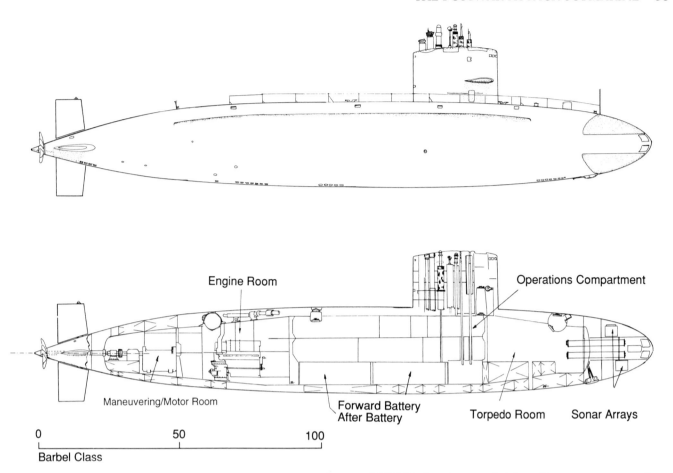

Engine Room

Operations Compartment

Maneuvering/Motor Room

Forward Battery
After Battery

Torpedo Room

Sonar Arrays

0   50   100

Barbel Class

Barbel as modified with sail planes. The bow sonars are SQS-4 above and BQR-2 below the torpedo tubes. The sonar room was the middle deck space just abaft the mast shown, below the control room/attack center. The small space just abaft the attack center was the Supplementary Radio room (ELINT space); the radio center was abaft it. Masts, fore to aft, are: Nos. 1 and 2 periscopes; BRD-6/ECM mast; BPS-12 radar; BLR-1 ECM (with VLF loop alongside, shown as dashed line); and snorkel induction and exhaust. Note the concentration of batteries amidships, typical of three-deck submarines. The structure above the engines is the muffler. Not visible in these drawings is the line of air-emitter piping, port and starboard, close to the keel, providing an acoustic shield around the hull. (Jim Christley)

battery tanks, fitting new motors; and fairing in the existing conning tower and deck fittings. At the $\frac{1}{2}$-hr rate, 396 cells would provide 5,300 SHP (12–13 kt). A few more cells would be better; 496 would provide 6,800 SHP at the $\frac{1}{2}$-hr rate (14.1–14.7 kt). In either case, battery voltage would fall quite badly after a $\frac{1}{2}$-hr discharge. As converted, Guppies actually had 504 cells.

All of this was promising. On 29 June 1946, OpNav approved the BuShips proposal to convert two submarines. The bureau promised that conversion would take 9–12 mo, but it actually did much better. OpNav offered SS 348 or 349 in the Pacific, and any one of SS 483–487 in the Atlantic. *Odax* (SS 484) was converted at Portsmouth, and *Pomodon* (SS 486) at Mare Island; Portsmouth did the design work. Because little was expected, few detailed requirements were imposed. The project was called Guppy, for "greater underwater propulsive power."

By October 1946, design work was going so well that 10 more conversions were on order. Portsmouth and Electric Boat were assigned the design of Guppy versions of fleet boats each had designed. Much attention went into streamlining; fairing the deck line alone saved 5 percent in underwater resistance. The submarines were rearranged, largely to accommodate new battery cells and more powerful air conditioning needed to dissipate increased heat output. The existing forward battery tank accommodated 184 cells; another 68 filled the former gun magazine and two freshwater tanks. The after battery tank was extended forward to the pump room, and the meat room and storeroom were relocated. A third air conditioner replaced the auxiliary engine. Four reload torpedoes were surrendered so that bunks could be relocated. Storage space was slightly reduced. On the other hand, existing direct-drive motors were retained, with the additional power being absorbed by new faster-turning propellers. They were noisy, but there was no space for larger slower-turning motors of sufficient power.

The extra air conditioning was not needed after all. At first, the new batteries heated badly when charging, but that could be avoided by never fully discharging the batteries.

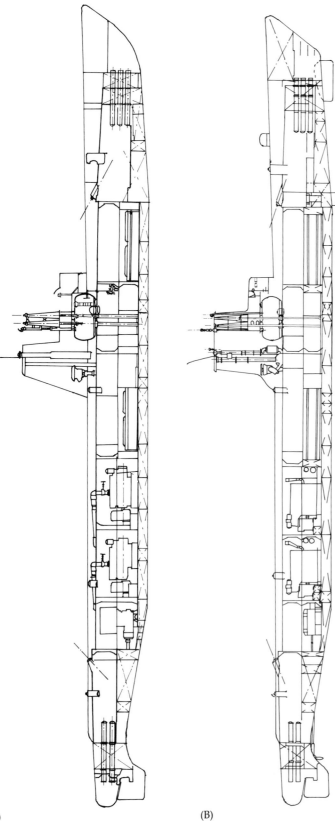

(A)

(B)

Fleet snorkels and Guppies show variations on the war-built fleet submarine hull. The separate conning tower, for the helm and attack instruments, was a standard feature of U.S. wartime and prewar submarines; the diving station was in the control room below (with the additional helm shown). Note the two separate main engine rooms abaft the after batteries, with the separate motor room under the main propulsion control cubicle. (A) is the most austere version of the fleet snorkel, in this case *Capitaine* (SS 336), as converted for Italy at Mare Island in 1966 (transferred 5 March) as *Alfredo Cappelini*. *Besugo* was similarly converted (as *Francesco Morosini*) at the same time. Similarly, partially streamlined fleet snorkels were transferred to Greece (*Lapon* and *Jack*, 1957–58), Turkey (*Blower* and *Bumper*, 1950) and Venezuela (*Tilefish*, 1960). Four boats transferred to Turkey were refitted with similar partially streamlined snorkels at Philadelphia in 1954 after transfer (*Blueback, Boarfish, Brill, Chub*). The torpedo-shaped objects are air flasks above her battery tanks. The sonar control room was on the level below the control room, abaft the pump directly under the diving station. Note that the snorkel induction and exhaust occupy the whole of the streamlined part of the sail (the large object at its base is the main air induction valve).

(B) *Torsk* (SS 423) was a standard U.S. fleet snorkel, with a fully streamlined sail; she is shown as in September 1964. At this time she had a plotting center below her control room, just forward of the pump room. The bow sonar done contains her BQR-2B passive sonar and a UQC underwater telephone (the dashed line shows its contour on the hull). The dome on deck houses a BQS-2 sonar and another UQC. A second BQS-2 transducer was in a retractable keel dome (the device above is an E-1/B hoist). Masts, fore to aft, are: SS radar antenna; Nos. 1 and 2 periscopes (VLF loop alongside No. 2 periscope); IFF (top)/UHF/ECM (AS-626/BLR fairing) mast; UHF stub; snorkel induction with whip attached (and ECM antenna on top); and snorkel exhaust.

(C) *Quillback* (SS 424) was a Guppy IIA converted in 1953; she is shown in December 1969. Compared to a fleet snorkel, she had a much more elaborate sail, with extra masts installed between conning tower and snorkel piping. Masts, fore to aft, are: Nos. 1 and 2 periscopes; SS radar antenna; BRD-6 ECM antenna (AS-1071 BLR dome, with AS-1649/B, AS-962/BLR, and AS-994/BLR angled dipoles further down); retractable whip; and snorkel head valve (induction) and exhaust. Note the fairing for No. 1 periscope to permit its vibration-free use at high underwater speed. The small objects at the fore and aft ends of the sail (and, in dashed form, abeam the BRD-6 mast) are transducers for the French-supplied DUUG-1C sonar intercept system. The chin dome houses a BQR-2B array, with a UQC-1 underwater telephone at

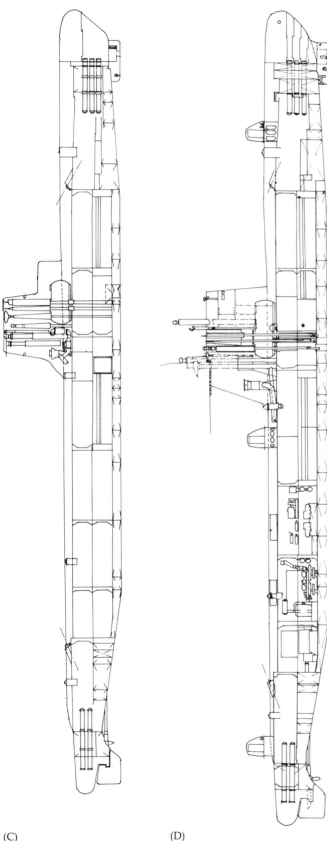

(C)

(D)

its after end. BQH-1 sound velocimeter transducers were on the side of the sail, above and somewhat abaft the DUUG-1 hydrophone, and, directly below, near the keel (they do not show here). The pumps have been moved aft into the former forward port engine room; the old pump room under the control room has been converted into an auxiliary radar operating space (including the WLR-1 ECM console) and sonar (fore end) and an electrical equipment space (aft).

(D) *Tiru* (SS 416) was a Guppy III fitted with PUFFS (three 10-ft vertical-line arrays); she is shown as in August 1972, after a refit at Charleston Naval Shipyard. Note her lengthened conning tower, enlarged to house new control instruments (such as a Mk 19 plotter and a Mk 66 torpedo control console). Note, however, that although the conning tower contained an azimuth-range indicator for the ship's BQS-4 active sonar and a bearing-time recorder (for BQR-2), it did not contain any console for the PUFFS passive ranger. That was in the sonar room a deck below. The 16-ft CW-406A chin sonar dome housed a DT-168/BQR-2B transducer (dashed lines) and a TR-141/BQS-4 transducer (the cylinder in the center of the passive array). Minor transducers in the same dome were, fore to aft: BQA-8 for self-noise monitoring (one of several distributed around the hull); BQH-2E (mounted on the bottom of the dome); two TR-232/WQC-2 for underwater communication; and a BQM-1 calibration transducer (for BQR-2). The four DUUG-1B hydrophones were arranged around the upper part of the forward PUFFS (BQG-4) sonar dome. The small darkened circles (on the SS-2 mast and on the hull well below it) are BQH-1 sound velocimeter transducers. Not shown are three air-emitting silencing belts: Prairie piping, near the stern, leading into the propellers; and vertical Masker piping (abaft the amidships PUFFS dome and about a quarter of the way aft from the fore end of the sail, extending up the sail). There was also a Masker piping line running along the bilge keel, as in *Grouper* (below). Masts, fore to aft, are: BRD-6 (port), with retracted IFF-UHF mast (carrying a retractable whip) alongside; SS-2 radar; No. 1 periscope (Type 8B) in its fairing; No. 2 periscope; ECM mast (AS-1071/BLR dome at top, below it AT-693/BLR to starboard and AS-371B/BLR to port, then the ring of AS-962/BLR, and then the array of short slanted dipoles of AS-994/BLR); the VLF loop (AT-317E/BRR); the snorkel intake (carrying an AS-1287/BRC whip); and the snorkel exhaust with its diffuser plate. The whip extended aft is AT-350B/BRC (it could be raised to the vertical). The device on the open bridge is a target bearing transmitter (TBT). In this ship the space forward of the control room was the sonar room (the pump room was still below the control room). The boxes aft over the engines are mufflers. Machinery shown in the former forward engine room is air compressors (both forward engines were removed). The two sections of the forward battery contained 126 (forward) and 68 (aft) cells; the two sections aft each contained 126 cells. By way of contrast, a fleet snorkel had 126 cells in each of her fore and aft sections.

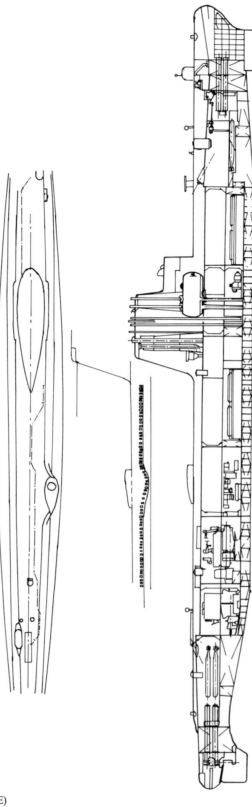

(E) *Grouper* (SSK 214), as newly converted to an ASW submarine. Her main sonars are the BQR-4 wrapped around her sail and the chin BQR-2, but she also has QHB (in the dome forward), JT (on deck forward), and BQS-3 (the two small ball-shaped objects, fore and aft). The small object on deck forward of JT is a QXB torpedo warning device. The sonar and intelligence room was built into the forward torpedo room, just below the QHB dome. The scrap views show the big radio buoy just abaft the sail (the buoy further aft is a messenger buoy, released by a bottomed submarine). Because it had to accommodate a big BQR-4 array, the submarine's sail was larger than that of a standard Guppy, but it had the same shape. Hence, the widened superstructure abeam the sail, shown in the scrap-plan view (the dashed lines in the plan are the safety line). Note that the JT hydrophone is offset to starboard. Masts, fore to aft, are: No. 1 periscope with ST range-only radar; No. 2 periscope; IFF-UHF mast; SS search radar; IFF/UHF mast to port; side-by-side ECM (ESM) DF mast (port) and UHF/ECM mast (starboard); MF-HF mast (port); VLF loop (starboard); snorkel induction (with AS-393/BLR on top); and snorkel exhaust.

(E)

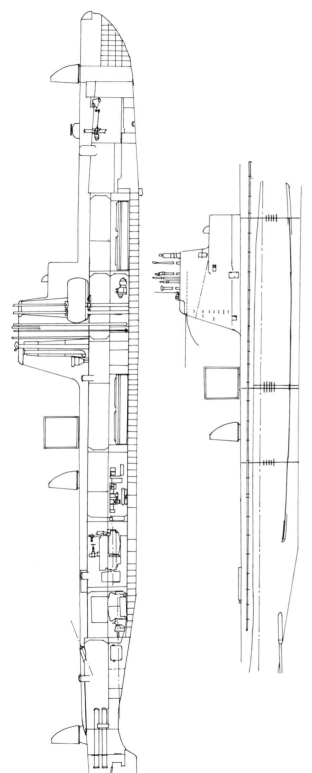

(F) *Grouper* (AGSS 214) was converted to an SSK and then to a sonar research submarine (AGSS); she is shown in May 1963, as modified at Philadelphia, with three PUFFS 10-ft line arrays on deck and a rectangular LORAD projector array (Colossus II) just abaft her sail. The scrap view shows air-emitting pipes used to sound-isolate her sonars by erecting bubble screens against noise transmitted through the water around her hull. They comprise three girth pipes (with guards) and a pipe running along her bilge keel (whose ends are shown). The long double line running along her side supports a line hydrophone. At this time she had not yet been fitted with a billboard array, to port. Her BQR-4 passive array was wrapped around her sail; it shows only in that the lower part extends somewhat further forward than in a Guppy. The dome on deck carries a BQR-3A trainable hydrophone (not shown is a BQM-1 calibration hydrophone on a short tripod mast forward of it). BQC and UQC underwater communications hydrophones were alongside this dome. The dashed diagonal line on the upper part of the sail is a floating wire antenna on the port side. Masts, fore to aft, are: No. 1 periscope (carrying an ST range-only radar); No. 2 periscope; SS radar; a mast (port side); the ECM mast (to port; the UHF-IFF mast was to starboard); the VLF loop antenna mast (starboard); the snorkel induction (carrying a whip and a Redeye missile seeker [the small rectangle on its after side]); and the snorkel exhaust. A lowered fairwater whip and a shorter mid-fed whip (to port) are visible extending abaft the sail. The pump room (which caused such trouble with the fairwater array) is visible directly under the control room. In this submarine both forward main engines were replaced by auxiliary machinery. An auxiliary generator was mounted between the two main engines. As in a fleet snorkel, there were 126 battery cells in each of the fore and aft tanks.

(F)

Because of the urgent need for the first two boats, they were completed without snorkels, which were not ready. The boats could be recognized by their narrow sails, bulged to house their SV air-search radars, and they were the fastest of the lot. No one could have expected their high speed. *Pomodon* made 17.9 kt at the 1-hr rate (18.2 kt at the ½-hr rate); *Odax* was slightly faster. She made 14.3 kt at the 1¾-hr rate. *Pomodon*'s captain considered her superior to a fleet boat in surface performance, although other captains found their boats quite wet.

Trials produced some unpleasant surprises. With full rudder, *Odax* heeled inboard about 8 degrees while turning at full power—a foretaste of the snap-roll problem. Fitted with a topside rudder for better maneuverability, *Amberjack* heeled about 15 degrees inboard. Rapid acceleration and radical application of rudder caused her to squat so badly that she often required as much as 15 degrees of dive angle on her stern planes.

As the Germans had found with their fast submarines, the Guppies had depth-keeping difficulties at high speed. A boat could too easily crash through her test depth. Snorkeling could be a problem. The designers provided stern stabilizing fins on the shaft lines. The fins lifted the stern,

so that rise was generally needed on the stern planes to keep the submarine level. A careful planesman could overcome the boat's instability, but the task was so difficult that on board *Odax* planesmen had to be relieved every half hour (and diving officers, at most, every 2 hr). *Odax* was modified with faster stern-plane action (3.85, rather than 2.73, degrees/sec) for faster recovery from stern-plane errors.

At high speed, everything happened extremely fast. At 11 kt, a boat with a 10-degree down-angle gained 200 ft—half her test depth—in only a minute. The submariners had been right to demand much more test depth in the *Tang*s. Existing gauges, which the planesmen followed, reacted too slowly. Moreover, the dynamics of the submarine were now so complex that the diving officer and planesmen could not always judge the consequences of their actions. It was now obvious that control itself had to be understood far better before the extraordinary capabilities of the fast new submarines could be fully exploited.

Like a Type XXI, a Guppy had devastating effects on existing ASW forces. Streamlining reduced active sonar detection range by about 10 percent, much as the stream-

The conversion of the prototype Guppies was so urgent that it could not wait for development of a satisfactory U.S. snorkel. *Pomodon* is shown at Mare Island, 27 June 1947. Note the retractable SV radar atop her sail and the retractable JT line hydrophone forward.

lining of jet engines reduced contemporary radar ranges. In anything over sea state 3, *Odax* could evade a destroyer escort by running directly into the sea, which did not affect her own speed. On the other hand, flow noise neutralized the submarine's own sonars; JT was useless above 7 kt, and WFA above 9 kt.

The first 2 boats were designated Guppy Is. The next 10, which were completed with snorkels, became Guppy IIs. In 1947, 12 more, including 4 *Tench* class suspended after WW II, were approved. Of these 24 boats, 7 were paid for out of remaining WW II funds; the rest came under FY 48–49 programs. The snorkel and extra periscopes cost a Guppy II about 10 percent in power near the surface.

These conversions were expensive, largely because their batteries required much more lead than in the past. The only overseas lead sources were in unfriendly hands (the Balkans) and in an unstable area (Burma). Fifteen conversions (SCB 47) were proposed in 1948 for the FY 50 program, but none survived the budget cuts. For FY 51, interest turned to a less expensive alternative, Guppy IA, in which Sargo cells replaced the special battery; she could make 15.0 kt submerged, compared with a nominal 16.5 for a full Guppy II. The results of a study by the Center for Naval Analyses strongly supported the Guppy IA concept on the theory that the more expensive battery could be added later. In 1949, the navy proposed 25 Guppy

IAs for FY 51. Initially, they were rejected, but 10 were restored early in 1950, together with 2 for the Royal Netherlands Navy and 2 for Italy (the latter were the only thin-hull fleet submarines converted to Guppies). The Dutch and Italian boats were sometimes called Guppy IBs because they had somewhat different equipment. Finally, 16 Guppy IIAs were authorized in the FY 52 program, for a total of 50 U.S. conversions (the Guppy Is were modified to Guppy II standards) and 4 for foreign navies. Two Guppy IIAs, *Razorback* and *Thornback*, had their hulls reinforced so that they could act as live targets for the new Mk 35 torpedo. They could be easily reconverted into full attack submarines (see Table 2–7).

Guppy IA was designed to be adaptable to a later SSK conversion, with a BQR-4 sonar wrapped around the bridge fairwater (see chapter 4). This was a hedge against the projected wartime need for large numbers of such craft. Guppy IIA had one main engine removed so that auxiliary machinery could be moved away from sonar transducers. Air conditioning was improved.

During the 1960s, many Guppies were silenced. Masker air lines produced a pair of bubble screens forward of the two engine rooms and others along the line of the bilge keel (and sometimes near the keel) outboard of them. Although the screens shielded the bow sonar from much of the engine noise, they did not protect the submarine

The sail of the Guppy II conversion, *Catfish* (shown at Mare Island on 28 April 1949 in the two photos above) contrasts with that of *Pomodon*. The large circular object is the snorkel induction. The portion abaft it, with the fins, lifts up to form the snorkel exhaust. The large circular hole is for the search radar, with the periscopes forward. Some Guppies had slimmer sails, the tops of which bulged out to accommodate the radar antenna and snorkel heads. The sonar dome forward of the sail accommodated a WFA transducer (from about 1954 on, this searchlight set was superseded by the BQS-2 scanning sonar). The retracted JT is barely visible further aft.

Table 2–7.   Typical Guppy Characteristics

	Fleet Snorkel	Guppy II	Guppy IA	Guppy IIA	Guppy III
Number	18	24	12	16	9
Displacement					
Surfaced (tons)	1,827	1,870	1,830	1,848	1,975
Submerged (tons)	2,400	2,440	2,440	2,440	2,450
Length overall (ft)	312	307	307	307	326.5
Beam (ft)	27	27	27	27	27
Draft (ft)	17	17	17	17	17
Surfaced speed (kt)	18.5	18.0	17.3	17.0	17.2
Cruise (kt)	13.5	13.5	12.5	13.5	12.2
Submerged speed					
Snorkel (kt)	6.5	9.0	7.5	8.0	6.2
Half-hour (kt)	10.0	16.0	15.0	14.1	14.5
Cruise (kt)	3.0	3.5	3.0	3.0	3.7
Engines	4	4	4	3	4
SHP	4,610	4,610	4,610	3,430	4,610
Battery	Sargo	Guppy	Sargo II	Sargo II	Sargo II

Note: Submerged cruise performance refers to 36-hr rate. Of Guppy IIs, only *Tiru* had three engines. Snorkel performance was on one engine. The figure for fleet snorkel conversions does not include the prototype *Irex* or conversions for foreign navies: seven austere fleet snorkels (two each for Greece, Turkey, and Italy; one for Venezuela), and eight standard fleet snorkels (four for Turkey, one for Italy, one for Greece, one for Spain, one for Pakistan). Four submarines already in Turkish service were given austere snorkel conversions (1954). Two Argentine and two Brazilian fleet submarines were fitted with snorkel-type sails but not with snorkels.

A special austere version of the fleet snorkel was developed for Turkey, Greece, and Italy. TCG *Inonu*, ex-USS *Blueback*, is pictured on 23 April 1953. She retained her 5-in/25 gun, and the front of her bridge was partly streamlined. The streamlined portion of the sail was limited to the new snorkel masts (induction forward, exhaust aft).

Fleet snorkels were a step down from Guppies. Streamlining was limited, no internal modifications were made, and plans initially called for the deck gun to be retained. Newly converted off Norfolk, *Runner* is shown on 17 April 1952. At least *Kraken, Torsk,* and *Medregal* also initially retained their 5-in/25 guns; within a few years, all fleet snorkels had surrendered their 5-in guns, although presumably they retained the necessary gun foundations. *Mapiro,* however, was converted to exactly this configuration (including the gun) for Turkey in 1960. A fleet snorkel could always be distinguished from a Guppy mainly by her bow, which was raked rather than rounded.

from detection as a result of that noise. Another silencer, Prairie, bled bubbles from the propeller to silence it. The Masker-Prairie air compressor replaced No. 2 main diesel engine.

A Guppy was far more than a minimum submarine conversion. The submariners wanted all active submarines to have snorkels. A total of 24 boats had been equipped: *Irex,* the snorkel prototype, and 21 Guppy IIs (*Cochino* already had been lost). As of early 1950, authorized active submarine strength was 75, including 10 special-purpose boats (SSP, SSR, SSG), *Manta* (torpedo target), and *Baya* (sonar test boat); 73 were in commission on 1 January 1950. The 9 boats under construction (six *Tang*s, three SSKs) would replace existing war-built units when they were completed. That left 32 attack submarines without snorkels. Particularly urgent were two snorkel-less Guppy Is. They received snorkels under the FY 52 program, which also included the 10 Guppy IAs and a snorkel for a missile submarine (SSG); however, the 1950 proposal for 16 more snorkel conversions was rejected. Instead, the navy converted 18 attack submarines to fleet snorkel boats by using FY 52 overhaul funds.

These were the most austere possible modernizations. The first and simplest version was applied in 1950 to two submarines, *Bumper* and *Blower,* for Turkey. Only the periscope shears were streamlined; the bridge had minimum modifications, and the 5-in guns were retained. Similar conversions were carried out for the Greek, Italian, and Venezuelan navies.

The U.S. conversions would have been similar. Instead, they were seen as the first stage of a possible ultimate Guppy IA conversion, providing only the snorkel piping and a streamlined fairwater at a cost of $450,000, compared with $9.2 million for a full conversion. Provision for the 5-in gun was retained, though few submarines ever carried

it. Nor was any fleet snorkel submarine converted to a full Guppy. A more elaborate conversion, in effect a Guppy minus the additional batteries, was considered but rejected.

Meanwhile, the outbreak of the Korean War resulted in an authorized total submarine figure of 120 (45 boats were recommissioned). This figure remained stable throughout the 1950s. Not all of the boats could have snorkels; it had to be accepted that those without them were adequate for simple ASW training.

By the late 1950s, the Guppies and fleet snorkels were clearly aging, but there was little hope of replacing them en masse. As with contemporary destroyers, the solution chosen in 1958 was the FRAM (fleet rehabilitation and modernization) program. In December 1958, the draft FRAM program called for 35 submarines (out of 48 surviving active Guppies) to be subject to FRAM II, which would extend their lives about 5 yr: 1 prototype under FY 59, 4 in FY 60, 8 in FY 61, and 11 in each of FY 62 and FY 63. In fact, the first 2 submarines were modernized under the FY 61 program, at which time 32 modernizations were planned. The number was later reduced to include only the 23 Guppy IIs and, finally, only 9 of them.

The result was called Guppy III. The main new feature was her ability to fire the Mk 45 nuclear torpedo, Astor. The submarine was lengthened by about 15 ft amidships to accommodate a new plotting room, and the conning tower was lengthened nearly 6 ft. She was fitted with the PUFFS (BQG-4) passive fire control sonar. The characteristic Guppy fairwater was replaced by a plastic nuclear submarine–style sail. Similar sails were installed aboard unrehabilitated Guppies and even fleet snorkels. The latter remained in service alongside Guppies as late as 1973. The last Guppy was not retired until 1975, well beyond its expected lifetime.

3

The Fast Submarine

THE U.S. SUBMARINE goal in 1945 was something far closer to Gemany's Type XXVI than to its Type XXI equivalents, the *Tang* and Guppy programs. The great surprise was that the Germans had done so little to realize a project advertised as nearly ready. (In June 1945, the British Commission in Germany asked whether the Blohm and Voss yard could build new Type XXVIs to order.) In fact, the Germans had neither the machinery nor anything like the hydrodynamic knowledge demanded by the project.

The United States and Britain had each received a scuttled Type XXVIB coastal U-boat powered by a 2,500-SHP Walter turbine.[1] The U.S. Navy salvaged the engine from its U-1406 and, together with a 7,500-SHP turbine planned for Type XXVI, set it up at the Naval Engineering Experimental Station in Annapolis. Many parts, clearly designed in a hurry, were inefficient and even dangerous. The U.S. Navy decided to examine alternatives to the Walter cycle.

Hydrodynamics was an unexpected problem. The Germans were proud of their wind tunnel tests of advanced submarine hulls, but that work had been superficial at best. The hull shape was dictated by the figure-eight pressure hull needed to accommodate large quantities of hydrogen peroxide. The German argument that so fishlike a form (much deeper than it was wide) must be efficient was no more than a rationalization.[2] The Germans also had not solved the high-speed underwater instability problem. Unless that could be overcome, no fast submarine, whatever its power plant, would be usable.

Work on a new power plant began with BuShips studies of alternatives (see Table 3–1). Type XXVI had been designed for a single 7,500-SHP turbine; apparently, because the new *Tang* would be about twice as large, the bureau decided that two Walter turbines or their equivalent would be needed. This power requirement, two shafts and 15,000 SHP, was maintained even after the plants had grown so large that they could not possibly fit a *Tang* hull. Full speed endurance was set at 10 hr, apparently because a larger U.S. submarine should exceed the 6.5 hr set for Type XXVI. BuShips also imposed a far more difficult demand of full power production at test depth (increased to 1,000 ft in May 1948). Any closed-cycle plant had to expend power to dump its exhaust product overboard against sea pressure. The Germans, for example, expected to lose power very quickly below 50 ft. The submarine would snorkel at 10 kt. The new power plant had to leave space for a large battery because the submarine would spend most of her time as a conventional diesel-electric boat. In 1948, she was expected to run at 15–20 kt for 1 hr and to make 18 kt surfaced while charging her battery at maximum rate. Minimum speed endurance was set at 48 hr.[3]

Because electric drive was not practical at the power levels contemplated, the turbines had to be geared to the propeller shafts.[4] Gearing was inherently noisy, and the program had to include work on quieter gearing. (BuShips had just gone through an elaborate program to eliminate the gearing that connected submarine electric motors to propeller shafts.) To eliminate reversing turbines, which would have consumed valuable space, the bureau invested in reversible-pitch propeller technology.

Later, the new plants were proposed for a very different role of providing a submarine radar picket (SSR) with a surface speed high enough to keep up with a fast carrier strike group. Existing diesels could not produce the 20,000 SHP needed for 25 kt. Characteristics for a fast SSR were issued in May 1952, and studies of gas turbine (e.g., Wolverine; see below) and steam (Ellis and Alton) plants were ordered that September. As in the case of the closed-cycle plants, nuclear power proved much more attractive. The only fast picket actually built was the huge *Triton* (see chapter 5).

The development of new power plants was hampered by postwar conditions. Defense funds were limited, and engineering talent was in short supply because it was attracted to the booming civilian economy. The prewar U.S. Navy had managed to finance its new high-speed diesels by adopting requirements specially suited to railroad use. Companies, such as GM, spent their own money on diesels suitable for naval use largely because they expected huge profits when the railroads adopted them. The prewar naval market itself had been far too small to attract large investments. Unfortunately, the new closed-cycle power plants had no apparent civilian application.

Nuclear power was the one important exception. It had

Ashore as a memorial near Portsmouth, New Hampshire, *Albacore* displays her hull form, her dorsal (sail) rudder, and her X-stern with contraprops. (Chris Cavas)

Table 3–1.   Closed-Cycle Submarine Designs, June 1948

	Tang	Gentry Gas Turbine	Ellis Steam Turbine	Wolverine Gas Turbine	Alton Steam Turbine
LBP (ft)	262	286	286	286	262
Beam (ft)	27	31	31	31	34
Draft (normal) (ft)	17	17.9	17.9	17.9	18.3
SHP (submerged)	4,750	15,000	15,000	15,000	15,000
Normal displacement (tons)	1,754	2,409	2,409	2,409	2,343
Maximum displacement (surfaced) (tons)	1,936	2,640	2,640	2,640	2,562
Submerged displacement (tons)	2,171	2,982	2,982	2,982	2,867
Standard displacement (tons)	1,553	1,860	1,860	1,860	1,810
Power plant weight (lb/SHP per 10 kt)	0.52	0.52	0.65	0.65	0.52
Speed submerged (kt)	18.5				
Speed at 15,000 SHP submerged (kt)	27.8	25.6	25.6	25.6	26.2
Fuel oil, normal (tons)	127	245	245	245	195
Fuel oil, maximum (tons)	311	480	480	480	418
Radius surfaced at 10 kt (nm)	15,300	22,200	17,800	17,800	17,950

obvious civilian applications, for which a naval power plant might become a sort of prototype. The Atomic Energy Commission (AEC) had been established partly to exploit nuclear power. It was able to finance any work that it considered ground-breaking. Thus, at least part of the expense of a prototype naval nuclear plant could be borne by an agency with fewer budget problems than the navy. Because of the AEC's special interests, it was quite willing to finance new kinds of reactors. That willingness, in turn, naturally influenced decisions on submarine design, probably most importantly the adoption of the submarine advanced reactor (SAR) for *Triton.*

Happily, the nuclear alternative was also the most attractive. None of the closed-cycle plants could run for more than a few hours at full power, whereas even the most primitive reactor surely could drive a submarine for an entire patrol. When a closed-cycle submarine's special oxidant had been exhausted, she had to revert to conventional snorkel operation unless the oxidant could be replenished at sea, an unlikely prospect. By 1946, most U.S. submariners apparently considered the closed-cycle project, like the fast battery submarine, an interim step toward their true goal, a nuclear submarine.[5]

BuShips held a conference on alternative closed-cycle plants in April 1946 and began a development program that June. It hoped, unrealistically as it turned out, that a plant would be available for installation in 1949. Each of the main alternatives was assigned a code name; in some cases, major components also were given code names, such as Widow for the Babcock and Wilcox pressure-fired boiler. The six major alternatives (with applicable code names) were:

1. Walter internal combustion condensing cycle (Alton)
2. external combustion condensing cycle (Ellis)
3. semiclosed-cycle gas turbine (Gentry and Wolverine)

4. free-piston gas generator, or gas turbine cycle
5. the closed-cycle diesel, the German Kreislauf (Gumbo)
6. nuclear reactor (Genie, a code name expressing the strong hopes it inspired)

Only the Walter and Kreislauf engines actually had been built. BuShips did not find either one directly usable. For example, the Germans had used a bed of porous ceramic stones impregnated with potassium permanganate in the Walter plant catalyst. The stones sometimes broke up and passed into the power turbine. BuShips substituted disks made of pure silver corrugated ribbon. Also, considerable effort was needed to achieve much performance at depth. By 1948, however, BuShips believed that its plant could achieve about 9 percent thermal efficiency at 1,000 ft, compared with the Germans' 6 percent at 300 ft.

In a Walter system, as hydrogen peroxide was decomposed in a catalyst chamber, it released enough energy to superheat the products (steam and oxygen) to about 1,450°F. This mixture was burned in a combustion chamber, cooled to about 1,300°F, and used to drive a gas/steam turbine. The steam was condensed, and the carbon dioxide exhaust was pumped overboard.

The plant was not usable on the surface because oxygen could not be substituted directly for hydrogen peroxide. Peroxide was also quite expensive.[6] In April 1948, the price was expected to be 60¢/lb, but the navy hoped to get it reduced to 25¢. About 9 lb were required per 1 lb of fuel burned, so each kilowatt-hour at full speed would cost $2–$3. This would total $20,000–$30,000/hr, or up to $300,000 per patrol. Existing diesel engines were rated at 1¢–2¢/kwh, or $100–$200/hr; a 75-day patrol consisted of 1,800 hr. On this basis, 10 hr on peroxide would cost as much as a full diesel-electric patrol. The use of peroxide would double total operating costs (the boat would still have to operate on diesel-electric power for most of her patrol). WW II experience suggested that, on average, each submarine would make 10 war patrols. In 1949, a fleet submarine cost about $10 million; peroxide operation would add $3 million.

The alternative oxidant, liquid oxygen, was far less expensive (about 4¢/lb, with 3.4 lb needed per 1.0 lb of fuel) and much easier to handle, but it had to be stowed in pressure tanks; special compensating tanks would be needed.[7] Oxygen for 10 patrols would cost $200,000. Fifteen oxygen submarines could operate for the operating cost of one peroxide boat ($3 million).

The Alton project was assigned to Allis-Chalmers.

External combustion (Ellis) meant a steam plant. When submerged, the boiler, using stored liquid oxygen, would run on a closed cycle. A pressured-fired boiler minimized size and improved efficiency. It had to run at 90 psi on compressed atmospheric air, when surfaced, but also at 600 psi on stored liquid oxygen. The latter was, by far, the highest in use for continuous combustion. The full Ellis plant would have included two boilers and two turbines, with only one boiler utilized below 10 kt.

Although no submarine was ever powered by an Ellis, the compactness of the pressure-fired plant was attractive for surface ships. The engines were used in U.S. ocean escorts of the *Brooke* and *Garcia* classes. Development contracts went to the Elliott Company, Babcock and Wilcox, Foster Wheeler, and Combustion Engineering.

The gas turbines Gentry and Wolverine resembled contemporary surface-ship plants. A modern open-cycle gas turbine uses air both as oxidant and as working fluid. Fuel is burned, but most of what passes through the turbine is hot air rather than combustion product. To operate in closed cycle, that is, to reduce the amount of air needed, Gentry and Wolverine required a separate working fluid. Oxidant was limited to the amout needed for mixing with fuel in order to heat it. On the surface, Gentry could be switched entirely to open cycle, but air could be used only as oxidant in Wolverine. The semiclosed-cycle plant was more complex, but it had the important advantage of needing far less air and was thus suitable for snorkel operation. Gentry had to be supplemented by diesels for snorkeling because it needed far too much air. In both versions, the closed-cycle working fluid was mainly carbon dioxide. It was compressed, heated (first by a regenerator, taking exhaust heat, and then in a combustion chamber), and run through high- and low-pressure turbines that drove both the compressor and the power shaft. The fluid then ran back through the cycle, with the exhaust gas removed at the compressor inlet and dumped overboard.

Gentry ran at constant temperature (1,500°F), with increasing pressure (up to 450 psi) to increase output. Wolverine initially ran at constant temperature (1,200°F), with increasing pressure (to 350 psi), and then temperature was increased to 1,550°F for full power. Because it offered so much power in a limited volume, Wolverine, in 1953, was considered a submarine radar picket power plant.[8] Unfortunately, a 20,000-SHP version was too massive:

93 ft long and a hull diameter of 20 ft. A plant redesigned for higher pressure likely would have come closer to acceptable dimensions.

Development contracts went to General Electric and Westinghouse. Surface ship gas turbine work was already well advanced; a big Allis-Chalmers engine was operating at Annapolis.

The free piston was a cross between a diesel and a gas turbine. As in a diesel, a combustion space lay between two opposed pistons. Instead of providing power via the pistons, however, the hot gas produced went into a turbine, which was far more efficient than a conventional cylinder. Some of the energy of combustion drove the pistons apart to build up energy for the next compression cycle. Free-piston engines were already being developed in Europe; the French Navy would later install them in *Sirius* class minesweepers and in the frigate *Commandante Bory*. In 1947, General Machinery Corp. was testing a free-piston gas generator, Westinghouse was building a turbine to be fed by two such generators (for ship service power), and Baldwin Locomotive Works was working on free-piston engines. No code name was assigned.

Closed-cycle diesel was attractive because it could be applied to existing submarines. It could not offer anything near the 15,000 SHP demanded of the other systems, so it appeared more applicable to auxiliary submarine types (see chapter 5) than to attack craft. U.S. forces had captured a German 1,500-BHP Daimler-Benz MB-501C (V-20) four-cycle submarine diesel adapted to closed-cycle operation. Some of the controls and most of the data had been lost or destroyed; the diesel was not set up until November 1946 (at Annapolis), but it was in operation by May 1947. When tests ended in April 1949, it was exceeding its wartime performance. Meanwhile, a U.S. project began in May 1946. As in the case of the snorkel, the question was whether the greater air flow requirements of a U.S. 2-cycle engine would be a problem. By December 1949, a standard General Motors submarine diesel (16-278A) was running under light loads. In January and March 1951, BuShips reported a variety of possible Kreislauf installations; by June, it seemed possible that one of them would be included in the FY 52 program.[9] BuShips suggested that the minelayer (SSM) then in the program be replaced by a Kreislauf or that an existing Guppy IIA or SSK be converted. In August 1951, however, the CNO decided that no Kreislauf would be installed in a submarine; the program died in October.

Initially, BuShips hoped to test each of the alternative closed-cycle plants in a submarine. By mid-1948, a common hull design had been selected for Gentry, Ellis, and Wolverine (Alton would fit a shorter hull); see Table 3–1. Funds were so short that one of the major alternatives had to be abandoned. The choice was difficult because none had reached the hardware testing stage. It fell on Gentry.

In 1950, the SCB assigned project number 67 to a closed-cycle submarine (SSX), with the hope of funding it and the nuclear prototype (SCB 64) in FY 52. Clearly, the new submarine would be far larger than a *Tang*. Preliminary characteristics, dated 28 April, called for nine bow torpedo tubes (six would be acceptable) and two stern tubes, with a total of 30 long torpedoes. That was impractical: it would be difficult to fit nine tubes in a conventional bow, and any attempt to do so might make it impossible for the SSX to reach the required 25 kt. At this time, BuShips hoped to have the prototype Walter (Alton) plant running by July 1950, the prototype liquid oxygen-steam (Ellis) plant by December 1950, and the prototype gas turbine (Wolverine) by October 1951. The plants would be subject to 18-mo testing before installation in submarines. Each would fit much the same dimensions, but details would vary. The Walter submarine might require increased beam (to 34 ft) to accommodate bags of hydrogen peroxide between its pressure and outer hulls.

It was now obvious that the SSX could not use the hull planned for the SSN. The closed-cycle power plant was only about half as heavy as the nuclear (lead shielding was very heavy), but the nuclear reactor was much shorter. Thus, as envisaged in 1952, the SSX was longer than the SSN (286 ft versus 250 ft) but about the same displacement (2409/2982 tons versus 2500/3000 tons).

None of the closed-cycle plants was on schedule. Moreover, as time passed, the submarine kept growing (see Tables 3–2 and 3–3). A quick study (September–December

Table 3–2.   Growth in Closed-Cycle Submarines, 1948–52

	Liquid Oxygen		Peroxide	
	1948	1952	1948	1952
LBP (ft)	286	321	262	293
Beam (ft)	31	30	34	33
Diameter (ft)	20	20	20	20
Standard displacement (tons)	1,860	2,170	1,810	2,085
Surface displacement (tons)	2,640	2,950	2,562	2,837
Submerged displacement (tons)	2,982	3,400	2,867	3,300
Surface speed (kt)	19	19	19	19
Submerged speed (kt)	25.1	24.0	25.6	24.5
Surface endurance at 10 kt	17,000	16,000	19,000	18,000
Underwater endurance (hr)	10	10	10	10
Underwater endurance (nm) at 3 kt (Maximum time underwater)	135	135	135	135
Oxidant (lb)	300,000	300,000	500,000	500,000
Battery (252 cells)	Guppy I	Sargo II	Guppy I	Sargo II
Reserve buoyancy	13%	15%	12%	16%

Table 3–3.   Reasons for Growth of Closed-Cycle Submarines, 1948–52

	Liquid Oxygen		Peroxide	
	Weight (tons)	Length (ft)	Weight (tons)	Length (ft)
Hydraulic ejection	25	——	25	——
Sargo II versus Guppy I	61	5-2¾	61	5-2¾
Hull fittings	50	——	50	——
Equipment and outfit	20	——	20	——
Machinery	46	10	22	7
Hull weight	108	20	97	26
Total	310	35-2¾	275	38-2¾

1951) showed that a closed-cycle plant shrunk to fit a *Tang* hull offered no real improvement in maximum underwater speed (16.5 kt), although endurance at that speed would increase from 1 hr to 10 hr. By 1952, the nuclear plant was so close to fruition that the intermediate step, the closed-cycle plant, was no longer particularly attractive. On the contrary, it was likely to be noisy and horribly complicated. SCB 67A was formally canceled on 26 October 1953; the relevant operational requirement was canceled four days later. The only closed-cycle plant to enter U.S. service was on board the midget submarine X-1 (see Appendix A).

Albacore was dramatically more maneuverable than her predecessors; at first, her gyrations were called "hydrobatics." Lt. W. J. Herndon is shown at her aircraft-style controls, 1955.

Albacore is shown off the Isles of Shoals on 5 April 1954. Note the auxiliary rudder at the after end of her sail and the enlarged rudder (taller vertical surface) at her stern. At this time, her propeller was still forward of the rudder.

The ballistic missile submarine *Ohio* displays two great innovations in control that were inspired by *Albacore* and introduced in the *Barbel* design: two-man aircraft-style control (at right) and push-button ballast control (at left). Each of two identical steering/plane consoles carries indicators of rudder angle, plane angles, course, and depth. Between them is the tactical display of the WLR-17 sonar intercept receiver; it provides the diving officer, who sits behind the planesmen, with assistance in evading an attacker. Although the submarine can be controlled by one person, normally both control positions are manned. The panels at the left control ballasting.

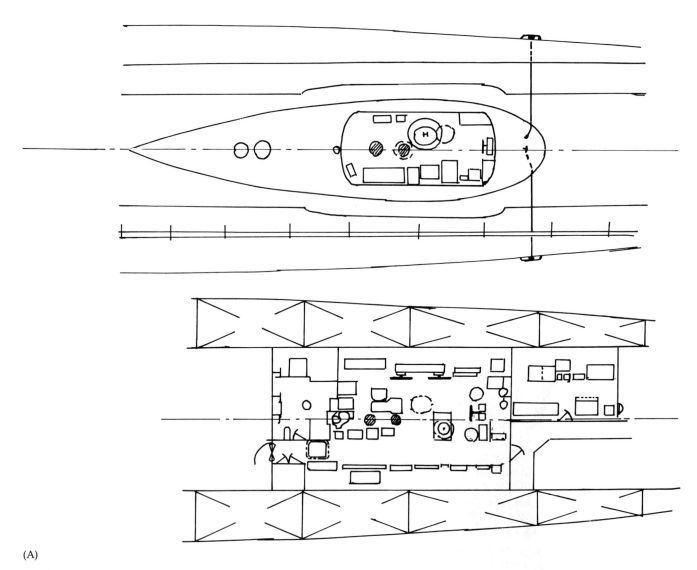

(A)

Submarine Control Arrangements

(A) *Grouper* (SSK 214) shows typical fleet submarine/Guppy control arrangements, with attack instruments concentrated in the conning tower (drawn above the control room in the pressure hull). The port side of the conning tower accommodated the console of the main search radar (SS) and, forward of it, the remote indicator of the QHB scanning sonar. The large box on the opposite side of the conning tower is the torpedo data computer. This side also accommodated the dead-reckoning tracer (DRT). At the fore end is the main steering stand. The control room below is devoted mainly to diving control (an ECM [actually ESM] room is located at the after port end). The main items on the port side are, aft to forward (left to right), the trim manifold, the diving station (with wheels for the fore and aft planes), and the hydraulic plant. On the other side are the air manifold and electrical control panels. This space also accommodates the auxiliary steering stand. Although these drawings show the ship as a sonar test unit, she retained much of her original control arrangement (she did have a special sonar room well forward). Note the piping for silencing air forward of the sail, and the hydrophone support to starboard. Periscopes are shaded in for clarity.

(B) *Tiru* (SS 416, shown in 1972, *facing page*) was a Guppy III with a conning tower enlarged to accommodate modern fire-control instruments. The main steering station in the conning tower has been eliminated, leaving only a steering stand in the control room below. Instruments in the conning tower, aft to forward, on the port side are: the TDC; a recorder; an intercom unit; the SS radar transmitter/receiver; a wiring plugboard; navigational electronics (UPN-12 and UQN-1B sounder); the SPA-4B radar repeater; and an amplifier. On the starboard side, aft to forward, are: a power distribution panel; the Mk 66 torpedo console (to control wire-guided Mk 48 torpedoes); the angle solver; the fire-control switchboard; the BQS-4A azimuth/range indicator; an azimuth recorder (BTR); the Mk 19 plotter (for TMA estimates and PUFFS plotting); and the DRT. In a separate sonar room below were the PUFFS electronics. The control room in the pressure hull surrounds a separate radio room (aft end) and a separate sonar room (fore end). The big handwheels controlling the planes are visible at the diving station just forward of the radio room. The steering stand is slightly to port, just abaft the sonar room. The big console on the after side of the sonar room is for PUFFS (BQG-4); atop it is a target simulator. Other equipment in this space includes BQS-4A and BQR-2B displays (along the forward bulkhead) and the DUUG-1 (Velox), the foremost item on the port side. The top of the bridge has been drawn in above the conning tower. The cutouts aft of the cockpit are for lookouts. The two side-by-side masts abaft them are for BRD-6 (to port) and for UHF/IFF (AS-523B/BPX, with an AT-818/BRC retractable whip protruding over the side) to starboard. On the centerline is the SS-2 radar antenna (the object to port is a TR-167A/BQH-1 transducer). Then come the two periscopes, with the ECM (actually ESM) mast abaft them (carrying AS-371B/BLR, AS-1071/BLR, and AT-693/BLR antennas). Abaft it is the loop antenna (AT-317E/BRR). At the after end are the snorkel induction (carrying an AS-1287/BRC whip) and the broad diffuser plate of the snorkel exhaust. On the port side is the AT-350B/BRC mid-fed whip.

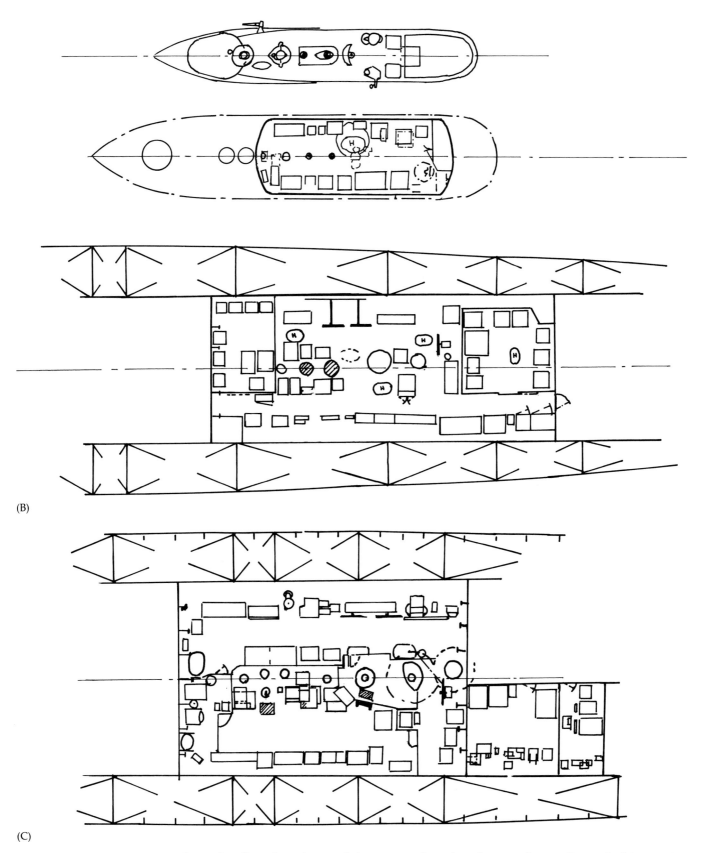

(B)

(C)

(C) *Trout* (SS 566, as in 1970) shows the effect of moving attack instruments down into the control room. Forward of the attack center (starboard side) are a radio room and, forward of that, a sonar room. As in World War II–fleet submarines, the wheels of the diving station are on the port side, with manifolds fore and aft. The steering stand is forward of the periscopes, just to starboard. Alongside it are sonar repeaters, with radar and ESM controls alongside the masts running roughly down the centerline. Most of the starboard side is occupied by the Mk 101 FCS and the Mk 18 angle-solver controlling wire-guided torpedoes. Mast control boxes are shaded for clarity. Portsmouth's *Tang*s (SS 563, 565, 567) all had side-by-side periscopes; Electric Boat's SS 564, 566, and 568 all had them in tandem.

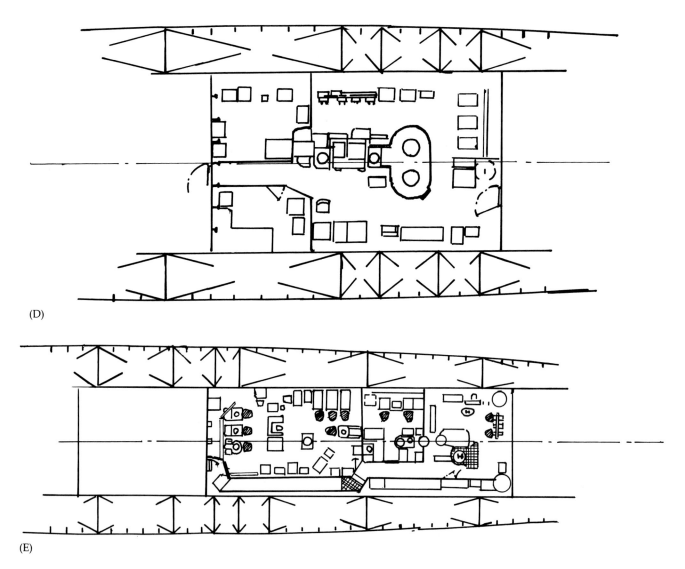

(D)

(E)

(D) *Darter* (SS 576) shows the next stage of evolution. At the after end of the control/attack space are the radio room (to port) and the sonar room (to starboard). The periscopes are side by side, to save length. The two-man airplane-type diving station is against the forward port bulkhead of the control room, but there are still conventional ballast controls (on the after port side of the space). The Mk 101 FCS and (abaft it) the DRT are arranged along the starboard side of the attack center. In the sonar room (on the forward side) is a BQR-2B indicator (steerable beam and BTR), alongside the BQR-2B azimuth indicator; the BQS-2 display is at the after starboard end of the sonar space. The contemporary *Skate*s had a similar transitional arrangement, retaining the older type of ballast control.

(E) *Sailfish* (SSR 572) shows a large air-control space abaft her control room. The cordoned-off space to port in the control room is the radio room; there is no separate sonar room. *Sailfish* was essentially a modified version of a World War II–fleet submarine, so she had much the same control arrangement: planes controlled from her control room, the main steering station (and attack instruments) above in the conning tower. In the big air-control center, note the row of three interceptor-control stations up against a status board, at the after end of the space. The U-shaped structure at the center of the space was an evaluation desk. Three radar repeaters are arranged along the port side. Operators' seats are shaded for clarity.

(F)

(F) *Barbel* introduced push-button ballast control and the modern arrangement of control spaces. On the forward bulkhead to port are the two helmsmen/planesmen. Abaft them is the ballast-control panel. The ECM (ESM) console is shown against the after port bulkhead of the control space. The starboard side of the space is the attack center, with the chart space at its forward end. The FCS and TDC are shown near the starboard side. In the center of the space is the raised periscope stand, on which the CO stands. Operators are shaded for clarity.

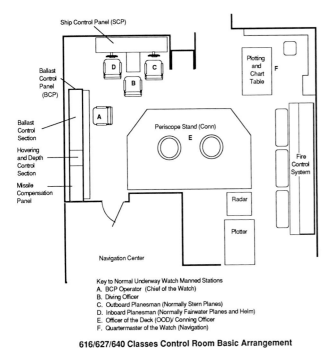

616/627/640 Classes Control Room Basic Arrangement

Ship Control Panel (SCP)

Ballast Control Panel (BCP)

Ballast Control Section

Hovering and Depth Control Section

Missile Compensation Panel

Periscope Stand (Conn)

Plotting and Chart Table

Fire Control System

Radar

Plotter

Navigation Center

Key to Normal Underway Watch Manned Stations
A. BCP Operator (Chief of the Watch)
B. Diving Officer
C. Outboard Planesman (Normally Stern Planes)
D. Inboard Planesman (Normally Fairwater Planes and Helm)
E. Officer of the Deck (OOD)/ Conning Officer
F. Quartermaster of the Watch (Navigation)

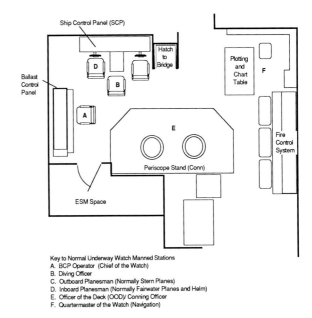

Skipjack Class Control Room Basic Arrangement

Ship Control Panel (SCP)

Hatch to Bridge

Ballast Control Panel

Plotting and Chart Table

Fire Control System

Periscope Stand (Conn)

ESM Space

Key to Normal Underway Watch Manned Stations
A. BCP Operator (Chief of the Watch)
B. Diving Officer
C. Outboard Planesman (Normally Stern Planes)
D. Inboard Planesman (Normally Fairwater Planes and Helm)
E. Officer of the Deck (OOD)/ Conning Officer
F. Quartermaster of the Watch (Navigation)

(G)

(G) Control/Attack Center arrangements for a typical SSBN (left) and for a *Skipjack*-class attack submarine (right). Both are similar to the arrangement in *Barbel*, with airplane-style controls and a push-button ballast-control panel. The SSBN has a Mk 113 fire-control system that is substantially larger than the Mk 101 on the *Skipjack*. Further aft is a sonar room. *Thresher/Permit*- and *Sturgeon*-class arrangements were similar to those in the SSBNs. (Jim Christley)

(H) Sonar, control, and attack arrangements in an "Improved" *Los Angeles*-class submarine (SSN 719 or later). To port, note the integrated control/ballast console, as in the *Ohio* class. To starboard, the sonar room (with four two-screen ICDC displays) is forward of the attack center (BQQ-5C and later versions of the earlier BQQ-5 sonar have four ICDCs; earlier versions of the sonar have three). This space also contains a performance-monitoring console and a raw video display. The consoles in the attack center are a Mk 92 attack-control console, next to a Tomahawk weapon-control console and three Mk 81 weapon-control consoles (for torpedoes and Harpoon missiles). Pre-Tomahawk ships, with the Mk 117 all-digital attack center (ADAC), had two Mk 81s next to a Mk 92, with another Mk 81 on the after side of it. Because all the Mk 81s are connected to the same digital computer (and because they have general-purpose raster-scan displays), they are interchangeable. Typically, a pair of Mk 81s is manned by a pair of target trackers; the attack-control console, which actually fires weapons, is manned by the weapons system officer. For example, one of the trackers may be responsible for a MATE TMA solution on the target, while the other watches a digital version of the classic pair of fire-control dials—showing submarine and target courses—to monitor the accuracy of the fire-control solution. Other Mk 81 display formats include

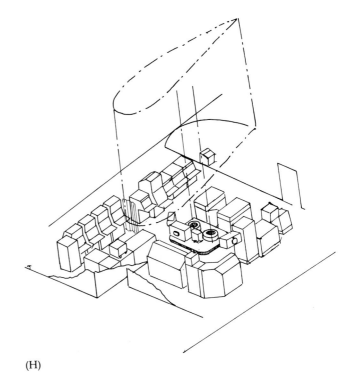

(H)

multiple-target tracking, weapon-attack evaluation, and generation of computer-recommended weapon presets based on the weapon model, target solution, and environment. The big console next to the ship-control console is for navigation. Other consoles in this space serve the surface-search radar and the ESM antennas; there is also a dead-reckoning tracer (DRT). Two bearing and range indicators (BRIs) hang above the periscope stand, the edge of which is shaded. The two periscopes have been omitted for clarity (their centerlines and wells are shown). Across from the sonar room are the CO's and XO's staterooms. Abaft the attack center is the radio/ECM room; abaft the control room is the navigational equipment space.

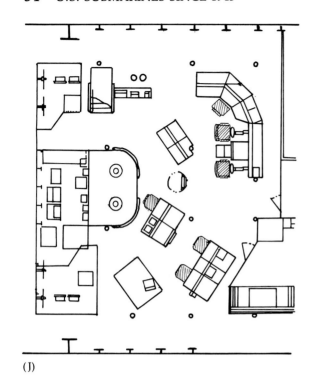

(J)

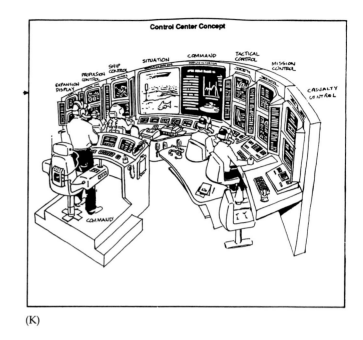

(K)

(L)

(J) The *Ohio* (SSBN 726)-class control space includes a much-simplified FCS limited to firing Mk 48 torpedoes and decoys. The ship-control console to starboard includes the ballast-control panel and the usual two-man airplane-type controls. The periscope stand occupies the centerline, overlooking the one-man command display console showing sonar data. Forward and to starboard of it is a two-man defensive weapons system (DWS) console. Aft of the DWS is the DRT table with a BRI above it

The experience of other navies suggested that the U.S. decision was absolutely correct. The British concentrated on the Walter plant and, by all accounts, were more than glad to abandon it.[10] The Soviets built a unsuccessful Walter submarine, Project 617. They had begun work on a Kreislauf plant before WW II and, in the 1950s, built the Kreislauf-powered Quebec class (Project 615). Once they

had a functioning nuclear reactor, however, they abandoned all such exotica.

As had been suspected in 1946, nuclear power solved the closed-cycle problem. On the other hand, it imposed high costs and demanded large submarines; therefore, some interest in closed-cycle plants survived. A new candidate, the fuel cell (originally called the primary battery),

(J, *Continued*) (another is off the periscopes, near the periscope stand). Both display target-position data. The DWS (FCS Mk 118) console consists of a pair of digital standard information displays (SIDs) flanking a Mk 92 attack console. The operators interact with their SIDs during target motion analysis (TMA) and use them to preset and control a weapon. A Mk 92 is used to select a weapon or countermeasure and launch it. Although typically one SID operator is responsible for contact position and motion analysis and the other for weapon orders, the SIDs are fully interchangeable (because they are merely displays, linked to the same computer), and either SID operator can conduct an entire attack, from TMA through launch and torpedo guidance. The console is linked to a three-bay UYK-7 computer. One peculiarity of the system is that it has no fire-control switchboard. Instead, each torpedo tube has its own firing circuit (one firing control per tube is provided on the Mk 92). Because there are only two tube-launched devices (a Mk 48 torpedo and a MOSS decoy), there is no need for any weapon-select switch. Instead, the unmanned console in the torpedo room has cables for both weapons, which are manually connected to the appropriate tubes (and which must be changed if a different device is loaded in the tube). The net effect is considerable simplification; a Mk 118 requires only about a quarter as many fire-control cables as its predecessor a Mk 113 in earlier strategic submarines. The SIDs also control decoys launched through the external 6-in countermeasures tubes under the sail, and they can control the separate 3-in countermeasures launcher. The computer software has some of the features planned under SUBIC for future strategic submarines. It has "search" and "avoidance" modes, in which environmental data are used to calculate and display detection areas around the ship to show those bearings that favor detection of a target or make own-ship detection least likely. An operations summary module displays own ship and target(s). Using a defensive-tactics module, an operator can ask "what if" questions to see the effects of own-ship and target maneuvers on attempts to trail the ship. Other software modules include evasive tactics and a system alert to indicate the presence of high-threat targets. Like that of a Mk 113/117, the software includes techniques for passive ranging. Initially, each contact is processed automatically (using Kalman automatic sequential target motion analysis [KAST]) to give a quick estimate of relative location. The operator can refine data for a particular target using techniques such as manual adaptive TMA (MATE), KAST edit, Ekelund ranging, and depression/elevation (angle) ranging. Seats are shaded for clarity.

(K) SOAS (Submarine Operational Automation System), a Martin-Marietta (formerly General Electric) project begun for the Defense Advanced Research Projects Agency (DARPA), is a possible future direction for submarine control. The hope is that very powerful distributed computers can integrate all available information on board the submarine, sharing it across all ship components. The submarine command function is broken down into functional units: control (navigation/steering), tactical con-

trol (sensor use and weapon control), mission control (executive function), power control, and casualty control. In a *Seawolf*, these functions require, respectively, 20, 36, 5, 51, and 22 men, for a total of 134. SOAS designers believe that each function can be reduced to a single display console, requiring a single operator (three for continuous manning), reducing the crew to 15 men. One argument in favor of such information integration is that, particularly in a fast-changing situation (such as an ambush by another submarine), the different functions are not really independent. For example, the proper reaction to an incoming torpedo will probably combine evasive maneuvers (ship control), acceleration (power control), weapon firing (tactical control), and preparation for a possible casualty. The success of such a program requires that the computers integrate information from all sensors, including the periscope, ESM, and radar. Thus, the success of programs for optronic (non-penetrating and unmanned) periscopes becomes a possible prerequisite for the appearance of SOAS and its analogs. SOAS concepts include automated multimission planning and tactical management, automated resource management, and automated sensor processing. The goal of a very small crew, which is attractive to cut life-cycle costs, can be met only if the submarine can operate essentially without maintenance at sea. As of mid-1993 Martin-Marietta is trying to sell SOAS ideas for inclusion in the new "Centurion"-class submarine.

(L) The submarine control space of the future (in the projected FY 65 ASW submarine), as developed under the SUBIC program. Note the absence of a periscope stand: this submarine would have had a non-penetrating electro-optical (television, in this case) periscope. The console on the left is the ship-control station, with its joystick for single-man control. Next to it is a three-man fire-control station, with a big CRT (tactical display) flanked by arrays of smaller ones (four target analyzers and a weapon and tube panel). It could direct four weapons to engage four targets simultaneously. Operators could interact directly with the evolving TMA solutions. Unlike existing consoles, this one could automatically evaluate weapon kill probabilities. The other three consoles shown are for sonar surveillance, to carry out five distinct functions: passive initial detection, frequency monitoring, classification, passive tracking, and active tracking. A DIMUS-type preformed-beam sonar would have been used for initial passive detection. DEMON and BSM recorders were added to present refined frequency analysis (Lofargrams). Passive ranging and active-range and range-rate analyses were automated. The shapes on the floor show an operations station (on the left) and a pair of monitoring stations. The operations station centralized control of radar, ECM (ESM), navigation, internal voice communications, and the television periscope. In the center is the command station. The ship-control station would have been used for steering/diving and for ballast and trim control. Its principal display would have been SQUIRE (Submarine Quickened Response). This drawing is based on one in the 1962–63 report of the SUBIC program.

surfaced in the late 1950s.[11] During the 1980s, several companies abroad began to offer low-powered closed-cycle engines for air-independent propulsion (AIP) that supplemented existing diesel-electric power plants and allowed submarines to loiter for extended periods without drawing down their batteries. This was a different proposition from the 1946 BuShips program. The main current candidates are Kreislauf, the fuel cell, and the Stirling engine (an external combustion piston engine); such engines are now being adopted by Sweden and Germany. The Soviets also tested AIP systems. Given the enormous tactical advantages of nuclear power, it seems unlikely that the U.S. Navy will reverse its 1953 decision.

The hydrodynamics and control problems were assigned to the David Taylor Model Basin. The first surprise was that virtually no work had been done on submarine resistance at high speed. The basin's approach, then, was to determine the fundamental factors in underwater resistance by running a series of abstract hull forms. It then planned to test the effects of necessary distortion and also of such appendages as the bridge fairwater and the control surfaces.

Airships seemed to be the closest analogs to submarines, so the basin tested airshiplike bodies of revolution, with varying length-to-diameter ratios and nose and tail shapes.[12] The models formed Series 58. As published in classified form in April 1950 (and later declassified), the Series 58 report amounted to a prescription for the fastest possible submarine hull. A length-to-diameter ratio of 6.8 was ideal, although anything between 5 and 9 was acceptable.[13] A smoothly tapered hull was most efficient, but a tubular hull of the right dimensions (which would be far easier to arrange internally) would not be too much worse. Supplemental studies showed that a single propeller would have, by far, the greatest propulsive efficiency.

None of these tests solved the control problem. In 1949, the Panel on the Hydrodynamics of Submerged Bodies of the Committee on Undersea Warfare, National Academy of Sciences, proposed that the navy build an experimental submarine, an underwater equivalent of the X-series aircraft that the air force was then buying, for the specific purpose of exploring control problems. This design became Albacore (AGSS 569). A proposal that both hull shape and control surfaces be variable was rejected, but Albacore was rebuilt several times to test alternative configurations.

The experimental submarine had to be faster than a Guppy, at least as fast, ideally, as the projected 25-kt closed-cycle and nuclear submarines. Otherwise, once completed, the new submarines might encounter conditions not yet experienced by the test submarine. Rear Adm. C. B. Momsen, ACNO for undersea warfare (i.e., for submarines), gave the designers a free hand to pursue speed by using a hydrodynamically ideal form, even though it might be entirely unsuited to operational service. To achieve high speed, the designers wrapped the smallest and most ideal Series 58 hull (circular section, with no parallel midbody, with a single propeller on its axis)

around a 7,500-SHP Westinghouse double-armature motor. For surface running, the submarine had half a Tang plant (two pancakes, which minimized length and weight devoted to diesels). To save space, the motor and engine controls were concentrated so that a single crewman could operate them. Albacore was given a double hull, apparently so that she could survive the impacts of dummy Mk 35 torpedoes if she was used as a target (as the characteristics envisaged; see below).[14] To keep her sail small, Albacore was not given a snorkel, although provision was made for future installation. For the same reason, she was also provided with a single multipurpose antenna mast, a concept followed in later designs.

Albacore was designed to the usual one-compartment standard; she could float on her ballast tanks with any one compartment flooded. Because the hull had so large a diameter, the only way to hold down compartment volume (and thus to satisfy the requirement) was to minimize compartment length. Previous submarines had ballast valves in their control rooms, but they would have crowded Albacore's much shorter one. The solution, which was applied to later submarines, was the push-button ballast control that is now standard. Lack of space also encouraged the designers to adopt one-man aircraft-type controls that integrated the planes and rudders.

The power plant, particularly the battery, was so heavy that pressure hull weight had to be cut. There was already a healthy respect for diving depth, however; at high speed it would be easier for a submarine to crash through her test depth. On the weight available, the usual high-tensile steel would buy only 500 ft of test depth. Albacore became the first U.S. submarine to use HY-80, then called low-carbon HTS. The outer hull and frames were ordinary HTS; the pressure hull shell was HY-80. Adoption of the new material bought another 100 ft, but this was still short of the current standard of 700 ft. Structural tests on a scale model using the new material showed that diving depth would be determined by new modes of collapse, so existing calculations were no longer valid.

The formal characteristics called for a speed of 25.5 kt; by February 1950, BuShips was predicting a maximum speed of 25 kt at the $\frac{1}{2}$-hr discharge rate.[15] These spectacular figures hinted at particularly high future speed. For example, a speaker at the Fifth Underwater Symposium (1950) pointed out that the 67,000-SHP power plant, easily accommodated by a 3,000-ton destroyer, would drive a 3,000-ton submarine at 50 kt. Similar figures were presented at a Submarine Officers Conference in 1956.[16] Also in 1956, Albacore, with a modified stern, was credited with about 26.0 kt, and she could make 22.6 kt at the 1-hr rate. Although perfectly straightforward consequences of the Series 58 tank tests, Albacore's speed runs made a much stronger impression than did the abstract test report.

It might seem that Albacore was conceived as a test of Series 58, the hydrodynamic prototype of a new kind of attack submarine. The record shows otherwise.[17] From the first, Albacore was intended as a control test vehicle. The project was so vital that she was moved back from the FY 51 program to FY 50, using funds initially earmarked to convert *Fletcher*-class destroyers to ASW escorts. To cover her true purpose, the new submarine was often described as a target (SST). That was a secondary role, to be assumed after the hydrodynamic/control tests were completed.

The body-of-revolution hull turned out to be dynamically stable at all speeds, yet easy to dive and much more maneuverable in the vertical plane than conventional hull forms. By way of contrast, Guppies and *Tangs* were unstable above 8 kt because their flat decks acted as diving planes, so small-pitch angles soon developed into larger ones. Because *Albacore* did not suffer from this problem (she had no flat deck), she could explore the question of just how stiff a submarine should be in the vertical plane. Should she maneuver very freely for evasion and attack, or should she be protected from accidental dives toward test depth? After all, at a 30-degree down-angle, a future 30-kt submarine would dive 500 ft in only 20 sec. *Albacore*'s controls were given variable stiffness. Vertical maneuvers, however, were so obviously valuable that she could not be completely protected against accidental dives. Instead, throughout her career, there was considerable interest in dive brakes for emergency recovery from uncontrolled dives.[18]

Albacore adopted the aircraft-style single-man controls that the Germans had used in their wartime fast submarines.[19] She was so much like an underwater aircraft that her first pilots trained on blimps before "flying" her. On early trials, the single pilot found it difficult to keep a steady course at high speed because he tended to overreact. He needed new instruments, such as a rate-of-dive indicator to help him know he was pulling out of a dive. *Albacore* also had an autopilot incorporating an analog computer, which helped smooth out maneuvers (e.g., reduce noise and turbulence).

The big control surfaces had unexpected effects. The worst surprise was snap roll. When the submarine turned, her sail acted as a hydroplane. Its lift, exerted sideways, flipped her over to one side. Now, the rudder acted partly as a diving plane. The sail, flipped over, also acted as a diving plane, and one far larger than the control surfaces. Any turn was inevitably accompanied by a dive—the sharper the turn, the steeper the dive. The faster the speed of the submarine, the worse the problem became. The after edge of *Albacore*'s sail carried a dorsal rudder (12.5 percent of the full chord of the sail) controlled by the pilot's foot pedals that was intended to alleviate snap roll. Using the dorsal rudder imposed great loads on the sail structure, however, and it was little used. Both the dorsal rudder and the large conventional rudder tended to act as brakes (sea anchors).

Interaction between turning and up-or-down trim was not new, but it had not been so drastic in earlier, more sluggish submarines. Both U.S. fleet submarines and German Type XXIs trimmed up by the bow as they turned while submerged because both had round bottoms and

flat decks. The hull itself generated lift when it turned but not when it ran straight. *Albacore* did not feel this particular effect because her hull was symmetrical.

Like *Albacore*, later U.S. submarines dispensed with the earlier combination of helmsman and two planesman (bow and stern) on the ground that they could not react quickly enough or fully exploit a submarine's maneuverability. Instead of single-man control, however, two men were retained (planesman plus one helmsman), specifically to deal with snap roll. As the submarine turned and began to dive, the helmsman used the rudder to fight the dive. Many navies later adopted single-man control, with the aid of a computer to coordinate the controls. The U.S. Navy has resisted this practice on the grounds that such systems can be fatally unreliable and that human reflexes are quite fast enough. Possibly, the coming generation of submarine combat systems, which may be required to make snap responses to short-range threats, will demand acceptance of some form of computerized helm/plane control.

During her career, *Albacore* went through five distinct configurations, or phases. Her designers wanted to place the control surfaces forward of the large propeller, but the idea was rejected on the ground that a similar configuration had failed in the original *Holland* of 1900 and in the World War I *S-3*.[20] As completed (Phase I), *Albacore* had control surfaces abaft her single large propeller, as in a German Type XVII. They were extremely effective at low speed but too effective at high speed (aircraft-type trim tabs were used instead). There were also small folding bow planes. Their machinery took up much of the space in the forward room, and it was difficult to align. The bow planes were not really necessary because *Albacore* rarely operated either at periscope depth or at low speed (situations in which bow planes would have been valuable). They also added drag.

In Phase II (1956), the stern control surfaces were moved forward of the propeller. As in later single-screw submarines, a plastic sonar dome carrying a BQS-4 sonar and a larger, quieter slower-turning propeller (14-ft, rather than 11-ft, diameter) were fitted. Silencing techniques were tested. All machinery and hull piping was sound-isolated from the hull on rubber pads. The interiors of all free-flooding spaces were coated with Aquaplas, a water-based plastic, to absorb vibration and dampen water-flow noise.[21] The dorsal sail was deactivated; operators found that they could reduce snap roll by turning the rudder more slowly. The bow planes were removed.

Work on SCB 182, a Phase III conversion funded under the FY 59 program, began in 1957 and was completed in August 1961. The ship was fitted with a new X-stern, inspired by airship practice. It was expected to make for sharper turns, so a bigger dorsal rudder was installed and its machinery reactivated, together with a circle of 10 hydraulically operated dive brakes (unfortunately hinged on their leading edges and inside the boundary layer) and a drag parachute taken from a B-47 bomber at the upper

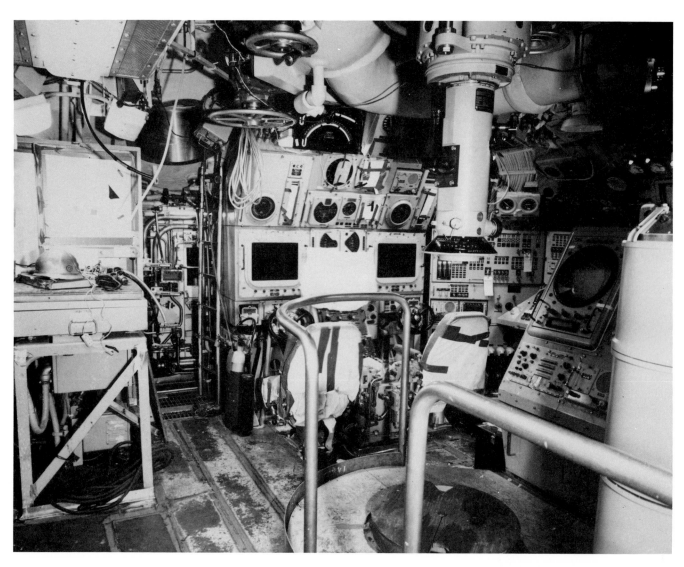

Combat operations center (COC) of USS *Archerfish* (SSN 678) as completed, 23 June 1971 (*above and facing*). Alongside the periscope stand (to port; the view showing the steering station has been reversed, left to right) is a display console for the BQS-13 sonar system. Note the rectangular window for the bearing-time recorder. The small CRT is the remote azimuth-range indicator (for active pinging); the larger one is for an A-scan. In the sonar space, the small CRT would be carried above the large one on the active-sonar console. On the starboard side is the Mk 113 fire-control system, with its digital computer against the hull of the submarine. The space has been named COC because it is no longer possible to separate attack and control centers.

after corner of the sail. (The parachute ripped off on the third or fourth trial.) The X-stern and dive brakes were potential solutions to the crash-dive problem. The planes in the X-stern had to turn in a coordinated way to dive, so no single mechanical failure could cause a crash dive. Because it made inadvertent dives much less likely, the X-stern itself could make violent maneuvers safer. With less chance of an accidental dive, a submarine could run at high speed much closer to maximum operating depth. The X-stern almost halved *Albacore*'s submerged turning circle, from 300 yd to 165 yd (*Tang* turned in 340 yd).[22] The control surfaces of X-sterns also achieved the same

effect as larger (draggier) conventional ones. The X-stern was rejected for production submarines, however, largely because it required computer control at a time when computers were justly distrusted as unreliable.[23] In practice, too, the X-stern aggravated control problems. A conventional rudder acted partly as a diving plane when a submarine snap-rolled; in the X-stern, the rudder was already at an angle to the vertical. Also, surprisingly, there was sometimes no control at all going astern submerged.

Alternative stern configurations considered at this time included a ducted propeller with control surfaces abaft it, a shroud ring mounted ahead of the propeller, and small

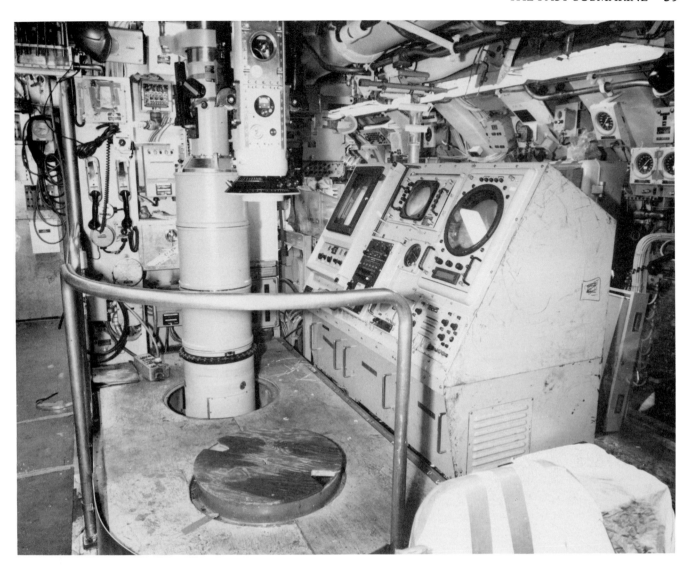

planes with pump outlets inducing controlled flow over the planes (equivalent to blown flaps in an airplane).

In Phase IV, under the FY 61 program conducted between December 1962 and February 1965, a new high-capacity silver-zinc battery (the metal for this had to be borrowed from the U.S. Treasury) and electrically driven contraprops were installed. (The second propeller was driven by a second 7,500-SHP motor.)[24] Maximum speed rose to 33 kt; in February 1966, *Albacore* was credited with the world record for underwater speed.[25] *Albacore* was tested with the propellers closer together or farther apart. For greater safety at high speed, a new vernier control system reduced control-surface movements as speed in-

creased. A new emergency hydraulic system of increased capacity powered the dorsal rudder and dive brakes. An aircraft-type semiautomatic propulsion control system was installed. During this period, *Albacore* tested a new, very high-pressure (3,000-psi) ballast-blowing system that was intended to correct the problem revealed when *Thresher* was lost (she was unable to blow her tanks at depth).

A Phase V conversion was carried out from August 1969 to August 1971; tests followed from September 1971 to June 1972. Reportedly, viscous polymers were blown from near her bow over her hull to improve laminar flow and thus drastically reduce resistance.[26]

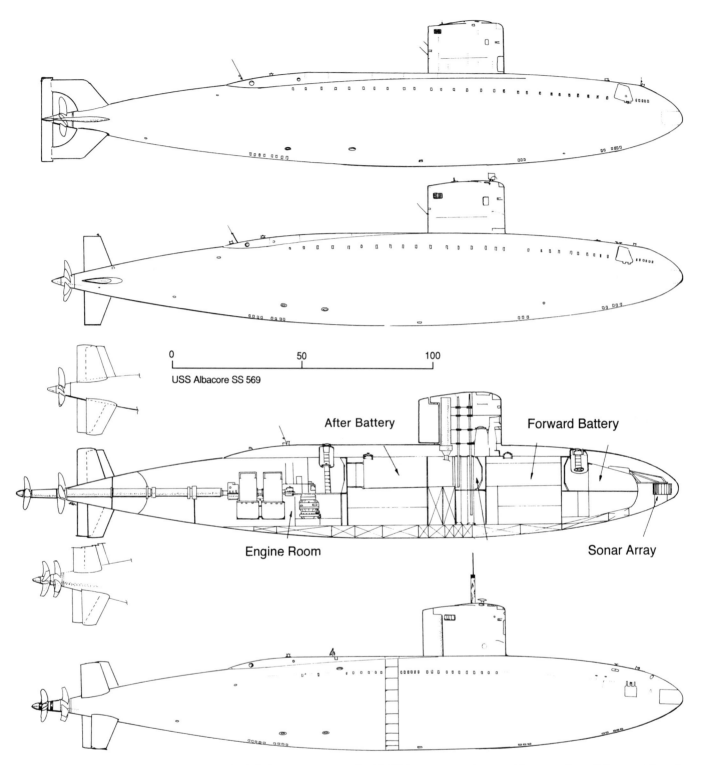

0   50   100

USS Albacore SS 569

After Battery

Forward Battery

Engine Room

Sonar Array

Albacore in various configurations: at top as built; below it as converted with SSN-type stern planes, with scrap view of X-stern; inboard profile showing final configuration with widely spaced contraprops and double electric motors, with corresponding outboard view below, and scrap view showing closely spaced contraprops. (Jim Christley)

Barbel is shown on 8 May 1963. The success of the experimental *Albacore* led to a proposal that a similar hull form be applied to a full-scale attack submarine. By this time, *Barbel*'s bow planes had been removed in favor of SSN-type sail planes.

By 1972, the pancake engines were nearly worn out and no spares were available. To keep *Albacore* in service for a projected Phase VI would have required replacing the engines with conventional diesels in a new 12-ft parallel midbody. This would have added considerable drag and made Phase VI too expensive. *Albacore* was retired and eventually became a museum ship.

The *Barbel* and *Skipjack* classes (see chapters 2 and 7), were the first operational applications of the *Albacore* hull form.

4

The ASW Submarine

ATTACK SUBMARINES ARE often considered mainly a means of dealing with other submarines, but that was not always so. Submarine specialization in anti-submarine warfare dates only from the late 1940s. Submarines sank other submarines in both world wars; in WW I, they were among the more successful ASW measures. In all but one case (in 1945), however, the victims were running on the surface. In effect, the attackers were executing their traditional anti-ship mission. Only well after 1945 did submarines begin to specialize in detecting and attacking submerged targets. ASW eventually became so important that it was the primary mission of all U.S. attack submarines.

Proponents of using submarines in ASW pointed out that U.S. WW II submariners considered Japanese submarines their most formidable and nerve-racking enemies.[1] For their part, U.S. submarines sank 32 Japanese boats, out of 132 lost, in about 90 attacks. HMS *Venturer* conducted a unique attack in 1945, in which both she and her U-boat victim were submerged throughout. It seemed to be a good prototype for postwar U.S. and British development.

The new fast diesel-electric submarines, typified by Type XXI, could evade existing escorts and probably nullify convoy tactics. The main alternative was to attack the enemy submarines "at source," at or near their bases. Carrier-based aircraft could attack the bases, but only submarines could survive long enough near the bases to ambush enemy craft as they emerged. In a protracted war, they might also destroy submarines on training missions, thus reducing the supply of new crews.

Such tactics were practical because submarines transiting to their patrol areas had to snorkel, and snorkeling submarines were loud. From a fire-control point of view, they differed little from surface ships. The new passive sonars, described in chapter 2, were clearly just what was needed to detect and track the submarines. Passive homing torpedoes, such as a Mk 35, were the obvious weapons. BQR-4 became the basis of a generation of specialist ASW craft called SSKs. Design and construction of prototype SSKs (anti-submarine warfare [ASW] submarines) were among the initial recommendations of the first OpNav-sponsored ASW conference in September 1946.

The U.S. Navy assumed that the Soviets were already mass-producing a local equivalent to Type XXI; in 1948, a Soviet admiral reportedly announced a goal of 1,200 submarines.[2] In 1950, a study of the security of overseas transportation in a future war (Hartwell report) estimated that the Soviets would build as many as 100 submarines per year. Following the same path as the U.S. Navy, the Soviets surely would develop naval nuclear weapons to attack both ships and ports. Other intelligence suggested that mass production had not yet begun, but this could be interpreted to mean that the Soviets might be waiting to stamp out the more formidable Type XXVIs. In fact, a somewhat smaller Sovietized Type XXI, the prototype Whiskey, appeared in 1949. It was soon followed by the larger, longer-range Zulu. In 1954, the official U.S. assessment was that the Soviets had a total of 345 boats, but only 47 Guppy equivalents (Whiskeys and Zulus) and another 83 conventional fleet boats (9 with snorkels). By then, Soviet construction was accelerating, but it never reached the predicted 100 or more submarines per year.

In 1956, the United States estimated an annual Soviet building rate of 160 submarines, although, in fact, only 75 (63 Whiskeys and 12 small closed-cycle Quebecs) were completed during that peak year. Unknown to the West, Nikita Khrushchev drastically cut the program (236 Whiskeys were built). He spared only long-range submarines, such as the Zulus' successors, Foxtrots, which would have been used against open-ocean convoys and naval formations. By then, however, the Soviet SSN program was well under way, as was the development of strategic attack submarines armed with cruise and ballistic missiles. The threat was very real.

Close-in ambush tactics demanded what would prove to be excessive numbers of U.S. or NATO SSKs. Improvements in sonar, however, made it practical to pull the ASW submarines back and thus to reduce their numbers. By 1954, it seemed that SSK barriers off the northern European coast would be effective. By this time, too, other

The great surprise of the early post–WW II era was low-frequency passive acoustics. *Flying Fish* is shown on 23 March 1951 after conversion for tests. Her fairwater is surrounded by a GHG array sonar taken from the cruiser *Prinz Eugen*.

forms of ASW were becoming effective against the diesel-electric threat, so SSKs were less vital.

Too, it seemed more apparent that the main submarine threat in a future war would be attackers armed with nuclear missiles aimed at the United States itself. Barriers would be essential, and only submarines could form barriers close to enemy ports. Thus, the first Long Range Objectives Group report (20 December 1955) envisaged five offshore barriers, the outermost consisting of 50 submarines (out of a total of 74 attack craft). Half would be needed by 1965, the rest by 1970. Because these numbers were so high, the report concluded that all attack submarines had to be dual-purpose—capable of both anti-ship and anti-submarine operation. By 1962, the war plan called for a combination submarine-air barrier off Argentia, Newfoundland, to bar Soviet missile submarines from the East Coast of the United States.

Beginning in 1955, the Type XXI story, in effect, was repeated. Nuclear submarines could overcome the measures so painfully developed to deal with their slower forebears. The Soviets completed their first nuclear submarine in 1958; clearly, it soon would be in series production. Unless the new SSNs suffered badly en route to the open ocean, they would overwhelm the escorts and ASW aircraft. Exercises strongly suggested that nothing short of an SSN could deal with an SSN. Only limited numbers of U.S. SSNs could ever be available. Each would occupy a large patrol area off a Soviet base or in a choke point leading from the base area to the open sea. All U.S. nuclear attack submarines would have to function as SSKs in wartime. In 1965, the Long Range Objectives Group used this reasoning to estimate the number of SSNs needed. It had to be able to impose a fixed loss rate on Soviet submarines passing through the barriers they formed.

Throughout the 1960s and 1970s, U.S. submarines often penetrated waters nominally controlled by the Soviets; it became obvious that they could actually conduct the sort of ambush warfare envisaged for SSKs during the 1940s

and early 1950s. Eventually it became clear that there was an alternative to the barrier strategy. At the outbreak of a war, the Soviets would be more interested in protecting their own SSBNs (ballistic missile submarines [nuclear]) and, incidentally, in attacking U.S. SSBNs than in attacking shipping in the open sea.

That opened an interesting possibility. The Soviets tried to protect their SSBNs by operating them within "bastions" protected by, among other things, their own attack submarines. Because they could threaten the only naval asset the Soviets valued, U.S. submarines operating in the bastions would tie down the protecting Soviet attack submarines. Without such pressure, the Soviets would surely reassign many of those submarines to attack vital shipping. This idea was formalized in the Maritime Strategy of the 1980s and led directly to the characteristics of the *Seawolf*-class submarine (see chapter 12).

The viability of the SSK depended on its sonar performance. In retrospect, it seems remarkable that the basic facts of sonar acoustics were all known within a few years of the end of WW II. Between 1950 and 1960, systems appeared that took complete advantage of the new discoveries, but their electronics was not yet reliable. Much of what has happened since combines more reliable electronics with much more powerful signal processing; the basic physics has changed very little.

The two key navy laboratories were the Naval Ocean Systems Center (NOSC) at San Diego and the Naval Undersea Systems Center (NUSC, originally the Naval Underwater Sound Laboratory) at New London. NOSC was assigned the submarine *Baya* for testing new sonars; *Flying Fish* was assigned to New London. Other submarines were later modified.

As described in chapter 2, it was obvious quite early that longer range demanded lower frequencies, which were best exploited by bigger, hence higher-gain, arrays. The other major advance was in signal processing. It made the most of a weak signal that is mixed with a great deal of random ocean noise—low-frequency sound can travel

Baya was converted as a laboratory ship; she is shown on 8 May 1956 after a San Francisco Naval Shipyard refit. The large tank probably accommodated a 14×14-element low-frequency (0.5–1.2 kHz) active/passive billboard array facing starboard. She also had a 50-element line array (2.5-ft separation) at deck level on the starboard side and an omnidirectional bow hydrophone. In this form, she tested Lorad, a proposed low-frequency active replacement for the passive SOSUS system then in use.

remarkable distances in the deep ocean and suffer only minimal losses.

Any sound can be analyzed into components at different frequencies. On average, a truly random signal (noise) carries all frequencies at about the same strength. A submarine is anything but random; her noise shows a distinctive spectrum (signature). Particular frequencies correspond to particular physical features. For example, the engine of a snorkeling submarine produces a strong signal at a frequency corresponding to the firing rate. If the strength of the different components is graphed against frequency to form a spectrum, narrow spikes (lines) appear at particular frequencies. A broad background corresponds to flow noise over the submarine hull and to flow within the inboard piping. The great surprise was that the low-frequency components of such sound could travel great distances through the sea without serious distortion (i.e., without much change in its spectrum). In many cases, moreover, a submarine could be expected to produce much the same spectrum for a considerable time. The Woods Hole Oceanographic Institution discovered this phenomenon in 1950.

To recover regular features from the noisy background, the sound heard by a passive sonar was put through a bank of filters tuned to different frequencies. As in a BTR, the output was a modified chemical recorder. Moving hori-

zontally, the stylus made a dot at each frequency detected in the signal; each horizontal line corresponded to a spectrum taken over a short interval. The next line corresponded to the next sample. To detect a target, an operator visually integrated over time, that is, looked down an output sheet corresponding to several minutes of such data in search of a consistent vertical line. The quieter the target, the longer the integration time to decide that a consistent line was in fact present amid the noise. Eventually, the filters were replaced by digital analyzers, and slices of the grams could be shown on the faces of CRTs. Because each submarine has her own characteristic spectrum, this type of analysis offers not only detection but also a measure of identification.

This spectacularly successful analysis was cloaked in the code designation of Lofar. The made-up word was often, although misleadingly, said to mean low-frequency analysis and ranging, but it actually had been chosen for its similarity to radar and sonar. The paper record is called a Lofargram, or gram. Lofar is also often called narrowband analysis because it detects on the basis of a particular, narrowly limited frequency line.[3] Each line corresponds to a specific sound tone, so the lines are often called tonals.

The noise of the continuous flow over a submarine is modulated, mainly by her propellers. It is detected at

Baya emerged from overhaul at San Francisco in March 1959 with a bulbous sonar bow accommodating a 1.5-kHz billboard projector. The receivers were a pair of 40-ft linear arrays on booms that could be swung out from just abaft the forward planes.

In January 1964, *Baya* (*above and facing*) emerged from another conversion with a second set of linear receiver arrays (at the bow) and a second transducer in a forward extension of the bridge fairwater (4.3-kHz active/passive unit).

somewhat higher frequency then the machinery noise picked up by Lofar. The regular modulating sound can be extracted by demodulation, a process called DEMON (DEMOdulated Noise), to display sounds below the usual Lofar frequencies. For example, a five-blade propeller turning at 300 RPM (a high speed) has a blade rate of only 25 Hz, whereas electrical machinery, such as a turbogenerator, often spins at some multiple of 50 or 60 Hz.

At first, Lofar seemed to solve the long-range passive ASW problem because it was so effective in detecting snorkelers. About 1956, however, the British discovered that they could grossly reduce Lofar range on their own snorkelers by sound-mounting their engines. Surely others, such as the Soviets, would follow suit, thus negating Lofar. The U.S. Navy became interested in very–long-range active alternatives.[4] The Soviets, however, never followed the British lead.

Nuclear submarines proved peculiarly vulnerable to Lofar detection. Much of their machinery had to function continuously or melt, so it produced sustained, well-defined lines, even at very low speed. This discovery led directly to the U.S. nuclear submarine-silencing program reflected in the *Thresher* design. By the mid-1960s, it seemed likely that the Soviets would follow the U.S. lead in silencing. Again, a radical change in sonar technology appeared necessary. The Soviets did not choose to silence their new submarines (Charlie and Victor I classes), however, and the crisis passed. Then, in the mid-1970s, the Soviets did silence the Victor III class, and the crisis returned.

The United States has applied Lofar to all areas of ASW since the 1950s. It was the basis of SOSUS, the long-range

fixed sound surveillance system. From 1956 on, a series of thousand-foot arrays, each carrying 40 hydrophones, was emplaced in the deep ocean off both U.S. coasts. An array that large was needed to form 5-degree beams at very low frequency. Design range against a snorkeler was 500 nm. It was natural to imagine Lofar detection applied to submarines, but they could not accommodate anything nearly as long as a SOSUS array. On board submarines, therefore, Lofar was initially considered far more important for identification than for detection or tracking. Lofar was also used in sonobuoys, initially under the code name Jezebel.

The first submarine Lofar contract was let in September 1950, the feasibility study completed in January 1954, and an operational requirement issued in May 1954. The resulting four-channel BQQ-3 spectral analyzer was not operationally evaluated until December 1962. By that time, it had been modified so that it could be fed either by the single scanned beam of a BQR-7 or by its own small arrays (15 hydrophones in the bow, 3 amidships, and 3 astern). The main Lofar channel (10–120 Hz) used only the small arrays (bow alone, bow and amidships, or all three on one side). The other three channels used either the bow hydrophones or one BQR-7 beam, all of which were in the part of the hull least affected by flow noise. They were (1) a Lofar channel at 65–175 Hz, (2) a DEMON (blade-rate) channel at 0–40 Hz (demodulated from 125–300 or 270–600 Hz, depending on which suffered less from background noise), and (3) a self-noise measurement channel (broadband noise at 125–300 Hz). BQQ-3 was later replaced by digital analyzers. The first contract for the single-channel BQR-20 was let in 1971; the dual-channel BQR-

22 followed in 1974. The current BQR-23 processes 64 channels.

By the late 1950s, a new kind of passive sonar, a towed array, was being proposed. Inspired by oil exploration technology, it promised extraordinarily low flow noise. The Office of Naval Research (ONR) and David Taylor Model Basin sponsored a special study of array flow noise in 1959–61. A 50-ft array carried 11 hydrophones on a cable up to 3 mi long and achieved, by far, the lowest self-noise to date over the full range from Lofar to medium frequencies (100 Hz to 10 kHz) at speeds up to 10 kt. The following year, a Towflex array developed by the Chesapeake Instrument Co. (which later became the towed array division of Gould) was used to measure the radiated noise produced by the experimental submarine *Albacore*.[5] Although submarines carried devices to measure self-noise, no on-board device could measure radiated noise. The Towflex was probably the first submarine-towed array.

The National Security Industrial Association (NSIA), an organization of major defense contractors, conducted a study of ASW during early 1964. By this time, SOSUS was clearly demonstrating its capabilities. It seemed likely that a submarine could tow a full 1,000-ft array at the end of a 10,000-ft cable, far beyond her own self-noise. That May, NSIA formally proposed that the next submarine sonar (which became BQQ-5) consist of a bow sphere, PUFFS, and the towed array. In July, OpNav released a Specific Operational Requirement (SOR) for a towed array that used much the same language as NSIA's. The array would be connected to an inboard beamformer, with signals being detected by the BQQ-3 spectrum analyzer already on board many submarines.

To use Lofar effectively, the U.S. Navy needed detailed knowledge of Soviet submarine spectra; otherwise, receivers, such as those in sonobuoys, could not be tuned properly.[6] U.S. submarines penetrated Soviet submarine operating areas to record their signatures. Unfortunately, hull arrays, such as BQR-7, suffered from flow noise at the low end of the Lofar spectrum; a submarine had to stop dead, with all machinery off, to collect data. That was unacceptable. The ONR experiment with towed arrays offered a solution. Isolated from much of a submarine's self-noise and suffering little flow noise, a towed array could be used while the submarine moved.

In 1965, the surveillance equipment program (including ESM [electronic support measures] and special periscopes) was formalized. The acoustic component, Tuba, would have three phases. Tuba I used existing submarine sensors with the addition of special recorders. Tuba II (BQH-4), the near-term (12–18 mo) upgrade, added a towed array (the first in U.S. service) and a special mechanically steered, high-frequency array on a pedestal. The 258-ft array (3-in diameter), towed on a 2,600 ft cable, carried three subarrays of 50 hydrophones each. The entire system was effective between 10 Hz and 20 kHz. The recorder was BQH-5. (The TB-16 array used in current BQQ-5 sonars is a modified version.) Tuba III (BQH-6), a longer-term program planned for service in 1977, was terminated in FY 78 because of overruns and delays after Raytheon built three prototypes. Eight production versions had been initially planned for FY 76. Tuba was sometimes called AIGS (acoustic information-gathering system).

Another immediate application of the towed array SOR was BQR-15, a special self-defense array for strategic submarines. Hull-mounted sonars could not look aft, so submarine commanders periodically turned for a look over their shoulders. Because a strategic submarine ran particularly slowly, such a turn lost considerable time. The array looked directly aft and also offered much longer-range passive detection than that of the submarine's BQR-7 hull array. It was relatively short (about 120 ft long, with a diameter of 3.5 in, and carrying 42 hydrophones) and simple (utilizing twisted-pair technology). BQR-15 used the submarine's existing inboard processor, BQQ-3 initially but, later, BQR-20, -22, or -23. It was operationally evaluated in 1970.

Array stowage was always an issue. Tuba arrays were reeled back onto the submarine when not in use. Because U.S. SSNs were largely single-hulled, these thick arrays could not be stowed internally (wound around reels in ballast tanks). The tubes were cumbersome. The simpler alternative was for a small boat (typically an LCM) to clip the array onto the stern of a submarine leaving port and then unclip and recover it when the submarine returned. This type of clip-on array was adopted by the Royal Navy but was later abandoned by the U.S. Navy because it could pull off as a submarine transited at high speed (e.g., to the Western Pacific). Also, the array was subject to considerable damage when streamed (e.g., from shark bites or even from snagging underwater obstacles). By the late 1970s, the U.S. Navy had gone full circle and was again installing retractable arrays.

By mid-1967, the experimental arrays were so promising that the formal characteristics for what became *Glenard P. Lipscomb* noted that, if successful, they might replace standard hull-mounted passive sonars altogether. A clip-on submarine tactical array sonar system (STASS), using the existing Lofar processor, was ordered for existing attack submarines. In March 1972, STASS was operationally evaluated in the Pacific aboard *Permits* and *Sturgeons* with their BQQ-3 and BQR-20 processors. It used a BQR-25 beamformer and wet end (a 298-ft, 350-Hz) array carrying four hydrophone modules (2- to 2.4-in diameter), streamed on an 800-ft cable; there were only 18 channels (elements) feeding signals through 18 twisted wire pairs. Tow points for the STASS clip-on array were installed on board *Tullibee*, several *Permits*, many *Sturgeons*, and at least three SSBNs (probably *George Washington* class).

In November 1970, a tentative SOR for a submarine integrated tactical towed array (SITTAR) was issued. It envisaged a longer array (500 ft), streamed 1,000–2,000 ft astern, to pick up low-frequency tonals more effectively. If the array were thin enough ($\frac{5}{8}$–$1\frac{1}{2}$ in), it could be wrapped around a winch in a main ballast tank and streamed through a line wiper. Integration meant that the array would be part of a new sonar system (BQQ-5), including the BQS-13DNA then under development.

SITTAR was too ambitious. Instead, the Tuba II array was adapted as TB-16 (240 ft × 3.5 in, carrying 50 hydrophones in a 186-ft acoustic aperture section, towed on a 2,600-ft cable). The TB-16 prototype was developed under a 1973 contract (the production contract followed in 1975), and the contract to integrate it into BQQ-5 was awarded in August 1982.[7]

Longer thin-line arrays increased gain and could operate more effectively at lower frequencies, first the 4X array (TB-23) and then the 12X array (TB-29). A stand-alone TB-23 was planned for the *Ohio* class, but it failed its initial tests; a long version of TB-16 (SPALT 9080) was substituted.[8] In each case, the X refers to the acoustic length of the TB-16 array; the TB-29 acoustic aperture is about 2,230 ft long, which greatly exceeded NSIA's original hopes. Such an array is so much longer than the submarine's hull, the only other triangulation baseline, that it pays to space special elements along it specifically for triangulation, using a special TARP (towed array range processor). Tested at sea in FY 87, TARP is part of BQQ-5E, the version incorporating TB-29. It turns out that a fatter array suffers less from self-noise per unit length, so it can perform better at speed; the longer thin-line array offers higher gain at low speed.[9] The *Ohios* and *Seawolfs* carry both types.

The other great post–WW II sonar discovery was the nature of sound propagation in the deep ocean. Typically, there is an upper mixing (isothermal) layer, in which temperature and, therefore, sound velocity are constant; sound travels in straight lines, so sonar behaves like underwater radar. Pre–WW II submarines generally operated in the isothermal layer, which might be 300 ft deep in the summer Atlantic or 600 ft deep in winter. Below the layer, sound velocity varies with depth. The ocean refracts sound waves, just as a stack of sheets of different kinds of glass refracts light. Wartime submariners soon learned to hide beneath the layer.[10]

In 1941, scientists at Woods Hole postulated that, in water deep enough, sound pointed down at the appro-

Baya was the initial test ship for the wide aperture array now being installed on board nuclear attack submarines. WAA, unlike PUFFS, forms beams and thus requires a two-dimensional array, rather than a vertical line hydrophone.

priate angle would bend around and refocus at a distance. This is now called a convergence zone. The first convergence zone in the Atlantic is usually about 35 nm (70,000 yd) from a sound source. Additional convergence zones occur at multiples of that range and form rings around the sound source (about 5 nm wide in the Atlantic). The convergence zone range differs from area to area and from ocean to ocean. A sonar that works at the convergence zone range could go far beyond the maximum direct-path range, which is usually about 20,000 yd. A target detected at the convergence zone, however, would vanish as it passes the inner edge of the zone.

Sound projected at a steep enough angle is virtually unrefracted. That is why fathometers work: they point straight down. At a shallower angle, sound hits the bottom but bounces off away from the sonar. It arrives at a range greater than direct path but shorter than convergence zone, often out to 40,000 yd (under some conditions, a submarine could achieve a long bounce out to 50 nm).

Because sound bounces back from any angle *less* than the maximum, a target detected by bottom bounce could be tracked continuously. Similarly, sound could bounce off the surface.

This phenomenon can be turned around. If a submarine is deep enough, looking up in a cone to maximum bounce angle, she can reliably detect submarines above her. She is said to be using the reliable acoustic path (RAP); it is reliable because it depends very little on the details of ocean layering. The deeper the submarine, the larger is the area that the cone covers near the surface.

Sound paths (ray paths) through the ocean can be calculated from the way temperature varies with depth. At many ranges, a submarine at a given depth can receive the same sound at several angles that correspond to different ray paths. Ray paths corresponding to those angles should cross at the likely position of the target. Such ray tracing is an alternative to the vertical triangulation described in chapter 2. Both became practical with the adop-

Much effort went into mapping out sonar propagation. This Mk 81 weapons control console, actually a simulator for training, shows a typical ray trace, with refraction (to form the convergence zone) and reflection off the surface. The same general-purpose console can display target tracking solutions and weapons data for attacks. (Hughes Aircraft Company)

tion of spherical sonars (see below), which could easily measure the angles at which sounds arrived.

The Woods Hole scientists also found that sound travels almost without loss through a deep channel, about 4,000 ft below the ocean's surface. Although clearly beyond any submarine's depth capability, the deep channel might be reached by a dangling hydrophone. SOSUS exploited the deep channel. Once really deep-diving submarines had become practical, the deep sound channel became an interesting, albeit too expensive, objective. During the late 1950s, RAP was used to justify proposals for submarines capable of diving deep (but not to the deep channel).

Although sound can travel along all possible paths, it is absorbed as it goes. The lower the frequency is, the less the absorption. For example, frequency must be reduced to about 3.5 kHz to reach the convergence zone in the Atlantic.

The first demonstration of convergence zone listening occurred in August 1947. As the fleet submarine *Quillback* was balanced dead in the water on a density layer off Bermuda, she suspended a hydrophone 300 ft below her. Practice depth bombs were heard at 35, 70, 105, and 140 nm (i.e., out to four convergence zones). They could sometimes be heard through the submarine's hull. A second demonstration, also off Bermuda, took place on 26–27 September 1947. While balanced on a layer, *Sennet* used two remote hydrophones (one at 200 ft below her and the other floating 100 ft above) and a band-pass filter (set at 400–800 Hz) to track the machinery noise of the destroyer *Witek* out to 70 nm. She then detected *Witek* at the third

convergence zone, a distance of 105 nm. The destroyer could be heard at the first convergence zone even in sea state 5, and depth charge explosions could be heard at 400 to 600 nm. This sort of performance could not be used operationally. The submarine had to be extraordinarily quiet. Not only her main machinery, but also such auxiliaries as air conditioners, had to be stopped. Even the noise of men turning over in their bunks could make long-range listening impossible. After everything had been shut off, *Sennet* required an additional 15 to 20 minutes to quiet down (e.g., to stop completely and thus eliminate flow noise). Proving the existence of the predicted phenomena much encouraged the development of quieter submarines and better passive sonars.

By the mid-1950s, interest had turned to big active sonars that exploited the convergence zone and bottom bounce. *Baya* tested Lorad, a very–low-frequency active sonar. Several submarines tested BRASS (bottom-reflection active sonar system).[11] Both systems required vertical beam steering. It had occurred to NUSC scientists that a submarine sonar should be able to steer its beam equally well horizontally or vertically and equally well up (for surface bounce) or down (for bottom bounce and convergence zone operation). Submarines had used paired deck and keel sonars for many years. In August 1956, NUSC suggested that future sonars have paired 8-ft bow hemispheres, above and below the torpedo tubes, scanned as a single unit. It claimed that this integrated sonar would roughly quadruple effective range.[12]

In December 1956, NUSC formally proposed that the two hemispheres be enlarged and joined together; the

Grouper is shown about 1965. The big Lorad (Colossus II) projector abaft the sail was fitted about 1963, together with a line hydrophone to starboard. Later, the billboard array to port, which could form beams in elevation as well as in bearing, was fitted. It was used for BRASS (bottom-reflection active sonar system) experiments.

entire bow of the submarine could be used. Completely smoothing the bow drastically cut self-noise, and the larger sphere worked better at lower frequency. In May 1958, Raytheon received a contract to develop and produce the NUSC sphere, BQS-6; the two prototypes were installed on board *Tullibee* and *Thresher*. Each sphere was 15 ft in diameter and covered by 1,245 transducers. Like the earlier scanning sonars, it formed its beam by using a commutator moving on (in this case, within) a scale model of the transducer (a compensator; in this case, a $\frac{1}{10}$th-scale sphere). BQS-6 had three compensators: (1) a passive scanner for a bearing-time recorder (BTR) at 1–2.8 kHz, (2) a receiver for active mode, and (3) a passive BDI tracker at 1–2.8 kHz. The transmitting beam was formed by a switching network (DT switches) that generally energized an orange-peel–shaped segment of the sphere. A transmitting beam could be directed in elevation by separate DE switches. For target classification, BQS-6 provided broadband audio output at 0.5–5 kHz.[13]

BQS-6 was combined with a BQR-7 conformal array (and with a BQA-2 secure submarine communications set [SESCO] and a BQA-3 Doppler analyzer) to form an integrated sonar, BQQ-1. A target initially detected and tracked by BQR-7 would be passed to the BQS-6 passive tracker. Just before attacking, the submarine could send out a single ranging ping. That single ping was the most important BQS-6 active mode, at least initially. Because

the receiver had to point in exactly the direction of the ping while waiting for an echo, the active receiver was stabilized against the yawing motion of the submarine (the passive tracker was not). BQS-6 also had a search mode sending out an omnidirectional pulse. Because the energy otherwise concentrated in a single ping had to be spread around the sphere, maximum range was considerably reduced; source level fell from 142.5 dB to 122 dB. A compromise mode, tri-beam, using three adjacent 6-degree transmitting beams, switched from one tri-beam to the next in about a minute. The sphere could also receive in tri-beam, with the three compensators working together. Displays included a radar-style PPI).

The SSBN equivalent of BQQ-1 was a combination of BQR-7 and the BQS-4 pinger. Apparently, the sphere would be important mainly for active fire control; a properly handled SSBN should not come close enough to another submarine to need one.

BQQ-1 was combined with what amounted to underwater IFF (BQQ-3) and a passive fire control system (BQG-1, PUFFS) to form the BQQ-2 integrated sonar. BQQ-1 had been designed in 1958 to deal with fairly noisy snorkelers. Lofar could detect quieter submarines at longer ranges, so the existing analyzer was connected to the BQR-7 low-frequency array. By 1962, the navy estimated that for Lofar/BQR-7, on board a 20-kt *Thresher*, to detect a quiet 10-kt nuclear submarine, such as *Skipjack*, at only

Conger, shown in 1963, carried a BRASS II transducer (4.5 kHz, 144 dB) in the forward extension of her bridge fairwater.

Tigrone, pictured on 7 June 1967, had the full BRASS outfit: a BRASS III parabolic bow transducer (2.15 kHz, 150 dB), a BRASS II transducer at the fore end of her bridge fairwater, and a prominent 85-ft line hydrophone (two 25-degree preformed beams) along her port side (in the squared-off tube). The object visible atop the BRASS III housing is a hydrophone (others were atop BRASS II, atop the periscope shears, and right aft).

4,000 yd would take 20 min of integration time. By then, the submarine would have long departed the sonar beam. Desired performance by 1964 was detection out to bottom-bounce range in 5 min. The obvious solution was to enlarge the passive array to increase its gain at low frequency. Unfortunately, BQR-7 already extended over the entire quiet part of the submarine's bow. This situation resulted in NSIA's 1964 recommendation that BQR-7 be abandoned altogether in favor of a towed array.

Because it was not stabilized against yaw, the BQS-6 tracker beam tended to swing back and forth past a target. This decreased signal strength enough for the system to lose track of a target. The active receiver was already fully stabilized; Raytheon had provided it with a broadband passive receiver. Because active pinging was used so rarely, it became a valuable tracking channel. The vacuum-tube version of this improvement was installed in *Thresher* before her loss; a solid-state version was installed in *Tullibee* and *Plunger*. It proved its value in Subroc tests in 1964.

BQS-6A (BQQ-1A) was installed in *Permit*-class submarines. The improved BQS-6B (BQQ-1B), for early *Sturgeon*s (FY 62–64), had an improved vacuum-tube transmitter and a better power supply. BQQ-1As were brought up to this standard by Retrofit I modification.

By the summer of 1962, OpNav wanted better active performance: sufficient power to reach the convergence zone in omni mode (i.e., for search) and two counters to reverberation (short pulses and autocorrelation detection). Like the BQR-beam, the search tri-beam scanned far too slowly; it depended on the bank of mechanical phasing switches. Raytheon developed a Retrofit II package (BQQ-1C). It could not much increase transmitter power (for omni to match single-ping range would have required a factor of 100 in power), but it could improve beam shaping by replacing the DT/DE switches. Raytheon met the reverberation problem by providing an FM pulse mode alongside the usual CW mode.[14] The dramatic success of the secondary passive tracking channel inspired Retrofit IIA (dual track) that incorporated the stabilized automatic tracking feature (ATF).

Compared with BQR-7, the sphere offered better passive directivity (e.g., to reject self-noise), but it operated at higher frequency. Its output was fed into the BQQ-3 DEMON channel.

By early 1964, a new version, BQQ-1D, was due. NSIA thought it should be a digital sonar that incorporated the new DIMUS technology, but it had to be ready for FY 68 (later FY 69) submarines. OpNav opted for a Retrofit III package, which was installed in new FY 65 ships. Work on defining it began in July 1964. As before, neither active nor passive performance seemed sufficient. BQQ-1 was not reliable enough; it showed a mean time between failures of only 30 hr, compared with an allowable minimum of 100 hr. The fleet reported an unacceptable availability rate of 0.7–0.8, observed between December 1963 and July 1964. Worse yet, the active system could not be tested at sea without revealing the submarine by pinging.

Raytheon offered solid-state technology to improve reliability and to increase transmitter power by a factor of 2.6. It had already developed a modular solid-state transmitter for a German sonar. Retrofit III also improved the switching network and the active receiver. *Permit*-class submarines received BQS-11; BQS-6B was replaced by BQS-12. New submarines, from FY 65 on, were fitted with BQS-13 (1,241 elements). The first was *Bergall* (SSN 667); her sonar was certified for service in June 1969. BQS-13 was incorporated in the later integrated sonars (BQQ-5 and BSY-1) of the *Los Angeles* class.

Active search speed was still a problem. The solution lay in forming the transmitting beam digitally so that one beam could quickly follow another in any direction. This problem was even more difficult than DIMUS because far more power had to pass through the digital phase shifters involved.

Much less could be done for the passive sonar. BQQ-1 could track up to 3 targets (BQS-6 plus BQR-7). Hopefully, a single operator using a digital sonar could double that number, and two operators could track 12 targets. The goal could be achieved by applying DIMUS to BQR-7. Unfortunately, DIMUS was still immature, although a 24-beam version of BQR-2 had been tested on board *Albacore* and *Hammerhead* had been testing a beamformer since 1963. Nor was automated TMA working. OpNav suggested using vertical triangulation, scanning the BQS-6 passive beam vertically between +15 and −60 degrees, and displaying the result on an elevation-time recorder

(equivalent to a BTR). Such a recorder, in theory, could localize a contact out to maximum bottom-bounce range, about 40,000 yd.

DIMUS was revived in the summer of 1967 by a group of OpNav officers who were aware of how well it had worked in experimental BQR-2 and -7 arrays. NUSC was pushed to accelerate work. SubDevGru 2 put narrowband processing sonars to sea on board some *Sturgeon*s and achieved good results. This led to interest in using the same sort of processing in a fire-control sonar (the bow sphere).

In 1967, Raytheon received a contract for a new integrated sonar, S70, to be installed in the contemplated FY 70 CONFORM submarine (see chapter 10). Although the CONFORM program soon collapsed, the idea of better integration survived in Raytheon's multipurpose sonar, BQR-24. It replaced the BTR channel of a BQS-6 series sonar with DIMUS. Although nominally only a sonar, BQR-24 included considerable short-range fire-control capability tailored to the new Mk 48 torpedo. Raytheon found that by analyzing precise Doppler measurements of the frequencies of narrowband lines, the system could work out target movement. The technique was called FLIT (frequency-line integration tracking); it provided BQR-24 with a situation display showing own-ship and target positions. The sonar's computer could determine the appropriate Mk 48 prelaunch settings far more quickly than earlier manual techniques. BQR-24 had two consoles, one for broadband passive detection (waterfall display) and one for digital Lofar analysis and a Lofar line tracker (narrowband tracking). The broadband preformed-beam facility was valued partly because it doubled torpedo detection range. BQR-24 would be approved for service use in 1974 and 11 sonars bought under the FY 76 program. By that time Raytheon had lost out to IBM in its attempt to provide the next integrated sonar, BQQ-5, although it still supplied the spheres (the BQQ-5 contract was awarded on 13 December 1969).[15]

The next step was the digital transmitter beamformer, a feature usually called accelerated active search. In 1968, BQS-13DNA (DIMUS, narrowband, accelerated active) was considered the ideal future sonar. It was planned for the next-generation integrated sonar, the BQQ-5 adopted for the *Los Angeles* class. As it happened, A was both difficult to achieve and less important than better passive performance. It finally appeared in the BQQ-5 successor, BSY-1, as SADS (submarine active detection system). BQQ-5 did incorporate vertical triangulation ranging in the form of numerous preformed depression/elevation beams.

When BQQ-5 was developed for the *Los Angeles* class in 1968, both BQR-7 and NSIA's towed array were rejected, the former because it was so difficult to install and the latter because it was expected to cost half a knot and a year's delay. The steel sonar dome dissipated some sonar energy and was hard to fabricate; it was replaced by reinforced plastic, which could not have supported the BQR-7 array. The new submarine would have a digital fire-control system, so one of the analog analyzers was

Analog scanning sonars used commutators turning inside scale models of their arrays (compensators) to form their beams. The big BQS-6 spherical array used three compensators: one a scanner feeding a BTR, one for the stabilized receiver for its active sonar, and one for the steerable tracker beam. The $\frac{1}{10}$-scale spheres are shown here before installation. Each transducer of the big sphere was wired to a corresponding point on each of the small ones. A commutator crawled around the inside of each sphere; note the glass observation port in each. This was the last and most complex analog beamformer; its successors were digital computers. This particular set, for a BQS-6B, was installed on board *Sturgeon*-class submarines of the FY 62–64 programs. The corresponding transmitter occupied six electronic cabinets; its design was based on an earlier radio transmitter built for the Voice of America. (Raytheon Corp.)

eliminated. Because, by 1969, it seemed that some type of low-frequency array would be needed to detect quieter second-generation Soviet submarines, such as Victors, a hull array (in this case, a chin array of 104 hydrophones) was revived. Contrary to expectation, BQQ-5 did not require any more space than its analog predecessor. It was later ordered backfitted in all *Permit* and *Sturgeon* class submarines during regular overhauls, beginning with the FY 76 program (which included 14 backfits at a total cost of $127 million). Ironically, BQQ-5 was soon modified to use a towed array that shared the narrowband processor of the chin array. A similar BQQ-6 for the *Ohio* class lacks any active element. Later *Ohio*s have a version of BQQ-5.

The BQQ-1/2 operational requirement (1958) also envisaged a submarine improved sonar system (SISS) to be installed in at least the two best pre-*Thresher* classes of nuclear submarine—*Skipjack* and *Lafayette* (SSBNs). It was required to track targets out to 30,000 yd, accurate to 2 percent at 10,000 yd and 5 percent at 20,000 yd. This sort of performance would have sufficed to control Subroc missiles, but it would not have approached the convergence zone and bottom bounce achievable by BQQ-2. SISS probably would have employed a conformal array like BQR-7 plus a new active array. Although BRASS was one possibility, it employed a single large trainable transducer and its loss would disable the system. Development was scheduled to begin in FY 63, but money was too tight. The idea did not die. An operational requirement for a *Skipjack* modernization sonar was issued in March 1966; it was to be operationally evaluated in FY 71 and all six installations completed by FY 76.[16] It would track at least two targets simultaneously, passively detect a target (another *Skipjack,* equivalent to a future Soviet submarine) at extreme direct-path range, and localize it at extreme bottom-bounce range. Active range would increase from 6,000–8,000 yd to 10,000 yd (6,000 yd when one submarine was in the layer and the other was below it). For self-protection, the system would detect a helicopter outside attack range while the ship ran at 5 kt, well below periscope depth. As in the newer sonars, it would add central maintenance and fault detection. This project died of tight money during the Vietnam War. A *Lafayette*-class SSBN sonar improvement project, which would have integrated BQR-21, DIMUS BQR-7, and BQR-15, was begun in the 1970s as BQQ-8. OpNav allowed it to die in 1982, reportedly for fear that it would compete with the new BQQ-5/6 series.

Effective SSK operation also required accurate navigation. Generally, boats would be assigned their own patrol areas within a barrier. Because it was nearly impossible to identify submerged submarines, each had to assume that any other submarine within her area was hostile; neighboring SSKs could not be allowed to wander across boundaries. This problem was eventually solved by the ships inertial navigation system (SINS).

SINS was not even imaginable in the heyday of SSK development. Nor could SSKs navigate by the stars. Several ingenious methods, some later applied to early missile submarines, were tried. In 1952, for example, Submarine Development Group 2 (SubDevGru 2) had tested RAFOS and gravimetric navigation. RAFOS was an inverse version of SOFAR (sound fixing and ranging) a means of signaling via the deep-sound channel. A hydrophone dangling into the deep-sound channel detected the noise of small charges exploded on a timed schedule. RAFOS offered an accuracy of 5 nm at 950 nm in the Atlantic. Gravimetry exploited the fact that local gravity varies from place to place. After a two-day survey by an SSK entering her operating area, she could find her position to within 12 nm. A few years later, RADUX, an improved version of the Loran radio system, was available. It was considered effective up to 2,500 nm, but it needed an antenna projecting from the water.

From the first, SSK design was dominated by the need for huge numbers. During 1948 for example, the General Board studied U.S. naval requirements for the 1951–60 period. SSK force levels were estimated for two alternative situations: one in which the existing force of about 360 Soviet submarines was upgraded to Type XXIs, the other in which the Soviets had used their full industrial capacity to produce 2,000 modern submarines by 1958 or 1960. Tables 4–1 and 4–2 show the results, which were horrifying. About this time, the national mobilization plan called for construction of 245 SSKs. The SSK would have to be built by yards with no previous submarine experience and constructed of mild steel (MS) rather than high-tensile steel (HTS). She would dive to 400 ft instead of 700 ft and be extremely simple. Equipment would be replaced, rather than maintained on board. Even the power plant would be a package replaceable by a tender. Operating range

Table 4–1. SSK Requirements, as Estimated in 1948 (356-Submarine Force)

	On Station	Total
North Cape-Cherry Island-Spitzbergen	56	168
Petropavlovsk	6	18
North end of Sakhalin	6	18
La Perouse Strait	7	21
Tsugaru Strait	2	6
Training	——	19
Total	77	250

Note: The associated 1950–60 program showed 5 SSKs in 1950, 3 in each of 1951 and 1954, and otherwise 2 per year, for a total of 27, and 2 attack submarines per year from 1951 on, with the exception of 6 in 1960 to begin Guppy replacement. In each of 1951 and 1952, 3 fleet submarines would be converted to SSKs. Guppy conversions would end in FY 53, with 11 in 1950, 11 in 1951, 10 in 1952, and 8 in 1953. This tentative program also included missile and other special-purpose submarines.

could be short because the blockade of the Soviet Union would be conducted from forward bases (e.g., in Scotland).

The SSK's sponsors hoped that she would displace no more than 350 tons. She would have only two torpedo tubes, with one reload each, for short Mk 35 torpedoes. Fire control would be simplified by combining a good passive sonar and the homing torpedo. At that time, no one knew much about passive sonar. The characteristics called for a passive attack sonar with an accuracy of 0.10 degree; the SSK would fire at 10,000–15,000 yd. Silencing might be achieved, not so much by careful construction

Table 4–2. SSK Requirements, as Estimated in 1948 (2,000-Submarine Force)

	On Station	Total
Greenland-Iceland-Scotland	124	372
Northeast coast of Kamchatka	10	30
Wales-Spain	86	258
Petropavlovsk	6	18
Kuril	30	90
Tsugara Strait	2	6
Kyūshū-China	42	126
Training	——	70
Total	300	970

Note: The same analysis showed, in addition, 50 missile submarines; 300 attack submarines, including training requirements; 280 barrier (SSR) submarines to support continuous deployment of 138; and sufficient transport submarines to lift one third of a division. These numbers were apparently based on the assumption that the surface of the sea, at least initially, would be very nearly unusable.

but by anchoring the SSK underwater, with slight positive buoyancy and all machinery stopped. The characteristics called for a snorkel long enough to permit hovering at a depth of 60 to 75 ft, but a practical limit later turned out to be 50 ft. First characteristics were issued on 24 December 1946.

Size depended partly on complement; the characteristics indicated a crew of 18. A June 1947 analysis showed that the submarine might need 9 men per watch when submerged and 11 when snorkeling. To cut the crew to 24 or 25 total, the submarine would have to be adapted to one-man control; diving and surfacing would be all-hands jobs.

A tentative SSK design was submitted in August 1947 (see Table 4–3). It showed a simple hull with saddle tanks, built of MS, rather than HTS, and powered by three pancake diesels or four or five Gray diesels, a standard navy type. The SSK was unusual in that she was expected to remain nearly immobile on station. The characteristics showed a 50-kw battery-charging engine, which could keep the batteries topped up while burning less fuel than a main engine. Unfortunately, the total load when cruising at very low speed was 120 kw, so the extra engine was deleted.

The tentative design was rejected as too large. Two more designs were presented in September (see Table 4–3). The designers considered the larger one preferable for operating on station for the specified 30 days, but OpNav asked for a revised—which turned out to mean lengthened—version of the 14-ft design. It was submitted in late November 1947.

Torpedoes were a problem. Because an SSK operating in forward areas might be attacked by enemy ASW craft, she would need a few defensive torpedoes. Under some circumstances, she might fire unguided long torpedoes. The November design showed long tubes. In February 1948, the skids were required to be long enough to accommodate either a long weapon or a pair of Mk 27/37 defensive torpedoes. That added 2 ft to the forward torpedo room (and to the submarine). Two tubes no longer sufficed. It would be nearly impossible to withdraw a long torpedo so that a short one could be loaded and launched. BuShips suggested that two short tubes be added; the submarine would carry six long and three short torpedoes. She would displace 515 tons.

Even when hovering, the SSK needed a lot of power, 70 kw, largely for living: the "hotel" load. Her battery would lose three fourths of its charge in only 8 hr. Even with a drastically cut load, the remaining fourth would last no more than 7 hr. About 3 hr would be required to top off the quarter-charged battery. That was absurd; surely the SSK would have to spend most of each day on her battery. The battery had to be much larger, which meant that the submarine, too, had to grow.

The fourth SSK design, submitted on 20 April 1948, allowed her to make do with 5 hr of snorkeling in every 24 hr. Enemy ASW forces might appear at any time, and the SSK also had to be able to evade for up to 24 hr (using minimum hotel load, partly to be silent). Battery weight was increased from 75,000 to 200,000 lb. The hull was now so large that it cost very little to lengthen all four tubes to full size (252 in). Space now sufficed for eight long torpedoes and one short torpedo. The four 180-BHP diesels were replaced by three 375-BHP units, and twin

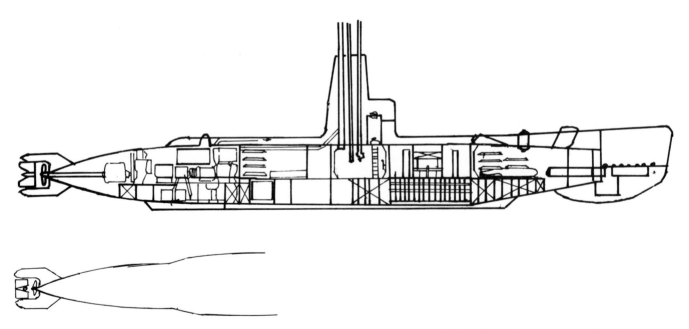

The SSK as designed, with a single screw and only a chin sonar (described as a 6-ft cylindrical transducer, presumably BQR-2). Note the unusually tall sail, which allows the submarine to run relatively deep while snorkeling (the head of the snorkel was to have been 50 ft above the keel). Snorkel induction and exhaust would have shared the same mast. Unlike contemporary U.S. submarine designs, this one had only a single battery, under the space forward of the control room. The scrap view, to a somewhat smaller scale, shows the arrangement of the stern planes.

Table 4–3.   SSK Designs, 1947

	14.8.47 (August)		19.9.47 (September)	28.11.47 (November)
LOA (ft)				175-0
Length waterline (ft)	161-6	155-0	142-0	166-0
Diameter (ft)	16-0	14-0	12-0	14-0
Beam (ft)	24-0	18-0	16-0	19-0
Draft (ft)	14-6			
Standard displacement (tons)	550	450	340	480
Surfaced displacement (tons)	630	510	385	540
Submerged displacement (tons)	750	600	455	640
Reserve buoyancy	19	18	18	18.5
Operating depth (ft)	400	400	400	400
Torpedo tubes	2 (163-in)	2	2	2 (252-in)
Torpedoes	6	4*	4	6†
Diesels	3 pancake or 4 Gray	4 Gray	2 Gray	4 Gray
Cells	252	252	126	252
SHP surfaced	640	540	270	600
SHP submerged	600	600	300	
Surfaced speed (nm)	10	11	10	10.5
Snorkel speed (nm)	6	6	5	6
Submerged speed (nm)	8–9	9	7	8.5
Endurance at 9 kt (hr)	3,000	3,000	3,000	3,000
Complement	5/22	4/24	4/23	4/25

* Six torpedoes if berths reduced by four
† Two full-length skids, each of which could accommodate two short ASW torpedoes

screws replaced the earlier single screw for superior propulsion and maneuverability. The safety tank was omitted as unnecessary; this meant the elimination of the last hard tank outside the pressure hull. These steps lengthened the hull from 175 to 194 ft (740, rather than 515, tons standard). An alternative submarine with a 140,000-lb battery would have displaced only 20 tons less, but underwater endurance would have been only 24 hr, rather than 38 hr.

By June, there was some question as to whether two larger diesels would be better than the three GM 8-268As (375 BHP each) that were planned. A third engine offered flexibility and dependability; it could also help charge the battery while the submarine ran faster (6 hr to charge at 5.75 kt or 4 hr at 3 kt). The issue was reopened the following February. Substituting two 16-338s would increase power from 1,200 to 2,000 BHP (some considered the SSK underpowered), adding over a knot, and the bigger engines were designed for sound mounting and snorkeling. About a fourth of the engine weight would be saved, and battery-charging time would also be cut by about a fourth. Larger engines would cost more, however, and would be less reliable. Alternatives studied at this time were three 750-BHP or four 500-BHP diesels. The original plan for three 375-BHP engines prevailed. At a July 1948 hearing on the planned FY 50 budget, the General Board sharply

criticized the projected 3,000-nm range. BuShips promised, and delivered, much more (see Table 4–4).

The SSK was needed so urgently that the design went ahead before the passive sonar, around which, in theory, the SSK would be developed, had any firm form. In September 1947, the U.S. version of the German GHG (Balkon: BQR-2) was chosen as its short-range sonar, but it was not yet clear what long-range set would be used. As of December, it appeared that 64 to 120 hydrophones would be spread over the skin of the outer hull with baffles inside the tank. The alternative was to mount a long-range array in a fairing around the horizontal perimeter of the hull.

Table 4–4.   The SSK Redesigned, 1949

Dimensions	196-3 × 24-5 × 14-11 ft
Displacement	750 tons
Diving trim	990 tons
Engines	3 (GM 8-268), 1,200-BHP (900-kw)
Surface speed	10 kt
Submerged speed	8 kt
Endurance	9,000 nm
Cells	126
Complement	6/33

If the hull was not quiet enough, the SSK could rely on a pair of PQN-1 hydrophones, one floating above and the other dropped below its hull (using JT controls and consoles). About October 1948, the new BQR-4 was chosen, its array wrapped around the bridge fairwater. In theory, the fairwater offered the best hydrodynamic position, protected the array from collision, and permitted emergency repairs on the surface. The planned active sonar had been eliminated that May on the ground that the SSK would not have to penetrate mine fields.

Unfortunately, silencing was little understood. The SSK was the first U.S. submarine designed specifically for sonar operation. She was arranged internally like a fleet boat, with the pump room and auxiliaries (refrigerating and air conditioning plants) directly under her fairwater,

hence directly under the big BQR-4 array. When the BuShips Submarine Branch raised the silencing issue early in 1950, construction of the first SSK was well along. Self-noise tests of the Guppy II *Grampus* had been scheduled for that July. An omnidirectional microphone was placed in her bridge fairwater. The results were shocking; machinery noise would have more than halved detection range. The bow was much quieter, however, so moving the array there largely solved the problem. The loudest machinery—two motor-generators, the hovering pump, and the trim pump—was relocated aft, and machinery not normally run while listening was moved to the former pump room.

The first SSK replaced one of the diesel attack boats initially planned for the FY 48 program and 2 more SSKs

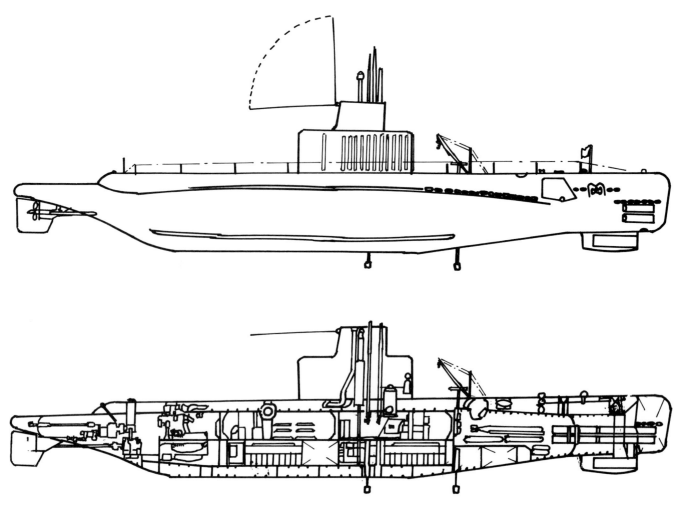

The SSK as redesigned (and much enlarged, to 196×24 ft [750 tons] from 162×19 ft [480 tons]) in 1949, with a BQR-4 array wrapped around her sail and with a 5-ft diameter BQR-2 (used as an attack sonar) in her chin sonar dome. On deck is a trainable BQR-3 (a modernized JT). The forward of the two hydrophones dangling from the hull is a remote listening device; the after hydrophone is for a UQC-1 underwater telephone. On deck forward of the torpedo loading hatch are a messenger buoy, a UQC-1 hydrophone, and a UQN-1 sounder (turned up and tiltable for under-ice navigation). The sound room is abaft the control room, and above the pump room. Note that the battery has been split in conventional fashion (66 cells forward, 60 aft). Masts, fore to aft, are: IFF antenna; No. 1 periscope (36-ft type with ST radar, the only radar on board); VHF-HF antenna; No. 2 periscope (40-ft attack type), with VLF loop alongside; SPR stub; snorkel induction with ESM on top. At this stage the ship had three GM 8-268 diesel generators (300 kW, i.e., 400 HP, each).

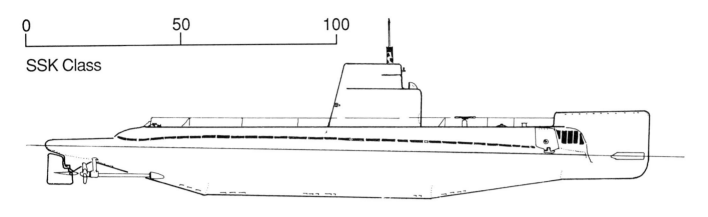

0   50   100

SSK Class

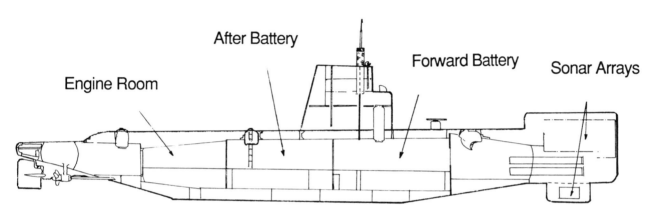

After Battery

Engine Room

Forward Battery   Sonar Arrays

SSK as built, with BQR-4 moved to the bow (BQR-2 in the forefoot, and JT on deck). (Jim Christley)

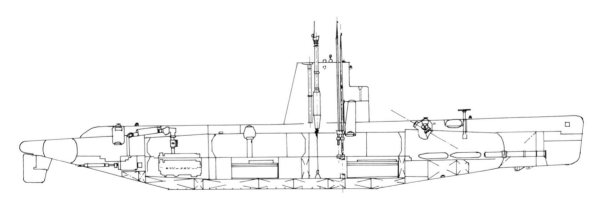

Barracuda (T-3) inboard profile, as in May 1971: an SSK converted to a target submarine. In this guise she lost her bow sonars (retaining only the trainable BQR-3A on its BQA-1 training shaft) and all but one torpedo tube (starboard side). Plans show only two torpedoes, both on the starboard side. Masts, fore to aft, are: an SS radar antenna on the top of the sail; then Nos. 1 and 2 periscopes (the former carrying an ST-1 range-only radar, the latter with a VLF loop to port); an HF-MF whip to starboard alongside a UHF antenna to port; and the snorkel induction, carrying a short whip and a submarine identification light. The short object between the big whip and the snorkel induction is a UQC-1 underwater communications transducer. Another is under a pipe guard forward (with a BSH-2D forward of it). The submarine retained all three main engines.

followed in FY 49. In mid-1948, the tentative FY 50 program included 10 SSKs, 5 with priority 5 and 5 with priority 18. (Guppies had priorities 12 and 21, and new attack submarines had priorities 15 and 26.) By that time, it was clear that the SSK was too elaborate for mass production or, for that matter, for construction by non-submarine yards. BuShips objected that, in wartime, she would compete with an attack submarine program. The austerity she still embodied was less and less acceptable. No SSKs (no new submarines at all, in fact) were included in the FY 50 budget. The three already under construction were initially known only by the designations *K-1* through *K-3*. They were named in 1955.

The only alternative near-term source of large numbers of hulls would be the mass of existing fleet boats. In November 1948, Capt. P. R. Heineman, who was then attached to Deputy Chief of Naval Operations (DCNO) for Operations, suggested to the General Board that at least one thin-skinned fleet boat (i.e., one not suited to Guppy conversion) be converted into an SSK to test the ASW potential of the hundred-odd boats in reserve. He considered it complementary, rather than alternative, to the special SSK. In December, BuShips estimated that conversion would cost $4 million, including $1 million for sonar; a new SSK cost $7.5 million. BuShips strongly favored conversion over new construction. The mobilization plan called for using the thin-skinned fleet boats against enemy surface ships, but the Soviets had few of those; ASW was a far higher priority. The fleet submarine conversion was also attractive because she would be large enough to accommodate alternative suites of SSK equipment, as well as elaborate test and recording equipment. If work were started late in 1949, it could be completed in about a year. In response to Heineman, Adm. C. B. Momsen, a submariner then serving on the General Board, said that it was unfortunate that the SSK had been started before any experience had been gained by converting an existing submarine. The only real drawback of the conversion was that she would require a larger crew and thus be inherently noisier.

Assistant Chief of Naval Operations (ACNO) for Undersea Warfare proposed to silence the conversion by removing two engines and either silencing or sound isolating auxiliaries. One of the torpedo rooms would be converted into a sound room. For the prototype, the arrays on board the existing Type XXI, U-2513, could be installed. The ACNO suggested that BuShips might also consider streamlining, installing a snorkel, and silencing propulsion with direct-drive motors and quiet propellers. Silencing also would include provision for silent living on board.

Work on characteristics for this SCB 58 conversion began early in 1949. She would have both directional and multiple (array) passive sonars, plus the pair of buoyant and sinking (to 1,000 ft below the keel) omnidirectional hydrophones then in vogue. BuShips proposed mounting a power-trained JT on a periscope or mast. A JT or BQR-2 might be mounted on the keel. A planned QHB active

scanning sonar would be mounted off center so that the existing WDA hoist could be used for future experimental sonars. An SCB work sheet, probably compiled in February 1949, called for means to stream and recover the sinking hydrophone while the submarine hovered. It also called for a retractable radio antenna buoy, by means of which the SSK could communicate with submarines (at 35 nm) or airplanes (at 105 nm) while hovering at maximum depth. Because the SSK would be operating in Soviet waters, she would be a valuable source of early warning of aircraft or rocket attacks. Therefore, the SCB wanted an automatic radio direction-finder (working at 2–3 MHz) usable at periscope depth. The SSK would anchor underwater and use up to 500 fathoms of cable.

The forward torpedo room, which was larger, was selected for conversion into a sound room, and the forward two engines were removed for silencing. It might be necessary to remove four or even all six forward torpedo tubes. In the end, two bow tubes remained, together with all four aft; the boat retained one reload per tube, 12 mechanically set 246-in–long weapons. The auxiliary machinery, all individually sound-isolated, was relocated to the former forward engine room. An alternative of sound-isolating them as a group had proved to be impractical. It turned out that relocation over even modest distances made for effective sound isolation. *Grouper* and her successors could listen effectively without shutting down auxiliaries, such as air conditioners.

The designers hoped that the converted fleet boat could support a larger passive array than the small, specially built SSK. One possibility was to put it in a chin (bulbous bow) like that being installed on the Guppy *Cochino*. Only after some months was an SSK-style fairwater installation chosen. Plans called for installation of both BQR-2 and -4; after trials, a passive attack sonar would be substituted for the less effective of the two. Later, an active scanning sonar might replace the passive attack unit. A requirement for single-ping ranging, using a BQS-2, was new; the small SSK had no active sonar at all.

The SCB initially wanted a maximum submerged speed of 13 kt, so the converted fleet boat had to be streamlined. The speed requirement was hard to meet without installing Guppy batteries. It was relaxed to 12 kt at the 1-hr rate; Sargo batteries were used.

Grouper (SSK Type I) was included in the FY 50 supplemental program. Her planned BQR-4 was not available in time; she was completed with a JT in her fairwater and a second in her bow buoyancy tank, the position planned for BQR-4 in the follow-on SSK Type II conversions. Low-speed (2.3-kt) noise tests showed little to choose from between the two locations. At higher speed (6.3 kt), however, the bow hydrophone was substantially noisier, perhaps due in part to structural vibration.

By this time a production version, SSK Type II, was being developed. The SCB wanted more firepower and better performance. The sonar room replaced the pump room, rather than the forward torpedo room, so more

Grouper is shown off Philadelphia on 25 May 1963, early in her conversion to a Lorad test boat. She retained her main SSK sensor, BQR-4 wrapped around the fore part of her fairwater; note the apparent thickness of material between her cockpit and the outside of the fairwater. The starboard side line hydrophone is clearly visible, as is her modified bow. The Lorad projector was not yet in place, but its turntable is visible. As completed *Grouper* carried both BQR-4 *and* BQR-2 for competitive tests; the loser (BQR-2) was then replaced by an active scanning sonar, BQS-2.

tubes could be retained forward. Initially, the designers had hoped to keep all six; by early April 1951, they accepted that two would have to go, leaving a total of eight tubes, with 16 torpedoes, fore and aft). To increase surface speed from 14.5 to 16.5 kt, a third engine was retained.

The big BQR-4 array was moved into the bow. In the first sketches, it was raised well above the waterline so as not to disturb water flow there. To clear its top, the BQR-

3 further aft had to be raised, but that added too much drag. The big array was lowered and a blunt waterline accepted. Ideally, BQR-4 would have had a circular array (eliminating the need for corrections in its scanning switch) within a sound-transparent fairing shaped for minimal resistance, but that was not yet practical. A BQS-2 active scanning sonar also would be mounted under the keel; a bottom BQR-3 under the torpedo tubes was sug-

Later SSK conversions had their BQR-4s wrapped around their bows; *Bream* is shown in 1956. What appears to be a small dome on deck forward is a support for a trainable BQR-3 line hydrophone, a modernized JT.

gested as an interim installation. Other planned sonars were a pair of BQR-3s on deck, fore and aft for passive ranging by triangulation, and a pair of remote PQN-1 hydrophones. Because BQR-3 was not yet ready, JTs could be taken from reserve fleet submarines and substituted. The remote hydrophones were never fitted, but they were evaluated in two submarines. Nor was the after BQR-3 installed. Six fleet submarines were converted to this SSK Type II configuration under the FY 52 program (up from three originally planned in spring 1950).

No other conversions were scheduled for FY 53 and FY 54, pending evaluation of the SSK concept. About 1955, however, three thick-hull fleet snorkel submarines, *Sterlet*, *Sea Owl*, and *Piper*, were fitted with BQR-4A sonars in bow domes. The domes were raised above deck so that they could retain all six forward tubes. No engines were removed. The work was done with overhaul, rather than shipbuilding/conversion, funds, and the submarines were not redesignated.

SSK construction and conversion constituted only one

K 3 (later renamed *Bonita*) shows her enormous BQR-4 array forward. The small object atop it is a BQS-3 searchlight sonar. The big bow array was removed when she and her sisters were reduced to training duty after 1959.

side of a larger submarine ASW development program. In 1947–48, both the Atlantic and Pacific fleets tried long-range listening by fully stopped, silenced boats, and they began to experiment with SSK tactics. Snorkelers were still so rare that, for many tactical trials, fleet boats were trimmed down aft to put more of their engine noise into the water. Early results were encouraging. At Panama and Guantánamo Bay (Atlantic Fleet), Submarine Squadron 2 detected snorkelers at distances up to 24,000 yd and held contact to 37,000 yd (echo ranges were only about 8,700 yd). Submarine Squadrons 3 and 7, out of San Diego, managed to detect a 10-kt snorkeler at 21,600 yd. Under excellent conditions, *Sea Dog* made marginal contact on *Diodon*, snorkeling at 10 kt, at 35 nm. The Pacific Fleet also conducted successful antisnorkeler firings with both straight-running and existing homing anti-ship torpedoes. All of these experiments were encouraging, rather than conclusive, because they were conducted in calm seas under excellent sonar conditions.

In 1949, each fleet commander was ordered to assign a submarine division to develop SSK tactics under Project Kayo. Some fleet boats were somewhat silenced, and better sonars were planned, but no boats were redesignated. The submarines turned out to have real ASW potential. During a late 1950 convoy exercise, for example, *Dogfish* zigzagged unannounced through *Halfbeak*'s patrol area. She was detected at an estimated 23,000 yd. *Halfbeak* was 10,000 yd off her track; based entirely on her passive sonar, she closed to a firing position at a 2,000-yd range. She did not sight the target's snorkel until just as she fired.

SSKs could do far better. Off Bermuda in 1952, *K-1* detected a snorkeler at 30 nm (60,000 yd) and tracked her for 5 hr. In May 1952, SubDevGru 2 used *K-1* and *Grouper* against a series of 43 transiters, half surfaced and half snorkeling, that were passing through an area 150 nm wide. More than half (23) were contacted at least once, 14 attacked (2 of them twice, which was not counted), and 11 counted as killed (not counting 1 killed twice) for a 26-percent rate, albeit under good sound conditions. A deep quiet submarine could still expect to evade an SSK barrier.

A February–March 1954 exercise off Iceland illustrated SSK tactics and performance. *Cavalla*, a converted SSK, and *K-1* simulated a transit to a forward base, resupplied there, transited to a patrol station, and returned. *K-1* was the target en route and *Cavalla* the target in the patrol area. Both relied entirely on passive sonar. In heavy weather, *Cavalla* could not snorkel for prolonged periods because her engines could not stand up to the frequent and prolonged closing of the snorkel head as waves swept over it. She therefore had to run on the surface; storm damage to her superstructure made her noisier when running submerged and limited her average detection range to 13 nm. Because she had smaller engines, *K-1* had no such problems snorkeling and suffered no noisy damage; her average detection range was 28 nm. *K-1* used the new TMA techniques, but she could not adequately measure her own movement because her gyro was not stable enough.

The most spectacular run began at a range of 60 nm, with *Cavalla* running for 2 hr at noncavitating speed (4.5 kt) and alternating with 1 hr of snorkeling at 6 kt

Sea Owl (SS 405), shown in 1964, was one of three fleet snorkel submarines fitted with the same BQR-4A sonar (about 1955) as the SSK conversions, but they were not redesignated. Nor were they elaborately silenced; they retained all four diesels. To listen, they turned off machinery and ran, for example, on a single shaft. The bow dome was raised above deck so that they could retain their six forward tubes. The other submarines fitted with a BQR-4A were *Sterlet* (SS 392) and *Piper* (SS 409). Other major sonars on board were an active BQS-2 or SQS-10 and a passive BQR-3.

K 2 (later renamed *Bass*) shows her antennas and some of her sonars, April 1952. Key (for a series of views; some antennas are not visible here): (1) MF-HF whip (NT 66053), (2) wire antenna for VLF, MF, and HF radio (not visible, on other side of sail), (3) VHF (NT 66134A as interim), (4) VLF loop for underwater reception (NT 66097), (5) AS-393/BLR ESM antenna (not visible), (6) SPR-1 ESM stub antenna, (7) AS-371/S (SPR-2) ESM antenna (not visible), (8) SS-1 surface search radar antenna, (9) IFF (AS-522/BPX) and UHF (AS-468/B) antenna (with AS-535/B to be added in future for VHF), (10) ST-1 range-only radar on the periscope, (11) JT line hydrophone (on deck), (12) BQS-3 single-ping ranging sonar (atop the big dome forward), (13) STT hydrophone (not visible here, on the lower fore side of the sail), (14) bathythermograph blister (40181, on the side of the upper part of the sail).

while zigzagging (short legs superimposed on longer ones to make TMA difficult). She was essentially undetectable while on batteries. Contact was made at 38 nm; 6 hr, 35 min later, the ambushing submarine was in attack position, 1,200 yds off the target's beam. The SSK concept worked. In moderate to poor weather, one SSK could cover a 40-nm front.

Clearly, the SSK offered another possibility as well. Her sonar performance far exceeded that of any surface ship. Performing as a manned variable-depth sonar within a

task force, she could call in surface ships or aircraft to attack detected targets that were well beyond torpedo range. Such tactics were limited by the difficulty of communicating with the submarine, but submarine sonar performance was so good that they kept reappearing, ultimately as the direct-support concepts described in chapter 10.[17]

The first full destroyer-SSK exercises were held in Japanese waters in mid-1954; the submarine relayed her information by underwater telephone. In one exercise, the SSK *Bluegill*, at a range of 15 nm (30,000 yd), vectored destroyers to within 1,500 yd of a target. To do that, she had to distinguish the sound of the target from that of a nearby steamer. SSK–surface ship tactics continued to be developed throughout the 1950s. On 1 April 1958, the U.S. Navy established ASW Defense Group Alfa (later Task Group Alfa) specifically to develop ASW tactics. It comprised a typical hunter-killer group built around an ASW carrier, a patrol plane element, and two SSKs, *Cubera* and *Sea Leopard.*

The main lesson learned was that the character of ASW had changed. In the past, a submarine lay in wait submerged as a formation passed over her. She announced her presence when she fired, and she had to reserve her limited underwater high-speed endurance for escaping afterward. For the defenders, this was a perimeter problem: the submarine had to be caught either going in or, more likely, coming out. The new submarines had so much high-speed underwater endurance, however, that they could fight within the area of the formation. Their new torpedoes could be fired from outside sonar screen range. These points had been suggested on theoretical grounds earlier, but they seem not to have made much impression prior to the Task Group Alfa trials.

Given the new perception, the submarine's superior sonar search rate was clearly valuable; however, the problems of communication and identification (to avoid attacks by friendly forces) remained. Similarly, cooperation between SSKs demanded good covert and secure underwater communication. This problem was never fully solved.[18] Acoustic communication is like one-way sonar. An underwater telephone is quite pratical at short range, but, like a pinging sonar, it gives away the presence of the submarine. Longer-range communication, in theory, can use exotic propagation paths, such as convergence zone and bottom bounce. Unfortunately, the message is an extended signal (the more covert, the more extended in order to keep volume down). It will generally propagate along several paths simultaneously, taking a different amount of time on each. At the receiver, the multiple signals interfere; the message is difficult to read. Several schemes for secure covert communication were proposed in the early 1960s, but none succeeded. In the late 1970s, a computer-driven system, which could automatically select the best propagation path and adapt messages to it, was announced, but it seems not to have entered service. Certainly, the U.S. submarine service has never shown the sort of enthusiasm for group operations that such a system would have inspired.

As for the SSKs, they were victims of their own success.

The special SSK designation was dropped in 1959. From that time, *all* U.S. attack submarines have had the SSK role.

The ultimate submarine-hunter is a quiet nuclear submarine. In Admiral Rickover's view, that required a specially silenced turboelectric power plant. Only one such craft was built, *Glenard P. Lipscomb*. This 22 November 1974 surface view emphasizes the sheer length (essentially the space abaft the sail) that the specially silenced power plant required. Length added wetted area, which increased resistance underwater. The turbo electric plant was also substantially less efficient than the rafted geared turbine installed in contemporary U.S. attack submarines. The combination cost several knots in maximum speed. It could be argued that the plant's inherent quietness was worth that sacrifice, however. The French and Soviet navies adopted simpler and more compact AC turboelectric plants in the *Rubis* and ''Alfa'' (Project 705) classes, respectively. DC had the important advantage that it could be reversed easily, allowing the submarine to pull out of a dive at full power or to maneuver with relative ease. Ironically, the conceptually simple and elegant DC plant turned out to be quite complicated and unreliable in practice. *Lipscomb* was retired well before her geared-turbine near-sisters.

5

New Missions

THE PRIMARY WW II submarine mission of attacking surface ships almost disappeared with the Japanese Empire. Naturally, the U.S. Navy began to search wartime experience for new missions that might become dominant in the future. Much the same might be said of the Cold War: the dominant ASW mission has shrunk, but now the secondary Cold War missions probably point the way. For a time, the special missions that emerged from WW II seemed so important that they might have eventually dominated the submarine force.

The post–WW II navy was clearly going to emphasize carrier attacks against shore targets. The main carrier-support submarine, the radar picket (SSR), was conceived for the invasion of Japan. Submarines were also natural allies of seaplanes, which were later considered potential strategic attackers. The Japanese had used submarines to fuel the large Emily flying boats during their second Pearl Harbor attack in 1942.[1]

The Germans had built special "milch cow" submarines to support their relatively small submarines in distant forward areas. (Prewar, the United States had considered a similar idea.) Although the milch cows had been located, mainly by breaking the coded messages needed to arrange fueling rendezvous, and wiped out, the support idea remained attractive after the war.

Submarines supported amphibious operations by beach reconnaissance, both through the periscope and by landing scouts. One large wartime submarine was converted into a special transport (APS) for marine raiders; another was used for that purpose but not redesignated.

Wartime submarines slipped through blockades with essential men and materiel; they could carry anything that was compact enough. For example, U.S. submarines evacuated the gold reserves of the Philippines, as well as some vital officers. In 1942, with U-boats sinking so many freighters, submarine pioneer Simon Lake proposed a program of submarine freighters. The idea was rejected because they could not carry sufficient cargo and building them would cut into the attack submarine program. The U.S. Navy considered (but did not complete) a special cargo conversion of a fleet submarine.[2]

In the fall of 1944, as part of his comment on the General Board's proposed new submarine program, Commander, Submarines, Pacific (ComSubPac) Vice Adm. Charles A. Lockwood formally proposed two special-purpose submarines: a fleet boat stripped to carry about 325 tons of cargo, and a new-construction tanker (milch cow) with sufficient capacity to top off at least four fleet submarines after they had used up about half their fuel. The tanker would keep the submarines in forward areas where they were productive, rather than in transit. Later, the same idea would be raised as a way of keeping SSKs in place. The postwar Submarine Officers Conference liked the cargo carrier but rejected the milch cow emphatically, although she eventually reappeared. The marines added a raiding submarine. In March 1946, CNO Admiral Nimitz, a former submariner, approved a program to produce a cargo carrier (initially designated SSK, later SSA to distinguish her from ASW submarines) and a troop carrier (SSP). Submarine oiler (SSO) and ammunition carrier (SSE) categories were also established, but conversions were not authorized. That fall, the Submarine Officers Conference considered a range of other auxiliaries specifically to support the ASW submarine barriers (see chapter 4), but nothing had been resolved before the small ASW submarine design was abandoned.[3]

The marines wanted a squadron of 12 SSPs, sufficient to carry the 60 officers and 1,380 enlisted men (5 officers and 155 men per SSP) of an assault battalion, with four 75-mm pack howitzers, six 57-mm recoilless rifles, five fire units per weapon (220 tons of ammunition), 158 tons of supplies (for 10 days), and engineer equipment. The marines would land in rubber boats, but they needed 12 amphibian tractors (LVTs) to carry their weapons and other equipment ashore.[4] To carry the LVT (with a jeep towing a 75-mm howitzer inside), rafts, and outboard motors, each SSP would have a pressure-proof hangar. The hangar could accommodate a small helicopter instead of

The greatest submarine virtue is stealth: for operating in the face of the enemy, but also for delivering men and materiel. *Perch*, newly converted to an amphibious transport shows off her hangar, big enough for an amphibian tractor (AMTRAC). She is shown alongside at Mare Island, 13 August 1948.

As a transport, *Perch* retained firepower to support a small-unit landing, in the form of a 5-in/25 and a 40-mm gun. She is shown at Mare Island, 13 August 1948.

an LVT. (A secondary SSP mission—reconnaissance or establishment of a covert post, such as a weather station—was proposed in late 1948.) The marines wanted a 4-in deck gun or a 105-mm howitzer for shore bombardment; the SSPs retained their forward 5-in/25 (the after mount made way for the LVT hangar) plus the forward 40-mm gun.

Troops required extra bunks, more showers and heads, and more air conditioning. They also needed so much more air that the SSP might have had to snorkel every 7 hr. To avoid that, she was provided with a CO_2 scrubber (developed by Mare Island Navy Yard and based on work at the University of Pennsylvania) and 50,000 cu ft of oxygen in high-pressure tanks (3,000 psi in place of the usual 2,000 psi). All torpedo tubes and two main engines were eliminated. The other two engines were fitted with a snorkel.

Two prototype SSPs, *Perch* and *Sealion*, were included in the FY 48 program. Despite some fears, the hangar did not interfere with diving. The LVT and rubber boats, however, were unsatisfactory in anything but the lightest surf. The marines abandoned the battalion idea in favor of commando operations.[5] One SSP, soon redesignated ASSP (then APSS and ultimately LPSS) was assigned to each coast, *Perch* in the Pacific and *Sealion* in the Atlantic. *Perch* fought in both Korea and in Vietnam; among other assignments, she landed a British commando unit in Korea in 1950. *Sealion* participated in the 1962 Cuban blockade; presumably, she was intended to land a beach reconnaissance party in preparation for a full-scale amphibious assault.

When the Regulus missile was withdrawn from service in 1964, the two recently built diesel SSGs were earmarked for conversion to second-generation LPSSs. Money was tight; only *Grayback* was converted (at Mare Island for the Pacific Fleet in 1969–70).[6] Her hangars did not accommodate LVTs but only the far smaller swimmer delivery vehicles (SDVs) developed for the SEALs.[7] A single SDV could be accommodated in a much smaller dry deck shelter (DDS). The DDS holds not only the vehicle but also a decompression chamber and an access section through which swimmers can enter while the submarine is submerged. *Grayback* was succeeded by a pair of obsolete ballistic missile submarines, *Sam Houston* (SSBN 609) and *John Marshall* (SSBN 611), that were converted at Puget Sound to carry two removable DDSs and up to 67 swimmers. Delays in DDS production limited each submarine to one each until May 1988. The two SSBNs were retired in 1992 after conducting a spectacular joint SEAL exercise in the Caribbean. Under the FY 92 program, they are being replaced by *Kamehameha* (SSBN 642) and *James K. Polk* (SSBN 645).

The DDS could be fitted to any properly modified attack submarine; the prototype, *Cavalla* (SSN 684), was converted in August–December 1982 to carry the DDS and 16 SEALs. Beginning in 1989 with SSN 680, additional *Sturgeon*s, SSN 678–680, 682, and 686, were converted. It is widely believed that special forces will become much more important in the post–Cold War world. Relying on a few special submarines is not attractive because they might be unavailable in a sudden crisis. This problem can be solved by converting numerous SSNs to carry DDSs on a temporary basis.

The SSA, intended mainly to support the raiders, was a much simpler proposition. The forward engines, after torpedo tubes, and all reload torpedoes were removed; complement was cut to 55. As in the SSP, a snorkel was added for covert transits. In October 1946, the design was ordered modified to add gasoline-carrying fittings in half the fuel tanks and a larger (36-in, rather than 25-inch standard) hatch into her main cargo space. *Barbero* was converted under the FY 48 program, but the cargo-carrier role was soon dropped and she was laid up until a later conversion to a missile submarine.

The marines also wanted an SSO to supply their battalion over the beach; *Guavina* was converted, under the FY 49 program, as SCB 39. She had to carry both diesel oil and gasoline for vehicles and aircraft and be able to discharge her cargo while submerged. As completed, *Guavina* had a snorkel and retained three torpedo tubes (one forward to discharge dry cargo, two aft for self-defense). Special saddle tanks could carry 150,000 gallons of jet fuel, diesel fuel, or gasoline. Her motors were replaced with the quieter direct-drive type. The formal characteristics noted that, in future, she might have to carry other fuels, such as missile fuel (in portable containers).

By October 1951, tests had shown that *Guavina* could fuel another submarine submerged, if both first hooked up on the surface. SubLant considered it doubtful that she would ever have to do that in practice or to fuel a beachhead. She took too long to empty her tanks (10 hr), and the external gasoline tanks would easily breach if she was bombed. She might, however, fuel a small carrier, seaplane tender, or group of seaplanes.

The SSO became important because she could support the new P6M Seamaster attack seaplane.[8] As a tender, the SSO would be no more vulnerable to a first strike than the stretch of sea from which the Seamaster would fly. The first Seamaster contract was let in 1953. *Guavina* was refitted at Philadelphia in 1955 with a flat plane-handling "flight deck" aft. Tests of the new mobile support concept began in January 1956, and characteristics for another seaplane support conversion (SCB 170) were approved in September 1957. The SSO would be able to fuel her seaplanes when submerged to 100 ft (at 400 gal/min), via a floating buoy. She would also carry out minor repairs and act as a navigation and weather reference.

The 1970 fleet projected in December 1955 by the Long Range Objectives Group included 72 seaplanes, to be supported by six converted fleet submarines (then designated ASSO), as well as numerous surface tenders. For the longer term, BuAer wanted a nuclear-powered seaplane, which required its own tender. The tender would provide the chemical fuel needed by the plane for takeoff, landing, and high-speed dashes, as well as replacement crews (the airborne reactor would have had only limited shielding, so no crew could make many flights). Around 1956, BuShips sketched a 342 × 30-ft tender (5,450 tons submerged) powered by an S5W reactor (20 kt submerged), to carry 180,000 gal of fuel, 120,000 lb of bombs, and 34 passengers. The

Cavalla is shown with a dry deck shelter. After the demise of the special amphibious submarines, this shelter was developed for use on board conventional attack craft. (J. Bouvia)

Guavina fuels an ASW seaplane while under way in the Caribbean on 3 March 1955.

attack seaplane project was canceled in favor of the Polaris missile. *Guavina* became a pierside trainer in 1959.

In 1945–46, another special role, that of radar picket, was already well established. Experience in the Pacific clearly showed that a task force needed the earliest warning it could get; this generally meant radar picket destroyers operating well away from the task group center. Such warning became even more urgent as aircraft speed increased so drastically after the war. The Japanese were well aware of the importance of the pickets, which they attacked quite effectively at Okinawa. The obvious solution was a submersible picket, a submarine equipped with as much of the destroyer's radar and air control facilities as possible.

On 6 July 1945, Cominch (Commander-in-Chief U.S. Fleet) ordered 24 fleet submarines converted to support the invasion of Japan (Operation Olympic) planned for that October. Spaced about 25 nm apart, they would patrol a picket line 50 to 100 nm from the fleet, each controlling a combat air patrol of 4 to 20 fighters. Submarines, however, lacked the combat information center (CIC) and high-powered radar such a role demanded. In mid-1945 tests, for example, *Conger* could not detect targets above 10,000 ft or beyond 27,000 yd with SV, her best radar.

SubLant concluded that a drastic conversion would be needed. One engine room could be cleared for radar consoles and a CIC. To support operations in 1946, conversion would require about six months, so work would have to begin immediately on several boats. No prototype could be tested in time. Details were developed at a late July 1945 meeting between the OpNav submarine staff and BuShips. The after torpedo room was used instead of an engine room; the tubes were retained, but they could be loaded only through their muzzles. A search radar (the big new SR) and a height-finder (SV mounted on its side to scan vertically) would be mounted on deck immediately above the after torpedo room.

Pearl Harbor had to provide 24 interim pickets for the planned October invasion. It managed to complete 2 (*Grouper* and *Finback*) and partly completed 4 more.[9] The SV air-search antenna was relocated to a new periscope mounting, developed by the Submarine Training Command at Pearl Harbor, so that it could be used at periscope depth. The second conversion had a small CIC in her chief's quarters. These austere pickets were effective enough for Admiral Lockwood (ComSubPac) to question the more elaborate program prepared in Washington.

The BuShips design became Project Migraine, a name reflecting the miseries involved in packing so much electronics into such little space and protecting high-powered microwave transmission joints from the effects of seawater and pressure. *Spinax* and *Requin*, the Migraine I conversions, were completed in the fall of 1946. They carried SR-2 and SV-2 radars on deck aft, where they suffered badly in most seas. As in the Pearl Harbor conversions, their SV radars could be used on a limited basis. Extra electrical and heat loads required another motor-generator set and an additional air conditioner.

When everything worked, a Migraine I was considered virtually as effective as a destroyer picket and much more survivable. She was not very fast, but destroyers rarely steamed much beyond her speed of 18 kt. On the other hand, the picket served as a reference point for her fighters. The submarine was difficult to see, and her aircraft lost touch with her homing beacon when she dove. In early tests, *Requin* had two broad yellow bands painted fore and aft, so that she could be identified from 10,000 ft.

With the two Migraine I submarines nearing completion in the fall of 1946, two more conversions were included in the tentative FY 48 program. They were initially conceived as arctic pickets (SCB 12), part of a larger program to extend naval operations into the approaches to the Soviet Union. By 1948, plans called for one conversion each year for a total of at least six. The FY 48 and FY 49 programs each included one Migraine II SSR: *Tigrone* and *Burrfish*, respectively. The two radars were raised onto masts. A pressurized version of the new SPS-6 air search radar, 15 ft across, was proposed (but not adopted) to replace SR-2. Electronic equipment was moved to the crews' store and the after battery compartment (rather than the after torpedo room) to raise the main antennas and improve the CIC arrangement. Half the battery was removed to make more space; capacity was maintained

Newly converted to a radar picket, *Spinax* demonstrates one reason why the project deserved to be called Migraine: her main antennas (SV-2 height-finder and SR-2 search radar) are only feet above the water. The CIC was right below them. The object just abaft the conning tower is her 5-in gun mount, minus the barrel. *Spinax* is pictured off Portsmouth Naval Shipyard, 13 November 1946.

by replacing the other half with Guppy cells. A snorkel was installed to feed two of the four diesels; the auxiliary diesel was removed. All four after tubes and the two upper forward tubes were removed to provide bunks and storage space. Each retained one reload, below the forward torpedo room flat.

Although not finally classed as arctic pickets, these Migraine II boats were fitted with topside fathometers. They also received QHB sonars and QXB torpedo detectors. The earlier Migraine I conversions were modified under the FY 48 budget to approach Migraine II standard. Their SR-2 radars were moved forward onto the boats' cigarette decks; the SV-2 remained aft. As in Migraine II, six tubes were removed and snorkels fitted. CICs were partly rearranged. All four boats were armed with single 40-mm guns (a twin mount specified for Migraine II was not available) that were later removed. (Their 5-in guns had been landed to compensate for the topside weight of the radar antennas.) The four boats were eventually fitted to control Regulus missiles fired by other submarines. In 1950, it was estimated that a Migraine II SSR could reliably detect a typical Soviet bomber (Tu-2) at 50 nm. The new standard air search radar, SPS-6B, on board a destroyer could detect

the same airplane at 125 nm. The submarine could conduct three simultaneous interceptions and the destroyer four.

By that time, the primary U.S. carrier mission was a quick strike against Soviet targets. The carriers would use their speed to avoid enemy attack, but no submarine could keep up with them. Submarines would have to be placed in advance of any strike. This would limit the flexibility of the carrier strike force. Interest grew in designing a submarine so fast that, when surfaced, she could actually cruise with the carriers.

An August 1950 OpNav presentation on the carrier task force of the near future showed 4 SSRs helping to protect a formation of 4 carriers. Because the navy hoped to operate 12 carriers, that implied a goal of 12 SSRs and, therefore, conversions beyond the four Migraine I and II boats. A new Migraine III (SCB 12A) applied to 2 SSRs in FY 51 and 4 in FY 52. The conversions were carried out on nearsisters (SS 267–272 and 274) to avoid any need for more than one set of conversion plans.

The navy had two new SSR radars: BPS-2, to match SPS-6B performance, and a BPS-3 height-finder, effective out to 55 nm, compared with 35 nm for SV-2. Existing Migraines were badly cramped for space; the SCB consid-

Spinax was soon rebuilt, with her search radar moved to a better position higher above water. The SV-2 height-finder could not be moved, however, and thus continued to suffer water damage. This photograph, taken at San Francisco Naval Shipyard on 19 July 1954, shows neither SV-2 nor the YE aircraft homing beacon, essential for aircraft control, that was also on deck.

Tigrone typifies the next stage of radar picket evolution, with the height-finder raised on a mast and the superstructure modified (the 40-mm gun has been brought down on deck). *Tigrone* later became an experimental submarine, with a partially streamlined sail.

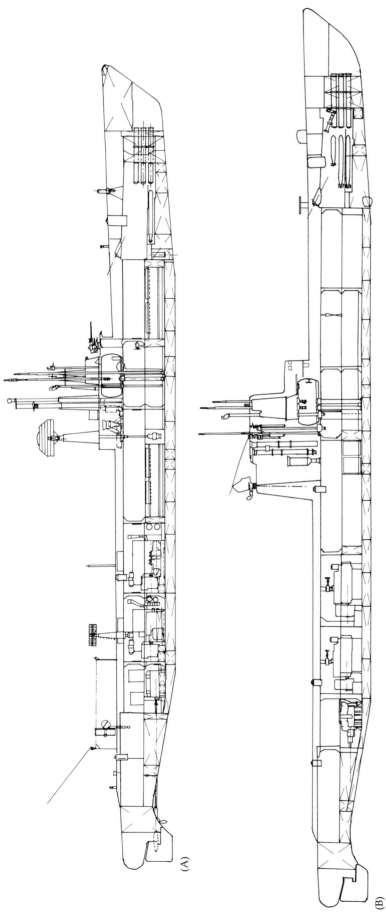

(A) *Spinax* (SSR 489) was one of the original "Migraine" SSRs. She is shown as in 1950. The air-control center is aft, under the SV-2 height-finding radar antenna shown almost right aft. Abaft this space was an electronic spare parts and storeroom; the two spaces replaced the former after torpedo room. Forward, the upper pair of torpedo tubes were demilitarized and converted into pressure-proof lockers (the four lower tubes remained in use). By this time the big search antenna (SR-2) had been moved to the conning tower fairwater (the other big antenna on deck is a YE-3 aircraft beacon). An auto-pilot replaced the main steering station in the conning tower (but not in the ship's near-sister, *Requin*). Note the whip antenna right aft, with radio antennas port and starboard forward of it. The pole forward of the YE-3 is an AEW antenna. On the fairwater, a new mast has been installed forward of the periscopes to carry an SPR-1 ECM (ESM) radar-warning antenna. No. 2 periscope carries antennas. Between the periscopes are the VLF loop and UHF and IFF antennas. Abaft the periscopes is an SV for secondary air search (the big air search antenna is SR-2). Snorkel induction and exhaust are also shown. Picket work invited air attack. Four 0.50-cal machine-gun mounts were arranged on each side of the main deck, abeam the fairwater, and three more on each side of the cigarette deck, roughly abeam the snorkel. The vertical tube forward is for a WFA sonar transducer (another projected down, using the trunk shown near the keel).

(B) *Rock* (SSR 274, shown in 1958) was one of the final series of fleet submarines converted to radar pickets. By the time of this drawing, the height-finding radar on deck abaft the sail had been removed, leaving her only with the big BPS-2 visible at the after end of her sail. The sonar dome on deck forward (to starboard) is for BQS-2; a similar dome (which was not retractable) is shown near the keel, on the starboard side almost directly below the JT-1 on deck (to port). The keel dome also contained the transducer of a UQC-1 underwater telephone. Conversion entailed the addition of a 30-ft section forward of the sail. Forward of the control room is the air-control center, with CPO and crew quarters added at its fore end. Below it is an electrical equipment space with a small sonar room at its fore end and air-conditioning machinery aft. As in earlier radar pickets, the stern torpedo tubes have been eliminated. The forward tubes survived (the mechanism above them is hydraulics for the bow planes). Masts, fore to aft, are: No. 1 periscope; a small UHF antenna to starboard (AS-468/B); No. 2 periscope; SV-3 air-search radar; AS-371/S (ECM) to starboard and an AT-365A/BL (ECM) stub, also to starboard; BLR-1 DF antenna (in a small dome) on the centerline; the IFF/UHF mast (extended: AS-522/B and AS-468/B, on the centerline); a retractable MF/HF whip; the VLF loop; the AEW mast (AEW beacon, AEW link, and UHF antenna AS-493/U); the snorkel induction with AS-393/BLR ESM antenna on top; and the snorkel exhaust.

ered suspending further conversions until it was convinced that living conditions would be satisfactory. In December 1950, an SCB member, Comdr. James S. Bethea, suggested adding length. The BuShips submarine designer, Capt. Armand Morgan, chose 27 ft 6 in; the original proposal of 20 ft would have given insufficient stability. Even then, no guns could be provided. The complement grew with the design, from 10 officers and 84 enlisted men to 12 and 95, respectively. All stern tubes were removed, and bow stowage was drastically reduced to 10 long and 2 short torpedoes in order to provide the additional berthing. Given the extra volume, the submarines could retain their original Sargo batteries. Regulus missile control was not included.

The converted fleet boats were fundamentally limited. The FY 52 program included the first new SSRs, *Sailfish* and *Salmon* (SSR 572 class, SCB 84). They brought the total to the desired figure of 12, but the earliest Migraines were clearly due for replacement. A third new SSR planned for the FY 53 budget, however, was dropped to provide money for the second large-deck carrier, *Saratoga*.

Because hull volume was clearly the key to an SSR design, the SCB 84 basic design, completed in May 1952, had a hull substantially larger than that of a fleet submarine. Its specifications were 343 ft × 28 ft 8 in × 23 ft 11 in, 1,907 tons standard, 2,428 tons in maximum surfaced condition, and 2,983 tons submerged. Unlike a postwar attack boat, SCB 84 would spend most of her time on the surface; she was more like the older sort of submarine. For example, she had considerable reserve buoyancy (33 percent in normal condition, 23 percent fully loaded) for surface seakeeping, even though that added wetted surface (resistance) when she submerged. Her power plant matched that of a fleet boat—four 2,000-BHP diesels, 252 Sargo II battery cells, 6,750 SHP surfaced, 3,390 SHP submerged. Armament was limited to six bow tubes (12 torpedoes), and complement matched that of a Migraine III.

The original hull design was that of a fleet boat with 25 ft of parallel midbody added, like a new-construction Migraine III, 334 ft long. The compact pancake diesel was abandoned, and the engine room had to be lengthened. The motors were pushed aft and the stern section fattened to accommodate them. Good surface speed, however, required a longer and more tapered stern. Structural problems were also evident. The conical after end of the pressure hull had to be flattened on its bottom to accommodate the motors. An attempt to keep the pressure hull nearly circular at its forward end (for strength) was abandoned because that made the bow too full for high speed.[10] In the end, the length was held to 343 ft only by shortening the engine and motor rooms. Control surface areas were based on those of WW II fleet submarines, except that a topside rudder was added. There were also weight problems.

Topside arrangement was another serious matter. The BPS-2 radar could retract into a fairwater, but the BPS-3 could not. A single fairwater carrying both would have been 85 ft long, which was unacceptable. Mounting one radar on a separate conical tower abaft well amidships cut the size of the fairwater but added about as much drag. The SCB saved the day by cutting the number of masts, including snorkel and periscopes, to only (!) 12. The BPS-3 pressure chamber was sunk deeper into the deck, and the TACAN radar beacon, which had replaced YE, moved close to the main deck abaft it. Surface speed was still inadequate. BuShips developed a pressure-fired plant (see chapter 3) for 20,000 SHP and 23 kt or more, but this work was abandoned about 1954.

Nuclear power was the obvious solution. The SSR was an obvious application of the new SAR reactor developed

Sailfish displays the antennas of her BPS-2 search radar and her BPS-3 height-finder. The small sonar dome is for BQS-2 (with another in a retractable keel dome); abaft it is a trainable attack sonar (BQR-3). By late 1960, the trainable array had been replaced by BQR-2. Note also the topside rudder. *Sailfish* was later converted into an attack submarine and equipped with PUFFS.

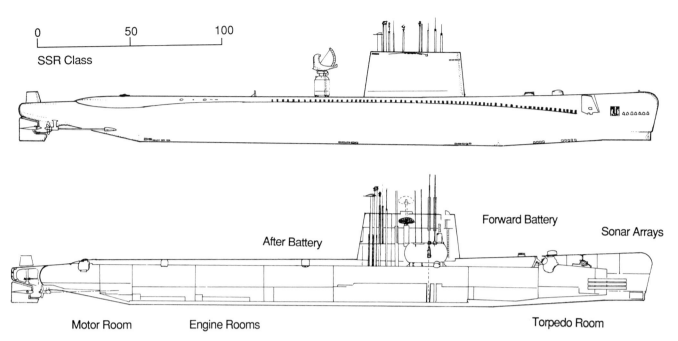

Sailfish (SSR 572). The sonar dome on deck was for BQS-2; a trainable BQR-3 (on the port side) is shown further aft. There was also a retractable keel dome for another BQS-2 transducer. The radar in the sail was BPS-2; that abaft the sail was a BPS-3 height-finder. A URN-3 TACAN beacon (replacing the YE-3 of earlier radar pickets) was emplaced on deck aft. (Jim Christley)

specifically for high speed. Work on a nuclear SSR began around 1954–55, and one was included in the FY 56 budget (*Triton*, SSRN 586, SCB 132). An early sketch showed a 400×38-ft (4,800/6,500-ton) ship carrying the usual BPS-2 and -3 radars in a big stepped sail. She was expected to reach 27 kt on the surface and to cost $78 mil-

lion. Then, the SAR plant began to grow. *Triton* ended up 448 ft long, with a displacement of 7,780 tons submerged and a price of $100 million. Her greater length balanced off her greater tonnage, so that she could still make her designed surface speed. She had only a single radar, initially SPS-26 (to have been replaced by the abor-

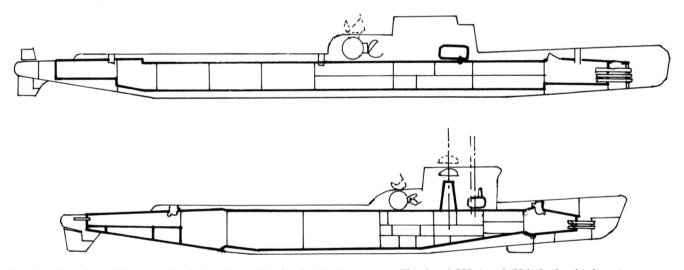

Diesel and nuclear SSRs were sketched early in 1955 for the FY 56 program. The diesel SSR (*not Sailfish*) had a third engine room, for a total of 12,000 BHP (six Fairbanks Morse 2,400 BHP diesels); estimated trial speed was 23.6 kt. Submerged, using 504 Guppy batteries, she would have made 14.1 kt at the 1-hr rate. The air control center would have been on the upper level, just abaft the control room under the small conning tower. The radar shown is the BPS-3 height-finder; the antenna of a BPS-2 search set would have been mounted in the large part of the sail. Dimensions: 387×31.1×18.2 ft (2,330 tons light, 2,930 tons surfaced, 3,950 tons submerged, for 35 percent reserve buoyancy). Estimated cost was $24 million. The alternative nuclear version, which became *Triton*, had a three-level hull, with the air center on the middle level. Dimensions: 400×38 ft (4,600 tons light, 4,800 tons surfaced, 6,500 tons submerged). Estimated performance (as of January 1955): 34,000 SHP = 27 kt surfaced, 23 kt submerged. Estimated cost was $78 million. By the time these drawings had been made, the exotic closed-cycle power plants proposed for SSRs had been abandoned.

At Philadelphia Naval Shipyard, 24 August 1953, *Pompon* displays her antennas. Barely visible is the emergency wire antenna extending to the left from the sail. The short whip protruding from the left side of the sail is an SPR-1 (ESM). The two very short antennas visible to the right of the search periscope, which carries an ST range-only radar, are AS-468/B UHF antennas carried port and starboard. To the right of the attack periscope is an SV-3 air search antenna. The mast to its right carries an AS-522/BPX IFF antenna and more AS-468s for UHF. To its right is a mast carrying a pair of retractable MF-HF whips. The stack of antennas on the mast to the right is an AS-493/U assembly for AEW (beacons and link) and UHF communication (mainly with an AEW airplane). To the right is the snorkel induction mast, carrying an AS-393/BLR ECM antenna at its head. The big BPS-2 air search radar antenna is visible, but not the SV-6 height-finder further aft or the YE beacon on deck.

tive BPS-10), an electronically scanned three-dimensional radar that could, in theory, replace both sets of an earlier SSR.[11]

The Long Range Objective Group's December 1955 description of a future fleet included five carrier strike groups, each supported by 2 SSRs for a total of 10. All but the 2 new *Salmon*s would be nuclear powered. As *Triton*'s cost began to grow, the long-range planners, by 1957, wanted only enough SSRNs (4) to protect a single nuclear carrier group. The four non-nuclear groups would make do with 2 SSRs each.

Then, the SSR died. A new generation of carrier radar

airplanes, the E-1B and its successor, the current E-2, could provide the necessary radar and fighter control service in virtually all weather and keep up with the fast carrier.[12] The new *Triton* no longer had any obvious role; she was too big to be an effective attack submarine. Her large two-level CIC did make her attractive for other roles. In 1957, a Regulus missile-submarine conversion was studied; later a Polaris conversion was proposed. The entire fore end of the submarine, including her sail and CIC, would have been replaced. Still later, she was proposed as an alternative national emergency command post afloat (NECPA, designated SSCN). None of the ideas quite worked. *Triton*

Ray displays her new BPS-3 height-finder, 1957 (it replaced the SV-6 height-finder). The YE homing beacon has been eliminated (aircraft were converting to an alternative beacon, Tacan). Some ships (e.g., *Raton*, by November 1958) lost their height-finders, too. The sonar dome forward is for BQS-4; a trainable passive attack sonar array is visible abaft it.

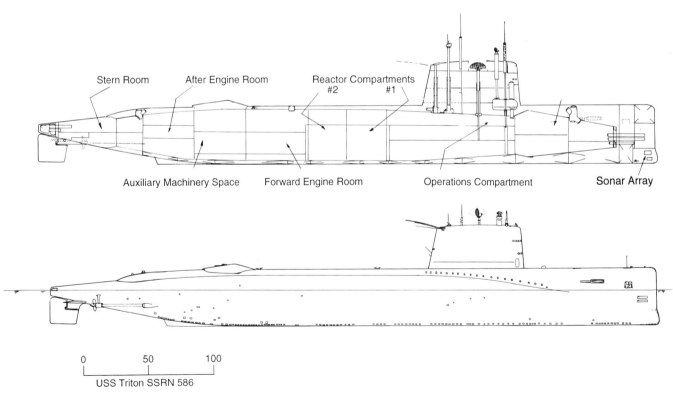

Stern Room   After Engine Room   Reactor Compartments #2   #1

Auxiliary Machinery Space   Forward Engine Room   Operations Compartment   **Sonar Array**

0   50   100

USS Triton SSRN 586

Triton had her air-control center on her second level, below the officers' quarters abaft the control room/attack center. Crew quarters were in the double-decked after portion of the torpedo room. This ship was unusual among nuclear submarines in having full-length torpedo tubes aft. Note also her conning tower, in the sail above the control room, with the single radar antenna abaft it. Her unusual bulbous bow was adopted to increase surface speed. The structure aft atop her superstructure was fitted just prior to her round-the-world cruise; it contained a predecessor of the BRA-3 towed communications buoy then planned for ballistic-missile submarines (the shape of the structure resembled that of the after end of the missile section of an SSBN). (Jim Christley)

Triton was built as an SSRN, but the submarine radar picket role was abandoned just as she was completed. She is shown as an SSN on 15 June 1963. Note the cutout in the sail for her big air search antenna. There was no provision for a secondary height-finder; *Triton* had a single 3-DSPS-26 radar, electronically scanned in elevation. The big fairing aft was for an experimental communications buoy.

was the first nuclear submarine to go into reserve. She is best known for making the first totally submerged round-the-world cruise in 1960.[13]

The 2 *Salmon*s, essentially fleet snorkels with fewer torpedoes, were reclassified as attack submarines and modernized in the FRAM program in 1964. Their CICs were converted into the plotting rooms needed for PUFFS and the Mk 45 torpedo.[14] The Migraines were all reclassified in 1959 and used as auxiliaries.

One SSR role survived. Because she is covert, a submarine can collect electronic intelligence that might be denied to a more visible airplane or predictable satellite. Typically, other platforms can monitor 93 percent of what a submarine obtains, but the other 7 percent—the signals that a target wants to conceal and turns off in the face of overt collectors—is the most important information. By monitoring potentially hostile signals before a battle group appears, a submarine can provide extremely valuable "indications and warning." Several *Los Angeles*-class submarines preceded carriers through the Mediterranean during the buildup to the Gulf War.

Intelligence gathering became a major Cold War mission after the February 1948 Czech crisis convinced U.S. planners that they might actually have to fight the Soviet Union in the near future. Atomic bomb production was drastically stepped up. Suddenly, it was terribly important to locate Soviet early-warning radars and measure their parameters. Later, recording Soviet submarine acoustic data became vital (see chapter 4). Surveillance work always has been extremely secret, but it was apparently a major U.S. Cold War submarine mission. This mission is likely to become more important in the unstable post–Cold War period.

SubLant seems to have made the first proposal for a special electronic surveillance submarine (2 April 1948). The Submarine Officers Conference considered a modified SSR with a standard Type 5 periscope sufficient, but it is unlikely that such submarines were ever used. No special

surveillance submarines were built, although this role certainly affected the *Sturgeon* design. It appears that no integrated program to develop the necessary equipment was formulated until 1965 (see chapter 4).

Reportedly, some submarines were modified for quite specific intelligence duties.[15] After service as a cruise missile submarine, *Halibut* was apparently modified to service divers. In 1972, she reportedly tapped the undersea cable crossing the Sea of Okhotsk; this operation (Ivy Bells) was compromised in 1981 by Ronald Pelton, a traitor in the National Security Agency. *Seawolf* and *Parche* were modified to service the tap placed on the cable. *Halibut* and *Seawolf* were described publicly as research submarines; special thrusters allowed them to maintain a precise position below the surface while equipment was lowered far below. Both were also fitted to handle deep-diving submersibles; photographs show *Halibut* carrying one aft, atop her hull. *Parche* was fitted to mate with a deep submergence rescue vehicle (DSRV) and thus, presumably, to operate with other submersibles. That might have obviated any need for the precise-positioning equipment used with an unpowered tethered device. Reportedly, *Halibut* lowered reconnaissance equipment (e.g., to photograph the sunken Soviet Golf-class submarine before the Central Intelligence Agency (CIA) used *Glomar Explorer* to try to retrieve it in 1974. *Grayback,* another former missile submarine, may have been similarly modified.[16]

Intelligence gathering inevitably brought U.S. submarines into contact with Soviet ASW forces. When such operations were first publicly discussed in 1975, there was much anguish that incidents involving U.S. submarines could escalate into (always unspecified) disasters. These incidents more likely demonstrated to the Soviets that U.S. submarines could, in fact, carry out their wartime missions and thus contributed to deterrence. Moreover, it is clear that neither side was anxious to use any incident, however embarrassing, to touch off a disastrous war. Incidents might be exploited for bargaining purposes, but they were more likely to teach lessons. For example, no reprisals resulted from the large number of U.S. reconnaissance aircraft that the Soviets shot down in and beyond their airspace. U.S. submariners presumably gained invaluable operational experience by operating in and near Soviet waters. The intelligence gathered was quite valuable in itself. Because they demonstrated that the submarines could perform as advertised, intelligence successes may have helped to convince Congress and the White House to buy more submarines.[17]

One abortive conversion, the minelayer (SSM) proposed for the FY 49 program (SCB 66), deserves brief mention. Existing submarines could not lay mines fast enough to produce a dense field, and, except for the Mk 27 self-propelled mine, they could not carry enough mines for a large field. Design work was protracted, and the conversion was dropped from the tight FY 49–51 budgets. It reappeared in FY 52; *Picuda* was chosen. A 35-ft mine stowage section would have been inserted between the

forward battery and the forward torpedo room. Dry stowage would have amounted to 108 Mk 49 mines in the forward torpedo room, a special mine space, and the aft torpedo room. Another 60 mines would have been stowed in the main ballast tanks. *Picuda* would have been streamlined and fitted with a snorkel. In July 1952, preliminary designers considered replacing two of her main diesels and the auxiliary diesel with a 6,500-SHP Walter closed-cycle plant (geared to two generators) for a faster (16-kt) run in and out of enemy waters. Hydrogen peroxide would have been stowed in bags in the outer hull tanks at a cost of about 400 nm in diesel endurance for every hour of full power on the Walter plant. The idea was rejected on the ground that such high-speed endurance was not worth its price in snorkel endurance (10,500 nm, rather than 13,800 nm, at 10 kt). Maximum surface speed would have been reduced from 17 to 14.5 kt. The conversion was cancelled on 1 October 1952, and *Picuda* became a Guppy IIA.

Converted to a special-mission submarine, the former missile boat *Halibut* enters San Francisco harbor with the rescue submersible DSRV-1 atop her stern, 6 April 1970. In 1994 it was revealed that carrying the submersible was only a cover for her real mission, photographing and recovering important debris (such as parts of a Soviet missile submarine) on the sea bottom.

6

The Nuclear Revolution

IN 1945–46 CONGRESS decided to place nuclear matters under central, but emphatically not military, control in the form of the Atomic Energy Commission (AEC). The naval nuclear program had to be half Navy and half AEC. The AEC answered not only to the usual defense committees of Congress but also to the Joint Committee on Atomic Energy (JCAE). Divided responsibility created unusual bureaucratic opportunities for Admiral Rickover, who was actually responsible for naval nuclear power plants. For example, as an officer of the AEC, he was considered half civilian; he could gain direct access to the JCAE and thus circumvent the naval chain of command. Perhaps most importantly, the members of the JCAE generally long outlasted CNOs and bureau chiefs.

Rickover's full independence probably dates from his successful fight for promotion to rear admiral in 1953. Two U.S. Navy selection boards refused to promote him from captain; in the normal course of events, he would have had to retire. The JCAE managed to reverse the Navy's official decision. Committee members argued that it would be insane to remove the man most responsible for so vital a program as naval nuclear propulsion. Rickover must have learned that he was no longer completely subject to naval authority—the reward and punishment system of naval advancement no longer applied to him. He now served, in effect, partly at the pleasure of the JCAE, rather than the secretary of the navy or the CNO.

The navy argued that Rickover was a narrow specialist within the larger field of naval engineering, hence ill-suited to hold flag rank and thus to command a bureau. The JCAE was convinced that nuclear engineering was a fully fledged field in itself. Although no formal steps were taken, the nuclear propulsion organization within BuShips, Code 1500, essentially became a separate bureau of (nuclear) engineering, with its own brand of engineering duty officer (EDO); Rickover became the senior nuclear EDO. Certainly, Rickover's own tough personality helped him to exploit the opportunity presented by split

control of atomic energy; certainly, too, the unusual prerogatives of his position tended, in later years, to shape his character. As a prime exponent of the "never complain, never explain" school of leadership, however, Rickover projected a more arrogant and arbitrary image than he probably deserved.

As early as 1939, a small navy group had been formed to investigate the consequences of nuclear fission but was dissolved when the atomic bomb project began. In 1945, many officers imagined that, as in every other sphere, nuclear energy eventually would be applied to naval propulsion.[1] Early in 1946, the wartime Manhattan Project, which would be turned over to civilian control under the AEC on 1 January 1947, began work on a power reactor at Oak Ridge, Tennessee. The Navy contributed five officers, the senior of whom was then Captain Rickover, and three civilians. Oak Ridge proposed to circulate helium gas through the reactor core to transfer heat to an electric generator. In June 1947, General Electric, which had received a contract to operate the wartime plutonium-producing reactor at Hanford, Washington, proposed a naval power plant using liquid metal, either sodium or a sodium-potassium alloy, for heat transfer. Initial studies suggested that such a plant might be available for submarine installation as early as the end of 1950.[2] BuShips let a $2.25 million contract for Project Genie.

The following December, CNO Admiral Nimitz formally advised the secretary of the navy that a true (i.e., nuclear-powered) submarine would be the most secure means of carrying out offensive (presumably strategic missile) operations; hence, the navy should immediately begin development of a nuclear submarine. Work on missile-firing submarines was already well advanced. On 20 January 1948, BuShips formally proposed to the AEC that a single organization, reporting both to it and to the AEC, be formed to design and build a naval nuclear power plant. The nuclear plant would meet the same requirements for power and operating depth as the closed-cycle

Nautilus began a revolution in submarine design and practice. Perhaps the most significant design decision was to equip her with torpedo tubes, rather than build her as a purely experimental prototype. The bulbous dome alongside the torpedo hatch covers a UQS-1 under-ice sonar normally carried by minesweepers (unique in 1958 among U.S. Atlantic Fleet submarines). Installed for the submarine's cruise over the North Pole, this sonar was the predecessor of under-ice sonars installed in many U.S. ballistic missile submarines. *Nautilus* also had a big BQR-4A in her forefoot and an SQS-4 Mod 4 active scanning sonar.

types then under development (see chapter 3). A single reactor, however, would heat a pair of boilers (heat exchangers), each feeding its own turbine. Reportedly, this pattern of duplication for the purpose of reliability was continued in later installations.[3]

The major AEC reactor development organization was the Argonne National Laboratory, but some studies were still being conducted at Oak Ridge. The AEC allowed General Electric to build a new Knolls Atomic Power Laboratory. Westinghouse, the other major electrical company, was also interested in reactor development. It established a laboratory, analogous to Knolls, at Bettis Field in East Pittsburgh. The navy welcomed competition between the two potential suppliers. BuShips awarded Westinghouse a contract for Wizard, a pressurized-water reactor. A contract with Allis-Chalmers to study Oak Ridge's helium gas-cooled reactor was soon dropped.

Reactors could be characterized by the energy of their neutrons: slow (thermal), intermediate, or fast. A thermal-neutron reactor used water to slow down (moderate) the neutrons within its core and also to transfer heat. Although it turned out to be the most successful type, that was hardly obvious in 1948. It produced relatively little heat and could not superheat steam. For about 15 years, BuEng had concentrated on increasing, not decreasing, steam conditions in the name of efficiency and compactness. It seemed natural, then, to pick a very hot reactor, using intermediate-energy neutrons, and an extremely efficient heat conductor, liquid metal.

Early in 1949, Captain Rickover chose the pressurized-water thermal reactor as the prototype because it was simplest, hence closest to maturity. It was also inherently safe. Pure water running through the hot core could not become radioactive. It could be piped outside the shield to heat the boiler. Radioactivity would be confined to the reactor proper. Because water was both coolant and moderator, the nuclear reaction would stop if, for any reason, it drained from the reactor. Later, reactors moderated and cooled by water were found to be inherently stable, with attractive control characteristics. On the other hand, a thermal reactor required about three times as much U-235 as an intermediate one. U-235 was also needed urgently both for bombs and for reactors to breed plutonium for more bombs.

The pressurized-water reactor was designated STR (submarine thermal reactor). Mark I was a land prototype; Mark II was the reactor installed aboard the prototype submarine *Nautilus*. Rickover saved considerable time by keeping the arrangements of the two nearly identical. Mark I was changed to reflect required changes in Mark II as submarine design progressed.

The intermediate-energy reactor offered efficient heat transfer, but the liquid metal running through it became radioactive and required shielding. The added weight could more than balance off the saving on the turbine. Too, unlike the STR, the metal-cooled reactor was not inherently safe. There was no liquid to drain and thus shut it down; the moderator was an array of solid beryllium reflectors. If water accidentally flooded the reactor, it would react violently with the sodium. For that matter, any leak in the heat exchanger piping would also bring sodium into direct contact with water. Later, the reactor was found to be inherently unstable thermally.

At the time, however, the submarine intermediate reactor (SIR) was considered a worthwhile alternative to the STR. General Electric had conceived it and was given the contract to build it. The land prototype was Mark A and the submarine prototype (in the *Seawolf*), Mark B. Comparing the SIR with the successful prototype STR demonstrated that its inherent problems were even more damning. Apparently, the decision to concentrate on pressurized-water reactors was made well before the SIR entered service at sea. Its initial problems confirmed the earlier technical judgment that it was better to concentrate on developing the STR series. Of the total $750 million investment in the nuclear program by 1958, about $225 million went into the SIR.

Work on the submarine reactor abruptly became more promising about August 1949; it shifted from a long-term to a near-term possibility, possibly available even before the inferior closed-cycle engines. In October, the submarine reactor moved from the bottom of the Argonne priority list to the top. Early in 1950, a prototype nuclear submarine (SCB 64, *Nautilus*) was inserted into the FY 52 program so that a hull would be available in time. This was an extraordinary step. Money was still very tight. Excluding AEC costs for the reactor, the new submarine would cost $40 million, more than twice as much as a new destroyer.

A second extraordinary decision was made. Although the new submarine was primarily experimental, she would be armed as an operational unit. When the General Board reviewed the project in 1950, BuOrd and submarine force representatives argued that some armament inevitably would be installed; it would be much less expensive to install tubes during construction than later. BuOrd suggested a compromise: the tubes could be installed, but no torpedoes should be included in the initial cost of the ship.[4] As in the contemporary SSX, the first draft SSN characteristics called for nine torpedo tubes and "as many torpedoes as can be carried, probably about thirty," but it turned out that only the usual nest of six tubes could be accommodated. Series 58 had shown that a single screw would be more efficient than the usual twin screws, so the characteristics omitted any stern tubes. Reportedly, Rickover personally preferred twin screws for reliability.

The *Nautilus* design changed as its reactor evolved. The concentrated mass of reactor and shielding was kept as close as possible to the center of gravity of the hull.[5] The pressure hull bulged into a single-hull section around that mass in order to provide buoyancy and thus avoid excessive strain on the hull structure. Fore and aft of the reactor, the submarine had a conventional double hull. Conical transition sections connected the two. They had to be fairly steep so as not to add too much unusable internal space. This structure required considerable theoretical and experimental work; $\frac{3}{16}$-scale models of portions of the *Nautilus* were tested at the David Taylor Model Basin. The full-diameter section eventually extended forward to the torpedo room, and provided two full decks over much of the length of the submarine. The hull pinched in abaft the reactor.

The submarine grew quite rapidly, through feasibility design, to about 250 ft long (2,500/3,000 tons) in March 1950. A 293-ft version was sketched in May 1950, and a 275-ft version in October.[6] By early 1952, the SSN was 302 ft 6 in long (3,237/3,747 tons). During contract design, further increases in reactor and machinery weight made it necessary to lengthen the submarine to 319 ft 6 in in early 1953 and ultimately to 323 ft. More than 100 tons of lead ballast had to be added. By this time, too, it seemed unlikely that the STR would deliver full power; she was expected to make 23 kt on 13,400 SHP.

There was no question of "unlimited" endurance. The 1950 tentative characteristics showed 15,000 nm at full speed (600 hr at 25 kt); this was the sort of endurance a wartime fleet submarine might have made on the surface at cruising speed. Fuel would be added or withdrawn in a 75- to 100-ton protective "coffin" or cartridge, but it turned out that even the prototype reactor had much longer endurance. *Nautilus* was first refueled in 1957 after 26 months of operation (69,138 nm); she was again refueled in 1959 after 93,000 nm in 26 months.

The reactor heated up the ship itself as it produced steam for the turbines. That would have been no great problem in a surface ship open to the atmosphere, but a submarine was sealed. A high-capacity air conditioner had to be installed.

A battery provided backup against a possible reactor failure and also backup reactor cooling power. The characteristics called for enough battery power for 24 hr at 3 kt (creep speed); BuShips offered half a Guppy battery (252 cells, 16 hr). The ship was built with 126 Guppy cells and four 420-BHP diesels. The battery was normally charged by the submarine's turbogenerator. In the event of a breakdown, the SSN could run on diesel-electric power (the diesels had a snorkel).

Nautilus had a large bow sonar dome for a BQR-4, which had to be usable while the submarine was surfaced. The array's sonar window was vertical in order to minimize internal reflections. The bow pinched in above the dome, but it was still quite full. Model tests showed that this unusual inverted arrangement, flat on the bottom but with a very narrow deck at the top, would bring the bow wave over the deck at 15 kt. There was a double irony here. Surface performance was important for a diesel submarine. Even when snorkeling, she could not travel very fast and therefore would make long transits surfaced. A nuclear submarine, on the other hand, could transit submerged; surface operation was essentially irrelevant. Neither the location of the sonar dome for surface use *nor* poor expected surface performance was particularly important.

Underwater operation was limited by the oxygen supply. The ultimate solution was to use the vast power available through the reactor to dissociate seawater, but no such oxygen generator was yet available. Instead, *Nautilus* was provided with oxygen tanks. The combination of tanks and air purifier had been designed for diesel submarines. Because her engines promised much longer underwater endurance, however, *Nautilus* had sufficient oxygen capacity for 30 days, rather than the usual 10.

Electric Boat was responsible for the detailed design.

No one could be sure about the effect of *Nautilus* on naval warfare. In January 1952, the Weapon System Evaluation Group (WSEG), which reported to the Joint Chiefs of Staff, compared the nuclear submarine with a Guppy and with the closed-cycle submarine as then designed:

Nautilus makes a highline transfer, 22 January 1964.

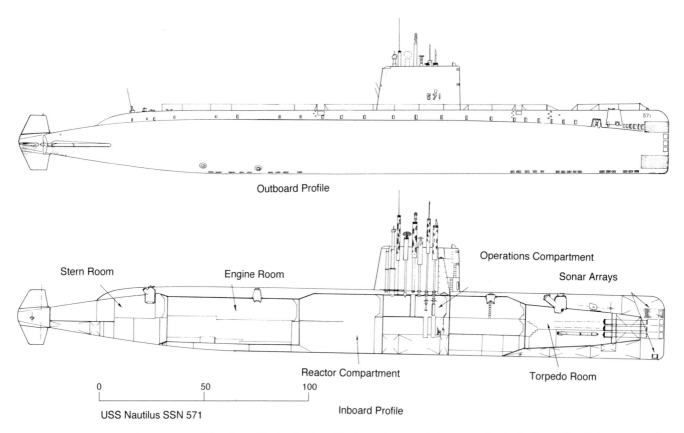

Outboard Profile

Stern Room   Engine Room   Operations Compartment

Sonar Arrays

Reactor Compartment   Torpedo Room

0   50   100

USS Nautilus SSN 571   Inboard Profile

Nautilus was unique in having control levels within her hull, with the periscope platform on the deck above the diving station. In effect, the two-level conning tower/control room combination of a fleet submarine was moved one level down into her hull. Masts, fore to aft, are: Nos. 1 and 2 periscopes; BPS-1 radar; ECM/directional mast with retractable whip (not shown) to starboard; BPS-4 radar; ECM-Omni (port) alongside IFF/UHF (starboard); snorkel induction; snorkel exhaust (housed). The large cockpit occupies the forward end of the sail. The sail top profile was changed just before her Arctic voyage (masts were recessed 8–12 in to prevent ice damage). Similarly, the sails of under-ice *Los Angeles*-class submarines are 12 in taller than those of near-sisters not designed to operate under ice. (Jim Christley)

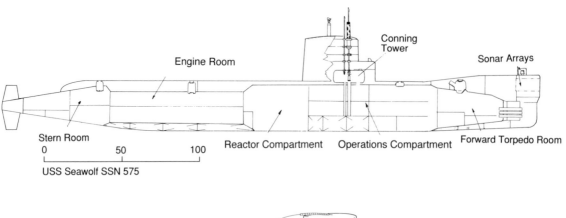

Engine Room   Conning Tower   Sonar Arrays

Stern Room   Reactor Compartment   Operations Compartment   Forward Torpedo Room

0   50   100

USS Seawolf SSN 575

Seawolf. Note that the periscope eyepieces were moved up into the small conning tower, but not the attack instruments or sonar readouts. That largely negated the value of the conning tower, both in this ship and in *Triton.* Late in her career, *Seawolf* carried thrusters (for precise maneuvering) forward, below the prominent line of limber holes. (Jim Christley)

"A possible unique role, which could not be filled by conventional or other [SSX] submarines under development, is the conduct of extended operations with and as an integral part of a fast carrier task force, as a replacement for, or an addition to, destroyer radar pickets. Another unique role may be that of serving as an advanced A/S [anti-submarine] sonar screen in the protection of convoys or task forces." High sustained submerged speed, in itself, would make it possible for a submarine to operate as part of the main naval strike unit, a fast carrier force. Actual capability, of course, would depend on other developments (e.g., in sonar and silencing).

Operating as part of a barrier against a transiting submarine with no effective sonar capability, one SSN or SSX would equal two to four Guppy II or *Tang*s in terms of submarines sunk per barrier submarine. If the transiter had a sonar, she could try to evade; the SSN would do better than any of the others, including the SSX. WSEG estimated that, excluding research and development (R&D) and nuclear fuel, an SSN would ultimately cost only 20–25 percent more than a diesel submarine.

The high speed of the SSN would help her in evading ASW weapons. For example, the kill probability of a Squid or Weapon Alfa was estimated as 5–40 percent against a Guppy (at 300 ft, 15 kt). Largely because she could run at greater depths, *Tang* had only a 0–8 percent probability of loss. At the same depth and higher speed, the SSN would suffer no more than a 1 percent kill rate. A Mk 24 and a Mk 27 homing torpedoes were far too slow; the pings of the new Mk 35 would warn a really fast submarine in time to evade.

The submarine community was apparently more impressed by the sheer size (hence cost) of *Nautilus*, which was a direct consequence of the much earlier choice of

Seawolf, despite her internal similarity to *Nautilus*, had a quite different appearance, with her BQR-4A passive sonar atop her bow (rather than in her forefoot) and a Guppy-like sail (to accommodate a small conning tower that *Nautilus* lacked). When this photograph was taken in 1958, *Seawolf* also carried a smaller passive-scanning sonar (BQR-2B, common to Guppies and other fleet submarines) and an SQS-4 active set (with TR-117 transducer).

15,000 SHP for all post–WW II closed-cycle power plants. No one was quite sure that the speed of *Nautilus* was worth that price. After all, no one had ever operated a 23-kt submarine, let alone one with effectively unlimited endurance at that speed.

A second nuclear attack submarine was included in the FY 53 program. Given the sacrifices (to military characteristics) made in the *Nautilus* design, there was initially some hope that she would be a combat prototype, quieter and perhaps with more torpedo tubes. Time limitations prevented the development of a new, more compact power plant. The second U.S. nuclear submarine, *Seawolf* (SCB 64A), had to be another prototype. The only major change that could be made was in the reactor—in this case, the SIR. In the normal course of events, the second submarine yard, Portsmouth, would have designed *Seawolf*. Portsmouth was busy with current conversion and construction work and could not assign a priority that was high enough; its first, and only, nuclear submarine design project was *Thresher*.

Because the SIR was smaller than the STR, the designers initially hoped to use a conventional double hull.[7] Code 1500 wanted to avoid the 9–12-mo delay entailed in a new design. Instead, STR work was used as much as possible. As in *Nautilus*, *Seawolf* had a large-diameter (27 ft 8 in) single-hull section around her reactor.

The most striking changes, compared with *Nautilus*, were in the sail and bow. As in the contemporary diesel-electric design, SCB 2A, a small conning tower was provided to keep the hull deeper at periscope depth. The control room was moved up from the first platform, as in *Nautilus*, to the second platform deck immediately below this conning tower. As in a Guppy, only the periscope shears were faired to full height. Unlike the sail of a Guppy, *Seawolf*'s stressed-skin structure supported the masts inside. To make the bow drier, the big sonar was moved to the upper deck; the requirement that it be usable when submerged was dropped.[8] BuShips wanted Sargo II cells, but the SCB ruled for Guppy batteries.

The land-based SIR prototype developed superheater leaks; during July 1955, leaks also appeared in the main steam generators. The superheaters could be bypassed (at a cost in power), but the main steam generators were much more serious. By January 1956, the land-based prototype had been fixed. The Mark B plant was installed aboard *Seawolf*. Soon after she went to full power, one of her superheaters developed a leak. Bypassing the superheater, *Seawolf* ran her full-power trial in February 1957 on reduced power. By then, Rickover had decided to abandon the SIR altogether.

Seawolf's SIR was replaced by an STR. Fortunately, Code 1500 had demanded an SIR-sized reactor compartment, but no evidence in the design history indicates that any such conversion had been contemplated. The decision to abandon the SIR as unworkable was made late in 1956, and authority for the reactor replacement was sought in 1957 for the FY 58 program. By that time, the shipbuilding budget was under considerable pressure. A whole series of postwar technologies, such as computers, advanced jet fighters, and surface-to-air missiles, were reaching maturity at costs far in advance of those projected.

Reactor replacement could be put off temporarily because *Seawolf* was nearly operational, albeit at reduced power and under restrictions. Further leaks that would require immediate correction were possible; she could not be used for war patrols. A replacement SSN would cost $47 million versus reactor replacement at $20 million. The reactor was replaced at Electric Boat between 12 December 1958 and 30 September 1960 (FY 59 budget). *Seawolf* was converted for special research operation at Mare Island between January 1971 and June 1973.

U.S.S. NAUTILUS   SSN571
STERN VIEW
JANUARY 21, 1954
ELECTRIC BOAT DIVISION
GENERAL DYNAMICS CORP.

Nautilus shows her stern details in this 21 January 1954 prelaunch photograph. Her hull tapered to a point at the extreme stern to take the single propeller the Series 58 trials showed was most efficient. In the interest of reliability, however, she was built with twin screws, one of which is shown here. Later twin-screw nuclear attack submarines had stern "countermeasures" tubes like their diesel-electric counterparts.

The ASW Crisis: Nobska and After

NAUTILUS SOON DEMONSTRATED what she could do. In her earliest tactical trials during July and August 1955, she easily overtook an ASW carrier force, HUK Two, operating at 16–18 kt. She easily outran homing weapons, such as a Mk 43 air-dropped torpedoes. She could not outrun nuclear depth bombs, but she was so agile that she was rarely caught. A postexercise evaluation showed that the seven claimed kills had occurred 40–50 mi away from the submarine's actual position. She managed this sort of performance even though her superstructure rattled so badly that her own sonar was useless much above 8 kt. Her big Type 6 periscope was an embarrassingly good radar target. She had to sprint at 20 kt between pauses to listen at 8 kt.[1] The most hopeful evaluation of the exercise suggested that about eight surface warships, including the carrier, would be lost for each Nautilus sunk, given a typical screening efficiency of 60 percent.

The submarine's commander, Capt. Eugene P. Wilkinson, found that his Mk 101 fire-control system could not react quickly enough to match the submarine's speed and agility. Of seven torpedo attacks, he made only two hits. One was achieved by sneaking in after breaking contact. Nautilus was fast enough to evade attack but, often, not fast enough to turn on her tormentors and sink them. Wilkinson felt that the nuclear submarine would not achieve her full potential until her speed matched that of the fastest surface ships.

During Strikeback, a NATO exercise, Nautilus presented a greater threat than all 21 snorkel submarines combined. Running at 24 kt and reattacking surface ships almost at will, she made simulated attacks on 16 ships—2 carriers, 1 unidentified heavy unit, 2 oilers, 2 cargo ships, and 9 destroyers. On one occasion, she detected a carrier and her escorts steaming almost directly away at 20 kt. To reach an attacking position she steamed 219 nm in 10¼ hr (averaging 21.5 kt); 16 hr after this attack, she struck a lone destroyer 240 nm away. Another time, Nautilus kept station under a formation for 15 hr. She maintained position from directly under it out to 400 yd from a heavy ship and was neither challenged nor attacked. From start to finish during this exercise, she steamed 3,384 nm at an average speed of 14.4 kt.

In a British exercise, Rum Tub, Nautilus showed that she could "do as she like[d]" in the face of modern ASW forces. While keeping station under a convoy, she detected and attacked the submarine Quillback, which was attempting to attack the ship above her. Thus, Nautilus demonstrated her potential as an underwater escort. Passing at 22 kt, she detected the British diesel submarine Auriga with her SQS-4 active sonar at just under 3,000 yd and made a simulated attack. During a later exercise, a screening helicopter jumped to a position within 50 yd of a green grenade fired by Nautilus, but she was already 3,500 yd away, clear of any weapon the helicopter might have dropped.

By the fall of 1957, Nautilus had been exposed to 5,000 dummy attacks in U.S. exercises. A conservative estimate would have had a conventional submarine killed 300 times; Nautilus was ruled as killed only 3 times.[2]

Using their active sonars, nuclear submarines could hold contact on diesel craft without risking counterattack.[3] The U.S. Navy abandoned construction of diesel submarines and accepted the higher cost of an all-nuclear fleet. Given Wilkinson's perception, the standard for submarine speed was substantially raised beyond that envisaged in 1950. The result was Skipjack.

In effect, Nautilus wiped out the ASW progress of the past decade. Not only was she difficult to find (partly because she never had to snorkel), but she was too fast for existing ASW torpedoes (see chapter 4). Counterattacked, she could break off and then reattack at will because she had no battery to exhaust. Along with Seawolf and Albacore, she soon showed that she was almost impossible to track as she quickly bounced in and out of a sonar beam. Her speed and agility made nearly all existing U.S. surface escorts obsolete. Only at very long range would the sonar

Thresher is shown on the slip at Portsmouth Naval Shipyard, April 1960. Nuclear submarines were terrifying, partly because they could jump up and down so quickly through a conventional sonar beam. The solutions included both lower frequency (for longer range) and a beam that could track in three dimensions: a sonar sphere. It first appeared on board the Tullibee and Threshers; in the latter ships, it was associated closely with the new Subroc anti-submarine missile. Incomplete on the slip, Thresher clearly shows her bow sphere, with its lower hydrophones in place. The triple row of hydrophones, wrapped around the outer hull, is not visible.

beam be so broad as to preclude such evasion. The only sonar with sufficient range, SQS-26, could not fit most existing ships, certainly not mass-produced escorts like those built during WW II.

The United States had two nuclear submarines in service by 1957; it was time to pit SSN against SSN. When running at high speed, each submarine easily detected the other at substantial ranges, but neither could hit because torpedo range was too short. At low (quiet) speed, each detected the other only when inside *minimum* torpedo range. Existing fire control systems were too slow to obtain useful solutions before one or the other had run off.

Later experiments showed that although existing passive and active sonars permitted a nuclear submarine to find and close another, existing torpedoes, such as a Mk 37, had neither the speed nor the range required. In some cases (1958), the SSN found that she was torpedoing herself, presumably because she was so noisy at high speed. In other cases (as in 1961), the torpedo was ineffective because a nuclear submarine did not put out the kind of noise for which the torpedo had been designed.

Even the first nuclear submarines were difficult targets because they were so fast and maneuverable. A few years later, *Skipjack,* much faster and more maneuverable in all three dimensions, appeared. Contacts were indeed made, but they were fleeting; it was quite difficult to get accurate bearings with existing cylindrical passive and active sonars.[4] The new spherical sonar, first installed in *Tullibee* and *Thresher,* solved this problem because it could track a fast submarine in all three dimensions. These new submarines had many other advantages. They were far quieter than their predecessors—comparable to diesel-electric submarines when they ran at low speed—and *Thresher* was quite fast. In their first submarine-versus-submarine exercises, (September 1961), *Thresher* and *Tullibee* clearly outclassed the slower *Skate. Tullibee* achieved spectacular active sonar detection range. Although not very fast, she could outrun the standard Mk 37 ASW torpedo.[5] The faster *Thresher* could go so deep and so fast that she seemed altogether invulnerable. The other submarines could not even get close enough to try to ram her.

Even the older nuclear submarines were difficult targets. In the Pacific, two *Skates* trying to dogfight ended up hopelessly milling after 30 min; their fire-control systems could not keep up with such fast targets. On the other hand, SSK operation was sometimes possible. In one exercise, a *Skate,* carefully quieted, picked up one of her sisters entering her patrol area at moderate speed. She never went active and was able to track her sister for 4 hr. She ended up practically alongside, with the other submarine unaware; she even called on the underwater telephone to ask whether anyone was nearby. Using passive sonar, she had been able to match turns and stops and remained quite close. When both submarines were stopped, she could even hear "bangs" and "klunks" aboard the target submarine.

In 1959, BuShips found itself seriously looking at a convoy escort submarine as an alternative to new frigates. She would have had a *Thresher* nose (with spherical sonar)

wedded to a less expensive after section (carrying an S3W reactor, as in the *Skate* class). Reviewing the study, Adm. Ralph K. James, head of BuShips, remarked that it might be wise to abandon building frigates altogether in favor of escort submarines. His idea was rejected for the usual reason—the escort submarines could not easily coordinate either with the surface force or with each other.

Project Nobska was one attempt to find a way out of the new ASW crisis. In the fall of 1955, Adm. Arleigh Burke, the new CNO, formally asked CUW of the National Academy of Sciences to conduct an ASW summer study, (i.e., of counters to the SSN).[6] CUW apparently felt that ASW in itself offered few new questions and a summer study was unlikely to produce a stunningly new approach. Committee members did feel, however, that the navy did not yet appreciate the strategic potential of its quiet nuclear submarines. In March 1956, the CUW expanded the study to include implications of nuclear submarines and naval nuclear weapons during the coming decade.[7]

The CUW tried hard to ensure that any ideas developed in its summer study would be taken seriously. It managed to have a senior submariner, Rear Adm. Lawson P. "Red" Ramage, assigned to the study full time. It asked for, and got, unprecedented direct AEC assistance, in the form of representatives of the weapons laboratories.[8] The study also included representatives of Electric Boat and of the two reactor developers, GE and Westinghouse. The bureaus, DesLant (Atlantic Fleet Destroyer Command), and SubLant all contributed officers. The 73 members of the Nobska panel included such luminaries as Dr. Isidore Rabi, the Nobel laureate physicist; Paul Nitze; and Dr. Edward Teller. Five panel members had served on the 1950 Hartwell study, and three had participated in Atlantis, an earlier ASW study. The new study was conducted between 18 June and 15 September 1956 at an estate at Nobska (near Woods Hole). The result, generally known as the Nobska Report, was released on 1 December 1956. Some members met again at Newport in August 1957 to discuss its implementation.

The participants studied a projected 1960–70 threat, on the theory that the Soviets would need at least five years to bring new weapons into service. Although the existing fleet could be considered largely defensive, especially given its poorly located bases, it would surely grow by an order of magnitude during the 1960s. The Soviets probably would build a mixture of expensive but noisy nuclear submarines and cheaper (and quieter) closed-cycle craft. Their armament would surely include nuclear missiles for use against ships at both long and short ranges and also against the U.S. coast. We now know that the Soviets fired their first submarine-launched ballistic missile in September 1955 and that they were then working hard on anti-ship missiles (as yet air- and ship-launched), but the Nobska panel—and probably the Office of Naval Intelligence (ONI)—did not know that. The panel was projecting such U.S. developments as Regulus.

It seemed unlikely that the fixed SOSUS system could defeat either the new, very quiet diesel-electric submarines, which the British were just demonstrating, or special deception, saturation, or jamming tactics (e.g., by underwater explosions). Long-range, low-frequency active sonar (Lorad) could overcome silencing, but it lacked the potential range of SOSUS. New means of detection and classification at very long range could be developed. Nobska proposed a submarine that could dive deep enough to exploit the deep channel.

Problems would get only worse once an enemy SSN was detected and localized. It was not clear whether any torpedo could home at 45 kt, the speed required to engage a 30-kt future SSN. The only alternative was nuclear ASW weapons carried by torpedoes or dropped from aircraft. The Betty (a Mk 90) nuclear depth bomb seemed to be the only operational weapon that could kill a fast submarine. The Nobska panel argued that it was wiser to devote valuable nuclear material to strike warfare than to ASW. Its hydrodynamicists believed that the 45-kt homing torpedo could indeed be built. A development program, RETORC (REsearch TORpedo Configuration), was begun. RETORC I became the Mk 46 lightweight torpedo; RETORC II is the a Mk 48 heavyweight that arms current U.S. submarines. An interim nuclear torpedo would have to be developed. It became Astor, a Mk 45. Reportedly, the discussion of compact low-yield torpedo warheads led Dr. Teller to propose a lightweight strategic warhead, which was the inspiration for Polaris.

The Nobska panel felt that U.S. submarine-launched ballistic missiles offered a different way out of the problem. Because the missiles could not be shot down, the only viable Soviet countermeasure would be to attack the submarines carrying them. The larger the fleet of U.S. missile submarines, the more difficult would be the Soviet ASW problem and, therefore, the fewer resources available for offensive submarine warfare. Although this was not quite the way the navy would come to see Polaris, it was a classic naval solution to a difficult enemy threat: disable it by confronting the enemy with a counterthreat, the response to which would neutralize the original threat. The Maritime Strategy of the 1980s would fit this category.

Nobska participants feared that the U.S. Navy could never build high-performance nuclear submarines in sufficient numbers. Cutting reactor weight to fit a smaller hull would carry a disproportionate cost in power because shielding could not be scaled down. The reactor might be carried in an external blister (a technique called shadow shielding) or in the lower cylinder of a figure-eight hull, or it could be wrapped in its heat exchanger, which would form part of its shield. Such technology promised 30 kt in a small submarine hull. The ongoing navy and air force nuclear aircraft program promised innovative lightweight reactors using, for example, a reflector (rather than water) moderator. The Nobska panel envisaged a 500-ton nuclear submarine carrying 30 tons of armament.

The success of the X-1 midget seemed to prove that a diesel using hydrogen peroxide oxidant was feasible for small submarines. (Ironically, X-1 soon exploded, proving once again that peroxide was less than safe.) For the longer term, Nobska's preference was the use of fuel cells (primary batteries), partly because they could be extremely quiet. Extrapolating from the performance of a single such cell, the panel predicted that a 1,500-ton submarine could achieve an endurance of 11,000 nm at 11.6 kt, with a burst speed of 19 kt. A small reactor might improve the efficiency of a fuel cell by heating it. *Nautilus* was then being credited with an endurance of only 15,000 nm (albeit at a much higher speed). It turned out to be relatively easy to extend *Nautilus* endurance and far more difficult than anyone had imagined to bring a fuel cell submarine into service. Fuel cells figured in many later U.S. studies of the potential of non-nuclear submarines, but the conclusions, at Nobska and later, were always that speed was limited because of the need for so much hull to accommodate the fuel and oxidant.

Nobska participants argued that building pre-prototypes, ships conceived as test platforms without real reference to operational requirements, could allow for bolder thinking and concentrate interest. After all, few in the defense establishment really appreciated the potential of a nuclear submarine before *Nautilus* entered service. The Nobska study saw *Nautilus*, *Albacore*, and *X-1* as exactly such pre-prototypes. Together with some exotic ASW surface ships, it proposed an SSK that was optimized for quiet operation (undetectable 100 nm from a SOSUS station at 10 kt), capable of detecting a snorkeler at 100–200 nm in relatively calm water.

It is difficult to measure the influence of the Nobska report. After it was completed, BuShips prepared a report showing that virtually all of Nobska's proposals were already being pursued in some form. On the other hand, Nobska presented a unique integrated picture of the ASW problem and its likely solutions. The report probably focused interest at a high level within the navy. To some extent, it must have been viewed as a kind of checklist—a method of determining if some promising approach had been overlooked. The Nobska report also might have changed priorities within the existing naval program. It helped to mold Polaris. Aside from the strategy shift, the most striking aspects of the report were its advocacy of very–deep-diving submarines and of alternative reactor technologies. Neither ever reached the point of operational hardware.

The Nobska panel was surely aware of BuOrd's two proposed nuclear ASW weapons, a torpedo (Astor, the A/S Torpedo) and an underwater-to-underwater missile, Stinger (later Subroc). In July 1956, NOL at White Oak formally compared the two. Astor fire control had to be based entirely on passive sonar data because a target alerted by pinging might be able to evade a relatively slow torpedo. Unless PUFFS (see chapter 2) succeeded, the torpedo would depend largely on inexact TMA solutions and be wire-guided to follow the target bearing as it rode out. NOL suggested that the torpedo might carry a short-range (500-yd) pinger that provided enough information for command detonation by the launching submarine.

Stinger was a torpedo tube-launched ballistic missile.[9] Flying through the air, rather than swimming, to its target, Stinger would arrive so quickly that no target could get away. It would rely on a single-ping range (the existing

SQS-4 could reach 5–15 kyd) or on PUFFS. At this time, NOL envisaged a torpedo-size weapon (21 × 176.3 in, 2,146 lb) carrying a small warhead (8 kT) to a range of 3–20 kyd (flight time 40.6 and 76.2 sec, respectively). Burn time would be 10 sec.

Astor (a Mk 45 torpedo) was clearly a shorter-term proposition; development began in January 1957 on virtually a crash basis. BuOrd began evaluation 1 November 1959; operational evaluation began the following summer. The prototype went into the new nuclear submarine *Scorpion* (SSN 589).[10]

PUFFS worked, so a Mk 45 needed no torpedo-borne pinger. It carried the new lightweight nuclear depth bomb, Lulu (the W34 warhead). A Mk 45 was the first important U.S. wire-guided torpedo. Submarines firing it had to have a new analog fire-control device, the Mk 18 angle solver, installed in place of the angle solvers (ballistic computers) of their Mk 101 and Mk 106 systems. A Mk 18 combined the roles of the earlier ballistic computers and of the torpedo director used with the earlier Mk 39 wire-guided weapon (see chapter 2). Like the earlier weapon, a Mk 45 could be fired either as a bearing-rider (always pointed toward the target) or in corrected-intercept (collision-course) mode. As in the earlier system, the operator literally steered the torpedo in 2-degree increments, so that only one could be controlled at a time. A second command channel ordered the warhead to burst; run-to-burst was set in 100-yd increments. A Mk 18 was designed for considerable growth in torpedo capability: it could handle speeds

up to 60 kt and torpedo ranges up to 35,000 yd. Maximum target depth was 1,400 ft.

A Mk 45 diameter was limited to 19 in, so that it could swim out of the pneumatic tubes of existing WW II-built submarines. Nominal speed was 40 kt, about the best that could be hoped for with existing seawater batteries. A Mk 45 ran out at a preset depth (100–1,000 ft), but its shock wave could destroy submarines at considerably greater depths, a unique capability at the time. Range was initially 12,000 yd, although later versions with seawater batteries did somewhat better. The original version had no set enabling range and so somewhat endangered the launching submarine. In Mods 1 and 2, enabling range was fixed at 2,050 yd, presumably somewhat beyond the weapon's lethal radius. Despite its limited yield, many submariners suspected that an exploding Astor would take them with it; few probably mourned its final demise in 1979.[11]

Nobska's prediction—a fast homing torpedo could be entirely practical—was realized in the form of a Mk 48 (initially designated EX-10). Conceived as a fast successor to a Mk 35, a Mk 48 homed both actively and passively but at longer ranges. Quiet electric propulsion could not provide the desired performance; a new internal combustion plant had to be developed. The feasibility study was completed in September 1957 and the operational requirement issued in November 1960.

BuOrd initially selected a turbine power plant but was surprised to discover that flow noise over the torpedo was

Pickerel, a Guppy III, off the coast of Oahu, 17 January 1963, shows the three domes of her PUFFS passive fire-control system (BQG-4). It was used to target the Mk 45 nuclear torpedo, one of the first major fruits of the Nobska study. Other submarines (including fleet snorkels) were fitted with the new plastic sail, but only Guppy IIIs and some postwar submarines got PUFFS and the associated fire-control system (in a lengthened section of pressure hull) needed for a Mk 45. Attempts to fit a retractable version of PUFFS to the more streamlined *Thresher* and her successors failed until the advent of the current wide aperture array (WAA, designated BQG-5 when used as a stand-alone system).

far stronger than engine noise. It adopted a less expensive and noisier alternative, a piston engine. This engine maintained its power level (hence the torpedo's speed) against the increased back pressure of greater depths. The engine used more fuel, however, and a Mk 48's range was sacrificed at depth. The British took the opposite path in their somewhat later Spearfish. They adopted essentially the losing Mk 48 power plant, a Sundstrand turbine, and guaranteed sufficient speed at depth (probably 55 kt) by requiring much higher speed (65–70 kt) at very shallow depths. Spearfish made a world speed record for torpedoes in a Scottish loch.

BuOrd originally planned to use 90 percent hydrogen peroxide plus diesel oil. In 1963, it switched to a new monopropellant, Ottofuel II, named after the bureau's Dr. Otto W. Reitlinger. Tested extensively from July 1963 on, Ottofuel proved far less tempermental than peroxide. It was formally adopted for the new torpedo in February 1964.

By 1961, the RETORC II program was using a pump jet to minimize self-noise. Its goal was 20,000 yd at 50 kt, which was somewhat faster than the Nobska goal of 45 kt but with shorter maximum range (Nobska called for 35,000 yd). By this time, too, the Nobska target acquisition range goal (2,000 yd, twice that of a Mk 37) had been increased by 50 percent so the torpedo could form an acquisition cone more than 20 times the area of the one then associated with a Mk 37. By 1965, BuOrd could announce proudly that its test vehicle approached the noise level of the quietest torpedo then in service (a Mk 37), while running at more than twice its speed (54 kt).

BuOrd also hit upon a novel way of minimizing the noise effect of high torpedo speed. Silencing for better seeker operation did not really matter until the torpedo approached its target. A Mk 48 ran out at high (transport) speed under wire guidance, then drastically slowed to search. At really short range, the pings from the target were so strong that flow noise was not too serious a problem, so the torpedo could accelerate again to attack and to prevent the target from maneuvering away. About 1962, the planned transport speed was 50 kt, and the search speed was 25 kt. Press reports credit the mature Mk 48 with a transport speed of 55 kt and a search speed of 40 kt.

Unlike previous wire-guided torpedoes, a Mk 48 was digital, that is, controlled by messages coded as a series of discrete tones rather than by analog signals whose meaning depended on their strength. It could therefore respond to more complex commands. Because digital signals tend to survive noise better than their analog equivalents, a Mk 48 was easier to guide at longer range. Existing analog systems, such as Mks 101, 106, 112, and 113, required the addition of a separate control console (a Mk 66) that translated analog commands into digital form (there was a separate tone generator).

The warhead was originally 250 lb of HBX-3. It was too small to sink large surface ships, so submarines continued to carry straight-running Mk 14 torpedoes well after

a Mk 48 entered service. To fire that mix, the submarine had to combine analog and digital fire control systems (a Mk 14 was decidedly analog). About 1968, in order to make the new Los Angeles completely digital, a Mk 48 was redesigned and fitted with a more powerful warhead to become a truly dual-purpose torpedo.

BuOrd took longer to begin serious work on Stinger. In 1956, few in the bureau or in the fleet imagined that the weapon could be targeted at any range beyond 10 nm, and money was scarce. The new spherical sonar solved the targeting problem. BuOrd conducted a feasibility study in October 1956, and a formal operational requirement was released that December. There was still no money, but then cancellation of the Triton strategic missile freed some funds. The idea was formally presented to OSD early in 1958. Informal agreement must already have been reached; formal development began on 2 January 1958. The contract was let in June 1958. Stinger (by then called Subroc) was service approved on 27 July 1966. The submariners insisted on retaining the shore bombardment capability, and the missile had an air burst option throughout its life that was never part of its formal operational requirement.

Stinger was soon renamed Subroc (for SUBmarine ROCket), formally Missile Mk 28 or UUM-44. It was considerably enlarged to reach the convergence zone (163-sec flight time). Because the convergence zone was 5 nm wide, the warhead had to be powerful enough to kill anything within a similar radius. Minimum safe range was therefore set at 5 nm, four times the safe range of a Mk 45. The ultimate range objective, never reached, was the second convergence zone (70 nm).

Because TMA was so slow, a target might not be engaged until it came quite close; an enemy commander might even choose to accelerate toward the U.S. submarine to get within safe range. In May 1962, therefore, an operational requirement was issued for a version to carry a lightweight homing torpedo, the submarine ASW rocket. Minimum range would have been set by the homing envelope of the torpedo (about 2 nm). Unlike a large nuclear warhead, a homing torpedo could not independently kill a target somewhere in the wide swath of the convergence zone. Consequently, a non-nuclear Subroc would have been limited to bottom- or surface-bounce range, about 40,000 yd. In 1962, the only available warhead was the slow Mk 44 lightweight homer. Calculations showed that its homing radius was so limited, however, that a submarine hearing the Subroc motor go off could well evade the torpedo. A version carrying the much better Mk 46 was later planned but fell victim to Vietnam War funding cuts; in 1962, operational evaluation of the torpedo-bearing Subroc was tentatively scheduled for 1969.[12] The idea survived as STAM (Submarine TActical Missile) and then Sea Lance (see chapter 10).

Subroc outlasted Astor because it was the only standoff weapon available to U.S. submarines. There was also a marked reluctance to concede the field of tactical nuclear submarine weapons to the Soviets, who fielded a wide variety of nuclear torpedoes and also a pair of Subroc-like missiles.[13] As an analog weapon, Subroc was not compatible with the new Mk 117 all-digital fire-control system; in the natural course of events, it would have been discarded along with its Mk 113 analog control system. In 1983, however, Congress directed that the new Mk 117s be modified to accommodate Subroc. The last Subrocs were withdrawn from active service in 1988. Apparently, they were held in reserve for a time: the Subroc warhead (W45) was not formally retired until the fall of 1990.

To automate TMA (mainly for Subroc fire control), BuOrd introduced the first U.S. digital computer for submarine fire control, a Mk 130, as part of the Subroc fire-control system, a Mk 113.[14] Fire control had two phases, the initial target estimate and position keeping for actual firing. Existing systems, such as a Mk 101, emphasized the latter, adding a limited analyzer to prepare an initial target estimate. In a Mk 113, the analyzer (now replaced by a combination of analog analyzer and digital computer) became the basis of the system. The position keeper, ballistic computer, and torpedo director (for wire-guided weapons) merged to become the Mk 75 attack director.

Given its heritage, a Mk 75 could function independently by using a manual TMA solution. This was a hedge against digital computer breakdown. Like earlier torpedo directors, a Mk 75 could control only one torpedo at a time, although it could set several free runners in quick succession. A Mk 113 used a pair of cross-connected Mk 75s; each director's position keeper could send its solution to the other director's. A Mk 75 plus one or two Mk 51 analyzers formed a weapons control station.

Either director could send its angle-solver data on to the Mk 129 leveling computer for Subroc control. The leveling computer sat in the separate weapon launching console in the torpedo room, between the banks of tubes. The name reflected the first fundamental operation in controlling a ballistic missile: its internal inertial platform had to be stabilized horizontally (against submarine pitch and roll) and pointed (aligned) at the target position. The missile had to be fed with initial submarine position and velocity data relative to the point at which it would intercept its target. The computer also made safety calculations to protect the launching ship from premature arming or circling.

The analyzer was the input/output device for the Mk 130 computer. The console displayed the picture produced by a chosen sonar, a blip or line of bearing. In earlier systems, an operator entered sonar data by setting dials to figures corresponding to readings from a scope. That was too slow for TMA. The position of an electronic marker on the analyzer scope could be read directly into the computer. The analyzer operator entered sonar data into the computer by matching the marker with the picture on the scope. This form of analog-to-digital translation was much like that used in contemporary radar-oriented systems, such as the naval tactical data system (NTDS). Each operator concentrated on a single target.

The analyzer used a stabilization computer in its base to correct sonar data (measured in the plane of the submarine

deck) for ship motion (roll and pitch). This function became more important as sonar range greatly increased. Each analyzer translated data, in stabilized own-ship terms, into geographic terms that canceled out ship movement; the ship herself could move quite far in the course of a TMA. The computer solution in geographic terms was translated back into own-ship terms (range, bearing, and target elevation or depression) for fire control.

The analyzer also automatically translated digital computer output into analog data suitable for the attack director. These data appeared on its face in the form of the traditional dials showing target- and own-ship course and speed. Thus, the operator could monitor the progress of the Mk 130 solution, just as the operator of a TDC or a Mk 101 watched the movement of the dials to tell when a position keeper solution had settled sufficiently so that firing torpedoes would be worthwhile. The analyzer operator chose the method of analysis to be used, based in part on how the solution was behaving.

The computer smoothed the data it received and sent. It also corrected automatically for refraction and reflection effects (i.e., tracing the ray paths of the sounds it used). In the past, that had always been done manually; hence, earlier analog fire-control systems were inherently limited to short ranges. Such corrections could not be done easily in the analog analyzer because they depended on local water conditions. The six operating modes were (1) bearings only (pure TMA), (2) bearing plus passive range (PUFFS), (3) bearing plus single-ping range and range rate, (4) bearing plus continuous pinging, (5) triangulation, and (6) calculation with constraints. Bearing measurements could be discrete, or they might be computer-smoothed averages of continuous measurements made when using an automatic tracking sonar. Target course, but not range (only the ratio of range to target speed), could be determined from three independent bearing measurements taken along a single own-ship track. The analyzer operator could then constrain the computer solution by manually inserting a range or speed estimate obtained, for example, by plot or turn count. The computer then calculated other elements of the solution (e.g., target speed given target range) to be projected forward and checked against further observation. A Mk 130 had four memories, one for each of four targets, time-sharing a central TMA section. That reflected analog practice. In a modern digital system, a single memory carries information on all targets. The computer can easily compare them to decide which to engage first.

A Mk 130 was very nearly a hard-wired (fixed-program) digital computer, a type quite common in contemporary fire-control systems. When the computer was turned on, it set its circuits by reading a taped sequence of 4,000 instructions (about as long as its entire memory). The tape was not a stored program in any modern sense. On the other hand, it could be changed, for example, to incorporate different TMA techniques. Once the techniques had been set up, however, a Mk 130 could not adjust them to account for circumstances.

A Mk 113 approached the concept of a combat direction system, in that the summary CRT of its Mk 50 attack-control console, mounted overhead, displayed all four targets simultaneously, together with own-ship and dead-reckoned wire-guided torpedo positions in PPI (radar-style) format. BuOrd envisaged the console as the battle station of the commanding officer (CO) and its CRT as the basis of tactical decisions. Naturally, the console also carried the firing panel that sent preset and firing commands. The PPI presentation also appeared well adapted to the future possibility of submarines working together and with surface ships. The position of a consort could be displayed, and the consort's sonar data fed in through the Mk 50. In fact, the necessary long-range acoustic communication never worked.

A Mk 113 was not quite up to such performance. Its semiprogrammable computer was intended for intermittent use, to be turned on (and set up, by tape) only when and if combat was imminent, whereas a true combat direction system always would be running. Nor did the tracking capacity of a Mk 113 suffice. As passive sonar range increased, more and more of the objects detected would be nontargets, sifted out only by their behavior. In practice, the CRT on the Mk 113 control console seems not to have been nearly as effective as planned, perhaps because engagement tended to be a drawn-out process more adapted to a paper plot than to the short-term picture on the PPI. Too, COs and conning officers were accustomed to basing their approaches on a combination of fire-control dials (comparing own-ship and target courses) and the plot. In effect, the officer, not the computer, integrated the system.

COs liked to run a parallel manual solution of the most important target in the sonar room. The manual technique could be adjusted if its conclusions seemed unrealistic, and new techniques (other than the ones programmed into a Mk 130) could be applied. For example, a manual TMA plot might give a range that was different from one produced by the computer. The computer operator could try different courses and speeds to check them against the estimated range. The operator could constrain the computer in range and recompute target course and speed. The solution might show that the original computation was indeed valid and the manual TMA wrong. Similarly, a turn count could be used to estimate target speed and then to constrain the computer in speed. Again, the computer could recalculate, given the inserted speed, to check the validity of its solution. This dual approach has persisted. After a solution was obtained, a single ping could be used to get a more precise range, to test or solidify the solution, and/or to feed more accurate data back into the computer.

A Mk 113 turned out to be more futuristic than necessary. Only the prototype, aboard *Thresher*, had the four analyzers needed to attack four targets in quick succession. A submarine could not fire a second wire-guided torpedo out of a tube as long as the wire of the first one was paying out. The production version for attack submarines, Mod 2, had only one analyzer per attack console.

Mod 3, again using the Mk 130 computer, was an abortive version of Mod 2 for the later ballistic missile subma-

rines (SSBN 616 and beyond). It was enough to track and engage one target at a time, on the theory that SSBNs probably would not encounter more than one attacker at a time. These submarines already had powerful Mk 84 digital computers fitted for missile fire control; their Mk 113 Mod 5s used these computers, rather than Mk 130s, for TMA calculations. Mod 5 was the first application of a programmable stored-program digital computer to submarine fire control and offered the ability to update TMA techniques. The computer's memory and precision were valued for bearings-only TMA conducted over a long time. This sort of time sharing was acceptable; it was most unlikely that the submarine would have to engage another submarine while preparing to fire off her missiles. In fact, a successful engagement or evasion might be the prerequisite for missile firing. Like its predecessor, Mod 5 could track and engage only one target at a time. Unlike the attack submarine version, it could not fire Subroc because the host submarine lacked the big sonar sphere needed for single-ping ranging.

Later, even Mod numbers were used for attack submarines and odd numbers for ballistic missile submarines. The versions adapted to a Mk 48 torpedo control (1967) were Mod 6 and Mod 7. For ballistic missile submarines, the advent of the Mk 48 torpedo became the occasion for rearranging the Mod 5 version of the system in order to bring the analyzer console closer to the plotting area.

When scanning operation became universal, particular sonars and processors no longer had specific roles. For example, Lofar was sometimes used for identification, but it could also be a means of long-range detection in the presence of noise. Clearly, the ideal was merging all available sonar data to form a unified tactical picture as a basis for decision making. If that picture was carried in a computer, data about a potential target could be instantly used to support the attack. That was much the concept of NTDS, which was under development for the surface fleet during the late 1950s and early 1960s.

To achieve integration, the system had to be fully digital. Otherwise, information would not flow freely through it and information from multiple sources could not be easily combined. Digital technology also offered the possibility of freely varying the format in which information was displayed, for example, to keep pace with a changing situation or to match different tactical situations. Above all, information would be presented in the form best suited for use, rather than in traditional forms that placed much heavier loads on the users. The new program was called SUBIC (SUBmarine Integrated Control). Integration is now commonplace, but on 30 June 1957, when Electric Boat produced its first brochure, SUBIC was quite futuristic. Work began in earnest in 1958 and continued until 1965.[15] SUBIC inspired the NSIA recommendation that the next-generation sonar suite be all-digital (see chapter 4).

SUBIC examined three alternative computer architectures: (1) a single central duplex machine, (2) a pair of computers working in parallel, and (3) a distributed computer network. By the early 1960s, solid-state machines had demonstrated that computers could be reliable, but small ones, such as UYK-20, did not yet exist. Even so, the 1963 SUBIC report showed that a modular (distributed) system was preferable, with about 1.6 times the figure of merit assigned to a single computer. The laboratory version actually used a single computer for the sake of simplicity.

By 1963, SUBIC had built a mock-up of a possible FY 65 integrated submarine control space, in which attack sequences could be tested. The sonar consoles were brought back into the control room, partly to reduce the need for verbal communication, which slowed operation and introduced errors (96 percent of verbal reports to command came from sonar and fire control, and 51 percent of all verbal commands went to those functions).[16]

The command station carried both a tactical display and a sonar effectiveness display that showed, for example, likely detection ranges and best listening depths. If the computer were powerful enough, the CO could ask "what if" questions, such as those necessary to evaluate the effect of changing speed or depth on sonar effectiveness. The sonar effectiveness display could, for example, be a PPI with range marks out to maximum sonar range or 50 and 90 percent probability of detection curves, an own-ship radiated noise curve, a mode indicator (e.g., quiet, ultraquiet), a speed indicator (e.g., in 3-kt increments), and a display of best listening depth.

Directly in front of the command station would be a one-person ship-control console with SQUIRE as its main display (see below). The fire-control station and three sonar surveillance stations continued a rough semicircle from the ship-control console, all of them visible from the command station. Across a passageway were an operations station and two ship systems monitoring stations.

The fire-control console was a more compact equivalent of a Mk 113, with a tactical display, four target analyzers, and a weapon and torpedo tube panel. As in a Mk 113, it would be limited to four targets. Unlike the Mk 113/130 combination, the all-digital system allowed the tactical display operator to interact with the evolving TMA solution and estimate target parameters from the way the solution evolved (an impossibility in the Mk 130/Mk 113 combination, introduced only in a Mk 117). The operator could use the computer to calculate kill probabilities for various TMA solutions and solve ambiguous target/consort triangulation problems. Given sonar data, target size could be estimated. The system automatically controlled weapons (e.g., steering wire-guided torpedoes).

Sonar operator stations were reduced from seven to the five needed to perform all functions simultaneously: passive initial detection, frequency (Lofar) monitoring, classification, passive tracking, and active tracking. Passive ranging and range rate analysis would be automated. DEMON and Lofar BSM recorders were added for better frequency analysis.[17] SUBIC seems to have introduced automated sonar ray path tracers to U.S. practice. It developed alternative presentations of sonar data.[18]

The operations station centralized control of radar, ESM, navigation, internal voice communication, and a proposed television periscope. A CO tactical and navigational display (a PPI) would solve maneuvering board–type problems and would also replace the DRT (dead reckoning tracer). Vectors would show courses and speeds; positions could be projected ahead. The PPI would replace the summary tactical display of the usual a Mk 113, the DRT, and the usual manual maneuvering board. Its operator could try different possible speeds and courses; its computer would automatically translate between coordinates centered on the submarine and the geographical coordinates needed to use external information or information from maps.

SUBIC inevitably concentrated much effort on the special problems of Polaris submarines, which used their Mk 113 systems almost entirely in the passive TMA mode. The SUBIC program developed mathematical models of the various TMA techniques, from which it could deduce the errors in target range, course, and speed associated with the ranges of error inherent in existing sonars. For example, it was essential to measure more accurately the rate at which target bearing changed (i.e., to improve the performance of automatic target followers [ATFs]). SubDevGru 2 suggested that a CO would want a display of the errors in target parameters that could be accommodated by any given aiming angle for a given torpedo (e.g., a Mk 37-0 fired in snake mode). The CO could then decide how many torpedoes (with associated deflection angles) to fire to provide any desired degree of coverage.[19] Early calculations suggested that its larger acoustic homing cone would make the new, very fast EX-10 (a Mk 48) torpedo particularly susceptible to TMA errors in target range because it could so easily pick up false targets (e.g., bottom and surface reflections).

Much effort was given to the displays needed by an SSBN to avoid and evade hostile submarines. It had to be assumed that an enemy would make the best possible use of the sonar environment. The SSBN could do the same, based in part on intelligence concerning enemy ship and sonar characteristics. An SSBN commander would also want meteorological information because of the effect of weather on enemy air searches. The system would have to meld local data taken by the submarine (e.g., with her bathythermograph [BT]) with remote oceanographic data supplied by communication link.

The SUBIC proposal was a special avoidance and evasion console. The avoidance half was a geographical plot showing cloud cover and the main bottom contours. It was divided into cells, each showing such data as enemy search rate as a function of depth. Given such data, the CO could choose the area in which the enemy would find it most difficult to search. The other half was to assist in evasion, once an enemy submarine had made contact. To help the CO maneuver into an enemy blind spot, it showed both own-ship noise pattern and assumed enemy noise pattern and sonar beam pattern. The own-ship pattern, based on measured data, changed with speed and depth. As soon as an enemy was detected, the display showed its line of bearing. Given estimated target parameters, a noise radiation pattern could be developed to obtain an approximate range, based on minimum and maximum probable ranges for which the submarine would receive signals of the same strength as those actually received. The same console could be switched to what the SUBIC developers called predictive scanning (PRESCAN). Half a PRESCAN display showed the existing situation; the other half showed predicted consequences of some possible action.

FRISCO (fast-reaction submarine control) was a companion program that produced several devices specifically for better dynamic submarine control: CONALOG (CONtact AnaLOG), SQUIRE (Submarine QUIckened REsponse), AMC (Automatic Maneuvering Control), and AUTOTAB (AUTOmatic Trim And Ballast). CONALOG showed the helmsman/planesman the path to follow, in the form of a synthetic highway in the sea, on a CRT (the video mixer of which could also display sonar and radar information). The CONALOG image was, in effect, a com-

bined instrument panel in visual form. Installed in several attack submarines, it was heartily disliked, partly because of maintenance difficulties. One former submarine CO recalled that it tended to put watch-standers to sleep. The first report describing CONALOG was issued in August 1958. The device was tested in 1961 on board *Shark* and later on board *Thresher* and *Permit*. By 1965, CONALOG was in production for all *Sturgeon*s and all ballistic missile submarines of the SSBN 640 class. By 1968, dislike of CONALOG was so intense that it was specifically deleted from *Los Angeles*.

SQUIRE projected ahead the consequences of control plane movements for the purpose of avoiding unexpected and dangerous maneuvers. Investigations of both linear and nonlinear forms of quickening probably began in the spring of 1958; the first report was issued in June 1958. On the grid display (vertical lines for course, horizontal for depth), the ordered position was indicated by a circle, the predicted one by a dot, and the actual one by a cross.

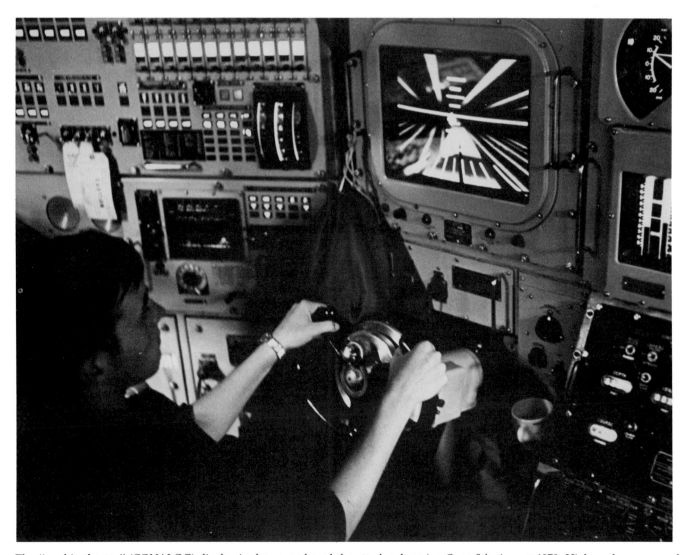

The "road in the sea" (CONALOG) display is shown on board the attack submarine *Queenfish*, August 1970. High performance and violent maneuverability made for interest in new kinds of piloting aids, but this sort of sophistication did not turn out to be necessary.

SQUIRE, shown on board *Tullibee*, was another attempt to improve crew performance in submarine maneuvering, financed by SUBIC. It displayed the consequences of maneuvers in the form of a quickened dot and bar. (General Dynamics Corp.)

Unlike CONALOG, SQUIRE provided a 360-degree view but did not indicate submarine speed. The nonmilitarized prototype went to sea aboard *Tullibee*. General Dynamics received a contract for the first two militarized prototypes in FY 63. According to the 1965 SUBIC report, SQUIRE cost from one third to one half as much as CONALOG, it was more reliable, it was easier to use, and it was preferable to CONALOG because it alone could project the consequences of various control actions.

AMC, a less spectacular outgrowth of these devices, was installed on board ballistic missile submarines. Its analog computer modeled the submarine's control characteristics. It had to be readjusted each time the submarine was refitted, but it conferred an unexpected advantage. A ballistic missile submarine had two crews; one remained ashore while the other operated the submarine. Thus, the CO had to orient the crew during the early days of each patrol. AMC could bring the submarine up to periscope depth much more smoothly (and much more quietly) than a slightly stale planesman.[20]

Automatic maneuvering reappeared in 1977 when Rockwell's Autonetics Aided Display Submarine Control System (ADSCS) was tested on board *Los Angeles* during a Mediterranean deployment. Course, depth, turning-rate limits, depth-rate limits, and a bandwidth for each were

input (e.g., periscope depth plus or minus 1 ft, with a relatively high depth rate). The system auto-executed when its button was pushed. It helped to quiet the submarine by reducing plane motion at high speed; this also reduced hydraulic noise. Although ADSCS was not adopted, it presumably inspired the computer piloting system on board the current *Seawolf*.[21]

AUTOTAB, an automated ballast-trim system suitable for automatic hovering, was developed and evaluated in 1963. It sought to minimize the associated flows and hence the associated noise. The stern planes were used to correct trim; the sail planes were not used at all. AUTOTAB was considered a direct outgrowth of SQUIRE, which used control surfaces to maintain the submarine at ordered depth and was most effective at some speed. AUTOTAB worked when the submarine had little or no way on at all, as in the case of missile firing.

SUBIC was far too radical to be implemented immediately, but it had considerable impact. When the SSBNs were refitted with Poseidon missiles and the corresponding Mk 88 fire-control systems about 1967, their geoballistic computers were replaced by new ones powerful enough to drive a CRT in a redesigned attack console that worked with a new Mk 78 analyzer. The new CRT could display a simulated version of the traditional combination of dials and counters, or it could show the corresponding geosit (geographical situation: PPI), a display formerly associated only with the big attack console. The analyzer operator could use it much more effectively as he interacted with the computer running the TMA program. This new version was Mod 9.

Mod 9 much impressed the ad hoc weapons committee that convened in 1968 in connection with the new fast submarine (to become *Los Angeles*). Committee members argued that fire-control performance would be the limiting factor in any submarine-submarine engagement. The key problems were inadequate sonar bearing input, the need to manually plot TMA, errors inherent in the analog-digital interfaces between computer and analyzer, and inadequate display/retention of target information. Manual TMA was credited with a 10–15 percent range error. That could be reduced by pinging a few times, but such operation was increasingly unacceptable as Soviet submarines improved. Digital systems offered an attractive solution.

Alan Marins, a civilian with the Naval Ordnance Systems Command (successor to BuOrd), realized that, given the bureaucratic barriers, it would be nearly impossible to develop a wholly new integrated submarine system. It would be relatively easy, however, to replace elements of a Mk 113 one by one. Marins's initial step was to replace the existing digital computer and the analyzers feeding it with a simple analog-to-digital converter and a single-bay UYK-7 computer that was far more powerful than the geoballistic units on board the SSBNs. This version, Mod 10, was installed on board the last two *Sturgeons* and early *Los Angeles*-class submarines. The computer's terminal was the new Mk 81 console, whose CRT could show dials, geosit (multitarget display), data storage and evaluation, multiple-mode tracking, multiple (alternative) TMA solutions for single targets for high solution confidence, and ray traces and other sonar data. This system was still fed by analog sonars, and it still commanded Mk 75 analog attack directors.

Unlike earlier versions of a Mk 113, Mod 10 could track many more targets than it had consoles. Typically, an operator could handle up to about 10 targets on a time-share basis; the central computer could run about 20 TMA analyses. Operators could time-share their efforts partly because they could call up earlier sonar data from memory; they did not have to handle each target in real time. Such numbers were needed not because the world had suddenly filled with enemy submarines, but because better long-range sensors, such as towed arrays, often picked up distant nonsubmarine targets. Only TMA could identify them so that they could be disregarded. Moreover, the computer was now so powerful that (as SUBIC's developers had hoped) operators could interact with the running TMA solution, a technique called MATE (manual adaptive TMA evaluation). Operators determined target course, speed, and range by trying alternatives and matching the bearings that were implied against the measured bearings.

Mod 10 was still saddled with $1\frac{1}{2}$ tons of heavy equipment, whose only purposes were to convert data between analog and digital form and to solve for torpedo deflection angles. The next step was easy. A pair of Mk 81 consoles, now designated weapon control consoles (WCCs), replaced the old Mk 75s. The single-bay UYK-7 was replaced by a two-bay version, roughly doubling target-handling capacity. The analog BQQ-2 sonar was replaced by the digital BQQ-5. The new system was renamed a Mk 117. Design work began under the FY 73 program, and development tests were completed in August 1977. The Mk 48 Mod 3 and 4 torpedoes were associated with this system. A Mk 117 was introduced in *Dallas* (SSN 700) and then backfitted in earlier ships.

Originally, a Mk 117 was designed to control only digital weapons, but a weapon data converter had to be installed to permit control of surviving analog weapons. Under the FY 83 program, many Mk 117s were connected to leveling computers (a Mk 129) for control of Subroc. This facility had to be eliminated when ships were converted to control Tomahawk land-attack missiles; there was not enough space for both types of equipment. When combined with Tomahawk control equipment, a Mk 117 was redesignated CCS (combat control system) a Mk 1. A parallel Mk 118 was developed to control torpedoes and defensive countermeasures on board *Ohio*-class missile submarines.

Mks 117 and 118 still did not reach the SUBIC ideal of full integration of sonar and fire control. In practice, the character of their sensor trackers and their man/machine interfaces limited performance; a Mk 117 could achieve less than one fifth of its theoretical track capacity.[22] The operational requirement for a fully fused system, BSY-1 or SUBACS (SUBmarine Advanced Combat System), was issued on 17 April 1980. It would be a *Los Angeles*-class block upgrade for FY 89 and later ships. SUBACS was conceived as a distributed system using a single type of multipurpose console for both target tracking (from processed sonar data) and fire control. It would be tied together by a fiber-optic data bus with sufficient capacity to carry both processed sonar data and tactical or fire-control data. A submarine would carry 11 consoles but could operate with only 4; the others provided spare capacity and could be brought on line instead of repairing consoles at sea. Multipurpose operation would be possible because the consoles used a new kind of high-density electronic card. Operators would use processed sonar data to conduct semiautomatic TMA, thus localizing targets to form a coherent tactical picture. An operator following a single target could switch the console from one sonar to another to make optimum use of each. The tactical picture would be carried in a UYK-43 computer, but most processing would be done by 68000-series microprocessors in the consoles. In theory, BSY-1 could handle 10 times as many targets as a Mk 117. Any separate fire-control system, as such, would no longer exist.

IBM received the SUBACS contract in March 1983. Its first task was a 6-mo study (at navy request) of an accelerated program. On the basis of this study, the navy decided to put a version in FY 83 submarines, with preplanned block upgrades in FY 86 and FY 89 ships (i.e., in the new *Seawolf*). Full integration of sonar and fire control was abandoned. Estimated RDT&E cost was $1.3 billion in 1983 dollars. By early 1985, the navy estimated an $800 million cost overrun, and there was some fear that the microprocessor network could not handle the information load. The navy proposed a new three-stage program, SUBACS Basic, A, and B. SUBACS Basic and A would be federated central computer systems using standard navy computers (UYK-43 central processors and UYK-44 minicomputers). Significantly lighter than BQQ-5, they would release weight for vital sonar improvements. SUBACS B might realize the original ideal of full distribution. An internal navy panel suggested that BQQ-5 should be modernized instead, but that option was rejected in July 1985 because it was expected to cost six times as much as the cost increase entailed by the three-stage program.

The main objective for SUBACS Basic and A was improved sonar performance through use of the new UYS-1 signal processor and installation of the SADS digital transmitter, the MIDAS (mine and ice detection system), and the projected long, thin towed array. The system would also add an improved weapons launch-control group to permit faster vertical launching. Common sonar displays (improved control-display consoles [ICDCs]) replaced the former types. In September 1985, IBM was chosen as the sole supplier of the new interim SUBACS. The General Accounting Office recommended terminating the program. In November 1985, the House Armed Services Committee deleted the entire allocation of $205 million, but the Senate kept the program alive. BSY-1 delayed the FY 83 submarines by three years. The BSY-1(V) development contract was awarded in February 1986.

Plans initially called for five interim versions with UYK-7 central computers and UYS-1 signal processors (to improve passive performance) but lacking SADS and MIDAS. Further production systems would have UYK-43s; improved active performance, thanks to SADS and MIDAS; and a more capable VLS (vertical missile launching system) controller. In fact, the fifth ship (*Miami*, SSN 755) received the full SUBACS Basic outfit. BSY-1/CCS Mk 1 uses four ICDC sonar consoles, two multipurpose consoles, four Mk 81 fire-control system (FCS) consoles (from CCS Mk 1), one command launch-control console (for the VLS), and four weapons launch-control consoles (one for the VLS).

A major embarrassment occurred. Upon delivery, the prototype BSY-1 did not fit USS *San Juan* (SSN 751), mainly because of excess wireways. Fitting her cost an overrun of nearly $100 million, which was settled in mid-1988. *San Juan* was upgraded to full capability in November 1989; the first full system had been delivered the previous February. BSY-1 was approved for full production in October 1989. *Miami* conducted BSY-1 technical evaluation in March–December 1990, followed by operational evaluation beginning in December 1990. The last of 24 ship sets was ordered under the FY 90 program.

SUBACS A was expected to provide common sonar and weapons system displays and to reduce solution time by using a new UYS-2 signal processor. Sensors would be improved. SUBACS B would have added a wide aperture array (WAA) to cut localization time to 2 min, as well as a much more capable ESM system (a variant of Sea Nymph) and a mission-oriented communications system, but neither A nor B was bought. Instead, the navy ordered a new competition for SUBACS B (BSY-2). GE, whose naval division has now been sold to Martin-Marietta, received the full-scale development contract in March 1988. Its BSY-2 is a fully distributed system using 68030 microprocessors (about 200), as well as UYS-2 signal processors and specialized array beamformers. The system has no central computers at all, only multifunction consoles (MCCs) and combat-system display consoles (CSDCs): a total of 11 consoles, 3 of them specifically for the CCS. There is a completely new bow sonar array.

In September 1988, Raytheon received a contract to replace CCS Mk 1 (in both BQQ-5 and BSY-1 submarines) with a new CCS Mk 2 built around a UYK-43 computer and 4 Mk 130 multipurpose consoles. The main computer carries the system software and down-loads it to the consoles. It also carries the system's tactical picture and works as the system's input/output device. CCS Mk 2 uses some BSY-2 software. Mod 0 is for *Los Angeles*-class submarines without a VLS; Mod 1 is for such submarines with a VLS; Mod 2 works with BSY-1, which already provides the UYK-43; and Mod 4 is for the *Ohio* class.

Project Nobska seems to have inspired a major study that was started in early 1959 by Capt. R. B. Laning of the OpNav Undersea Warfare Division.[23] Laning doubted that any advance in technology could greatly increase the volume in which a single submarine could detect and kill

others. Surely, the new technology could be used to mass produce low-cost, high-capability submarines conceived more like airplanes than traditional ships. Equipment and machinery would have to be substantially automated to reduce manning. Maintenance at sea would be abandoned almost completely; the submarine would rely on its base or tender.

The airplanelike submarine would lack all rescue facilities, backup bulkheads, and double closures, as well as emergency propulsion and any means of reactor start-up. Reserve buoyancy would be only 5 percent, compared with 15–18 percent in a conventional submarine. No machinery units would be duplicated. Detail simplification included no anchor, no sail planes, integrated and miniaturized electronics and control, reduced electronics suit, no repair parts, limited access, and minimum masts. Torpedoes would be carried externally. For greater depth, a stronger hull material (HY-150) would be used. Laning hoped that the nuclear airplane program would provide his submarine with a lightweight, unmanned 5,000-SHP plant (50–65 lb/SHP, then altogether unattainable). A closed-cycle plant might be a viable alternative.

The project became the proposed FY 65 submarine. Laning convinced those responsible for SUBIC to make the FY 65 combat system their goal; he strongly supported the SUBIC program. He discussed the concept with the material bureaus (BuShips and BuOrd), ONR, and the industry in February 1959. BuShips conducted a series of envelope studies that March. DCNO (R&D) held a conference in May. In June 1959, BuShips released a letter (echoed by an August OpNav letter) stating the following goals:

$10–15 million unit cost; displacement 500–750 tons
30 kt maximum, endurance 30 days at 10 kt if non-nuclear
5,000-ft operating depth
12 crew
10 external, deep-running wire-guided torpedoes

Laning went to aircraft manufacturers (Grumman, Lockheed, and probably others; the Lockheed version was called EMPIRE), rather than to traditional shipbuilders for most of his industry studies. The aircraft and aircraft engine industries considered lightweight nuclear power plants a major opportunity. Their optimistic engineers believed they could easily outperform conservative naval machinery engineers. They revisited two of the earlier rejected alternatives, liquid metal and gas cooling, and also considered a boiling water reactor, which would not need separate primary and secondary loops.[24] Code 1500 considered none of the commercial plants particularly realistic, but the companies persisted in their claims for some years.

Weapons could be carried in a saddle that fired fore or aft and allowed multiple simultaneous shots without interfering with a large sonar transducer. However, it would add considerable drag (2–3 kt), require large shutters, and be difficult to load. Alternatively, tubes could be inclined at 20 degrees, loaded from above, and fired down, leaving space in the bow for a sonar. The tubes would be easy to load but could not fire at high speed. Finally, torpedoes could be carried in a bomb bay and dropped one by one to fire. The bay could carry five torpedoes on each side that could be fired forward or aft. It would be easy to load and allowed space for a big sonar transducer, but it could fire only two torpedoes at a time and would have had wiring and firing problems.

BuShips presented its own advanced-concept submarine alternatives in November 1959. They were rather larger, hence more expensive and a lot less expendable than Captain Laning had hoped. The bureau looked at two depth options (2,500 and 4,000 ft) for each of three power plant alternatives: nuclear (half a *Thresher* plant), diesel-electric, and closed-cycle (Alton, using hydrogen peroxide). In each case, 10 external tubes (each 27 × 200 in) were arranged in a ring around a tank (a trim tank for SSN, diesel oil for the diesel-electric submarine) that also surrounded a sonar. The closed-cycle submarine had a hydrogen peroxide tank forward and another externally, abaft the pressure hull.

The deeper the diving depth, the larger the submarine that was needed to accommodate her heavier pressure hull. Thus a 2,500-ft nuclear submarine would be 152 ft 3 in × 25 ft (1,400 tons submerged); her deeper-diving companion would be 183 ft long (1,840 tons) and correspondingly slower. Estimated costs were $34 million and $39 million, respectively, compared with $65 million for the new *Thresher*, hardly the sort of saving to justify the program.

The shallower-diving diesel-electric option would not dive nearly as deep as the nuclear one; she was 170 × 24 ft (1,385 tons). The deeper-diving version would have been 213 ft long (1,975 tons). In each case, the planned underwater power plant was 8,500 SHP; this could have driven the smaller boat at about 28 kt for 2¾ hr. Both versions had silver-zinc batteries sufficient for about 100 hr at 5 kt. Estimated costs were $22 million and $29 million, respectively, compared with $29 million for *Barbel*. Although the deep diver was smaller, she would be no cheaper than a conventional submarine.

The closed-cycle (Alton) 8,500-SHP (for 10 hr) alternatives had the same 24-ft diameter hull form as the diesel-electric boats; the shallower diver would have been 190 ft long (1,515 tons) and the deeper, 219 ft (1,910 tons). Estimated costs were $23 million for the shallower diver and $29 million for the deeper.

The aircraft companies were more optimistic. Like the BuShips sketch designs, theirs showed 10 oversize external tubes wrapped around the hull forward (around a fuel tank in the case of a diesel-electric submarine). A composite diesel-electric boat, with the same diving depth as the shallower of the BuShips designs, would have been smaller—110 × 23 ft, rather than 170 × 24 ft (800 tons, opposed to 1,385 tons). On the other hand, she would have had a much less powerful motor (2,000 SHP for

19.3 kt), and much less endurance (15 hr, rather than about 100 hr, at 5 kt). Estimated cost was $18 million.

The commercial nuclear submarine would have been powered by a 5,000-SHP plant then being developed for aircraft by North American Aviation. Some of the aircraft designers thought they could produce a 121 × 20-ft submarine (580 tons) capable of 27.5 kt and of diving to 4,000 ft. They quoted a $23 million price tag, but it was estimated that the reactor itself would cost $500 million to develop. This plant never materialized (the nuclear aircraft program died), and the estimated development cost probably was grossly optimistic.

By January 1959, the smaller, mass-production submarine had been officially accepted as a complement to conventional attack craft. A Long Range Objectives Group projection of the 1973 fleet consisted of 65 full-size attack submarines and 25 Laning-type submarines; mass production of the latter was expected to begin in FY 65. The larger submarines would operate mainly in close coordination with other ASW forces (e.g., in escort roles). The smaller submarines would operate individually in barriers and in surveillance roles.

With the failure of the nuclear aircraft program, the March 1962 ASW program (GOR 23) had to accept BuShips' more pessimistic displacements. On the other hand, higher burst speed might be possible, for example, by smoothing the submarine's boundary layers with polymers (see chapter 3 for experiments with this mechanism using *Albacore*). The projected FY 65 submarine was expected to displace 1,000–1,500 tons, with a test depth of 3,000 ft; it would achieve 45–60 kts for 10 min. It would be armed with both the new long torpedo (a Mk 48) and short-range underwater rockets and have an inherently quiet direct-drive nuclear power plant.

The March 1959 BuShips long-range R&D program had envisaged a 4,000-ft submarine, although that specific goal was dropped from the December 1960 version of the plan. A CUW special task force on deep-diving submarines, formed in May 1960, had held a symposium that September. The acoustic arguments for deep diving, both to the deep channel and for using an upward-looking RAP sonar, were pressed. Some members argued that a deeper diving hull would be stronger, hence more resistant to explosions (e.g., of nuclear depth bombs, a popular submarine antidote at the time) at shallower depths. However, very strong materials are often brittle and thus may succumb more, rather than less, easily to the shock of an explosion. On a more exotic plane, it appeared that deep-diving hulls might ultimately approach the compressibility of water, in which case they might be altogether transparent at some sonar frequencies. This idea was never tested.

CUW was quite optimistic. It estimated that, within two or three years, a 2,000-ft *Thresher* could be built at a 2 percent increased cost in engineering and entirely without operational sacrifice. In March 1961, CUW suggested that a *Thresher* equivalent capable of diving to 4,000 or 5,000 ft might be developed in time for the FY 64 program. The committee hoped that by 1965 hull and machinery component work and testing and evaluating such a ship would cost only $5–10 million. Operational submarines might dive to 12,000–15,000 feet by the end of the decade. Very few deep-diving submersibles had yet been built. In addition to new strong materials, these deep divers probably would be radically different from conventional submarines: they would be weight- rather than volume-limited. Thus, CUW hoped that drastic cuts in component weights in a conventional design (like *Thresher*) could be translated into a much heavier, hence deeper-diving, pressure hull.

These expectations translated into official requirements. For example, GOR 23, the March 1962 official long-range ASW development plan, called for 2,000-ft diving depth in a FY 65 prototype; 4,000 ft in a FY 66 operational prototype; 12,000–15,000 ft in an experimental deep diver, a systems test for a very deep diver, in FY 67; and an operational deep diver (10,000-ft operating depth) in FY 75.

Official projections of the number of Soviet submarines were horrifying. It was assumed that the Soviets would prefer quantity (diesel submarines) to quality (nuclear craft). Thus, according to the official May 1961 ASW threat summary, the Soviets, by mid-1971, would have 578 submarines: 316 SS, 50 SSN, 24 SSB, and 36 SSBN.

The Nobska idea, that the Soviets might well concentrate on exotic forms of non-nuclear propulsion, such as fuel cells, was accepted. They might increase submerged endurance at 5–20 kt to 15–30 days. On the other hand, they probably would not dive deeper. By 1971, it was believed, Soviet nuclear attack submarines would be armed with standoff missiles (equivalent to Subroc but usable against surface ships), might achieve 40–45 kt, and might dive as deep as 4,000 ft. Its SSBN probably would

not exceed 25 kt and a 2000-ft operating depth. The expected diving depths almost certainly reflected CUW ideas, not intelligence.

The first step toward the CUW goals was to develop a new generation of hull penetrations, such as propeller glands, torpedo tube closures, and periscope seals. A deep-diving prototype, *Dolphin* (AGSS 555, SCB 207), was therefore included in the FY 61 program. She was the last new submarine designed at Portsmouth. Because she did not use any new stronger hull material, *Dolphin* had to pay heavily for her depth. About 54 percent of total displacement was devoted to her 15-ft diameter HY-80 pressure hull, compared with 20–25 percent in a conventional submarine.

In 1964, Project Seabed suggested that deep diving might be even more important for an SSBN. At or near the bottom, she might be virtually indistinguishable from bottom features. An SSBN with a test depth of 8,000 ft could sit on the mid-Atlantic ridge; she could operate anywhere in 98 percent of the ocean volume if she could dive to 20,000 ft. Even shallower test depths might be worthwhile. Positions 2,000 ft above or below the deep sound channel would be best for evasion; this was assuming that bottom-bounce propagation could not be exploited.

The "go-ahead" point for a 4,000–6,000-ft SSN seemed reachable in three or four years. A deep-submergence rescue vehicle (DSRV) already in development would reach 6,000 ft, and new oceanographic submersibles could do much better. It appeared that a *Sturgeon* redesigned to triple her operating depth could be built of titanium (yield strength, 120,000 lb/sq in) in a sandwich structure. She would displace 4,670–5,300 tons, compared with 4,120–4,640 for *Sturgeon*, and would be about 10 ft shorter

Billfish is shown with *Avalon* (DSRV 2) on board at Rota, Spain, September 1992, for NATO exercise "Sorbet Royal 92." She was to practice deep-sea rescues with British and Italian submarines. The deep-submergence rescue vehicle was one of the main legacies of interest in deep diving. Many submarines were converted to carry it.

and a knot or two slower. Unlike *Sturgeon,* she would be weight-limited, unless much stronger hull materials were developed.

The Vietnam War swallowed the R&D money that might have gone into a new generation of hull materials and hull penetrations. Even had the war not occurred, the push to dive deeper might not have succeeded in competition with numerous other thrusts then under consideration. Ultimately, the U.S. position was that putting very high performance, which included diving, into weapons, rather than big, expensive submarine hulls and other platforms, achieved the greatest economy. When the Soviets deployed deep-diving Alfa-class submarines, the response was a new generation of deeper-diving torpedoes. No one came close to reaching the sea bottom, or even the Mid-Atlantic Ridge, in anything bigger than a research submersible.

Initially, *Dolphin* was unarmed. Soon after completion in 1968, a single tube was mounted in the center of her bow, with BQS-4 and BQS-8 (obstacle detector, later replaced by BQS-15) active sonars below it, plus standard passive sonars (BQR-2B and BQR-7). A powerful low-frequency (2.5 kHz) projector with a narrow conical beam (15 degrees wide) was mounted in the front of her sail; the associated receiver was a 46-ft array with preformed beams. The transducers of a BQQ-3 Lofar classifier were mounted to port abaft the sail.

The 30-in ram-catapult bow tube fired an experimental DEXTOR (Deep EXternal TORpedo) in the deepest torpedo shot to date. The tube's ram pushed against the torpedo guide stud. BuOrd saw it as the prototype of future torpedo tubes, three times as efficient as existing piston-pump tubes. Its large diameter accommodated many components that were more usually fitted externally. Also, because water circulated freely around the emerging torpedo, the tube did not need an external WRT tank or piston pump. BuOrd claimed that it weighed only two thirds as much as a conventional tube.

Built at the Naval Underwater Ordnance Station at Newport (the old Torpedo Station), DEXTOR was a test bed for future torpedoes diving to 4,000–6,000 ft. It could dive to 4,200 ft and was expected to crush at 5,600. The main new feature was a new type of body using sandwich construction to withstand pressure. It was somewhat shorter than standard heavy torpedoes (21 × 230 inches) and used the motor of a Mk 45 Astor (16,000 yd at 26.8 kt at half power and 12,000 yd at 38.2 kt at full power). DEXTOR had neither seeker nor warhead, but it did have space and weight for both, and it was wire-guided.

By the time DEXTOR and its tube had been installed, the deep submarine program had been largely abandoned. BuOrd admitted somewhat sheepishly in its own journal that "although other nations are not expected to employ deep-submergence tactics (below 2,000 ft) during the decade from 1970 to 1980, such a development remains a distinct possibility." Ironically, the Soviets were then building exactly the sort of deep diver that GOR 23 had predicted, the famous Alfa-class submarine, which could make 42 kt and could operate at about 2,300 ft.

Dolphin's tube was removed in 1969 to make way for a new set of sonars, this time to test the upward-looking RAP concept. A planar transmitting array was built in the main ballast tank forward of the pressure hull. The receivers were two 30-ft line arrays (52 elements each) near the bow in a Mills Cross protruding vertically and horizontally from the outer hull, with a 15-ft array (24 elements), mounted fore and aft, passing through it. Presumably, *Dolphin* later tested towed arrays. She also tested submarine-air laser communications.

8

From Nuclear Prototypes to Production

WITH THE FIRST two nuclear prototypes well under way, Captain Rickover sought the next step. STR and SIR reactors embodied design choices made in 1949. Surely, newer basic technology could do far better, for example, in power-to-weight ratio, so that a much faster submarine could be built. In 1951, Rickover persuaded CNO to ask BuShips to investigate design criteria of a very fast submarine. He asked the two reactor companies to prepare 6-mo studies. Although GE wanted to concentrate on commercial work, Rickover persuaded it to develop a new two-reactor submarine plant, which was designated SAR (submarine advanced reactor). The CNO, Adm. Robert Carney, signed the operational requirement for the fast submarine in February 1953. Because SAR was expected to involve new technology, AEC would pay for much of its development. It was accepted into the AEC program in April 1953.[1]

The outcome was unhappy. Rickover soon found himself shifting the SAR goal from high speed per se to a much improved power-to-weight ratio, which, in any case, would be essential for a new generation of fast nuclear submarines and surface ships. Even early, and overly optimistic, estimates of the weight of SAR made for very large submarines. As the reactor's weight increased, it became less and less attractive. The project survived because its new-technology status guaranteed AEC support.

Apparently, STR had been surprisingly close to the peak of available pressurized water performance. That technology now had to be made available to the naval architects, in the form of power plants sized to ship requirements, rather than the other way around. By 1953, the *Nautilus* design was complete, but the fleet considered her far too large. Thus, the first offshoot was a scaled-down reactor, with half the output of the STR, to power what amounted to a nuclear *Tang* or Guppy. Naturally, it was designated SFR (submarine fleet reactor). As S3W and S4W, it powered the *Skate* class.[2] There was no land prototype because SFR was merely an extrapolation of the existing STR.

No SFR submarine could match *Nautilus* in speed. Rick-over had not lost his faith; he expected *Nautilus* to prove just how valuable speed could be. With the SAR program already in some disarray, Rickover ordered Westinghouse to redesign the existing *Nautilus* reactor, STR.[3] He designated it AFSR (advanced fleet submarine reactor). It became the standard U.S. nuclear submarine reactor, S5W.

The SAR never did meet expectations. Within the submarine community in 1953–54, however, the SAR designation was synonymous with the ideal of high, not moderate, speed. A January 1954 Submarine Officers Conference accorded it high priority, even though studies of SAR-powered fast submarines, such as a missile submarine, showed that they would be quite large. Thus, SAR powered only a single submarine, the large picket *Triton*.[4] GE applied its SAR expertise to HPR (high-powered reactor), a destroyer/cruiser reactor. As with SAR, it was vital to hold down the power-to-weight ratio. HPR became the D1G land-based prototype and the D2G production reactor. Except for the very large *Long Beach*, two D2Gs powered each U.S. nuclear cruiser (actually a large nuclear destroyer). Although D1G/D2G was never intended as a submarine reactor, it was the most powerful unit available in 1963, when much more power was suddenly needed, and it became the basis of the S6G reactor that powers the *Los Angeles* class.

A third natural line of development led to a reactor for carriers and large cruisers. This LSR (large ship reactor) project was assigned to Westinghouse, which produced the related A1W/A2W carrier plant for *Enterprise* and the C1W cruiser plant for *Long Beach*. LSR and HPR had about the same unit output, but HPR was a simpler proposition because it could be heavier per horsepower. The carrier *Enterprise* was powered by eight LSR reactors, far too complex a plant. Therefore, Westinghouse began to scale up its plants. It produced an abortive four-reactor A3W about 1960. By that time, there was considerable interest in cutting the cost of nuclear escorts. One way to do so was to halve the number of reactors. Westinghouse received a contract for a unitary reactor, D1W, with twice the output of a D2G, about 60,000 SHP. Work began in 1962. As in

On the slip at Portsmouth, *Seadragon* (SSN 584) shows her bluff bow form, similar to that adopted for *Nautilus*. The vertical object visible amidships is the access tube to her bridge (the bridge fairwater has not yet been fitted). Despite the bow form, the sonars inside were more those of a *Tang* than of a *Nautilus*: BQR-2B and SQS-4 (with TR-131 transducer).

the case of the D2G, D1W was important to submarine development because it was available, at least nominally, in the late 1960s, whereas any wholly new reactor of similar power-to-weight ratio would have taken far longer to develop. D1W was never used, but it was scaled up (output roughly doubled) to become A4W that powers *Nimitz*-class carriers.

SAR and AFSR were both designed for about the same output. To extend nuclear power to much of the fleet, Rickover had to offer a menu of power plants with very different outputs. That mirrored the standard BuEng policy of the past. By 1954, Rickover apparently believed that his design group understood the new technology well enough to scale it up or down at will; after all, it had successfully halved STR power to produce SFR. That could be halved, and then halved again. At the other end of the scale, SAR power could be doubled. That made a total of five new reactors. (Because AFSR was a modernized version of the existing STR, it was not considered a future development program.) Rickover called them the "family of five," and CNO approved their development in April 1954.[5] The smallest of the lot, which would have produced 1,500 SHP, was never built.

The half-SFR reactor (the small power reactor, or SPR, later redesignated SRS [submarine reactor, small] and then S1C) powered *Tullibee*. Planned output was 2,000–3,000 SHP. One S1C could power a small submarine, or two could power an attack submarine.

At this time, estimated SFR output was 6,000–7,000 SHP. One reactor could power an attack submarine; two could power an SSG, SSR, or a relatively slow surface ship.

Estimated SAR output was 15,000–17,000 SHP. SAR was designed only for two-reactor operation; two could power an SSR or SSG. For a time, it seemed that two pairs of SARs would power a nuclear destroyer. Hopefully, SAR would have about 60 percent of the power-to-weight ratio of SIR, itself assumed to be lighter than STR in *Nautilus*. An SAR land prototype was included in the FY 56 AEC budget.

At 30,000–40,000 SHP, LSR was the highest-powered member of the family. Later, HPR was hived off. In 1954, it was hoped that HPR would have about half the weight per SHP of SAR.

In 1955, all reactors were redesignated with letter-number-lettercodes that indicated application serial number and manufacturer (G for GE, W for Westinghouse). Thus, the STR land-based prototype (a Mk I) became the S1W (the operational version became S2W). Parallel SIR designations were S1G and S2G; the SAR land-based prototype was S3G. Combustion Engineering, a third manufacturer, worked on only a single reactor—the small SPR, which became S1C.

The "family of five" resulted in a major surprise. OpNav liked SPR because it was small enough to make a nuclear SSK affordable and ordered development for *Tullibee*. It turned out that the scaling laws had not been well understood. The small reactor became quite heavy,

possibly because its shielding could not be scaled down in proportion to its output. That sort of problem even affected the larger SFR, which had half the output of the original STR but weighed 60 percent as much. The small reactor grew large enough to ruin hopes that any small SSK(N) could be built.

Rickover probably learned a larger lesson. Nuclear power plants were extremely difficult to design. With limited personnel, he could not keep many designs running in parallel. Any sudden, unpredictable change in requirements could be met only by adapting an existing reactor to a new role. That happened in the mid-1960s with the D2G.

SAR was little better than SFR or, for that matter, SIR. Even the first seagoing reactor was much farther up the learning curve (in power-weight ratio) than Rickover probably imagined. There was still some room for improvement, but it would be very difficult to make even slight gains. Code 1500 soon learned that enormous improvement in core lifetime was possible. This was partly a matter of fuel efficiency (relating to how much usable fuel could be packed into a given core, as well as to operating practice).

Refueling a nuclear plant is an enormously expensive and elaborate operation. For a nuclear-powered ship or submarine, this is the most natural time for a major refit. Because a nuclear submarine costs relatively little to operate between fuelings, anything that reduces the number of fuelings in its lifetime greatly lowers the cost of owning it. Actually, it might be far less expensive to buy a more expensive power plant that needs few refuelings than to buy a cheaper one that requires frequent refuelings. Core lifetime is generally measured in equivalent hours at full power, typically well over 1,000 hr/yr. Submarine lifetime is conveniently measured in refuelings. It can be assumed that no submarine capable of running on the fuel still on board would be discarded.

The same reactor might carry quite different cores without changing its designation. About 1955, it was believed that the *Nautilus* core would last 900 hr at full power (600 hr would have met the design requirement for a 15,000-nm endurance at 25 kt). The new SFR core intended for the *Skate* class was then credited with 2,000 hr at full speed; later, the figure increased to 2,500 hr. S5Ws installed in the *Skipjacks* were each credited with 5,500 hr, the culmination of first-generation core design. The next generation, in *Threshers* and *Narwhal*, was rated at 10,000 hr, equivalent to 8 years of operation. Second-generation power plants (and the submarines carrying them) were credited with a lifetime of 24 years with two refuelings. Hulls could probably last somewhat longer, so the ideal core would last about 30 years. By the 1980s, naval reactors had reached the point at which a submarine would have to be recored only once in her career. The submarine force justified procurement of substantially more expensive submarines (*Los Angeles* class) largely on the ground that, because of rarer refuelings, ownership costs would fall so far that total submarine costs would not rise significantly. Much the same argument was later made for the *Seawolf* class. Conversely, when dramatic cost cuts were needed, submarines had to be laid up or discarded instead of being refueled. That is why many relatively modern units were retired from 1989 on: retaining them in service would have entailed the major expense of refueling. Some may be laid up before their first recoring.

In 1956, Oak Ridge suggested that the natural tendency of water to rise as it was heated could be used to circulate it through a reactor core without resorting to pumps. Even at very high power, natural circulation would be strong enough that only small pumps would be needed. The pumps were noisy and potentially unreliable. Rickover liked this natural circulation reactor (NCR) for its simplicity, which guaranteed reliability, and financed its development. The main technical question was whether circulation would be disturbed as the submarine maneuvered, so a prototype was mounted on a special rolling, pitching platform. Others liked NCR because it was inherently quiet (at this time Rickover was not much concerned with pump noise). The seagoing NCR prototype, the S5G, powered *Narwhal*; a larger version, S8G, powers *Ohio*-class strategic submarines.[6]

NCR reactors are taller than their pressurized water equivalents because the pumping action depends on a combination of heat difference and height; much the same physics favors tall smokestacks. With about half the power, *Narwhal* had the same hull diameter as *Los Angeles*. Similarly, *Ohio*, with about twice the power as *Narwhal*, has the same hull diameter as the abortive big missile submarine, which would have had twice the power of *Los Angeles*.

No other completely new submarine reactor technology has emerged in the quarter century since NCR. That might be taken as evidence of Rickover's gross technical conservatism; however, nowhere outside the United States has any radically new technique turned up. The British, Soviet, and French navies adopted pressurized water reactors, although the French flirted unsuccessfully with liquid metal and the Soviets actually deployed liquid metal reactors in their Alfa class. No one ever deployed a gas-cooled submarine power reactor.

The S5W proved extremely successful. The British tried to develop their own submarine reactor but lacked sufficient technical manpower; the Magnox civilian power reactors had higher priority. In negotiations with the U.S. Navy in 1958, Britain was offered the *Skate* reactor but ended up with the more powerful S5W. HMS *Dreadnought*, the prototype British SSN, had, in effect, a *Skipjack* tail welded onto her slightly larger-diameter British front end. The British believed that they returned the favor by providing the U.S. Navy with the rafting (silencing) technology that proved crucial at just about the same time. All later British submarine reactors incorporate some S5W technology, although just how much is a matter of dispute.[7]

The sale to Britain probably was approved partly because the British submarine power plant was already well advanced. In mid-1958, the Royal Netherlands Navy thought that it had a similar agreement in train. Admiral Rickover apparently believed that the overall submarine reactor technology was so obvious that it could not be kept secret. Reportedly, he changed his mind after a visit to the new Soviet nuclear-powered icebreaker *Lenin*, the details of whose plant appalled him. He obviously had secrets worth keeping, and the Dutch agreement was scuttled. The Royal Canadian Navy tried to buy nuclear submarines at this time; Rickover personally approved an offer, valid for a year, of the *Skipjack* design. When the Canadians could not decide (they became interested in the superior *Thresher*), the offer was allowed to lapse. The French may have approached the U.S. government about 1959 after their liquid metal project failed. If so, the proposal was rejected. Reportedly, the power plants of the French strategic submarines closely resemble S5W but without permission. More recent French nuclear power plants have a quite different native design.

The first SSN design study to follow the two prototypes was a fast attack submarine, powered by two SARs, that was investigated in 1952. The preliminary estimate was about 5,000 tons; by May 1953, it had grown to 8000–10,000 tons, mainly to accommodate the power plant. A memo on her armament was marked, "The price of speed is going up." This growth was so disturbing that, at one point, Electric Boat went so far as to suggest placing the reactor in the bow, where the forward-facing part could be left almost unshielded. Although the increased displacement was needed mainly to gain speed (i.e., power), it allowed for increased payload beyond the normal attack submarine armament. Possible alternatives were Sea Dart aircraft and Regulus missiles. Either probably could be accommodated by adding another 500–1,000 tons at the cost of 2–3 kt. No further details of this design seem to have emerged, and the Regulus submarines sketched early in 1954 were substantially smaller.

No nuclear submarines were included in the FY 54 budget. There was little point in duplicating the two prototypes, and the follow-on SFR reactor was far from ready. Late in 1952, an early version of the FY 55 budget showed only two diesel-electric boats and two closed-cycle boats (SSX), the latter to test the competing power plants then still under development. Nuclear power would be expensive, so most U.S. submarines probably would be diesel boats. Therefore, replacement diesel craft had a higher priority than the more exotic types. By August 1953, BuShips wanted 10 diesel submarines, plus a new small SSN, an SSX, and a fast SSR for FY 56.

Then, the land-based *Nautilus* prototype reactor completed a simulated Atlantic crossing without incident. In September, BuShips moved the small new SSN to the top of the priority list, and it was closely followed by the radar picket. The bureau strongly recommended against postponing the SSN to FY 56. Hedging was no longer so important; the SSX moved well down the list. The FY 55 program submitted to the secretary of the navy in January 1954 showed the new SSN as priority 3 and two new diesel submarines as priority 6. The SSN was attractive partly because she would not cost that much more than a diesel submarine, $40.0 million compared with $28.5 million.[8] By this time, the SSR and SSX had been dropped.

In February, BuShips recommended an annual program, beginning with FY 55, of at least two SSNs (one SSN replaced one diesel submarine), which meant that both main submarine yards, Electric Boat and Portsmouth, could participate in the program. Clearly, diesel submarines were being edged out. BuShips wanted a third submarine, an SAR-powered radar picket, in the FY 56 program.

Nautilus had not yet entered service.

The two FY 55 SSNs and two of the FY 56 ships became the first class of U.S. nuclear submarines, the *Skate*s (SCB 121 design). In effect, this design was a *Nautilus* scaled down to *Tang* dimensions, with the hope of producing something more affordable. *Nautilus* had not yet demonstrated the enormous value of high speed, so it seemed sufficient to combine the speed of a *Tang* or a Guppy with effectively unlimited nuclear endurance. The scaled-down SFR (later S3W/S4W) reactor provided only slightly more power than *Tang*'s electric motors. Compared with the *Nautilus* reactor, it offered greater endurance. Scaling down power did not bring a proportional reduction in plant weight, perhaps largely because shielding could not be scaled down. A plant producing less than half the output of *Nautilus* weighed about 60 percent as much. This type of arithmetic, which was unavoidable, implied

that really small nuclear submarines could not be built, a point further reinforced by the experience of *Tullibee*.

As of January 1954, estimated characteristics included a submerged displacement of 2,500 tons (comparable to 2,270 tons then estimated for a diesel-electric submarine), dimensions of 240×25 ft, and a speed of 18 kt. By mid-1957, the design had been lengthened to 261 ft (2,250 tons light and 2,700 submerged); ultimately, the length came to 268 ft 8 in (2,861 tons submerged). As a nuclear equivalent of *Tang*, *Skate* carried a pair of short stern (countermeasures) tubes in addition to her long bow tubes. Small size and nuclear power did impose a sacrifice in the number of torpedoes she could carry. The earlier standard allowance of three reloads per bow tube and two per stern tube had to be cut to two and one, respectively.

The design was modified several times during construction. In January 1957, the characteristics were amended to show wire guidance for four of the bow tubes and both stern tubes; in September, power torpedo handling was specified to allow reasonable freedom of maneuver while reloading. This last feature had been conceived to take full advantage of the radical maneuvering powers of the next, and quite different, class—*Skipjack*.

The sonars were SQS-4 and BQR-2. Provision was also made for a torpedo warner (QXB-3, to be replaced by WLR-2). The original standard submarine design task, to locate and destroy enemy submarines and surface ships, was supplemented by a requirement to assist in guiding Regulus missiles.

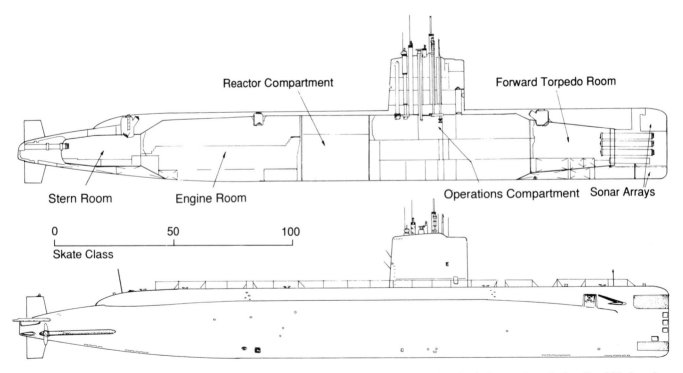

Skate class. The small tube at the stern is for a reelable towed array. All ships of the class had clip ons installed at Pearl Harbor, but two later had reelable ones fitted. The bow sonars are SQS-4 Mod 1 and BQR-2B. Masts, fore to aft, are: No. 1 periscope; ECM mast (for the BLR-1 precision DF system and the wide-open WLR-3) alongside BRA-34 radio mast; No. 2 periscope; SS-2 search radar; retractable whip; snorkel induction (with whip and AS-371 ESM omni-directional antenna); and snorkel exhaust (stowed). The maneuvering room in this class (and in *Nautilus* and *Seawolf*) was aft (to starboard, on the upper level); all later nuclear submarines had the maneuvering room forward. (Jim Christley)

Ready for launching at Portsmouth, *Seadragon* (SSN 584) shows her twin stern tubes. As nuclear analogs of the *Tang*s, the *Skate*s had stern countermeasures tubes. *Nautilus* was similar in general configuration, but her shaft fairings extended out to the propeller tips, her vertical fins were sharply tapered on their after edges, and she lacked stern tubes (which, ironically, had been the reason for adopting twin screws). Alongside, on the right, are hull sections for *Thresher*.

The FY 56 program, first sketched in 1953, was much more ambitious than the FY 55 program. By June 1954, it included no fewer than seven new diesel-electric attack submarines (SCB 116), another small nuclear submarine (SCB 121), the big radar picket (SSRN), and a cruise-missile (Regulus II) submarine (SCB 118).[9] The submarine part of the program was revised at least twice. First, the diesel submarines were cut to four to finance the recommended annual program of two nuclear attack submarines. Sec-

ond, CNO Admiral Carney eliminated another diesel submarine in May 1955 in order to pay for a third SSN. Buying three SSNs in one year brought a third yard, Mare Island, into the SSN program.

As of July 1955, the FY 56 program included three diesel submarines (SCB 150, the *Barbel* class), three SSNs, and two missile-firing submarines (SCB 137). Although the SSNs were listed as repeat *Skate*s, notes to a memorandum of this period describe one of them as a new design incorporating the best features of *Skate* and *Barbel,* which meant combining the SFR reactor with a multilevel *Albacore* hull. This combination would bring speed back up to that of *Nautilus,* 23 kt.[10]

The idea of abandoning the apparent security of twin screws was not altogether popular; Admiral Rickover, in particular, opposed it. Hydrodynamics left him no real choice. For example, in August 1955, Electric Boat compared a variety of possible designs, all of them with the AFSR (S5W), a more powerful reactor than the earlier SFR. At this time, the S5W was expected to deliver about twice the power of the SFR (actually it did much better) and to drive a slightly enlarged *Skate* hull at 23.4 kt, which was about what the SFR could do in an *Albacore*-shaped hull. About 1 kt might be gained by changing the hull aft to accept a more efficient single screw. Applying an *Albacore* hull form to exactly the same power plant, however, would add more than 3 kt to the original 12,000-SHP design. The point was obvious: the single-screw *Albacore* form was the only way to get high underwater speed without excessive (and unavailable) power.[11]

The added speed came from a combination of reduced hull form drag and much higher propulsive efficiency—as much as 90 percent compared with about 70 percent for a twin screw. Because the single screw could turn more slowly for a given speed, a single-screw submarine at a given depth could go considerably faster before she began to cavitate. The *Albacore*/single-screw hull form also promised much better maneuverability and control. It was estimated that such a submarine would typically enjoy a tactical diameter of less than two hull lengths, compared with about three lengths for a conventional design, which would also be longer for a given usable internal volume. She would reach a given depth more quickly, but she would also recover from an inadvertent dive in both less time and less excess depth. The latter was an important safety consideration.

By this time, *Nautilus* had made it quite obvious that such speeds were extremely desirable. In August, Admiral Burke, the new CNO, formally decided to raise the required level of attack submarine speed above that initially required (but not met) in *Nautilus.* On 13 September 1955, Burke reviewed characteristics for the nuclear ships of the FY 57 program. He decided that, although two of the FY 56 submarines would be repeat *Skates,* the third would be redesigned as the prototype of the FY 57 submarines, "to be of large diameter [i.e., of *Albacore* hull form], of increased speed, and of slightly increased size."[12] She became *Skipjack,* the first really fast nuclear submarine. Burke also decided that all subsequent U.S. submarines would be nuclear powered.

The new preliminary design was completed on 1 March 1956, and a contract design followed on 11 June. Speed was so important that the protruding sonar domes common in earlier designs were eliminated. The usual flat superstructure (casing) atop the pressure hull was reduced to a narrow spine covering the exhaust leading from the diesel generator. The torpedo tubes had to be arranged in double horizontal, rather than vertical, rows, with sonar above

(SQS-4) and below (BQR-2B) them, in streamlined domes faired into the hull. The single screw precluded placing any tubes aft. On the other hand, the larger hull diameter made for more torpedo stowage; the earlier attack submarine standard of three per tube was regained. For the most efficient use of internal space, the submarine employed a single hull over most of her length (a cylinder/cone configuration, as in *Nautilus*), with main ballast tanks at the ends. Because it was on the axis of the hull, the single screw could be much larger than earlier twin screws.

The large-diameter hull provided four deck levels, rather than the three of *Nautilus.* Usable submarine space is a function of usable floor area, not of total volume; thus, an additional deck resulted in a more efficient use of volume. Resistance is a function of submarine surface (wetted) area, (i.e., the area wrapped around the volume needed to support vital functions). In the case of *Skipjack,* the more efficient use of volume was reflected in length reduced by 50 ft and reduced displacement, 3,500 tons (submerged) compared with 4,040 for *Nautilus.* The combination of a more efficient hull form, a smaller wetted area, and a much more efficient propeller made for spectacular performance. *Skipjack* turned out to be even faster than expected, partly because her hull was smoother than those of earlier submarines.[13]

Skipjack introduced another feature that became standard on later U.S. nuclear submarines. Her bow planes were moved up onto the sail where they would not contribute to turbulence around the bow-mounted sonar and the noise of their machinery would not affect sonar operation. Moreover, sail planes were considered better for near-surface operation (e.g., while controlling cruise missiles). They also conferred an unexpected benefit: the submarine could change depth slowly without changing her trim angle, so she did not have to develop any great upward or, more important, downward momentum. This configuration was practicable because the sail was mounted well forward.

Because *Skipjack* was expected to be capable of the sort of violent maneuvers achieved with *Albacore,* she needed power torpedo handling; the torpedoes always had to be under positive control. Horizontal racks extended across each side of the torpedo room abaft each row of breeches, for a total of six ready-use reloads. Additional torpedoes stowed beneath the racks could be moved up by block and tackle after the first reloads were fired. This was the first U.S. submarine design to incorporate such a handling system, although it was soon adopted for other submarines under construction. *Skipjack* also tested a new hull material, HY-80, the special new steel under development since the late 1940s. HY-80 promised, but did not immediately grant, increased diving depth.

Skipjack proved much more maneuverable than any other submarine, with the exception of the short-endurance *Albacore.* The combination of speed and maneuver was devastating. A former *Scorpion* (*Skipjack* class) officer recalled an encounter with Task Group Bravo (equivalent to the older Task Group Alfa), in which his CO waited for the destroyers, then deliberately raised his

The official model of *Skipjack* (top) shows her *Albacore*-shaped hull. *Thresher* (below) had a larger hull, but resistance was cut almost to the same total figure by drastically reducing the sail and other appendages. Note that *Thresher*'s fairwater planes are placed close to the top of the sail to improve near-surface seakeeping (to keep the hull as far below the planes as possible). The deck fittings shown are all retractable. (Naval Sea Systems Command)

radar to radiate. As two pouncers ran down the line of bearing toward the radar, he lowered masts, turned, and dove at full speed, leaving a prominent "knuckle" in the water. A magnificent sonar target, it fully occupied the destroyers while *Scorpion* ran back toward the carrier. She soon came back up to periscope depth and deliberately raised her masts to create a visible "feather." By the time the closer-in escorts could react, *Scorpion* had retracted her

masts and moved out of the way. Once the ships of the task group had become thoroughly confused, *Scorpion* closed in for the attack.[14]

Skipjack was a step up in unit size and cost. In April 1956, the projected FY 58 program included four SSNs to cost about $45 million each. The SCB suggested that smaller, less expensive submarines should be built in place of two of these. BuShips' current "sketch book" showed

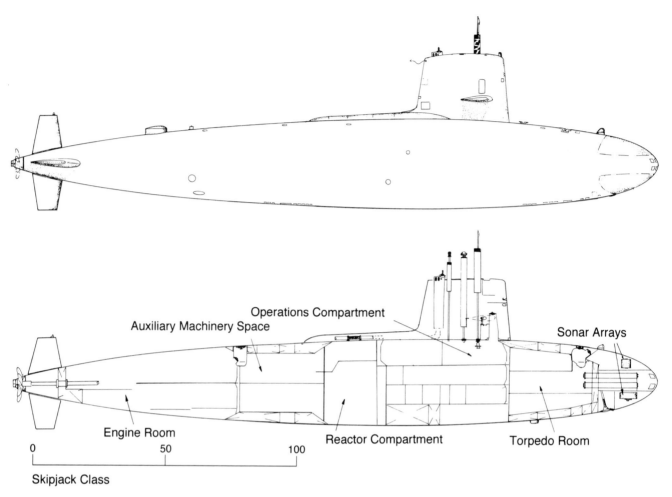

Operations Compartment

Auxiliary Machinery Space

Sonar Arrays

Engine Room

Reactor Compartment

Torpedo Room

0   50   100

Skipjack Class

Skipjack class. The bow sonars are SQS-4 Mod 1 (above the torpedo tubes) and BQR-2B (below the tubes). The two sonar domes in the hull are for the WLR-9 acoustic intercept receiver (forward) and the GNATS sonar jammer (aft). Abaft the control room/attack center were a radio room and a space for Regulus guidance equipment. The space below was the officers' quarters and crew's mess; below that was crew's berthing (above the battery and the negative and auxiliary tanks). Masts, fore to aft, are: the two periscopes side by side; the SS-2A radar mast; and the ECM mast. The VLF loop, not shown, was near the periscopes. The snorkel is shown raised slightly. There was also a retractable whip. The diesel muffler/expansion joint shown abaft the sail was made of titanium. Note that the S5W power plant matched that of an SSBN, but occupied only about half the space; it still worked quite well. A former crewman recalled this class as the "Maserati of the fleet: small, fast, loud." This class introduced the small extendable secondary propulsion motor (SPM), a 325 HP electric motor that could turn through 360 deg. It was intended to help these single-screw craft maneuver. All nuclear submarines also have an electric motor that can turn the main shaft at low speed, to get them home if the reactor fails. (Jim Christley)

several small submarines (see Table 8–1). The SCB recommendation led to construction of *Tullibee* (FY 58 program), the one regression in size in the U.S. submarine program.

While *Skipjack* was being designed, *Nautilus* was run past a SOSUS array. She was quite noisy, mainly from the whine of her gearing and the sound of her pumps. This was narrowband noise (i.e., caused by rotating machinery), which was exactly what SOSUS and other forms of Lofar could best detect. In April 1956, immediately after completion of the *Skipjack* contract design, OpNav decided to emphasize silencing.

Little could be done about the basic *Skipjack* design. A feasibility study completed in June 1957 concluded that *Skipjack* should not have her main machinery altered but her sisters could be quieted to some extent. In *Skipjack*, flow noise could be reduced by sharply cutting the number of tank vents (at the cost of slower crash diving—a rela-

tively insignificant factor for a nuclear submarine submerged most of the time), and hull damping (not included in the original design) could be applied to keep her from rattling at high speed. Later ships of the class (SSN 588–592) had quieter main reduction gears. Auxiliaries, such as generators, were replaced by quieter units. Major silencing improvements would have to wait for the next classes, *Thresher* (see chapter 9) and *Tullibee*.

By 1955, *Albacore* was demonstrating that, once submerged, she could dive much faster than earlier submarines. SCB feared that a fast maneuverable nuclear submarine could crash through the 700-ft test depth in less than 30 sec, far too quickly to recover. A deeper-running submarine might evade ASW weapons more effectively. They might miss altogether because it would take them longer to reach the submarine; whole classes of ASW weapons would be rendered obsolete. In November 1955, SCB or-

Table 8–1.   BuShips Small Submarines, 1955

	1,000-Ton	SRS	SSK(N)
Length (ft)	211.5	195	208
Beam (ft)	23.5	25	17
Light (tons)	1,000	1,500	825
Surface (tons)	1,285	——	900
Submerged (tons)	1,465	1,810	1,025
Complement	6/45	——	——
SHP	——	3,000	1,500
Submerged speed (kt)	15.7	16.8	15
Surfaced speed (kt)	15.5	——	12
Snorkel (endurance at 10 kt)(hr)	8,200	——	——
Snorkel (endurance at 7 kt)(hr)	10,000	——	——
Submerged (hr)	57	——	——
Torpedo tubes	6 bow	6 (22 + 4 CM)	2 (8)
Cost (in millions)	$15	$28	$15

Note: SRS, submarine reactor (small); SSK(N), ASW submarine (nuclear); CM, countermeasures (i.e., homing torpedo). Both SSK tubes were angled out from the hull to clear a bow sonar.

dered BuShips to investigate the feasibility of building a submarine capable of operating at 1,600 ft. The Operational Evaluation Group (OEG) studied the operational advantages of greater test depth. Both studies were completed in mid-1956.[15]

Increased operating depth required more than replacing high-tensile steel with the stronger HY-80, although that did buy the necessary hull strength without increasing pressure hull weight. Critical components, particularly hull penetrations (periscope bushings, propeller shaft glands, and large pipes for condenser flow), had to withstand much greater water pressures. Development of components good to 1,600 ft would have taken too long for them to appear in the last FY 57 submarine, *Thresher*.[16] Existing components, however, could be quickly modified to stand a 1,300-ft depth, and that figure was adopted. Some officers, including Admiral Rickover and the first nuclear submarine commanders, fought the new test depth on the ground that it was too chancy, but they lost their fight in the SCB. Much later, there was some feeling that their fears were justified by the loss of the *Thresher*.

The FY 57 program included six nuclear attack submarines. All were initially planned as *Skipjack*s. Because shipbuilding capacity was limited, award of the final unit (SSN 593) had to be delayed. This made redesign possible. At first, it appeared that the sixth submarine would be a deeper-diving *Skipjack*, with a new bow sonar consisting of a new active cylindrical transducer (probably SQS-23) and a new conformal passive array, better adapted than BQR-2 to the new streamlined hull form. The cylinder was expected to reach bottom- or surface-bounce range (then estimated as 50,000 yd) but not the convergence zone (70,000 yd). Direct-path range would have been at least 20,000 yd. Although not nearly comparable to BQR-7, the passive array offered about 75 percent better performance

than the earlier standard BQR-2B. It seemed likely that the FY 58 SSNs would repeat the modified design.

The Long Range Objectives Group argued that ASW was so vital that all future U.S. submarines would have to be adapted to ASW. In 1956, this apparently meant that silencing and excellent sonar performance would be more important than the speed and agility represented by *Skipjack*. CNO Admiral Burke opted for an SSKN in the FY 58 budget as a prototype of a numerous new class of inexpensive submarines. When three of the four SSNs in the projected FY 58 budget were switched to SSGNs in October 1956 (to supplement one SSGN and one SSBN already in the budget), the prototype SSKN *Tullibee* survived.

Flow noise would clearly limit effective listening speed. Improved single-screw efficiency might be used to achieve maximum listening speed, something like *Skate* speed, by using the small reactor included in the "family of five." Thus, on 5 April 1955, BuShips submitted a nuclear SSK, along with five diesel-electric alternatives, in response to an SCB request, issued earlier that year, for a small SSK with simplified systems and minimum equipment. The diesel-electric craft could not dive very deep; the smallest would have displaced about 1,000 tons, with a speed of just over 13 kt. The nuclear version offered higher speed (15.5 kt) and much greater operating depth. All of the sketch designs eventually showed four torpedo tubes (initial SSKN sketches showed only two, set well back from the bow). The SSKN was so attractive that the diesel-electric alternatives were abandoned in June 1955. Work on a preliminary design began in May 1956.

Unfortunately, the original estimates for the weight of the smaller "family of five" reactors proved optimistic; a new machinery study came out 50 percent heavier. A new sketch design showed 1,725 tons submerged (1,400 tons

Construction photographs of *Scamp* (SSN 588) (*above and facing*) show her bow torpedo tube openings (left photo, January 1960) and her stern planes and conventional propeller (right photo, April 1960). The blade rate problem was as yet unknown.

light ship). This was no longer a small, inexpensive SSKN, but there was no hope of starting an entirely fresh lightweight, low-powered reactor design for installation in the near future. The design also grew because its reserve buoyancy was increased. The preliminary design submitted on 24 October 1957 called for a ship much larger and more expensive than anyone had imagined: 2,400 tons submerged (1,980 tons light ship, 258 ft×23 ft 4 in). She was also fairly slow. Late in 1956, some consideration was

given to a redesign in which an S3W power plant would be combined with the SSKN bow.

By this time, Admiral Rickover strongly advocated turboelectric propulsion as a preferred solution to the gearing noise problem, and it was used in *Tullibee*. She could operate quietly by shutting down her reactor and running her main motor on the battery. Clearly, it was desirable to keep the bow array as far as possible from even quiet machinery, so the designers chose a relatively long, nar-

row hull over a short, fat one that would have been better hydrodynamically—speed was not that important. The SSKN thus reverted to the two-platform arrangement of earlier nuclear submarines.

By the fall of 1956, plans called for a standard two-dimensional sonar in the chin position below the nest of tubes. A conformal array of passive Lofar hydrophones extended around and back from the bow. PUFFS arrays were mounted in the casing (superstructure).

In December 1956, NUSC formally proposed that the entire bow of the FY 58 SSKN be used for an integrated sonar in order to place the largest possible sonar in the quietest possible position. The single row of passive hy-drophones was replaced by the much larger three-row BQR-7, and the chin cylinder replaced by NUSC's big sphere. This new BQQ-1 required about 20 percent more equipment than the conformal array and two-dimensional sonar then planned for *Thresher*, but it offered a dispropor-tionate improvement (e.g., 140 percent of the passive range of the existing BQR-2B, compared with the projected 75 percent for the attack submarine array).

Removing the torpedo tubes from the bow would greatly improve sonar behavior, particularly at high speeds, because it would drastically reduce flow noise. The torpedo tubes, therefore, had to be moved back and angled out at 10 degrees. This arrangement was tested in

Scamp is shown on 9 May 1961. With their very streamlined hulls and their powerful reactors, the *Skipjack*s realized the promise inherent in *Nautilus*. The superstructure (casing) has been eliminated almost completely; the low spine abaft the sail carries the auxiliary diesel induction and uptake.

1957 on board the oiler *Neosho,* with the torpedoes firing down through her bottom. It turned out that torpedoes could be ejected safely at up to 20 kt and could swim out at up to 15 kt. The new design was adopted, not only for *Tullibee* but also for the new dual-purpose attack/ASW submarines. An alternative arrangement, in which six tubes were angled aft from the bow (with eight reloads), was rejected.

Given all of this evolution, final characteristics were not completed until early 1957. The contract design was completed on 3 February 1958. *Tullibee* proved quite successful in service. She was extraordinarily quiet, even though her power plant, apart from electric drive, was essentially unsilenced. Thus, she was a generation behind that of the *Skipjack*s, largely as a consequence of her low power. Her big spherical sonar was described at the time as "a revelation," capable for the first time of fully utilizing the different acoustic transmission paths. Moreover, she demonstrated that a relatively small nuclear submarine was possible. Although manning had increased considerably from the time of conception, she still required a much smaller crew than a fast fleet submarine.

Tullibee was not repeated. The design of the last FY 57 submarine was totally revised in parallel with the new SSKN design. By the time the new design was completed, it was clear that a fast submarine could achieve excellent ASW performance without sacrificing the sort of speed needed for dealing with fast surface ships. Given the surprisingly high cost of *Tullibee*, that was surely an attractive proposition.

As submitted early in 1957, the FY 58 program included only three SSGNs and the SSKN. The SSBN was deferred to FY 59 because the navy had decided to adopt a new solid-fuel missile, Polaris, rather than a modified version of the army's Jupiter. By this time, the FY 59 program was being planned. As of 24 April 1957, the tentative FY 59

program included three SSGNs, one SSBN, and three SSNs. A priority list showed the SSBN as second only to a nuclear carrier; she was closely followed by the SSGNs, with the SSNs low on the list at priorities 22 and 23 (albeit above missile destroyers). As the new Polaris missile developed, it soon became so attractive that supplementary funds were provided for three SSBNs. Some of the money came from cancellation of existing programs, including

Tullibee introduced the spherical bow sonar of all modern U.S. attack submarines. The vertical fins house her PUFFS (BQG-2A) passive ranging arrays (a third was in her sail). She is shown running trials in October 1960. Later she was fitted with standard large PUFFS arrays (BQG-4).

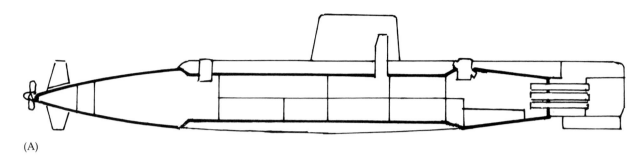

(A)

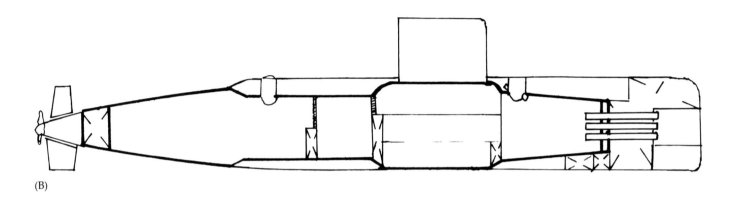

(B)

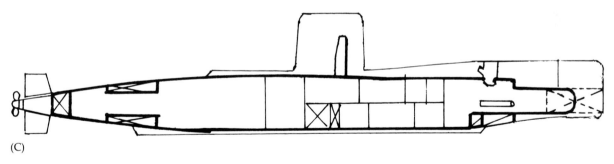

(C)

Small submarines included in the January 1955 BuShips "dream book." (A) is a 1,000-ton diesel submarine, probably one of the SSK alternatives developed at that time. Dimensions: 211.5×23.5 ft (1,000 tons light, 1,285 tons surfaced, 1,465 tons submerged). Estimated performance: 15.7 kt submerged, 14.3 kt snorkel, 15.5 kt surfaced; endurance 57 hr submerged at 3 kt, 8,200 nm/10 kt on snorkel, 10,000 nm/10 kt surfaced. Complement would have been 6 officers and 45 men, and estimated cost was $15 million. The arrangement duplicated that of *Darter*, on a smaller scale. (B) is an abortive 3,000 SHP SSN (195×25 ft, 1,500 tons light, 1,810 tons submerged, 16.8 kt), carrying 22 torpedoes plus four countermeasures (Mk 37s), all in a single forward torpedo room. She was expected to cost $28 million. Note the early application of a three-level arrangement amidships, with the control room and attack center (plus officers, aft) above the crew spaces, themselves above the battery. This design was the low end of nuclear attack submarines. (C) is the 1,500 SHP SSKN as conceived early in 1955: 208×17 ft, 825 tons light, 900 tons surfaced, 1,025 tons submerged, carrying eight "countermeasures" (i.e., homing torpedoes) fired from two tubes angled out from her hull. Estimated speed was 12 kt submerged and 15 kt on the surface; the SSKN would have cost $15 million. The dashed lines at the bow indicate a BQR-4 passive sonar. In this design, the crew was berthed on the lower level forward, below the officers (who were just forward of the control room/attack center). The after part of the submarine was occupied mainly by the reactor and the engine room. The SSKN design presumably evolved into the rather larger *Tullibee*. At this time, early in 1955, the submarine community was coming increasingly to doubt the value of diesel-powered SSKs. They could not afford to snorkel on patrol, and they had to conserve their batteries to sprint toward targets they could expect to detect well beyond firing range. They were effectively immobile, hence needed in vast numbers to fill picket lines. By way of contrast, if a nuclear SSK could be quiet enough, it could patrol the picket line without expending its sprint capability. Hence the preference for the SSKN, before it became clear that it was too expensive.

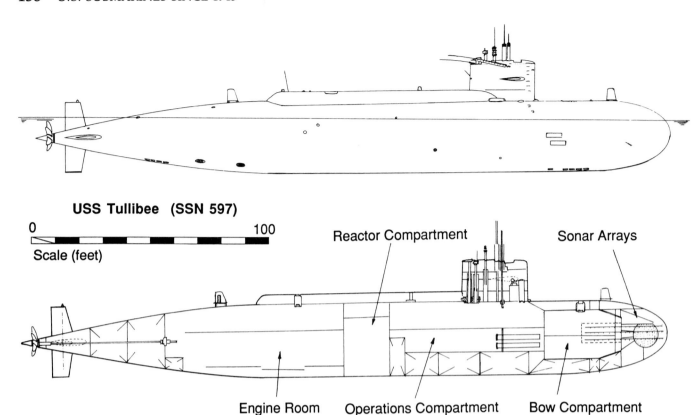

USS Tullibee (SSN 597)

0   100

Scale (feet)

Reactor Compartment   Sonar Arrays

Engine Room   Operations Compartment   Bow Compartment

Tullibee as built, with two external PUFFS arrays, a third inside her sail (at the fore end), and a fourth inside the superstructure abaft the sail (it protrudes slightly and thus is visible in the outboard view). Later, all were replaced by much larger arrays, all external. A design sketch showed two reloads per tube, side by side, for a total of eight plus four in the tubes (which were angled outboard at 10 deg). (Jim Christley)

Regulus II. The SSGNs for FY 58 and FY 59 no longer had missiles. The three SSGNs for FY 58 and one for FY 59 already had been ordered, but they were reordered as attack submarines.[17] The other two SSGNs in the FY 59 program were ordered as SSNs, for a total of five. Of six SSBNs ultimately included in the FY 59 budget, two had

been planned for FY 60 and were brought forward, and four were added by the House of Representatives.

By mid-1957, a total of nine new SSNs, beginning with SSN 593 (*Thresher*), were on order or authorized. The last FY 57 ship was worth redesigning because the cost of any radical change could be spread over a sizable class.

Table 8–2.   BuShips Concept Studies, 1955

	LSST	CVSS-N	SSO-N	SSO-N
Length (ft)	565	460	670	450
Beam (maximum; ft)	81	38	63	94
Light (tons)	8,000	6,700	11,100	11,100
Surfaced (tons)	8,700	——	——	——
Submerged (tons)	26,000	9,000	31,200	31,200
SHP	15,000	70,000	45,000	45,000
Surfaced speed (kt)	16	——	——	——
Submerged speed (kt)	12	28	20	20
Torpedo tubes	2	6 (22)	2 (CM)	2 (CM)
Payload	500 tons	3 *Sea Dart*	——	——
Cost (in millions)	$85	$92	$139	$139

Note: LSST, submerged tank landing ship (LST); CVSS-N, submarine aircraft carrier (CV)—nuclear; SSO-N, submarine oiler—nuclear. Of the two tankers, the shorter one has two parallel hulls. The LSST draws 3½ ft of water forward in landing trim; she can beach on a 1:50 slope and carry 500 passengers and crew.

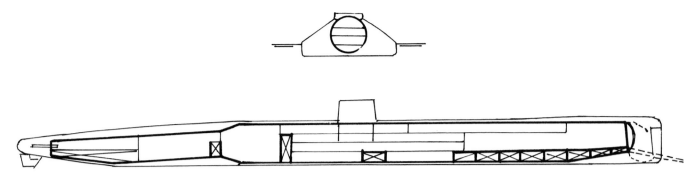

The LSST was sketched in 1955 by BuShips for its "dream book." Powered by an S5W reactor, it would have attained 16 kt in landing trim (and 12 kt submerged). Dimensions: 565×81×3.5 ft (forward, in landing trim); light displacement would have been 8,000 tons (8,700 tons surfaced, 26,000 tons submerged). It would have carried 500 tons of cargo and 500 troops, at a unit cost of $85 million. The four-level arrangement provided two levels for troop messing and berthing, with the control room/attack center and ship's officers on the upper level (but with troop berths at the fore end of the upper level), and stores and fresh water on the lowest level. Compensating tanks are shown at the fore end. The LSST could have beached on a keel slope of 1:50.

Decisions on deeper diving depth, quieter drive (then planned as turboelectric), and a sonar bow were pending. *Thresher* became the prototype of a new class, the basis of all later U.S. attack submarines.

Nuclear power offered some other possibilities. In 1955 BuShips began work on a menu of alternative concepts. The Bureau of Aeronautics (BuAer) and BuOrd already had "dream books" of their own, which they hoped would lead to future formal operational requirements. BuShips included several nuclear submarines: a landing ship (LSST), submarine carrier, tanker, and oiler (see Table 8–2). The BuShips briefing book also included early versions of submarines, the nuclear radar picket *Triton* and the ASW submarine *Tullibee*, that actually were built. The "naval engineer's sketch book" was first briefed early in 1956. A later edition was widely briefed during 1958—for example, to Admiral Burke, Senator Henry Jackson, and the BuAer planning board. In addition to the earlier concepts, it included missile submarines armed with both Jupiter and Polaris, a submersible seaplane tender, and a variety of new submarine design approaches, such as counter-rotating propellers, electrostrictive and electromagnetic pumps, and a "silent" submarine.

The submersible tanker and the weapons replenisher might be necessary to support sustained carrier operations in the face of a serious enemy submarine threat. The tanker was the twin-hull 1955 design, with a beaver-tail stern and water jets for stern control; conventional planes were carried forward. On a ton-mile basis (about $0.013/ton-mile), she was expected to cost about 10 times as much as a commercial tanker or about 6 times as much as a typical naval tanker.

The ammunition ship would carry nuclear weapons and the smaller missiles (not Polaris or Regulus); on a displacement of 15,000 tons (400×70 ft, with a hull depth of 40 ft), she could carry 2,000 tons of cargo (180 cu ft/ton) at 12 kt. BuShips pointed out that greater volume costs more to submerge. Cargo cost would be about $0.20/ton-mile.

The submersible LSST was conceived as part of a larger program of dispersing amphibious forces to counter the nuclear threat; the means ultimately accepted was vertical envelopment from helicopter carriers. The hull of the LSST had to be large enough to provide not only normal ballasting but also tankage to bring the bow up to beach.

The sketch book also included two midgets. One was a submersible workboat for swimmers hunting mines (26 ft×4 ft 6 in diameter, 8 tons submerged, 6 kt, 17-hr endurance), carrying an active minehunting sonar. A wet boat was already under development, but this workboat would have a dry cockpit. The other midget was a rescue submarine that would operate between submarines or between a submarine and surface ship. She was eventually built as the current deep submergence rescue vehicle (DSRV). In the 1958 version, she was expected to carry 18 men at 4.5 kt for 4 hr (30×10 ft, 46 tons submerged, test depth 2,000 ft). She would be towed to the scene of an accident or carried there on board a large ship or an LSD (landing ship dock). The greatest technical problem envisaged was mating her to a submarine.

A sketch of possible submarine sterns showed the usual cruciform type, as well as the "X" stern then planned for *Albacore*. Both types might be replaced by a shroud ring, in effect, a tail with infinite aspect ratio. Although never used in submarines, a shroud ring did control the Mk 44 torpedo. Boundary-layer control was an alternative. Water would be pumped over small movable control surfaces. Boundary-layer pumping also could be used for low-speed emergency propulsion.

9

Nuclear Submarines: The Second Generation

WORK ON THE new *Thresher* design began about October 1956. CNO Admiral Burke was determined to emphasize underwater performance in the new submarine (i.e., to combine sonar, which included silencing, with high speed and deeper diving). By April 1957, the *Tullibee*-type sonar bow had been chosen; *Thresher* and *Tullibee* were designed almost in parallel and their sonar arrangements modified in tandem. The test depth was definitely set in May. The reactor was the same as in *Skipjack*, but silencing would make the overall power plant larger and heavier. The new sonar bow would be bulkier than *Skipjack's*. The great question was how to maintain high underwater speed.

Little could be gained from improved propulsive efficiency; the single slow-turning propeller probably already exceeded 90 percent. A proposal to use contraprops did not survive the early design stage.[1]

Drag had to be cut. The fatter and blunter *Thresher* hull had a less favorable length-to-beam ratio than *Skipjack's* (8.7 versus 7.9), but it was not enough to make much difference: the curve of resistance per ton was fairly flat in that region. Added displacement (14 percent) made most of the difference in hull drag. *Skipjack* had already eaten up most of the improvement to be expected from smoothing the hull (e.g., by reducing the number of flooding holes).[2]

In previous submarines, appendages had amounted to as much as 50 percent of the resistance of the bare hull (a third of total resistance), with 45 percent in *Barbel* and 40 percent in *Skipjack*. A drastic purge cut this figure to 27 percent in *Thresher's* preliminary design. At this stage, calculated total resistance was only about 3 percent greater than that of *Skipjack*; the purge very nearly balanced off all the growth.

The sail was the main offender; one study suggested that it cost 1.5 kt. In February 1957, SubLant and SubPac suggested that it be eliminated altogether. This also would have cured snap roll and made for a smoother wake. BuShips refused. In a study produced in July, BuShips argued that any acceptable submarine needed some sort of housing for her masts, a housing that would add about as much drag as a carefully designed small sail. The sail was also needed for surface navigation and for depth-keeping near the surface.

BuShips shrank the sail to a quarter of the size of that in the earlier submarine. The number of masts had to be reduced drastically, leaving only one periscope, a radio mast, a VLF radio antenna, a combination snorkel and ESM mast, and one radar mast. The emergency diesel generator, required to bring the submarine home in case of a reactor failure, was relocated from the machinery spaces aft to a position under the sail, so that its exhaust could pass directly upward through a tube in the sail, rather than forward under a spine as in *Skipjack*.[3] That eliminated the last remnant of the old superstructure/casing. The sail's position was determined largely by the need to provide space in the small double-hull section for external valves and piping.

The combination of silencing (often associated with low speed) and high maximum speed may seem paradoxical. It was not; indeed, it became particularly rational with the introduction of the new long-range sonars. A very quiet submarine with excellent sonars could expect to detect relatively noisy Soviet submarines at very long range, tens of miles or more, far beyond weapon range. Therefore, she had to run in to shoot. Alternatively, she could make a deep high-speed end run outside the target submarine's detection range to get ahead for a bow sector shot. Such shots were particularly important when U.S. submarines were equipped with a homing torpedo, a Mk 37, which was only about as fast as its likely Soviet SSN targets (a problem cured by the advent of a Mk 48). Only Subroc could be fired from long range, but it was a special (nuclear) weapon and had to be used sparingly, if at all.

Too, there was already considerable interest in using submarines to escort fast surface ships. They had to keep up. Although the call for battle group speed (typically

---

The *Thresher*s (now called *Permit*s) were the direct ancestors of all modern U.S. attack submarines. *Plunger* is shown on sea trials in San Francisco Bay, 17 October 1962, with her snorkel and her two periscopes raised. This view emphasizes the small size of her sail (for reduced resistance) and her fat midbody (to contain her rafted power plant). The position of the snorkel, forward of the periscopes (and directly above the diesel generator) was strongly criticized, and it was not repeated. It was adopted to eliminate the piping run abaft the sail, which provided the last vestige of a superstructure in the *Skipjack*s.

more than 30 kt) is generally associated with *Los Angeles* of the late 1960s, SubLant and SubPac badly wanted it as early as February 1957 when the *Thresher* design process was beginning.

To free space for the big new sonar, the torpedo tubes had to be moved aft and angled out from the hull. They could not angle out from the pressure hull because they would have made elliptical holes, a source of weakness. Instead, they were cut into the forward cone of the pressure hull, the angled section connecting the full-diameter part with a smaller-diameter section ending in the sonar sphere. As in *Skipjack*, deck height limited the battery to two rows of tubes; in this case, however, each row could include only one tube on each side, for a total of four. The torpedo room was at least as large as that of the earlier submarine, so it could accommodate as many torpedoes. Late changes in design added one more to help make up for the loss of two in the tubes. Hopefully, too, new power-loading equipment would increase the rate of fire sufficiently to make up for the loss of two tubes. The anchor had to be moved to a less favorable position aft; this position also reduced flow noise.

As a modified *Skipjack*, *Thresher* was initially to have had a similar Mk 101 fire-control system. Adapted to the new long-range passive and active sonars, this system became a Mk 112 (as in *Tullibee*). By January 1959, however, *Thresher* had been earmarked for the new partly digital Mk 113 (see chapter 7) required to control the Subroc missile.

The main machinery design issue was silencing, particularly to overcome gear whine. That was not a new problem; before WW II, U.S. submarines had their high-speed electric motors geared to the propeller shafts. When that turned out to be a dangerous source of noise, bigger direct-drive motors were substituted. Admiral Rickover, then a captain in BuShips, had been in charge of that program. The reactor could drive a turbogenerator, which would not need gearing, and a big motor could drive the propeller shaft, again without gearing. As heir to a BuEng tradition of turboelectric power plants in very successful battleships and then carriers built after WW I, Rickover was confident that such an approach would work. *Tullibee* could use the turboelectric approach because her single shaft ran at about the same power as those of existing direct-drive diesel-electric submarines. Initially, it was assumed that a scaled-up equivalent would be installed in the new attack submarine (*Thresher*) and in her FY 58 cruise-missile submarine counterpart (SCB 166A). The 15,000 SHP of a fast submarine, however, was a different proposition from *Tullibee*'s 2,500-SHP plant. A slow-turning electric motor that was large enough did not exist. Something else was needed.

The turbine itself could be enlarged to run slowly enough to drive a shaft directly. Because turbine size was more than inversely proportional to RPM, the propeller would have to turn faster; it would be noisier and less efficient. Some efficiency could be won back by connecting a direct-drive turbine to contraprops, but such an arrangement was rejected as too complex to be developed quickly

enough. Other possibilities dismissed at this time were electrically driven contraprops (epicyclic gearing was not considered at this time), mixed geared and electric drive (the latter for low speed only), and hydraulic torque converters (in effect, larger versions of car transmissions).

The British offered an alternative. They had silenced a generation of new minesweepers against the threat of acoustic mines by mounting the offending machinery on rigid platforms (rafts). The rafts were sound-isolated on flexible supports. This same technology had been applied to British diesel submarines. Rafting was a brute force solution. It did not eliminate the source of noise altogether. The designer and the builders still had to be very careful to keep the noise from flowing out of the raft via an acoustic short circuit.

Rafted, geared turbines were formally chosen in April 1957 as the lightest, most compact arrangement—and also requiring the least additional development. The same arrangement was soon chosen for the FY 58 SSGN (SCB 166A) and the SSBN then in the design stage (SCB 180). In the case of *Thresher*, the combination of silencing and increased depth added about 30 percent to the volume of the machinery and reactor box and about 60 percent to the volume of the engine room itself.

Only after the new *Skipjack* had entered service, and well after the *Thresher* design had been completed, did the previously unsuspected noise problem of blade rate appear. The submarine's propeller does not work in a perfectly smooth flow. Instead, each of its blades periodically hits the wake produced by all the hull appendages, the largest being the submarine's sail. A blade vibrates each time it cuts into this wake, and the vibration produces noise. In the past, the main source of propeller noise had been cavitation; the cure was a large, slow-turning propeller. It now turned out that such a propeller could be so large that its blades would hit the wakes only intermittently. The blades of smaller propellers turned in the relatively uniform, streamlined flow of the hull. They could be heard, but they were not a major contributor to submarine noise.[4]

BuShips found blade rate a nasty surprise. One possible solution was a pump jet; this was adopted three decades later for *Seawolf*. Another was contraprops, the type of machinery rejected earlier during the *Thresher* design, that allowed for smaller propeller diameter without much increase in RPM (i.e., in propeller noise). In a redesign of *Jack* (SSN 605), her two propellers were driven by a pair of direct-drive turbines on concentric shafts. This installation turned out to be quite cumbersome and not particularly successful. The theory of contraprops was correct, but the only practical installation would have used epicyclic gearing, which was not yet considered practical.

Ironically, it turned out that scythe-shaped propellers largely solved the problem; they entered the turbulent wake more gradually. The propellers required very careful design. For many years, even their overall shape was closely held, although similar scythe-shaped propellers were adopted by most Western navies. This type of propeller was adopted by the Soviets around 1985 after they had obtained special milling equipment from Toshiba. Only when the Toshiba scandal broke (about 1987) was blade rate publicly mentioned; its importance can be gauged from widespread official comments that the Soviets had just been handed the means for a drastic cut in their submarine noise signatures. Blade rate is particularly important because its low-frequency noise can carry a considerable distance.[5] For example, a five-blade propeller turning at 300 RPM presents a blade to a turbulent part of the wake at 1,500 RPM (25 Hz).

Characteristics for *Thresher* were approved late in July 1957. Contract design was assigned to Portsmouth Naval Shipyard; the radical new submarine was that yard's first and, as it turned out, only nuclear design. At the end of preliminary design (October 1957), estimated dimensions were 273 ft × 31 ft 8 in (3,451/4,081 tons). After that, the ship kept growing. The machinery spaces filled out; by March 1958, the end of contract design, overall dimensions were the same but displacement was 3,612/4,182 tons. That July, length had increased to 278 ft 6 in and displacement to 3,788/4,311 tons (the stern was somewhat fattened). Estimated submerged speed at this stage was only 0.4 kt slower than *Skipjack*.

Thresher was the first modern U.S. nuclear submarine, the lineal predecessor of all attack types. Unlike previous nuclear submarines, she was a true general-purpose warship. In addition to the nine FY 57–59 units of the class (see chapter 8: SSN 593–596 and 603–607, of which SSN 594–596 and 603 were initially ordered as SSGNs), three

were added in FY 60 (SSN 613–615). The FY 61 program initially included three more; two were deferred to provide more funds for Polaris submarines, thus leaving *Haddock* (SSN 621). *Thresher* turned out to be a very tight design. The last three ships built (SSN 613–615) were lengthened to 292 ft (3,600/4,650 tons compared with 3,450/4,300 tons for *Thresher* herself), partly to correct weight and stability problems (SCB 188M version). The design was then completely revised to become the *Sturgeon* class (see below).

Thresher was lost on 10 April 1963. That was a severe shock, particularly since her design had been duplicated on so large a scale, both in general-purpose submarines and in the vital SSBNs then under construction on a crash basis. Was there some basic design flaw? Had the decision to go to deeper test depth been fundamentally wrong? There were no survivors, and the wreckage on the sea floor could not tell the full story.

It seems likely that a leak started in a seawater connection, such as a condenser pipe. The leak could not have been contained quickly, perhaps mainly because *Thresher*'s valves were distributed around her machinery spaces. Shutting the sea valves would have denied circulation water to the power plant; this would have quickly shut down the reactor and precluded any restart. It appears that the captain tried to plane up and blow main ballast tanks when power died, probably because the reactor electrical power tripped out due to flooding. Existing operating practice precluded a quick restart. Latent heat in the system could not be transferred into the turbines; that

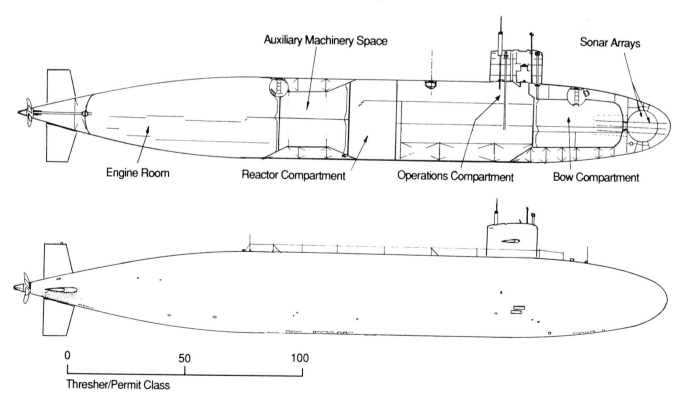

0   50   100

Thresher/Permit Class

Thresher/Permit class, showing the offending periscope in the after part of the sail. Masts, fore to aft, are: snorkel/air induction; SS-2A radar; VLF loop; UHF/IFF and MHF antenna; ECM; and periscope. The emergency diesel generator was in the lowest-level compartment of the bottle-nose, directly under the snorkel, with a sonar equipment room forward of it. Crew's quarters were above it. The sonar room was on the upper level near the ship's control center and attack center. (Jim Christley)

Haddo (SSN 604) (*above and facing*) is shown under construction at New York Shipbuilding Corp., Camden, New Jersey, 13 February 1962, with *Pollack* (SSN 603) alongside. Atop her sail, cutouts are clearly visible for the snorkel air induction (at the fore end), the VLF loop (abaft it: a small circle on the port side), the SS-2A radar (diagonal slot), the cockpit, the communications mast (UHF/IFF and MF), the ECM mast, the periscope (alongside it), and the snorkel exhaust (large circle).

practice had been avoided because a sudden loss of heat and pressure in the reactor would have had serious consequences. Thus, her crew could not plane up out of trouble, nor could they blow their main ballast tanks. In accordance with earlier practice, high-pressure air was led through long narrow pipes. Inevitably, they contained some moisture. As the air expanded through them, it cooled adiabatically (an inevitable consequence of the laws of thermodynamics) and quickly froze the moisture into ice. This last, previously unsuspected phenomenon was later demonstrated in a dockside experiment. Air pressure had been increased from 3,000 to 4,500 psi to maintain the same blowing capacity despite the increased test depth. It later turned out that all components of the system had been

tested individually but not the system as a whole. The combination of loss of the reactor and loss of blowing air doomed *Thresher*.[6]

The basic design was not at fault, but it had to be modified to preclude any repetition. The new program was called SUBSAFE. It delayed attack submarine deliveries by several years. The main SUBSAFE features were:

All seawater piping had to be redesigned to withstand full sea pressure. It had to be treated as though it were an external part of the pressure hull, and its length had to be minimized.

New centralized emergency valves were installed so

that one person could quickly shut down internal piping circuits.

Emergency reactor operating procedures were changed so that any heat remaining after a shutdown could be used for emergency surfacing.

The high-pressure blowing system was changed to vent directly into the main ballast tanks, instead of through manifolds in the control room. Piping was widened to overcome the adiabatic cooling problem.

Reengineering had been ordered for *Thresher* in December 1961. Her designers had sacrificed too much in hopes of cutting drag. For example, she had only one periscope, and it was poorly placed abaft her snorkel. Because the sail was so short, *Thresher*'s hull was very close to the surface at periscope depth, and depth-keeping was diffi-

cult. The engine room arrangement was awkward and, as the *Thresher* disaster later showed, dangerous.

The margin for redesign was limited; production of vital nuclear attack submarines could not be lightly interrupted. Electric Boat, which had already designed a rafted-machinery SSBN (SSBN 608 class) during *Thresher*'s construction, was assigned the job. The submarine was rearranged internally for better habitability and for more torpedo stowage in the form of longer racks, each of which could now accommodate two 161-in short torpedoes, such as Mk 37s.

The obvious solution to poor surface sea-keeping was a taller sail that could carry planes farther down; the deeper the keel, the less subject the submarine was to surface waves. A new secondary mission, electronic surveillance, was formally introduced as a design requirement.[7] That, in turn, added new masts and further en-

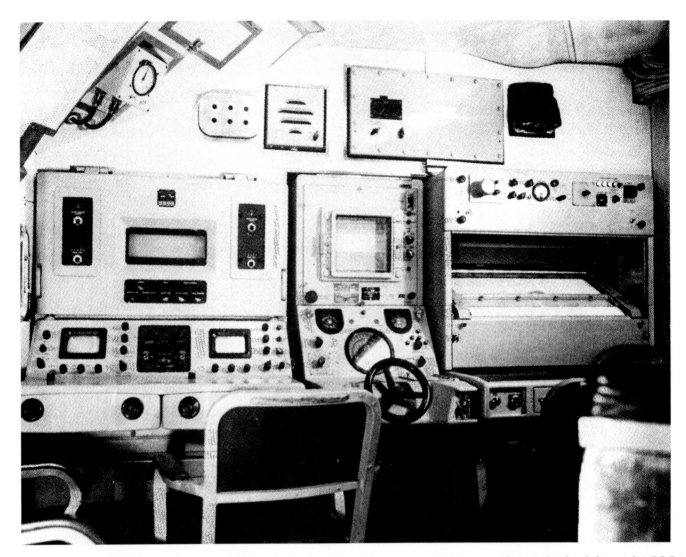

Thresher was designed around her sonar. This is the passive side of the sonar control room, with consoles for (left to right) BQG-1 (PUFFS), BQR-7, and BQQ-3. BQG-1 correlated the outputs of a pair of subarrays, hence the two small displays and the big screen to match them. BQR-7 had two beams, one steered manually (using the handwheel, with a bearing indicator above it) and one continuously scanned (feeding a bearing-time recorder, whose paper output showed in the rectangle above). BQQ-3 was a Lofargram recorder; the pen moved across the paper along the bar visible in the middle of the paper. (Raytheon Corp.)

larged the sail. To balance the fin area, end plates were added to the horizontal fins aft; the vertical fins could not be enlarged because the lower one could not be extended below the line of the keel. The redesigned SSN introduced a periscope fairing to reduce the feather at low speeds that was later applied to the *Thresher* class, except for SSN 612.

The solution to crowding was a longer hull (292 ft 2 in, rather than 278 ft 6 in, a difference of 13 ft 8 in).[8] Both the bigger sail and the longer hull added drag, but there was no hope of increasing either reactor power or propulsive efficiency. The net result was that the new submarine was at least 2 kt slower than *Thresher*, herself slower than *Skipjack*. The negative tank of the earlier design was eliminated, but a hover system was fitted. Silencing goals, introduced in the *Thresher* characteristics, were strengthened.

So much had been done that, in October 1962, the modified design was redesignated as a new class, *Sturgeon* (SSN 637, SCB 188A). *Thresher* was lost before the new design was complete, so the class was again modified to meet SUBSAFE requirements. The first *Sturgeons* appeared in the FY 62 program.

By this time, U.S. submarine designers thought they understood the important noise sources. *Sturgeon* was expected to be far quieter than *Thresher*, which had been designed at a far earlier stage. USS *Gurnard*, the first ship built at Mare Island, however, was surprisingly noisy. It was determined that no particular flaw existed in the design. Instead, the ship's relatively high noise level was traced to a large number of minor imperfections in equipment supplied by contractors and insufficiently checked by the yard. Silencing had to be a combination of very careful design and very tough—and

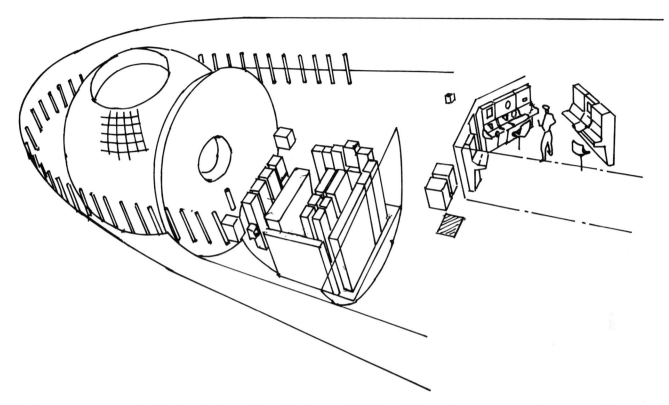

Thresher sonar arrangement, showing the bow sphere, the staves of BQR-7, and the equipment space and sonar control room (which was *not* in the control room or attack center).

costly—quality control at the subcontractor and shipyard levels.

The *Sturgeon* design evolved continuously during her production life (FY 62–69).[9] FY 64 units had de Laval main turbines with integral condensers (designated Mod 4 of the design). Mods 1, 2, and 3 (FY 62 and FY 63 ships) used de Laval, GE, and Westinghouse turbines. FY 65 units (Mod 5) contained new sonars: BQS-13 replaced the earlier BQS-6 sonar sphere, and a new under-ice/mine-avoidance sonar, BQS-14, was added. In the FY 66 units (Mods 6, 7, and 8) new air conditioners and GE main turbines with de Laval main condensers were installed. To check the new machinery arrangement, a partial mock-up of the engine room was built.

All of these submarines were equipped with existing surveillance equipment; some of it used antennas dating from the Korean War. An integrated surveillance equipment development program began in 1965.[10] In March 1966, OpNav ordered a study to determine how much space and weight would be necessary to accommodate Tuba II/III acoustic surveillance equipment (AIGS), including a towed array.

The FY 67 units were lengthened 8 ft 3 in. Estimated added cost was $3.7 million. A new periscope, Type 15D, was also fitted. FY 67 and FY 68 units (Mods 9, 10, 11, and 12) had a combined ESM/radio room, but the FY 69 craft had an ESM space (SUPRAD B) combined with the radar space.[11] This version was expected to be quieter than its predecessors, and it was fitted with a satellite navigation system. A new version of PUFFS, called a tacti-

cal range finder, was planned, but it was not ready in time. These submarines could all mate with DSRVs. Finally, all craft combined their low-pressure blowers with their diesel exhaust. Nine submarines (SSN 678–684 and 686–687) were built to this long-hull design.

In December 1967, a further redesign was proposed for FY 70, but *Sturgeon* production ended with the FY 69 program. The main features would have been provision for Mk 48 torpedoes (i.e., longer torpedo racks), a new digital command system (like the all-digital attack center actually fitted to the *Los Angeles* class), and quieter machinery (the goal was to match the quietest *Sturgeon* with all known corrections; also, a new low-RPM [i.e., quieter] propeller).

Admiral Rickover disliked rafted geared turbines; at best they were a brute force solution to the gear noise problem.[12] At worst, that solution could fail because of some minor imperfection. In 1964, OpNav made one of its periodic attempts to obtain a less expensive SSN. *Tullibee* had been far too expensive for mass production, but she was also much less expensive than a production *Sturgeon*. OpNav asked whether a somewhat more capable version could be produced.

Rickover saw the request as a chance to reopen the silencing question. He began work on a turboelectric version of the *Sturgeon* power plant. *Tullibee*'s big DC motor would be simply scaled up by a factor of six. A big AC motor would have been much smaller and would have presented fewer design problems, but DC was conceptually simpler. A submarine so powered could easily back

A week prior to launching (26 May 1967), *Pogy* shows the end plates on her horizontal stabilizers and also the scythe-bladed propeller adopted for silencing. Such a propeller demands precision machining; in the mid-1980s, illegal exports of computer-controlled machine tools (by Toshiba and Kongsberg) were credited with giving similar advantages to the Soviets. End plates were introduced in this class, presumably to provide more vertical fin surface. The centerline vertical fins are limited in size (e.g., by the requirement that the lower one not project below the submarine's keel).

down by reversing polarity. That might be rather important for her safety in an unintended dive. Too, a big DC motor could be run very quietly off the submarine's battery, with the reactor turned off altogether. To do this with an AC motor and turbogenerator would require extra equipment, such as an inverter to turn AC current into DC and vice versa. Rickover personally rejected this complication.

As it turned out, the theoretical simplicity of the DC plant masked some terrible practical problems, such as the sheer size of the bus bars needed to carry its current. Quite soon, it also became clear that the DC turboelectric plant would be massive; the submarine would have to be considerably larger than a standard *Sturgeon*. Some in BuShips tried to hold down the size by offering an S3W-powered turboelectric submarine. Rickover rejected it. His reasoning was obvious: If turboelectric drive was the cor-

rect, though bypassed, solution to the silencing problem of the standard attack submarine already in series production, little could be gained by developing a prototype plant that was not applicable to later units of this type.

The turboelectric drive submarine (TEDS) was tentatively included in the FY 67 budget, but OSD rejected it as too expensive and unsuited for series production. Rickover objected vigorously. He justified TEDS as a test bed for future silencing techniques on the ground that eliminating the loudest source of noise altogether (gear whine) would make it much easier to test for other sources. After a brutal fight, a TEDS, *Glenard P. Lipscomb* (SSN 685), was included in the FY 68 budget. The extent to which she was conceived as a straightforward machinery replacement in a *Sturgeon* hull shows in the fact that she was not allocated a separate SCB number during her design phase.[13] The TEDS did not turn out particularly well. The

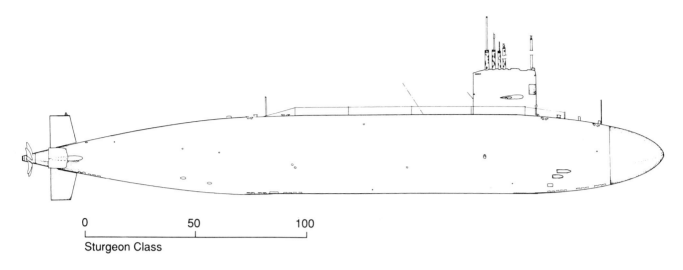

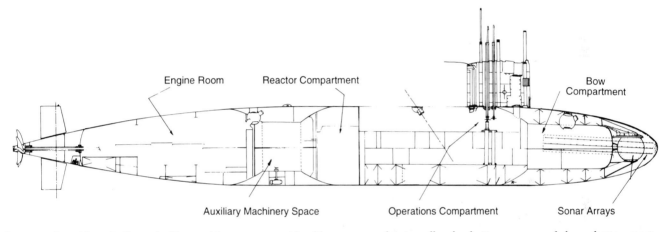

Sturgeon class (short-hull type). These ships were considerably rearranged internally, for better access and for a better mast arrangement. The diesel generator space is at the front end of the lower level of the bottle-nose, with berthing above and abaft it. The large space immediately abaft it is the torpedo room. Above it are more berths, the sonar equipment space, the wardroom, and the mess. The control room/attack center are on the uppermost level, with sonar control and the radio room (and the ELINT space) further aft. Many units had PUFFS arrays in the vertical end plates on the tail fins, with the other two arrays on each side, inside the outer hull. (Jim Christley)

turboelectric machinery was unreliable and inherently less efficient than geared turbines. Because she was also considerably larger than *Sturgeon*, *Lipscomb* was much slower. She operated very little after Admiral Rickover retired in 1981 and was stricken in 1989 after only 15 years of service.

The TEDS fight did make OSD more wary of attacking Admiral Rickover; as a result, TEDS deeply influenced the later decision in favor of *Los Angeles*.

Another contemporary design deserves mention. *Narwhal* (SCB 245, SSN 671) was powered by the natural circulation S5G reactor. To the extent that *Thresher*, *Sturgeon*, and *Lipscomb* were all variations on the same theme, *Narwhal* was the next attack submarine design to be built (FY 64 program). She had to be completely new because the S5G reactor demanded a much greater pressure hull diameter. The configuration was a bridge between the earlier series and *Los Angeles*. Design work began with a June 1962 BuShips letter, so it did not incorporate full SUBSAFE features.

By 1962, the NCR was valued mainly for its inherent quietness; reactor pumps had been a major source of noise.

With a quiet reactor, it was natural to avoid gearing altogether; *Narwhal* used a direct-drive turbine. A somewhat faster-running and less efficient propeller was accepted (see the discussion above on the direct-drive turbine for *Thresher*). Because the S5G was more powerful than the S5W of the *Sturgeons*, the designers did not expect to lose much speed from either lost efficiency or considerable additional displacement.

More generally, the design philosophy was to treat the causes of noise rather than the symptoms. Those sources that could not be eliminated altogether (like gearing) could be shut down at some speeds or could be slowed down; often the noise generated is proportional to the square of RPM. In some cases, equipment could be changed to avoid noise in the first place.

For example, *Narwhal* had a circulating water scoop. Other submarines used pumps to circulate condenser water at all speeds, but the scoop (roughly analogous to an airplane's air intake) sufficed at any speed above very low. No main circulating pumps were needed. The concept was tested on board *Scorpion*.[14] The long pipe involved

Thresher's BQS-6/BQA-3 sonar room: passive BQS-6 console, active BQS-6 active console, and BQA-3 graphic indicator, which measured target Doppler. As in BQR-7, there were two passive beams, one steered for tracking (using the handwheel, with bearing indicated on the dial above) and one continuously scanning (feeding the bearing-time paper recorder above the handwheel). Raw video, its beams formed by an amplifier-scanner, went to the passive console. A sonar receiver processed video to extract echoes for the active console and for BQA-3. The active console could also receive pings extracted by a separate receiver-scanner. The triangular indicator (SSI, sector-scan indicator) alongside the PPI allowed comparison of right-hand and left-hand beams for finer measurement; it also could be used to measure depression/elevation angle. Above the main PPI of the active console are direction and depression/elevation indicators for the single-ping pencil-beam active mode. Retrofit III sonars (BQS-11, -12, -13) had a new active sonar receiver in place of the earlier receiver-scanner. Signals passed via the active console to the BQA-3 (BQS-11 and -12) or via a new data computer and processor to an auxiliary active console. In Retrofit III sonars (BQS-11, -12, -13), the up/down and left/right indicators were moved to the lower panel; their place was taken by a small-diameter CRT for active operation and the lower displays were replaced by a large-diameter CRT for an A-scan. These sonars also lack the SSI, because they auto-track. Only in BQS-13, the BQA-3 electronic cabinet and display were replaced by a data computer and processor (fed by the active receiver) feeding an auxiliary active console with a single rectangular window. BQS-12 (but not BQS-13) had a modified passive console without a handwheel. Shown here is First Class Sonarman R. E. Steinel, who was on board *Thresher* on her final dive. (Raytheon Corp.)

became unacceptable under SUBSAFE rules; it was never duplicated in any other submarine.

Turbogenerators were drastically slowed down.

The earlier complicated combination of cylindrical and coned pressure hull sections was replaced by a simple cylinder, with all main ballast tanks at the ends. This configuration was also used in the *Los Angeles* class. It was much simpler structurally and allowed for better internal arrangements. By this time, too, it had been found that

double-hull sections were themselves a source of noise. The necessarily thin outer hull fluttered at high speed and produced its own louder flow noise (note the work on hull damping on board *Albacore* described in chapter 3).[15] The sail was moved aft because it had been discovered, unsurprisingly, that placing it over the discontinuity between the cylinder and forward cone of the pressure hull could also cause noise. With the forward cone omitted, the torpedo tubes now emerged at a much shallower angle

The BQQ-2 operating concept included a secure underwater communications system (SESCO, BQA-2). Its console is shown on board *Thresher* (across a passageway from the BQS-6 passive console). SESCO died, mainly of multipath. That turned out to be fortunate because space for additional sonar equipment was soon needed. (Raytheon Corp.)

from the big domed bulkhead that closed off the front end of the pressure hull. The larger-diameter hull accommodated a few more torpedoes than in *Thresher* or *Sturgeon*.

The simple cylindrical pressure hull did introduce one complication. PUFFS was still required (though it would never be fitted). In the past, its arrays, which had to be lined up precisely, had been sunk into tankage forward and amidships, but now there was no double-hull section amidships. The designers proposed to solve the problem by placing the arrays in blisters along the surface of the single hull. Although that was never done, it presaged the arrangement of WAA, the PUFFS successor, in *Los Angeles* and *Seawolf*.

Narwhal was quite successful; when she was completed, however, she was not suitable for further production (e.g., because of the scoop problem). Instead, her NCR power plant became an important element of the CONFORM (concept formulation) submarine proposed in 1968–69 (see chapter 10).

The push to build enough nuclear attack submarines

to deal with a vast Soviet threat (see chapter 7) coincided with an even more urgent program to build SSBNs that came out of the same shipyards and used the same power plants. In 1959–63, the lifetime of a modern submarine was set at $17\frac{1}{2}$ years; to maintain the generally accepted force of 90 attack submarines would have required an annual program of something over 5 per year. *Thresher*, however, had made earlier U.S. SSNs obsolete. To reach the goal of 65 modern SSNs by 1973, the Long Range Objectives Group had to advocate a higher rate of production, an average of 6 per year for about a decade. Then, smaller SSNs would begin edging out the large ones. To get 25 by 1973, the 1959 building plan envisaged buying a prototype in FY 64, then 5 every two years from FY 65 on—an average of 8.5 attack submarines each year.

By this time, the projected size of the SSBN force had been set at 40 to 50 submarines; the final figure was 41. To reach that objective quickly, as many as 9 SSBNs would have to be ordered each year in the peak years of the program, FY 62–64. The Long Range Objectives Group

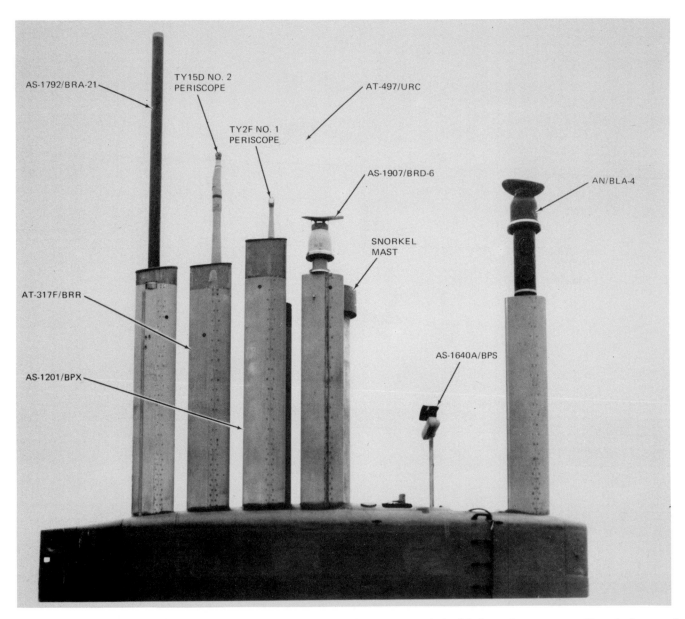

The *Sturgeon*s were designed partly for reconnaissance. As completed (June 1971), *Archerfish* shows her antennas. Note the button of the radar warner atop the Type 15D search periscope. Note, too, that many of the masts (BLA-4, BRD-6, BPS) have fairings atop them, so as to minimize turbulence when they were retracted. (This U.S. Navy photo was declassified when it was retired to the U.S. National Archives.)

accepted that orders for large SSNs would have to fall from 6 in FY 61 to 4 in FY 62, rise to 5 in FY 63, fall to 4 in FY 64, and then rise back to the annual rate of 6 in FY 65. On a crash basis, U.S. submarine-building resources were expected to produce as many as 14 ships in the peak year, FY 63.

These estimates were not far off. The FY 61 program ultimately included 11 submarines, 10 of them SSBNs. The FY 62 program actually did include the 13 submarines envisaged by the Long Range Objectives Group; however, 10 were SSBNs. This left only 3 SSNs, the first *Sturgeon*s. FY 62 was the peak year for SSBN production, whereas the 14 FY 63 submarines included 8 SSNs. The FY 64

program fell to 12 units, of which 6 were SSNs (including *Narwhal*). That made a total of 18 attack submarines in FY 61–64, compared with 19 proposed by the Long Range Objectives Group.

By this time, the U.S. defense budget was badly strained. Worse was coming. Many sophisticated systems had been developed during the 1950s and were nearing production. Heavy bills would soon be due. Incoming President John F. Kennedy named Robert S. McNamara as secretary of defense in 1961, apparently in the hope that McNamara would sharply cut costs by bringing modern management ideas from his former employer, Ford Motor Co.

A *Permit*-class submarine shows her short sail at Subic Bay, October 1986. The raised mast carries her broadband radio antenna; her snorkel induction, marked by a small pimple (the radar warning receiver) atop the sail, is forward of it. The submarine in the background is probably *Darter*.

McNamara evidently believed that the budget could be rationalized; if the services could be forced to reduce duplication, many programs might be curtailed or canceled. This would require careful analysis of each mission area. McNamara suspected, too, that often the various services bought different equipment for comparable missions because of traditional, rather than rational, reasons. The most celebrated example of his reasoning was to combine air force and navy requirements in a single airplane, the F-111 (or TFX). McNamara's techniques were also im-

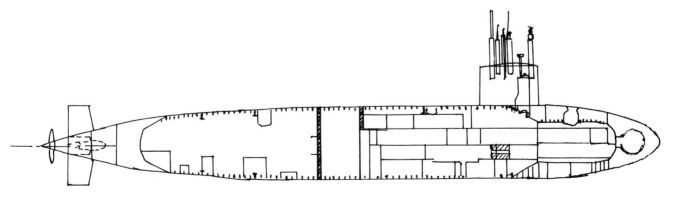

Narwhal, showing the configuration of her pressure hull. She lacked the wasp waist of a *Sturgeon*, but still retained the bottle-nose double-hull section of the earlier design. The breeches of her torpedo tubes are shaded. The preliminary design drawing on which this sketch is based shows no diesel generator forward, only crew living space on the lower level of the bottle-nose. There are two auxiliary machinery spaces (one atop the other) on the two lower levels of the after end of the central compartment, just forward of the tanks separating that space from the reactor compartment. Presumably, they include the diesel generator (its fuel tank is under the reactor compartment). According to the drawing, rated capacity is 22 long (252-in) or 44 short (161-in) torpedoes.

Since 1978, *Richard B. Russell* (SSN 687) has had a communications buoy, "Bustle," in an aft extension of her sail (*Silversides*, SSN 679, is similarly fitted). The after dome houses a GNATS (General Noise and Tonal System) sonar jammer, a common fitting in many U.S. submarines. This photograph was taken in September 1986. (G. Arra)

portant to the navy of the 1960s. Analyses were conducted by the Office of the Assistant Secretary of Defense for System Analysis, OASD(SA).

One peculiarity of the techniques used was that they could not take into account the effect of nonhardware choices, such as strategy, by each side (United States and Soviet Union) on the other and thus on the efficacy of given weapons. Such reactions, which are often dominant in real warfare, could have been approximated only by gaming (incidentally, an extremely important factor in shaping the pre–1941 U.S. Navy). McNamara's OSD largely rejected gaming as an analytical tool because its results were not sufficiently precise or repeatable or, for that matter, grounded in sufficient understanding of the basis of enemy behavior.[16] Not accidentally, gaming flourished in the navy of the 1980s because the Maritime Strategy of that time was precisely an attempt to alter Soviet behavior. It used much the same kinds of ships and aircraft as in the past but in a very different way. McNamara's approach, which is still standard, would have been to examine the way in which alternative technologies could handle the changing Soviet fleet on the unstated assumption that overall strategy would remain fixed. Apparently, neither McNamara nor his many critics made this difference explicit.

McNamara developed a series of Draft Presidential Memoranda (DPMs) that laid out overall needs and priorities for various mission areas, including ASW forces and major fleet anti-air warfare (AAW) escort forces. Such issues as the overall number of SSNs were discussed at this level. All proposed major new systems would be subject to concept formulation/concept definition (CF/CD), in which all reasonably practical solutions to a tactical problem would be compared mathematically before any one solution was chosen. This was the level, for example, where

Los Angeles was compared with alternative submarines.[17] Before heavy investment in R&D could begin, the sponsor of a program had to estimate its consequences in terms of long-term impact on the overall defense budget. In theory, this review would weed out extravagant programs before they gained enough political support to become unstoppable.

With CF/CD came a more formalized system of program management. System performance objectives had to be stated without direct reference to how they would be achieved (so that trade-offs could be calculated), and alternative proposed technical approaches (PTAs) had to be documented. Thus, a ship project during the McNamara era (or later) began with a specific development objective (SDO) and progressed through PTAs and formal management plans. Operational requirements (ORs), both general (GOR) and specific (SOR), already existed, but the SDO/PTA system was new.

McNamara's new techniques greatly increased OSD control over the defense program, partly because none of the services quite understood them at first. Trade-off analysis, for example, required a precise definition of the mission. This definition could be chosen to favor one solution or another.

The more formalized planning and budgeting system drastically slowed new development programs. Decisions involved many more actors; they naturally took much longer. Time was never explicitly included in the analysis process. A cynic might observe that, with central war against the Soviets largely excluded by mutual nuclear deterrence, McNamara felt that much of the urgency had gone out of the very expensive programs designed to deal directly with the Soviets. Delays would save money, which had to be spent on the one really urgent problem, Vietnam. On the other hand, it could be argued that, by the 1960s, the main technologies affected by McNamara's form of analysis were so mature that little more could have been squeezed out of them for some years. Early investment in producing new systems, then, would have been wasted. Ever since McNamara, periodic attempts have been made to redress the balance between technological progress (through risk taking) and insurance against budgetary disaster. The most recent were the "Black Programs" so common during the Reagan administration.

One consequence of the high hurdles placed in the way of any new program was that no completely new U.S. submarine design went all the way from concept to working plans for about two decades after 1968. In effect, none of the numerous proposals was considered sufficiently superior to the submarine then in production (*Los Angeles*) to make worthwhile the disruption necessary for a production shift. That carried a considerable and unseen cost: designers did not gain experience in translating their early sketches into producible submarines.

When Secretary McNamara took office in 1961, the U.S. Navy operated a total of 105 attack submarines (92 of which were diesel-powered), plus 11 auxiliary submarines (AGSS) for training and R&D. Through FY 61, a total of 28 SSNs (including *Triton*) had been authorized; 3 more followed in McNamara's first budget (FY 62). As the SSBN program tailed off, it became possible to shift effort to a higher rate of SSN production in order to head off the impending block obsolescence of the many surviving WW II submarines.[18]

It appears that Opnav divided the diesel-electric submarines into a group of 44 reasonably modern boats that could soldier on (12 postwar units, including 2 ex-SSRs, 23 Guppy IIs scheduled for FRAM, and 9 other Guppies) and a remaining group not worth keeping in service much longer that required urgent replacement. After that, a steady building program would eventually produce the desired all-nuclear force.[19] As formulated in 1961, the FY 63–67 shipbuilding plan provided the 30 most urgently needed SSNs by FY 66 (8 in FY 63, 6 in FY 64, then 8 in each of FY 65, FY 66, and FY 67). Nearly all of the remaining non-FRAM diesel submarines would be replaced by 8 SSNs in FY 67.

McNamara accepted the 105-submarine goal but hoped to stretch out the replacement process by modernizing the 35 best diesel-electric submarines (Guppy IIs and postwar units). On that basis, he decided to cut the annual rate (from FY 65 on) to 6 SSNs. The figure of 30 SSNs would be reached in FY 67, and replacement of the modernized units would begin in FY 69. The FY 64–68 program, formulated in October 1962, showed 7 FRAM Guppies in each of FY 65 and FY 66, and 6 modernizations of postwar diesel submarines in each of FY 67 and FY 68. Modernization could save a great deal of money: each FY 62 FRAM cost $4.7 million, compared with $62.7 million for a new SSN.

McNamara must have feared that the demand for 105 modern nuclear submarines would break his budget. In January 1963, he proposed to meet a FY 68 goal of 100 modern attack submarines (in the FY 65–69 shipbuilding plan) by reaching a total of 65 SSNs; the other 35 submarines would be modernized diesel boats.[20] Later, the figure of 65 SSNs would take on a life of its own and survive even after most of the modernizations had been abandoned. OSD hoped to maintain a total of 105 attack submarines through FY 68–69 by keeping older diesel-electric submarines in service.

The FY 66–70 plan formulated in October 1964 cut the annual building rate to 4 per year, enough to maintain 96 SSNs at the 24-year, 3-core lifetime then expected. This figure hardly would be reached immediately. In FY 62 (beginning 1 July 1961), the U.S. Navy had a total of 104 attack submarines, including 88 diesels and 9 AGSSs. Two years later, there were 84 diesel attack submarines and 19 SSNs (total 103). In October 1964, OSD projected that by FY 68 there would be 47 operational SSNs and only 58 diesel-electric submarines, a total of 105. By 1969, the two groups would be nearly equal (52 SSNs, 53 diesels); in 1970, SSNs would outnumber diesels, 56 to 49. The navy wanted slightly faster SSN production in order to reverse the 1969 numbers and make the FY 70 ratio 58 to 47.

By early 1965, it was obvious that the Soviets had not chosen the predicted route of concentrating on less expensive diesel submarines to maintain the sheer size of their fleet. The Guppy IIs were hardly worth modernizing, and those planned for FY 65 were dropped. McNamara accepted 6 (rather than 4) SSNs in FY 66, and the SSGN *Halibut* was converted into an extra SSN under the same program. The 12 postwar modernizations were moved up to FY 66 and FY 67, but Congress rejected the FY 66 units.

SUBSAFE was drastically slowing SSN deliveries. In February 1965, McNamara announced that he was 4 submarines short of his goal for FY 66. He expected to be back on schedule shortly, but that did not happen. A year later, only 24 nuclear attack submarines were in service against 31 planned, largely because of SUBSAFE.

By this time, McNamara was under intense pressure to control the defense budget despite the escalating demands of war in Vietnam. The SSN program was a major expense. In 1966, McNamara announced that a total of 64 SSNs would be needed. In the past, it had been assumed that about 64 SSNs were needed *alongside* 35 diesel submarines, all of which would be eventually replaced by SSNs. Now, the diesels would be gone without replacement. Within a few years, the remaining SSNs would be bought and the program capped until sometime in the 1970s.

McNamara probably saw the SSN program as an uncontrollable hemorrhage in the defense budget. Although production came nowhere near meeting delivery schedules, he was unable to convince Congress to hold down fresh authorizations. Considering the usual give and take of Washington politics, McNamara may have felt that congressional reaction to his decision to cap the program would be an attempt at compromise, thus reducing annual purchases to something closer to what he could afford.

The submariners were outraged. In 1965, the Long Range Objectives Group had estimated that 98 submarines would constitute a more appropriate figure.[21] OASD(SA) much preferred to minimize the number of platforms and maximize their effectiveness by buying better expendables, such as weapons and sonobuoys. That was largely a matter of politics and economics: a platform must be paid for in a single year, whereas no single year's worth of expendables is generally very expensive. OASD(SA) was particularly impressed by the P-3/SOSUS combination, using DIFAR (directional Lofar) sonobuoys and Mk 46 lightweight torpedoes. It also considered that the new Mk 48 submarine torpedo would greatly improve the capability of each submarine.

OSD's view was that, over the course of a 30-day ASW campaign, the P-3s would probably kill virtually all Soviet submarines. Until this was accomplished, convoy operations would be extremely dangerous. OSD therefore strongly supported efforts to build up stockpiles of materiel in Western Europe.

The navy's view of essentially the same situation was rather different. Stockpiles might well be eliminated prior to the war (e.g., by saboteurs); convoys then would be terribly important. Unless many Soviet submarines were eliminated before they reached the open ocean, the convoys would be massacred. NATO would not have 30 days to wait for the death of the Soviet submarine fleet. On this basis, the appropriate measure of required U.S. submarine numbers was the requirement to exact a percentage loss rate as Soviet submarines transited from their bases to patrol areas.

OASD(SA) also reviewed standing war plans. Submarines were assigned set patrol areas (e.g., in barriers across choke points). The size of each area was partly set by sonar range. That depended, in turn, on just how noisy current and future Soviet submarines would be; U.S. submarines were likely to detect their targets mainly by passive sonar.

Much depended on assumptions. In June 1969, for example, OASD(SA) argued that the navy was artificially inflating requirements by demanding that submarines cover minor stations as insurance against an unlikely dispersal of the Soviet fleet. It argued that allied ASW could be relied on in the Mediterranean, with U.S. submarines limited to a barrier to close it off. Using sufficiently optimistic assumptions of sonar performance to estimate the number of submarines needed to cover any specific choke point, the analysts calculated that 57 modern (post-Skipjack) attack submarines could cover both oceans from tenders at Holy Loch, Midway, and Palau. OASD(SA) could increase patrol time by 10 days (almost 17 percent) and reduce required numbers simply by moving the planned bases closer in (e.g., to Sasebo) and cutting turnaround time (in this case, from 20 to 30 days). The combination of forward basing and quick turnaround theoretically increased submarine time on station from 50 to 63 percent, so that 1.6 submarines would be required per station, rather than 2. The requisite number fell to 41; a 60-SSN force would allow a 50 percent hedge (e.g., for other submarine missions). Numbers could be cut further if the submarines were based closer to their patrol areas.

The navy tended to consider OASD's assumptions sanguine to the point of absurdity. Admiral Rickover was fond of quoting a claim that U.S. submarines could achieve an exchange rate of 25:1. On the other hand, the navy's assumption that the Soviets would soon quiet their submarines to the level achieved in the Skipjack class did prove premature.

The FY 67–71 program was formulated in October 1965. Congress had authorized a total of 54 first-line SSNs (of which Thesher had been lost; this figure did not include Triton, the interim Halibut, or the two prototypes). McNamara proposed that production be cut to 5 submarines per year in FY 67 and FY 68 and then terminated with a single submarine in FY 69. Triton and Halibut would serve as interim SSNs, and the diesel submarine modernization program was pushed back to FY 68 and cut to 7 boats (3 Tangs, Darter, 2 Salmons, and Grayback). In the end, these modernizations were done with overhaul rather than shipbuilding funds (the main improvement was PUFFS/Mk 45). The navy proposed a continuing program of 6 submarines per year, but Congress approved McNamara's plan for 5 SSNs for FY 67.

During planning of the FY 68–72 program in September 1966, McNamara again proposed 5 SSNs for FY 1968, with 1 more to end the program in FY 69. The navy proposed going back to 6 per year in FY 69. McNamara decided to save some money by pushing 2 of the FY 68 submarines forward to FY 69, for a total of 3 each year. The 3 FY 68 boats included the turboelectric prototype, Glenard P. Lipscomb, which McNamara had resisted.

Although McNamara had managed to cut the yearly production rate drastically, he knew that Congress would not cheerfully accept capping the program. Admiral Rickover was in a particularly good position to oppose him, thanks to his quasi-civilian status with AEC.

In January 1968, McNamara announced that new studies had cut the requirement to 60 first-line attack submarines. On the other hand, 5 more existing SSNs (the Skates and the slow Tullibee) were demoted to second-line status. That left 4 boats to build in FY 69–70. The FY 69 program was cut to 2; these became the last Sturgeons. The final 2 SSNs were scheduled for FY 70. The navy argued for 3 in FY 69 and then reversion to 5 per year.

Deliveries were still lagging. This was due partly to SUBSAFE and partly to late delivery of materials and components, presumably caused, in large measure, by the competing pressures of Vietnam War production.

As an economist, McNamara almost certainly thought in terms of the current cost of buying more SSNs than were needed, without reference to the cost of restarting an entire submarine construction industry that might be destroyed by ending SSN production. The nuclear submarine industry had already been hard hit by the end of the crash SSBN program. Of six yards building SSNs or SSBNs in the early 1960s, two (Ingalls and New York Shipbuilding) had soon dropped out. When McNamara decided that, in future, naval shipyards would not build U.S. warships, two more, Mare Island and Portsmouth, were excluded. That left only two nuclear submarine yards, Elec-

Puffer (SSN 652) is shown in Western Australia, probably in 1984. The fairing running down her port side covers a TB-16 towed array sonar, which pays out through her starboard horizontal stabilizer. The small sonar dome forward of her sail covers a WLR-9A sonar intercept receiver, part of her acoustic warfare system. The window on the forward edge of the sail covers the 30 scanned hydrophones of the BQS-14 receiving array; below it are the three vertical projector staves. Early *Sturgeon*-class submarines, such as *Puffer*, had BQS-8 or -8A mine-avoidance sonars; FY 65 and later units were built with the solid-state BQS-14, and earlier units were replaced. BQS-14 and the corresponding BQS-15 (*Los Angeles* class), the last descendants of the WW II QLA mine-avoidance set, used continuously transmitted FM (and therefore were necessarily bistatic). BQS-15 equips the *Los Angeles* class. (Royal Australian Navy, by LSPH E. Pitman)

tric Boat and Newport News, of which only Electric Boat had much contract design experience.

Construction of *Gurnard* had demonstrated that building nuclear submarines required a degree of expertise well beyond the capability of nearly every shipyard. To be certified for nuclear construction, a yard had to maintain special facilities and specialized workers. It seemed unlikely that either the small nuclear surface ship program or any submarine refit/recoring program could justify sufficient investment by the private corporations that owned the two remaining nuclear submarine yards. Once SSN production had stopped altogether, it might be far too expensive to restart.

The situation recalled the period after WW I when submarine construction virtually ceased for about a decade. At that time, design expertise survived because the government continued to maintain its own yard at Portsmouth. Moreover, the pre-1933 navy was able to build submarine engines, probably the most specialized large items then on board a submarine, at one of its own yards, but the yards had little ability to develop new engines. In the 1960s, there was no prospect of assigning a navy yard to make any of the numerous components of a modern submarine, let alone build or even design a reactor.

The submariners sensed that OASD(SA) had been far too narrow in its view of the way SSNs would be used in wartime. The new SSNs were clearly so capable that they could do far more than barrier ASW. The submariners spent some time in developing the appropriate missions. Initially, they argued that the ASW barriers should be supplemented by traditional submarine missions, such as attacks on shipping and minelaying. (OSD had argued that submarines on such missions would have to pass through the barriers, a very risky proposition.) The submariners became interested in carrier escort and in long-range missile attacks on enemy surface formations (see chapter 10). Ironically, all of the analyses omitted one of the most important missions, reconnaissance/surveillance, because it was so highly classified that it could not be discussed in any detail at the level of the official reports. Also debatable was whether barrier tactics would always dominate ASW. After McNamara left office, for example, the annual defense department reports mentioned open-ocean ASW operations cued by long-range sensors, such as SOSUS. This was quite aside from a sense that OSD had been far too optimistic in its ASW assumptions.

By 1967, Admiral Rickover practically personified the submarine production base. He would not quietly accede to its destruction. The CNO and most other naval officers could not directly oppose McNamara because of his position as secretary of defense. Rickover's position was more independent because he was also an AEC employee and, in that position, had developed his own base of congressional support. McNamara surely saw Rickover as a major reason why his attempts to trim the expensive SSN program had failed in Congress. His efforts to end the program altogether could be seen as an attempt to remove the one element in the defense department that could effectively oppose him. Ultimately, McNamara or Rickover would have to go.

Although McNamara was probably far more affected by the strains of the Vietnam War, his last personal battle in office ended in failure. He could not prevent the navy from buying a Rickover prototype, the turboelectric *Glenard P. Lipscomb*. Even before that, new submarine designs were in train. In his last annual report, Secretary McNamara noted drily that "we maintain the option of continuing SSN construction. The Navy is also investigating the characteristics of new submarines which may be required to meet the potential threats of the late 'seventies.'" These new submarines became *Los Angeles* and her abortive rival, a design developed by CF/CD (CONFORM) (see chapter 10).

McNamara resigned in February 1968. Some of his system analysts (the "whiz kids") survived briefly, but the struggle against Admiral Rickover could not be sustained without the secretary's political support. McNamara's successor, Clark Clifford, admitted that only continued production could preserve the industrial base. He also allowed that the McNamara studies might need reassessment, in terms of both submarine quality and base numbers. Better submarines might well be needed during the mid-1970s and beyond. Because cuts in nuclear attack submarine procurement were no longer possible, the necessary reduction in the FY 69 budget was achieved by discarding 3 diesel attack submarines and all 10 diesel training submarines (AGSSs).

Under construction at Portsmouth Navy Yard, *Thresher* displays the sphere of her bow sonar, as yet without any transducers in place. More recent submarines have an eyebrow plate above the sphere, shielding it from noise coming down from the surface (e.g., reflected self-noise). Behind the sphere is the forward bulkhead of the bottle-nose part of her pressure hull (note the flat bulkhead surrounding it, closing off part of her double hull section). This design featured a very short sail for minimum water resistance; an early concept was to do away with the sail altogether (hence with the ability to navigate on the surface). The submarine would then have to be towed out of her berth to the open sea. The short sail contained a short snorkel. The ship's single Type 8 periscope was much longer. It was therefore provided with two stands, one in the upper level and one on the middle level (later the ship's office), the latter to be used when snorkelling (i.e., to avoid putting a very long, unsupported mast out of the water). For simplicity, the periscope lacked any fairing, so it was usable only up to about 6 kt. To keep the sail small, it had room for only two hull penetrations. Because the Type 8 periscope lacked ESM capability, the other position was reserved for an ESM mast. When *Flasher* was built, a Type 15 periscope with ESM capability became available; at the operators' request, it replaced the earlier Type 8 periscope and a Type 2 attack periscope replaced the former ESM mast. This design introduced the retractable SPM motor, which could turn 360 deg for maneuvering. The *Skipjacks* (and all other submarines powered by the S5W reactor) had a small DC motor (EPM) wrapped around their propeller shafts, abaft the clutch (which was abaft the bull gear). It had to be DC, because only a DC motor could easily reverse to run astern. The ship's emergency diesel generator therefore had to produce DC power for emergency propulsion. The EPM guaranteed against damage to the reactors or to the reduction gears, but not against the loss of the main shaft and the single screw. The SPM solved that problem. Because it could turn 180 deg to run astern, it could be a more compact AC motor. The ship's diesel generator could therefore be a diesel, which was more compact (and which could share the AC bus with the ship's service turbogenerators: it charged the ship's battery via a motor-generator set, which converted AC to DC power).

10

Los Angeles and Her Successor

MANY IN THE submarine community were concerned about the trend to slower speeds, from *Thresher* to *Sturgeon*. The Soviets were beginning to field SSNs of their own. A U.S. submarine could expect to detect a Soviet craft at long range, but generally she would have to run in to reach a firing position. In 1968, when the fast *Los Angeles* was being considered, it was argued that a sprint/drift barrier submarine needed at least a 5-kt speed advantage over a fast submarine passing through the barrier.[1] The barrier submarine might well lose contact, which she would have to regain. A submarine that was fast enough could intercept a target even if she was detected first. Once the two submarines were close, they might well maneuver while each sought a favorable attacking position. A speed edge might make all the difference.

High speed also seemed valuable for open-ocean attacks on targets detected by long-range acoustic arrays. In most areas, patrol aircraft would deal with the targets they found. In other areas, such as the Norwegian Sea, where the Soviets might control the air, attack submarines would be needed for interception. The faster they were, the better their chance of arriving at a contact area early enough to search it before the Soviet submarine was gone. In peacetime, a quiet U.S. submarine would be able to pick up the signature of the Soviet submarine without alerting her. On the other hand, a patrol plane dropping sonobuoys would alert the target, which might then abandon the sort of typical behavior associated with her wartime signature. A submarine might have to cross much of the Atlantic before reaching a Soviet submarine, and a few knots' advantage would be quite valuable. A burst of high speed also could save a submarine on surveillance duty from enemy pursuers.

Most importantly, speed came to be associated with a new mission, direct support (escort) of surface ships. By late 1962 or mid-1963, it was known, at least within naval intelligence, that the Soviets valued their fast new nuclear submarine mainly as a means of attacking U.S. strike carriers. Soviet tactics called for the submarine to fire her nuclear torpedoes from off the carrier's bow. An attacker did not have to be as fast as the carrier, because she would be cued into position by the growing Soviet ocean surveillance system. She only had to be fast enough to reach the attack position from a considerable distance.

This was a new and terrifying capability. Diesel submarines could attack fast carriers only from very limited arcs ahead of their targets. The faster the target, the narrower the arc and the better the chance that it could evade attack altogether. Fast carriers were considered almost immune, to the point that their escorts were designed primarily to deal with air attack. It was assumed that submarines detected ahead of the carrier generally could be evaded. Rickover justified nuclear power for carriers largely on the basis that they could sustain so high a speed as to evade attack by diesel submarines. Clearly, SSNs were a different proposition.

It seemed that a fast submarine with the new long-range sonar could sweep the area ahead of the carrier. A submarine escort would listen (drift) at low speed, then accelerate (sprint) to keep up with the carrier. For surface ships, escort work was generally equated with speeds beyond 30 kt. Although many unofficial books credit virtually all nuclear submarines with such speeds, they are actually quite rare. The *Skipjacks*, the fastest of the existing fleet, had just touched a speed of 30 kt (see chapter 8).

This was not a new idea. As early as the summer of

Cincinnati (SSN 693), shown in 1990, demonstrates typical modifications to *Los Angeles*-class submarines. The window on the sail covers the trainable tracking receiver of a BQS-15 mine- and obstacle-avoidance sonar (the three vertical projectors run below it; this sonar also has four LF transducers to pick up pulses from the main sonar sphere, and it can have up to two additional HF and LF transducers). The tube running up her starboard side covers a TB-16 towed array, which pays out through her port horizontal fin. Unlike earlier designs, *Los Angeles* shows no separate sonar dome for an acoustic intercept receiver, so presumably her WLR-12 arrays are behind windows faired into the sail; for example, some photographs suggest that there is an acoustic window on the after part of the sail. The button barely visible atop her Type 15B search periscope (at right) houses ESM antennas (for WLR-8 and -10). The other periscope is a Type 2F attack unit, distinguishable by its very tapered stem. The mast between (and abaft) the periscopes carries a broadband (VLF/LF up through UHF) helical radio antenna (BRA-34; a second antenna of this type is retracted). At the after end of the sail, retracted, is the ECM mast, with its BRD-7 direction-finder. The submarine also has a broadband buoyant cable antenna and two emergency antennas. Paneling visible on the hull is anechoic coating (special hull treatment). (Leo van Ginderen)

1955, characteristics for the new *Skipjack* class included task force or convoy escort as one of several duties. A few years later the British designed the sonar and fire control system of their prototype SSN *Dreadnought* specifically for direct cooperation with surface ships. The U.S. Navy was well aware of the British work. It experimented in 1962 with some form of direct support.[2]

As envisaged in 1966, the escort submarine would operate 10–30 nm ahead of a force, just beyond the escorts' active sonar range. She could attack approaching enemy submarines directly or vector in carrier aircraft. Alternatively, the submarine could actually replace one or more surface ships in the screen around a major combatant, or it could serve as a "pouncer" to intercept submarines penetrating a spread-out surface screen. As of 1968, experiments suggested that it would take a 7-kt speed edge to maintain contact with an attacking submarine bent on evasion.

The rub in any such scheme was communication—between submarine and surface ships and between submarine and aircraft. For example, many submarine commanders shrewdly suspected that ASW air crews would shoot first and identify their targets later. In the early 1960s, it seemed that several programs for covert and secure acoustic communications might solve the problem. Too, the surface fleet was receiving a new computer system, NTDS (naval tactical data system), that maintained a current picture of surface, air, and subsurface activity around a force, partly on the basis of a digital data link, Link 11. Given its own NTDS computer and a one-way (receive-only) version of Link 11, the escort submarine could make better sense of the tactical situation and perhaps avoid being attacked by friendly forces. The British had greatly simplified the problem by running *Dreadnought* within direct-path sonar range of a frigate, which communicated with her by two-way acoustic data link. The U.S. Navy planned much more dispersed formations.

Whatever their doubts, the submariners were vitally interested in direct support by 1967. It was the first specific example of a new nonbarrier submarine role; moreover, this role could easily elicit the political support of naval aviators. Because escorts would have to be provided in addition to any barrier submarines, acceptance of the new role would immediately add up to 30 submarines (2 per carrier) to the agreed force level. The submariners knew that they would have to do much more than barrier work in wartime; the direct escort concept allowed them to circumvent OSD's narrow analysis.

It is not altogether clear how interest in a much faster submarine arose within the navy. The design that became *Los Angeles* was first proposed late in 1963, by which time *Sturgeon* speed estimates were available. The two rationales, the need to regain the lost speed of the *Skipjack*s and the need to protect carriers against Soviet nuclear submarines, were both often used.

In the spring of 1963, the navy fought and lost a bruising fight with Secretary McNamara over the power plant of the next carrier, CVA 63, which became *John F. Kennedy*. One of the losing arguments was that a nuclear carrier would be fast enough to gain immunity from submarine attack. Presumably, a conventional carrier, which could not run at maximum speed for very long, would indeed be vulnerable.[3]

In November 1963, Admiral Rickover proposed a solution to the submarine speed problem. He already had the D1G/D2G, a destroyer reactor twice as powerful as the S5W. It could be redesigned for submarine installation and wedded to the *Sturgeon*-class bow and weapons system. Rickover seems to have envisaged a shift to the new power plant in the FY 67 program.[4] The following April, he ordered Electric Boat to make preliminary studies of a high-speed submarine; in July, he presented the results to Rear Adm. E. P. Wilkinson, who was then Director of the Op-Nav Submarine Warfare Division (Op-31). Wilkinson had commanded *Nautilus* in the dramatic 1956 exercises; he certainly appreciated the virtues of high speed. In September 1964, the CNO ordered NAVSEA to make a feasibility study of the fast submarine. That October, Electric Boat was ordered to design the appropriate submarine machinery space, which had to be fixed before the overall design of the new submarine could begin. Responsibility for this project was transferred to Newport News in September 1965.[5]

NAVSEA took a year to produce a cost/feasibility study, presumably, at least partly, because nothing could be done without a preliminary machinery arrangement (to fix the weight and dimensions of a major portion of the ship). Rickover initially estimated that the new power plant would add 1,600 tons (to about 6,200 tons) and that the *Sturgeon* hull would grow from 292 to 314 ft. A FY 68 preliminary design study completed in March 1966 for what was then called an AGSSN, however, showed a 360-ft, 6,670-ton hull. Every foot of length cost some speed because it added wetted surface (i.e., frictional resistance) and because it took the form of the submarine farther from the ideal, rather fat length-to-beam ratio. Every extra ton added hull volume, hence wetted surface and drag. Measures to limit displacement included attempts to minimize the size of the crew; every man added weight and volume. Calculations predicted that the D1G submarine would still exceed the 30-kt escort limit but not by a very great margin.

The new submarine design adopted and elaborated on the simplified hull structure first chosen in *Narwhal*; the necked-in forward pressure hull section was eliminated altogether. Thus, virtually the entire length of the pressure hull formed part of the outer hull. The sonar sphere inside the forward main ballast tank was mounted on a long stalk emerging from the front dome of the main pressure hull. That reduced the cone over which the pressure hull blocked its aft-facing lines of sight, and it also reduced the level of sound transmitted by the sonar into the hull.

The main weights were the machinery and the pressure hull. Little could be done to reduce machinery weight; improved silencing techniques might actually increase it. Therefore, the designers were driven to shave some pressure hull weight. No improved hull material was in prospect. Any reduction in hull weight translated into reduced test depth (about halfway back from *Thresher* toward the pre–*Thresher* standard). The designers could not go all the way back to the pre–*Thresher* era because the new submarine always had to be able to operate her sonar well below the layer. In 1966, they estimated that it would cost 900–1,000 tons to return to the *Thresher* standard.

A nuclear submarine normally ran below cavitation depth; the faster the submarine, the greater that depth. On the other hand, some stern plane accident might cause the submarine to dive uncontrollably. Recovery would take time and depth—the higher the speed, the deeper the uncontrolled dive. The submarine would also lose depth when making tight high-speed turns because of snap roll. A wise submarine commander would operate in a depth range sandwiched from above by cavitation depth and from below by a safety cushion. The greater the test depth, the broader would be the operating range.

The required safety cushion could be shrunk by adopting an X-stern, as tested on *Albacore* at about this time (see chapter 3). The X-stern would be so much more effective than the conventional cruciform type that its surfaces, a major source of appendage drag, could be made smaller. Consequently, the X-stern became a design fixture of the big fast submarine.

It was assumed that the new submarine would be equipped with a new sonar, which would add 28 ft to overall length.[6] She also would be equipped with PUFFS. Later proponents of a cruciform stern, rather than an X-stern, would argue that PUFFS arrays could be installed at the tips of the horizontal fins. The amidships PUFFS arrays would have been recessed into the hull for minimum drag.

As in the earlier *Thresher*, much effort went into shrinking the sail, the major source of appendage drag. Its very presence made for larger (hence draggier) stern stabilizers. As in 1957, BuShips concluded that it could not be eliminated altogether. It protected the hull against surface collisions, and the bridge atop it was needed for surface control, as in docking. Some housing was needed for the masts. Sail planes made for better near-surface depth-keeping and they helped the submarine to recover from a stern plane casualty, although their value declined as speed increased. The designers planned to use a big towed radio buoy (with a 4-ft wingspan) as the primary means of communicating with the surface force escorted by the AGSSN.[7] The buoy had to have some dry accessible stowage for maintenance. Only a trunk in the sail offered this, and the sail could not be eliminated altogether. The designers chose a shorter and narrower sail than in the *Thresher*.

Cutting sail height had an unexpected consequence. The sail planes on a *Sturgeon* sail were high enough off the hull to turn vertical (e.g., when the submarine had to crash up through thin ice). The sail planes of the new submarine were mounted too low to turn vertical, so she could not operate in the Arctic. That became important as the new class came to comprise the bulk of the U.S. submarine fleet. Too, Arctic operations became more important in the 1980s. *Los Angeles* had to be redesigned with retractable bow planes in place of sail planes.

A *Los Angeles*-class submarine in drydock shows her silenced skew-bladed propeller and also the tube from which her towed array emerges, near the tip of her port fin. In 1985 it was revealed that the Soviets had obtained the automated milling machine technology required to mass-produce just such silenced propellers. This denied the West much of its ability to detect Soviet submarines through blade rate (very low-frequency tonals). (G. Arra via *Ships of the World*)

The new submarine would be much larger than her predecessors, thus much costlier, yet it would have substantially the same torpedo battery, including about the same number of reloads. Any alternative would have carried an unacceptable price in extra drag. For example, calculations showed that a second row of torpedoes above the first (for twice the loadout) would cost 9 ft more in length; however, a subtler improvement was possible. Earlier submarines had been designed to fire half-length wire-guided torpedoes, such as a Mk 37. The standard full-length torpedo skid could accommodate a short torpedo plus its wire dispenser. With the advent of the long Mk 48, that was no longer possible; a full torpedo space was needed for Mk 48 wire dispensers. The new submarine had skids long enough for the new torpedo plus its wire dispenser, thus gaining one torpedo within much the same internal volume. Her increased diameter added two more. The larger torpedo room could also accommodate a pair of weapon hoists, rather than the single centerline hoist of the earlier class.

The submarine would still suffer from one major problem of her predecessor. Torpedoes fired forward would tend to break their guidance wires.[8] When fired at high speed, they might slam into the side of the tube. Both problems could be avoided in a twin-screw design with its tubes aft, but that would have cost 900 tons and probably far more than a knot. To carry the tubes forward but angle them to fire aft would have greatly complicated pressure hull design.

In July 1967, the CNO ordered a new cost and feasibility study on the basis of the AGSSN report; by this time, displacement had grown to 6,900 tons. Newport News completed a design study of the D1G submarine in December 1967 that showed a length of 366 ft and a displacement of 7,040 tons.

Rickover's proposal collided with McNamara's new way of analyzing programs before they entered production. It is not clear whether the application of concept formulation (CF) to the submarine was merely a matter of timing (McNamara's fiat was in force), or whether it was OpNav's attempt to stall off Rickover's budget-destroying proposal at a time when it seemed difficult enough merely to keep nuclear attack submarines in production. The first two warship programs to be affected were the next-generation submarine and a proposed amphibious fire support ship, the LFS. Within the Navy, the concept formulation study was called CONFORM.

The whole idea of CONFORM was foreign to Rickover. Surely, the appearance of Soviet nuclear attack submarines presented an urgent problem. He had found a solution. It might not be the best conceivable, but it was clearly workable. Studies might produce something better; however throughout his entire naval career, he (and virtually all his contemporaries) had learned, often very painfully, that a reasonably good decision made today is far better than an optimal decision made five years later. To Admiral Rickover, CONFORM was part of an emerging culture that preferred not to take time into account. It was the opposite of Soviet Adm. Sergei Gorshkov's famous warning that "the best is the enemy of good enough."

Once the trade-off process had begun and before it had been completed, no single solution to the tactical problem could proceed to production. The D1G submarine project could survive only as an experimental prototype. Admiral Rickover had to agree, in writing, that it would be followed (probably in FY 71) by whatever submarine the CONFORM process recommended. Almost certainly, that was never Rickover's actual view. He had conceived the new submarine as the *Sturgeon* follow-on, another series production submarine. Although the AGSSN designation in the 1966 design report suggested an experimental craft, the escort mission was hardly speculative. It demanded a substantial force of very fast submarines, at least one per carrier. In that sense, it was also a direct challenge to McNamara's decision to cap SSN production based on the existing barrier ASW mission.

As McNamara's rules required, Rickover's D1G submarine was soon mired in bureaucracy. On 18 August 1966, OpNav issued a formal SDO (specific development objective) for a high-speed nuclear attack submarine to super-

sede the *Sturgeon* class. The basic assumptions were that the speed trend had to be reversed and improved basic systems (beyond those *Sturgeon* could accommodate) added to meet an improved Soviet submarine force in 1975–85. A PTA (proposed technical approach) to SSN development was published on 17 April 1967, after which OpNav ordered a cost and feasibility study (16-67) for the new submarine (25 May 1967).

The SDO was not quite what Rickover had in mind because it established performance objectives, not solutions. Moreover, as McNamara generally demanded, it called for a predesign trade-off study. The SSN program was established as a formally funded ship development program, beginning in FY 68 and continuing through FY 70, to be run by a new organization, PMS 81 (program manager for sea systems command). The associated CONFORM study was formally chartered on 22 September. At this point, McNamara still had not included any submarines beyond FY 69.

By then, it was accepted that Rickover's prototype D1G (high-speed attack) submarine would be built under the FY 72 program, with project definition in 1968. Based on completion of the concept formulation planned for FY 68–69, it was assumed that a new design could be ready to enter production in FY 73.

The study compared the performance of a series of possible submarine designs against a series of five missions. In priority order, the missions were:

1. forward area (i.e., operations near enemy bases, which would test the undetectability of the submarine)
2. track/trail (e.g., of enemy ballistic missile submarines)
3. escort (direct support)
4. coordinated operations (open-ocean attacks on enemy submarines cued by friendly forces or fixed detectors, such as SOSUS)
5. ancillary (e.g., anti-ship, mining, surveillance, landing of personnel, training, development)

Definite choices required that scores, or measures of effectiveness, be developed for each mission, then prioritized. At least at the beginning of the study, they existed only for the first two missions. In the forward area (a barrier), it was the number of kills/opportunity (i.e., per enemy submarine trying to pass through). In the second mission, the score was the ratio of time during which a passive contact could be held to the total time during which the submarine tried to track the target. It was not really practical to evaluate submarine performance in the other areas of direct and coordinated support, in which high speed might have been more important.

Any new submarine design eventually would be adapted to accommodate the new digital sonar and fire-control system specified in 1966. A prototype was expected in FY 74–75, with the first production system to follow in FY 77–78. The submarine eventually would be constructed of a new steel, HY-130. At this time (around 1966–67), the navy expected that a small nuclear submarine built of HY-130 would be launched in FY 74–75 and completed in FY 75. In 1969, however, it seemed that HY-130 could be incorporated into an FY 73 submarine. Politically, this was important because the new material would have restored the diving depth sacrificed in the design of the D1G submarine. Most of her subsystems had been taken from the *Sturgeon* design and were therefore designed for her test depth. In fact, HY-130 stayed just out of reach. In 1970, for example, the earliest possible date for HY-130 advanced to FY 74. The new *Seawolf* is built of HY-100.

In 1966, it seemed that a new submarine incorporating both the new weapons system and HY-130 could complete concept formulation in FY 70, be launched in FY 75, and be completed in FY 79. The first-generation CONFORM submarine would make do with existing fire control systems and HY-80 steel.

The main platform alternatives were:

Power plant: S5W, boosted S5G (NCR), and D1G, all driving contrarotating propellers through gearing (turboelectric drive was not considered viable for a fast submarine)

Weapons: Two, four, or eight tubes (11, 22, or 44 weapons)

Test depth: *Skipjack*, *Thresher*, or 2,000 ft

Sail size: *Thresher* or *Sturgeon*

To virtually everyone except Admiral Rickover, CONFORM was developing the next production submarine. It attracted many of the best submarine operators (to define the mission) and designers (to get the most out of each alternative combination of reactor and weapons). The naval architects working on CONFORM sought to increase speed by adopting the smallest possible hull (for minimum drag) and the most efficient propulsor. To minimize size, they tried to make do with a smaller reactor driving smaller turbines. Likely, the existing S5G could be boosted to 20,000 SHP without any growth in size. Adopting geared contraprops in place of *Narwhal*'s direct-drive single screw would cut turbine size and weight. CONFORM favored this solution, which could be combined with *Thresher* diving depth and *Sturgeon* armament.

Rickover differed fundamentally from the naval architects who shaped CONFORM. He preferred to rely on increased power, despite the corresponding increase in tonnage, which itself reduced the increase in speed that such power conferred. Almost certainly, Rickover did not trust the estimates of the hydrodynamicists. Wartime experience had taught him that the traditional skepticism of the old BuEng, in which he had matured, was well placed: naval architects could not always deliver the speeds they promised.

Rickover looked beyond the D1G submarine to one powered by the much more powerful D1W then in development. This was the 60,000-SHP reactor later incorrectly reported as the Trident power plant. The D1G submarine had barely met the speed requirement, and she might be outperformed by some new Soviet submarine. A subma-

rine powered by the D1W would gain about 5 more knots, despite the great upward jump in size required by the new power plant. Sheer hull size would buy more torpedoes and a pressure hull strong enough for much deeper diving. She might well be available in 1974–75 (FY 77 program). Although some calculations placed a CONFORM submarine powered by the boosted S5G at about the same speed as the D1G design, none would give her the sort of speed the D1W offered. If a few knots really mattered, only the D1W solution made sense.

Rickover also had to consider his own reactor development resources. In 1968, the Naval Reactors Division was still working on the submarinized D1G and was beginning work on a submarinized D1W. It was also developing the D1W into what would become the A4W carrier reactor. Although the S5G already existed and was about to go to sea aboard *Narwhal*, this plant likely would have needed more work before being approved for series production. For example, it was larger than the S5W; it probably would have been redesigned more tightly for the CONFORM submarine. Boosting would have required additional design work. Rickover did not have infinite resources. By early 1968, he had, in effect, already made his choice between S5G and D1G/D1W. He was unusually well placed to enforce that decision. By refusing to certify the boosted S5G, he made speed the issue.

CONFORM then offered a submarine powered by the basic unboosted S5G reactor, as in *Narwhal*. The contrarotating propeller might be so much more efficient than a conventional propeller that, even without boosting, the submarine could match D1G speed. Admiral Rickover refused to accept that argument and personally forced down the speed estimate. Thus the CONFORM submarine powered by the unmodified *Narwhal* reactor came out substantially faster than *Narwhal* but still a few knots too slow. The CONFORM submarine would have been intermediate between *Sturgeon* and *Narwhal,* probably about 305×33 ft (4,500 tons).[9]

At this time, the current production submarine, *Sturgeon*, cost $83 million each (up from $79 million for *Permit*). The prototype D1G submarine would cost $179 million, but production follow-ons were expected to cost $129 million each. A CONFORM submarine powered by a boosted S5G reactor was likely to cost about $140 million.

In February 1968, the Soviets dramatized the situation when a November-class submarine intercepted the fast nuclear carrier *Enterprise* en route to Vietnam. Although somewhat slower than the carrier, the November was able to execute interception instructions provided by the Soviet ocean surveillance system.[10] At about the same time, the Soviets suddenly introduced two new classes of attack submarine, Charlie and Victor. The existing November-class submarine was generally assessed as comparable to (but somewhat faster than) a *Skate* and equipped with a medium-frequency sonar. The U.S. Navy assumed that the Soviets would follow its trend toward better silencing and that their new submarines would be at least comparable to *Skipjack*. It was known that the new submarines had low-frequency sonar, presumably a long-range set broadly similar to the U.S. BQS-6. The *Enterprise* incident showed that the November was faster than had been imagined (though not as fast as the carrier), so it was reasonable to guess that the Victors and Charlies would be faster still—faster than *Sturgeon*s or even *Thresher*s.[11] Worst of all, the Soviets were credited with a single-shift capacity to build 20 nuclear submarines each year.

Some members of the OSD staff thought that two prototypes, the D1G submarine and the S5G CONFORM submarine, would be built and tested against each other to determine which would enter series production. By this time, however, OSD had gone through its unpleasant battle against the turboelectric submarine (to become the *Glenard P. Lipscomb*). Director of Defense Research and Engineering Dr. John E. Foster wanted no more prototypes; he wanted a new production submarine. Dr. Foster was strongly influenced by a short trip aboard a *Sturgeon*-class submarine. She ran a series of mock attacks against a *Skipjack*, which was considered typical of future fast Soviet submarines. Despite the skill of the *Sturgeon*'s captain, he was unable to reach an attack position against the faster target.[12] Speed clearly mattered, and the Soviets had apparently gained the edge.

The D1G submarine design had not yet proceeded to the detail stage. Much more effort would be needed to put the submarine into production. Thus, in February 1968, the submariners argued that substantial funds had to be earmarked in FY 69 in order to lay down a prototype in FY 70. It became *Los Angeles*; her submarinized D1G reactor was renamed S6G.

In mid-1968, the projected program consisted of the D1G prototype in FY 70, two D1G submarines in FY 71, and a D1G submarine and the prototype CONFORM submarine in FY 72. Rickover maintained that the CONFORM alternative would represent a regression in speed. By this time, Foster felt that more than one D1G submarine should be built in FY 70 to avoid a slowdown of this urgent program for fast submarines. Rickover's influence in Congress reportedly ensured that more than one such submarine would be ordered that year. Some FY 68 RDT&E (research and development, test and engineering) funds were reprogrammed. Consideration was even given to placing production of the new submarine on a super-priority (Brickbat) basis (as had been done with Polaris submarines), but this did not occur.

The CNO convened an ad hoc panel of experienced submarine officers in March 1968 to assess the new design. They approved the main features and repeated Rickover's contention that the only possible rival power plant, the S5G, was too immature to consider. They did demand a new weapons system, however; the all-digital attack center and the new digital sonar (BQQ-5) were actually adopted. By this time, DDR&E was interested mainly in the weapons system (the front end) and regarded the new submarine as a perfectly reasonable compromise with Admiral Rickover. A better sonar was much more important than a more efficient hull and power plant.

In June 1968, the navy formally proposed the D1G submarine as: "the best new class of submarines attainable by the technology which can be made available in time with high confidence in successful, reliable, operational performance." On 1 July 1968, it was authorized for inclusion in the FY 70 budget. That month, the CNO forwarded the new characteristics that reflected the ad hoc committee's recommendations. A new cost and feasibility study, dated 30 September 1968, estimated that the lead ship would cost $234 million and follow-ons, $156 million each. The SCB and CNO approved formal characteristics in November 1968.

It was not yet clear just how many fast *Los Angeles*-class submarines would be built. One outcome of the ad hoc study was a CNO ruling that CONFORM would not be ready for the FY 72 program, so a second fast submarine was substituted. The CONFORM submarine was pushed ahead to FY 73; a D1W submarine might be ready for the FY 74 program. In mid-1969, the CNO ruled that, to save time, the fast submarine should be placed in production without waiting for some important items, such as a new radar intercept receiver and 10-in decoy. They would be installed later in a preplanned class improvement plan (CIP). Rapid inflation of shipbuilding costs was also likely. Thus, the CIP might save money as well by making possible faster construction of the class. Later installations of CIP items, however, would carry their own costs.

The inflation argument won. Foster had already decided that at least 2 submarines would be included in the FY 70 program; in December, the deputy secretary of defense authorized 3. OSD now planned 3 per year in FY 70–74, rather than the 2 per year of the original program. The navy suggested 4 in each of FY 71 and FY 72 and then 5 in FY 73. OSD decided to ask for 3 in each of FY 70 and FY 71 and 4 in each of FY 72 and FY 73. Rickover's allies in Congress added more, so the navy got 4 submarines in FY 71, 5 in FY 72, and 6 in FY 73.[13]

The incoming Republican administration abandoned CONFORM altogether in 1969. McNamara's capping plan was also gone; the projected SSN fleet was set at 90 units. Submarine lifetime was three core lives, 24 years at the rates of the late 1960s, but considerably more with new cores that might last 12 or 13 years. To sustain a 90-SSN force on a 24-year basis required an average of 3.75 new submarines each year, but the backlog of the early 1960s and early 1970s made it possible to cut this figure to 3 in each of FY 74 and FY 75. By that time, the D1W submarine was no longer seen as a *Los Angeles* successor.

In 1974, the secretary of defense proposed that 5 submarines be built every two years from FY 76 through the end of the 1970s: 2 in FY 76, 3 in FY 77, 2 in FY 78, 3 in FY 79. That proved too expensive; in 1976, the planned FY 77–81 program was cut to 2 per year. Even that was too much. In 1977, Secretary of Defense Donald Rumsfeld announced that only 1 submarine would be bought in each of FY 79 and FY 80, with 2 in each of FY 81 and FY 82. In fact, an additional submarine was added to the FY 77 program; in compensation, the FY 78 figure was reduced to 1. The Carter administration retained Rumsfeld's FY 79 plan, but increased the number to 2 in FY 80, a rate maintained through FY 83. The Reagan administration then increased the projected size of the submarine force to 100 ships as part of its 600-ship program. Thus, 3 submarines were bought in FY 84 and then 4 per year from FY 85 through FY 87. Purchases tailed off as the follow-on *Seawolf* class moved toward production: 3 in FY 88, 2 in FY 89, and the last unit in FY 90. Because of defense cuts 4 more were cancelled: 1 in FY 90, 2 in FY 91, and 1 in FY 92. In all, 62 ships were bought over a period of two full decades.

Preliminary design of the D1G submarine began in March 1969. Much effort went into simplifying the ship to reduce costs. By mid-August, overall length had been cut 16 ft to 350 ft and submerged displacement to 6,600 tons.[14] By November, length was up to 360 ft, and projected tonnage was 6,125 surfaced and 6,900 submerged, about what had been estimated two years earlier. This was much the design ultimately adopted. Once contract plans had been completed, changes were likely to be quite expensive. A new policy was adopted: each design change required approval by the CNO or VCNO (vice chief of naval operations). This cost-control technique was revived during the Reagan administration (then, changes had to be approved by either Secretary of the Navy John Lehman or the CNO). The design program included a formal noise review, and the larger-diameter hull accommodated better silencing than in *Sturgeon*.

By mid-1968, it was accepted that the new submarine would have an improved Mk 113 fire-control system in which a central computer complex (dual UYK-7) replaced the earlier Mk 130. Hopefully, this system would support two simultaneous TMA plots; each of two attack directors could track two targets and attack one. The system was expected to triple the effectiveness of a *Sturgeon* faced with a *Skipjack*. In fact, the improved Mk 113 turned out to be far more powerful than expected (see chapter 7). The central computer complex also assisted in navigation, presumably including special TMA maneuvering. As in the SUBIC study, there was substantial sentiment in favor of an alternative distributed computer system. Two bays in the UYK-7 gave some redundancy, but not enough, because the computer now also performed functions outside the weapons system proper.

The submarine was limited to digital weapons. Eliminating analog equipment would save weight, and simplification would make for a much more reliable submarine. The fire-control system would have only a single type of interface with all the weapons it controlled, no matter what their variety. In 1968, the only digital weapon was the Mk 48 torpedo.[15] The loss of Subroc capability seemed acceptable in a battle group escort because aircraft would be available to prosecute distant contacts.

Torpedo tube design was changed so that weapons could be fired at maximum submarine speed. Earlier submarines could not open their shutters at full speed and did not provide strong enough impulses to overcome water pressure. Moreover, because a Mk 14 took a few minutes to accelerate to speed, a submarine running too fast could overtake her own weapon. The shutter problem was solved by having the shutter rotate, rather than slide.

Automatic maneuvering (steering, diving, and hovering) controls and CONALOG were eliminated. The hydraulic system was simplified. Other sacrifices included an after capstan, an oxygen generator, and some emergency endurance on the auxiliary diesel. Rescue arrangements were changed. To ensure that at least some of the crew would survive if she bottomed above her crush depth, the new submarine incorporated an internal holding bulkhead strong enough for collapse (not test) depth. Rescue almost certainly would be attempted by a DSRV, rather than the far more limited McCann rescue chamber. The number of standard escape trunks was greatly reduced in favor of a 30-in hatch, with which the DSRV could mate. The same hatch led into the storeroom for quick loading and therefore quick turnaround at a base.

Compared with *Sturgeon,* the most important sacrifice was surveillance capability. *Los Angeles* had four masts, instead of six, although it did gain something back by introducing a microminiaturized ESM receiver. It also introduced a new periscope, Type 18, that provided 18 times, rather than the previous 8, magnification at high power. Kollmorgen won the competition (against Itek) primarily because it offered the ability to use a camera without removing the face plate of the periscope. Ultimately, that led to the common use of television cameras, whose images are piped throughout the submarine (a system called Pereviz) and recorded.[16] With higher magnification, a submarine could observe targets without having to come within detection range.

The X-stern was eliminated in the fall of 1969 on the ground that the associated computer would not be reliable enough. As might have been imagined, eliminating the measure intended to compensate for reduced test depth had unpleasant consequences. A self-propelled model of the final design, with a cruciform stern, was tank-tested for maneuverability. Like other modern nuclear submarines, the model snap-rolled and lost considerable depth when that happened at high speed. *Los Angeles*-class commanders would have to limit their maneuvers to avoid crashing through test depth.

The lead ship was originally scheduled for completion in August 1974, but she was not actually commissioned until November 1976. Contractors delivered equipment late, and the work force at Newport News built up more slowly than expected. Newport News had never designed a nuclear submarine before, and some minor embarrassments also occurred. Electric Boat found it much more difficult than expected to deliver attack submarines while it was building the large Trident strategic submarines. Through FY 76, a total of 27 (through SSN 715) had been authorized, but none had been delivered.

Parallel to the design study was another ad hoc study that related to submarine weapons systems. It necessarily looked further ahead because of the time needed to develop anything new. On the other hand, the committee strongly supported the ongoing work in digital sonar and fire control, inspired partly by experience with the Mod 9 system in SSBNs.

As might have been expected, the ad hoc committee was unhappy with the total number of weapons, with the

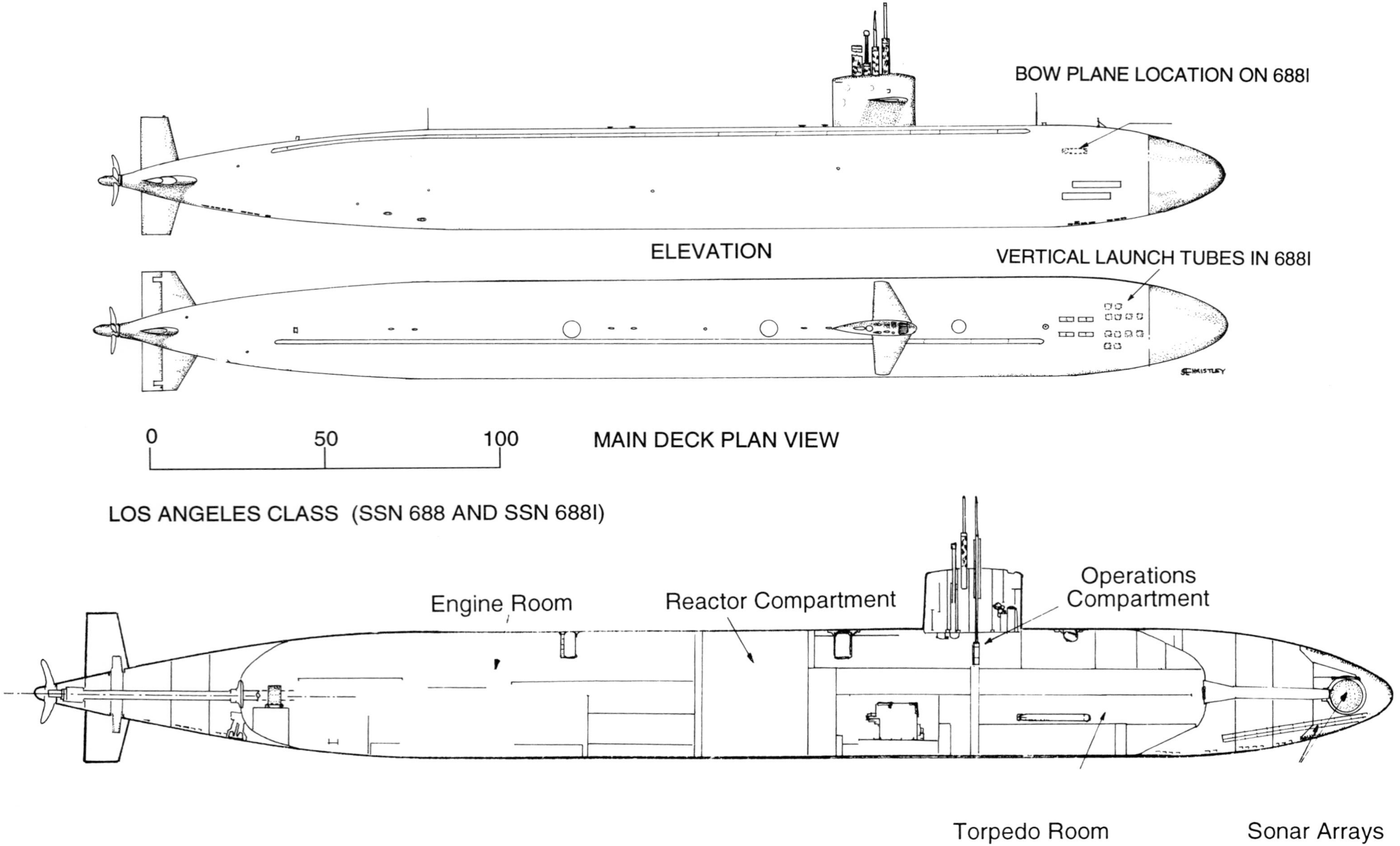

BOW PLANE LOCATION ON 688I

VERTICAL LAUNCH TUBES IN 688I

ELEVATION

MAIN DECK PLAN VIEW

0   50   100

LOS ANGELES CLASS (SSN 688 AND SSN 688I)

Operations
Compartment

Reactor Compartment

Engine Room

Torpedo Room

Sonar Arrays

Los Angeles, plan, elevation, and inboard profiles. Compared to a *Sturgeon*, a *Los Angeles* is somewhat squeezed, presumably because she lacks the space of the former's bottle-nose. The two middle decks have only limited clearance. Unlike a *Sturgeon*, a *Los Angeles* has her sonar room *forward* of the control space and attack center. The diesel generator is shown in the auxiliary machinery room, just forward of its fuel tank (on the other side of the reactor compartment). (Jim Christley) new Mk 48 torpedo, and also with the location of the torpedo tubes. Wire-guided torpedoes could best be fired straight ahead from a position *under* the hull, the tubes being canted down.[17] Subroc, already unusable in many situations, could be replaced by a non-nuclear missile carrying a new short torpedo that might achieve something close to a Mk 48 acoustic performance (albeit rather lower speed) in Mk 37 dimensions. To allow for future torpedo growth, a new 25×300-inch tube could be available by FY 75.

The committee called its new non-nuclear missile STAM (submarine tactical missile). Because it was non-nuclear, STAM could not achieve the definite kill associated with Subroc. Therefore, a submarine firing it could not afford the final ranging (and alerting) ping associated with Subroc; a STAM submarine would have to fight passively.

STAM could fly far beyond usable ASW ranges. Soviet surface ships could be tracked by the submarine's acoustic sensors, and targeting data developed by other sources could be transmitted down to the submarine. The same missile could carry a small nuclear warhead, so the STAM submarine could supplement the strategic submarine force. The missile would be too large for a torpedo tube: 30×300 in, 6,000–8,000 lb, with a range of 5–30 nm.[18] It appeared that vertical launch tubes could be backfitted to *Permit*s and all later nuclear attack submarines. In March 1969, the STAM concept formally replaced the earlier requirement for a non-nuclear version of Subroc.

Admiral Rickover saw the D1W-powered submarine as the preferable solution to the speed problem. By August 1970, he wanted to marry the D1W to the STAM missile. On 15 August, the CNO asked for concept studies for a 33–35-kt submarine armed with torpedoes and missiles (i.e., with STAM) and equipped with a sonar at least comparable to that on the new *Los Angeles*. She would probably have to be built of HY-80, but she would dive as deep as a *Sturgeon*.[19]

The CNO formed a new ad hoc committee on 1 October. Its 28 November 1970 report emphasized a new mission made practical by the STAM missile: ocean area control through standoff missile attacks on enemy warships, such as the surface action groups the Soviets were then deploying in the Mediterranean. Improvements in Soviet ASW might well make conventional torpedo attacks difficult. One or two of the new submarines would be included in each fleet. Their high speed would bring them into position to deal quickly and suddenly with surface action groups. Ideally, missiles would be fired in salvo. The committee favored a radar-guided sea-skimmer over a ballistic weapon, on the theory that a radar-guided weapon could overcome inexact targeting data by searching while it swept down a line of bearing. At least 1,000 lb of warhead apparently would be needed to deal with a destroyer or small cruiser.

By 1971, STAM had grown into an impressive long-range cruise missile (ACM). The encapsulated Harpoon, which would enter service in 1975, was seen as an interim step toward a subsonic ACM, which would enter service

in 1979. Initially, it would have a range of 140 nm, but that would eventually increase to 400 nm. Using the existing Harpoon terminal seeker, the ACM would be modified for expanded search because the target would move much farther away after the missile was fired. It seemed possible that the submarine's own sensors could target the 140-nm missile, but external data supplied by some sort of high-capacity data link would be needed for 400 nm. The ACM would be fired from a 40×360-in tube; it was assumed that limiting it to torpedo tube dimensions would unduly restrict missile performance. The three projected versions of ACM are described in Table 10–1.

A typical Soviet surface action group might consist of two cruisers and six destroyers. If 2 or 3 missiles were fired at each target, that amounted to a total of 16 to 24 missiles. For a single target, the committee wanted the submarine to be able to attack 9 or 10 times without rearming, for a total of 18 to 20 missiles. Therefore, the committee settled on a total of 20 missile tubes.

Several alternative missile launcher concepts were rejected. A revolver wrapped around the hull could jam and had limited growth potential. Similarly, one jam could cripple a reloadable launcher (with two or three tubes) in the sail. Horizontal pods would be ineffective at periscope depth or on the surface. They would also break the submarine's streamlined shape and thus would be a noise source. Combined missile/torpedo tubes were rejected as too complex, and it might be difficult to move heavy missiles around a small torpedo room.

The committee agreed with the CNO's call for higher speed. As with *Los Angeles*, speed was clearly helpful in dealing with fast Soviet submarines. It was also quite valuable for the new missile attack role: to close fast surface targets and also to allow the submarine to leave the missile launch point, the location of which would be revealed as the missiles flew out of the sea. Much of this logic probably applied to the Soviet Oscar class, which had much the same surface attack role as was planned for the big U.S. submarine.

Also, the committee wanted to restore the depth lost in the *Los Angeles* design. This would require major system redesign for such elements as hull penetrations, condensers, and piping. Depth was increasingly valued because it allowed more flexible sonar operation and more space for evasion after a missile attack revealed the submarine's position.

Firm conceptual design guidelines were set on 21 January 1971. The combination of high speed and big missiles

Table 10–1.   ACM Alternatives, 1971

	Subsonic	Supersonic	Strategic
Dimensions (ft)	34×336	34×340	34×336
Launch weight (tons)	8,600	11,420	9,950
W/O Booster (tons)	6,183	7,519	——
Warhead	1,000 AP	700	260
Speed (Mach)	0.8	2.0	0.8
Range (nm)	400	400	1,800

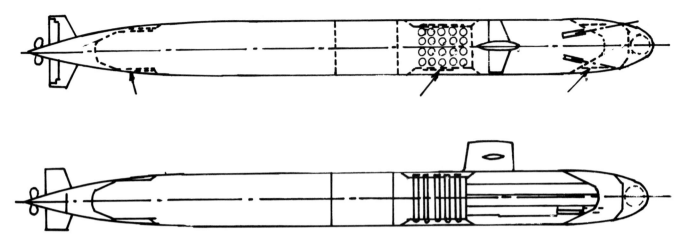

APHNAS, attack submarine of the mid-1970s, armed with torpedoes (four tubes) and 20 cruise missiles. As in a strategic submarine, the reactor was abaft the missile tubes. Arrows indicate the positions of the three elements of the wide aperture array (WAA) sonar on each side; a BQQ-5 DNA sphere is in the bow. Dimensions: 472×40 ft (13,000 tons).

implied, as might have been expected, that the new submarine would be powered by the big D1W. That, in turn, set hull diameter at 40 ft, compared with 33 ft for *Los Angeles*. As the ad hoc committee had recommended, the new submarine would carry 20 STAMs (in tubes abaft the sail), as well as more torpedoes than *Los Angeles*.

The new submarine was the first one designed for an entirely passive operation, that is, detecting targets passively at long range and then obtaining an entirely passive fire-control solution. She was therefore designed from the outset to have a towed array. The active bow sphere had to be retained as a hedge against Soviet silencing.

The passive alternative to a single ranging ping was rapid (virtually instantaneous) localization (RAPLOC) by triangulation. Limited by its high frequency and limited gain, the existing PUFFS could not reach STAM range. The new design substituted much larger, lower-frequency planar (rather than line) arrays exploiting the same propagation modes previously available only from the bow sphere (bottom and surface bounce and convergence zone). This WAA made the anti-submarine version of STAM a practicable proposition. It could also detect quite distant surface ships, perhaps out to extreme STAM range. A single array panel was demonstrated on a simulated submarine on Lake Seneca in 1967. WAA was successfully tested aboard *Baya* during FY 71. A developmental prototype was tested at sea on board *Barb* between January and April 1980. Beginning in July 1987, *Augusta* tested the prototype array. WAA is part of the current *Seawolf* sonar; a stand-alone version is designated BQG-5.

Table 10–2 shows the baseline design of the new submarine, compared with *Los Angeles,* as of 16 April 1971. The missiles were accommodated in a wasp-waist section abaft the sail (four rows of five missiles each) between the operations compartment and the reactor. The new submarine was soon designated APHNAS (advanced performance high-speed nuclear attack submarine) to distinguish it from HSNAS (high-speed nuclear attack submarine, or *Los Angeles*). Among the variations considered at this stage were using a new HY-100 steel, using bow rather

Table 10–2. The Big Submarine, 16 April 1971

	Baseline	*Los Angeles*
LOA (ft)	472	366
Diameter (ft)	40	33
Surfaced displacement (tons)	12,075	6,105
Submerged displacement (tons)	13,649	6,927
Mean draft (ft)	32.8	27.2
Officers	12	12
Chief petty officers	15	12
Enlisted	84	84
Reserve buoyancy	13%	13.5%

than sail planes, omitting WAA, and varying the missile load.

Chief of Naval Materiel released the APHNAS report to CNO on 26 June 1971, and the project was presented to the CNO Executive Board on 3 August. The CNO formally requested a preliminary design on 18 August. It seemed that at least a few such submarines would be built; however, they would be extremely expensive. The new CNO, Adm. Elmo Zumwalt, feared that a few APHNASs soon would become a large number of standard production submarines, just as the single prototype *Los Angeles* had turned into the new standard attack submarine.

In September 1971, Zumwalt ordered his systems analysis arm, Op-96, to supervise a new overall study of future submarine employment over the next two decades. APHNAS was clearly in trouble. To those who had survived (and fought) CONFORM, a new trade-off study must have seemed eerily familiar. Moreover, the terms of the study, a comparison of *Sturgeon, Los Angeles,* and APHNAS, hinted at Zumwalt's likely intention of cutting *Los Angeles* production short (never mind APHNAS) in favor of a return to the less expensive *Sturgeon.* To have abandoned APHNAS altogether late in 1971 would have been to accept Zumwalt's unstated desire to revive the issue that apparently had been settled in 1968 when *Los Angeles* superseded *Sturgeon*. As long as the study proceeded, APHNAS would attract criticism that might otherwise have been concentrated on *Los Angeles*.

The submariners argued that the big power plant offered enough extra speed to enable them to evade Soviet torpedoes fired back in response to their own shots.[20] Moreover, the higher the maximum speed, the higher was the tactical speed at which the submarine could effectively use her sonars. A larger submarine could accommodate new sonars, such as WAA, that would restore the ability of U.S submarines to strike at quieter Soviet submarines at long range. Finally, STAM offered a new and valuable capability, particularly against the growing Soviet surface fleet.

In August 1972, it appeared that the lead ship would cost $500 million to $600 million; follow-on ships would cost $300 million to $400 million. By way of contrast, five FY 74 *Los Angeles*-class submarines would cost a total of about $900 million. A serious APHNAS program might consume as much as 20 percent of the overall nonstrategic shipbuilding/conversion budget, just as the expensive Trident strategic submarine program loomed.

Most unusually, Op-96 appended a critique to every copy of the study. It chose to concentrate on ASW, which automatically excluded STAM. Nothing else really justified a 14,000-ton submarine. The study had not considered a *Los Angeles* enlarged to accommodate the WAA or the towed array. Op-96 estimated that the WAA would increase ASW effectiveness of *Los Angeles* by about 35 percent. It considered the study's treatment of torpedo attack and evasion unrealistic. Although the big submarine might survive by evading, in doing so she would break torpedo guidance wires and thus probably fail to sink the counterattacking target. Moreover, merely because it was so much larger, the big submarine would be easier to detect with active sonar. Soviet submarines probably would use mainly active, rather than passive, sonars.

STAM was interesting, but it did not necessarily require the new submarine. Indeed, there was some suspicion that STAM had deliberately been made larger than a torpedo tube so that it could be carried only by a big new submarine (i.e., one powered by the new reactor). Rickover certainly needed an application to justify the cost of the submarinized D1W, but it also can be argued that anyone primarily interested in STAM would have found Rickover's support well worthwhile. When Admiral Zumwalt killed the APHNAS project late in 1972, he ordered development of a tactical version of the new Tomahawk strategic cruise missile. It turned out that much the same performance could be achieved within the volume of a conventional torpedo tube. The interim ACM, the encapsulated Harpoon, was attractive because it could be fired from outside effective ASW range.

For Tomahawk attacks at really long range, intelligence data were collated to provide a submarine with an anti-ship targeting picture held in an on-board computer, the basis of a new OTH-T (over the horizon targeting) system.

The picture was updated every so often by a flash message describing new items. This idea was first tested about 1975 in the Mediterranean during an exercise called Outlaw Shark. OTH-T projected ahead the maneuvers of the ships in its tactical picture, so that the missile could be fired at an expected ship position, rather than at the last reported position. That reduced search time once the missile appeared at the target area, about half an hour after it had been launched. The longer it searched, the better the chance that it would be shot down before it found anything.

Submarines were weight-critical. It turned out that a fully fueled Tomahawk, plus its launch capsule, was too heavy for some (presumably, *Los Angeles*-class) submarines. For a time, therefore, submarine-launched land attack Tomahawks carried only partial fuel loads. This problem was solved in the late 1980s with a new lightweight launch capsule. Even so, missiles fired at Iraq from the Mediterranean (during the Gulf War) had to be specially modified to take full fuel loads.

The combination of a Mk 117 and the OTH-T system, Combat Control System Mk 1, was approved for service use in July 1980 and first appeared on board SSNs 716–725 and 750. The OTH-T and a Mk 117 replaced a Mk 113 Mod 0 on board the first *Los Angeles*-class ships (SSN 688-699); from FY 84 on, it upgraded the Mk 117 Mods 2 and 3 on board *Sturgeons*.

The ASW version of STAM became the standoff weapon (SOW) and eventually Sea Lance. It was canceled in 1991.

The demise of APHNAS effectively guaranteed that *Los Angeles* production would continue through about FY 76; a design begun in 1973 would not be ready for production for some years. To maintain a steady force level of 90 nuclear attack submarines, the United States would have to buy 29 in FY 77–88. In 1973, Secretary of Defense James M. Schlesinger requested a "high-low" study of submarine alternatives. The fleet was already a high-low mix; it might be necessary to replace the less capable submarines with new low-mix submarines. The high-low idea had been popularized by Admiral Zumwalt, and it died when he left office on 1 July 1974. The new high-low study, begun late in 1973, was presented to the CNO Executive Board in May 1974. Its goal for unit cost was $125 million to $175 million in FY 74 dollars.

The low-mix submarines (Type A) were imagined as replacements for *Thresher*s and their predecessors that would fill the many barrier positions. The high-mix Type B submarines would operate in forward areas and might also directly support the fleet. Any return to diesel submarines was rejected as fundamentally uneconomical.[21]

It turned out that something like a *Sturgeon*, equipped with the BQQ-5 digital sonar (with a towed array), would be quite effective in the barrier (A) role. The existing S5W reactor would provide enough power for the submarine to evade a modern torpedo (a Mk 48).

For the B role, Commander in Chief, Atlantic (CinCLant) and Commander in Chief, Pacific (CinCPac) were both much interested in interdicting Soviet surface forces

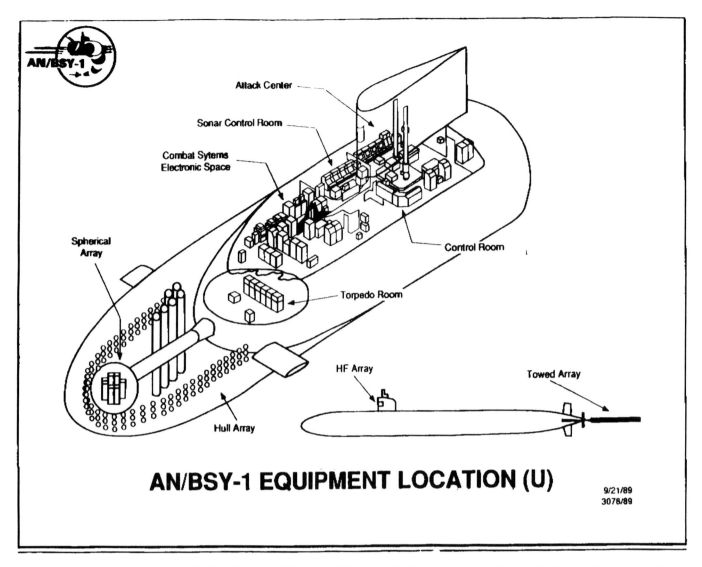

AN/BSY-1

Attack Center

Sonar Control Room

Combat Systems
Electronic Space

Spherical
Array

Control Room

Torpedo Room

HF Array

Towed Array

Hull Array

AN/BSY-1 EQUIPMENT LOCATION (U)

9/21/89
3078/89

This illustration of BSY-1, as installed on board an "improved" *Los Angeles*-class submarine, shows the bow sphere, hydrophones of the hull array, and (in the smaller drawing) HF array for mine avoidance and the towed array. Note the standard arrangement of control room to port and attack center to starboard, separated by the periscopes. Also shown are 6 of the 12 Tomahawk vertical tubes. (U.S. Navy drawing)

before they could engage U.S. task forces. They expected submarines to operate in target-rich, high-threat areas, where they would be most endangered when passing in or out. More weapons would translate into longer survival and greater effectiveness. The most obvious solution was to modify the existing *Los Angeles* to accommodate 8 tubes and about twice as many (40 to 50) weapons at the cost of about 1 kt. By this time, such missiles as Sub-Harpoon were clearly in prospect. Because they were not wire-guided, they could be fired in large salvos; more tubes translated into more hits. This was much the same logic as the choice of 20 tubes for APHNAS. A follow-on modified *Los Angeles* was expected to cost $207.6 million ($25.96 million plus the cost of an unmodified *Los Angeles*). A Type B, based on Type A, would cost $172.5 million ($30.5 million plus the cost of the unmodified Type A).

ASW STAM (now called ASW SOW) was still attractive. Available technology made a good torpedo, a Mk 48, more

effective. However, if the Soviets developed their own towed arrays, U.S. submarines might find it impossible to reach appropriate firing positions. In that case, a quick shot with a SOW might be the only possible solution. One possible form of SOW would be Tarpon, an encapsulated Harpoon carrying a Mk 46 torpedo. It was not adopted, but the idea was later seriously considered by the Royal Navy.

The high-low study concluded that the United States should buy 18 barrier (Type A) submarines and 11 high-performance (Type B) craft. It proposed that the first Type A submarines be ordered as soon as possible, with the clear implication that *Los Angeles* would be succeeded in production by a modernized *Sturgeon* with a somewhat quieter propeller.

Op-02 objected that this particular mix would not save much money. Moreover, U.S. submarines would never be so numerous that some could be assigned to specific low-threat missions, nor would underwater communications ever be so effective that several low-mix submarines could combine to deal with a high threat. The U.S. Navy would have to build standard submarines. Meanwhile, the planning horizon became shorter. The next trade-off study (April 1975) examined submarines to be built in FY 78–82.

At this time, the extended planning annex to the long-term defense plan showed a new submarine (SSNX) in the FY 81 program. It would embody the fruits of post–*Los Angeles* R&D: an improved hull steel, an advanced reactor (D1W), an improved sonar, and a long-range missile (which turned out to be Tomahawk). The 1973–74 study was restructured to compare five alternatives: Type A, an eight-tube Type A, an eight-tube *Los Angeles,* a WAA version of *Los Angeles,* and an advanced SSN (with eight torpedo tubes and the D1W power plant). Conceptual designs of the five basic alternatives were developed and Class F costs for FY 78 computed (see Table 10–3). To be worth buying, any new near-term design had to be so much better than a repeat *Los Angeles* that it would be worth building in small numbers until SSNX entered production. The 1975 study turned into a counteroffensive against those attempting to kill off *Los Angeles.* Later, in ASW, *Los Angeles* was found to be 40 percent more efficient than the low-mix submarine; the big advanced SSN was 60 percent more efficient. Weapon loadouts also mattered; the low-mix submarine could barely accommodate only eight tubes. She lacked space for future growth an embodied lower shock standards than *Los Angeles.* Speed was vital, as well. Even in a barrier, a faster submarine was attractive because it could better avoid counterattack by transiters.[22] It was impossible, however, to quantify the advantage of a particular speed.

The study concluded that it would be best to buy nine submarines of the eight-tube *Los Angeles* class in FY 78–82, based on the current rate of production (five every two years). The bigger D1W submarine was not yet cost-effective. It was assumed that the new high-powered plant would complete development in FY 82, in time for installation in a large new submarine during the mid-1980s.

In May 1975, the CNO directed that SSNX be a fast, quiet, multipurpose submarine no larger than *Los Angeles.* A preliminary NAVSEA study showed that the new requirements, particularly more weapons and more torpedo tubes, could not be achieved within such dimensions until new technology became available in the early 1980s. Nothing that was sufficiently better than *Los Angeles* would be available before FY 85, at the earliest. NAVSEA believed it best to build an improved (reengineered) *Los Angeles* in FY 83 and FY 84 and continue work on a successor, SSNX. The improved *Los Angeles* might have WAA, more weapons with a faster launch rate, and better and quieter machinery. It would be armed with the new ADCAP torpedo (advanced capability follow-on to a Mk 48) and ASW standoff missile. Another possibility was a submarine air defense missile; the submarine force was using more and more weapons, such as Harpoon and Tomahawk, whose air trajectories provided datums for enemy searchers.

This view was not universally popular. The Carter administration sought once again to reverse submarine growth with a new fleet attack (F/A) submarine. The F/A would combine the existing S5W power plant with a fatter (hydrodynamically superior) hull and six, rather than four, torpedo tubes in order to achieve somewhat better speed than *Sturgeon.* The submarine force preferred SSNX; by the late 1970s, this was envisaged as a new

Table 10–3.   Submarine Alternatives, 1975

	Low	Multi-Low	688/WAA	Multi-688	Advanced SSN
LOA (ft)	304.5	341.5	380	415	463
Diameter (ft)	31-8	31-8	33	33	40
Submerged displacement (tons)	5,060	5,810	7,336	8,080	13,500
Plant	S5W	S5W	S6G	S6G	D1W
Lead cost (millions)	$455	$517	$367	$526	$935
Follow-on ship cost (millions)	$268	$299	$352	$412	$602
Complement	12/108	12/112	12/115	12/119	12/119
Relative cost (millions)					
Procurement	$1	$1.26	$1.13	$1.51	$2.34
Life-cycle	$1	$1.19	$1.08	$1.32	$1.89
Relative effectiveness					
Barrier	1	1.4	1	1.4	1.6
CV Pro	1	1.5	1	1.5	2.1
ASSW/coastal interdiction—ASSW	1	1.4	2.0	2.1–2.4	2.5–3.5
Vector interception	1	1.6	1	1.6	2.1

Note: The advanced submarine had no missile tubes, but it had eight torpedo tubes and many more weapons than the more conventional submarines. "Multi-" means twice as many torpedo tubes (eight rather than four) and twice as many weapons.

Asheville is a typical "improved" *Los Angeles*-class submarine; the visible change is the elimination of sail planes in favor of retractable bow planes for easier operation through ice. Not visible are the vertical missile launch tubes in the bow, the improved mast sensors (including an IR periscope and an improved direction-finder), the improved combat system (BSY-1, including the improved mine-detection sonar), the paired towed arrays (the fairing covers the TB-16 low-speed array; there is also a long thin line array for high speed), the hull and sonar dome coatings (hull treatment), the quieter machinery (quieter propeller, quiet pumps, and electrical silencing), and the improved navigational equipment (presumably a better gyro/SINS, partly for better TMA for fire control) of this class. Unlike the original *Los Angeles,* the improved version can deliver mines. These improvements finally expended the weight margin of the *Los Angeles* design; the navy credited them with doubling the submarine's overall performance. The markings on the hull are to assist a mating DSRV.

six-tube hull wrapped around a substantially boosted *Los Angeles* power plant. F/A and SSNX were conceived for initial production in FY 83; the FY 78–82 production run already had been fixed, in effect, by the 1975 study. Versions of these designs are compared in Table 10–4.

The alternative was a reengineered *Los Angeles,* the first new submarine design taken almost to the point of detailed design between *Los Angeles* and *Seawolf.* It began in November 1975 with an OpNav request for a modernized *Los Angeles* design. WAA would be the main improvement. Like the earlier PUFFS, WAA required that all three arrays on one side be precisely in line. Accuracy at maximum range demanded that they be as far apart as possible. One solution would have been to lay them out along the parallel body section of the hull. The alternative adopted was to place the forward and after arrays inside the main ballast tanks at the ends. Amidships, the pressure hull was lengthened and necked in to accommodate the two middle arrays. This neck would be the only double-hull section of the submarine. The operations compartment had to be lengthened slightly to maintain the balance of the hull. Adding 28 ft of length (bringing displacement to 6,661/7,538 tons) was expected to cost about a knot in speed.

The sail would be enlarged, with the hope that careful design would avoid any added drag, to accommodate Dark Eyes, the new infrared periscope. Other improvements would include a six-tube version of the 6-in countermeasures launcher then being installed on board SSBNs,

the new integrated acoustic communications system (IACS), a new submarine communications buoy (BIAS, BSQ-5), and the new electrically suspended gyro navigator (ESGN) intended to replace the earlier SINS. Preliminary design was completed in June 1976, but contract design was deferred. Another long-hull *Los Angeles* preliminary design, presumably a return to the reengineered design, was completed early in 1978.

By May or June 1980, it was clear that neither F/A nor SSNX would be ready by FY 83. The reengineered *Los Angeles* was dropped. The next-generation submarine was deferred to FY 85. To meet that date, the basic design would be chosen about December 1980, with contract design between January 1982 and January 1983 and detail design between January 1983 and January 1985; the contract would be awarded about January 1985. The design schedule could have been compressed to permit an award in FY 84, but the new combat system would not have been ready that early.

When Jimmy Carter lost the 1980 election, major pending procurement decisions were naturally delayed until the new administration took office. Both F/A and SSNX were quite cost constrained, and it was clear that the Reagan administration would be willing to take a fresh look at submarine alternatives. That took somewhat longer than might have been expected, so the new *Seawolf*-class submarine was not funded until FY 89.

Meanwhile, the *Los Angeles* class remained in production. Much could be done short of redesign. The subma-

Table 10–4.   Submarine Alternatives, Early 1981

	F/A	SSNX	SSN 716
SHP	15,100	38,700	30,000
Length (ft)	237.5	301.25	360
Diameter (ft)	38.0	38.75	33.0
Draft (ft)	35.4	36.0	32.3
Submerged displacement (tons)	4,965	7,263	6,926
Torpedo tubes/weapons	6/32	6/32	4/22
VLS	——	12–24	——
Planes	Fairwater	Bow	Fairwater

Note: Because of improved hydrodynamics (and, presumably, a more efficient propeller), F/A gained about 3 kt over *Sturgeon*. SSNX would have been faster than the D1W submarine, albeit not nearly as well armed. Both F/A and SSNX used slower-turning, hence quieter and more efficient, propellers than *Los Angeles*. All three alternatives had the same test depth.

rine still had substantial weight and buoyancy margins and thus would not have to be lengthened to accommodate a variety of improvements. The design also could be made more produceable. For FY 82 and later submarines, tanks, supports, and control surface structures could be redesigned, as well as the electrical power distribution system. Welding and test procedures also could be revised. Such improvements come under the head of "learning curve savings" in a very long production run. The submarine could be further silenced, with quieter generators and pumps and possibly a new quiet propulsor. (The latter turned out to be the pump jet of the next class, *Seawolf*.) *Hartford* (SSN 768, FY 88) was the first to incorporate the extra silencing features; she also acquired a new propulsor and extra tail fins, as in *Seawolf*. By this time, the class had run out of growth margin.[23]

During the late 1970s, the navy had been developing a vertical launcher system for the surface fleet, specifically to enable ships to fire Tomahawk cruise missiles. Submarines could also fire Tomahawks but only out of torpedo tubes, in which case they competed with torpedoes for limited space. Typically, up to 8 Tomahawks might be carried, but no more than 3 could be preloaded in the tubes because the submarine had to reserve at least 1 tube for self-defense. In 1979, a redesigned bow intended mainly to cut production costs turned out to be readily adaptable to installing 12 vertical launching tubes in the forward main ballast tank. The bow was immediately ordered for two new submarines (SSN 719 and 720, the FY 78 and FY 79 units). This step increased standard Tomahawk capacity to 20; up to 15 of these could be instantly ready for firing. The firing interval also would be much shorter. With more available Tomahawk firepower, new missions became attractive. For example, a submarine with vertical

Tomahawk vertical launch tubes are open on board *Oklahoma City* (SSN 723), February 1991. They were worked in around the stalk between the pressure hull and the sonar dome and, thus, did not require any major redesign of the submarine. Fortunately the submarine already required some trim ballast forward, some of which the tubes replaced. Two submarines of this type, *Louisville* and *Pittsburgh*, fired Tomahawks during the Gulf War; they were the first U.S. submarines to fire guided missiles in combat. Many submarines *without* vertical tubes carry 8 Tomahawks in lieu of torpedoes, so a *Los Angeles* with vertical tubes probably carries 20 Tomahawks. The main drawback of the vertical tubes is that, at this writing, they cannot carry anything other than Tomahawks.

tubes might suppress air defenses in support of a carrier air strike, thus greatly amplifying the effect of the carrier.[24] FY 78 and all later units received the 12 vertical launch tubes for Tomahawk. SSN 712 was the first unit declared operational with Tomahawk (initially, in her strategic form) on 30 November 1983. During the Gulf War, *Louisville* fired 8 Tomahawks against Iraq; *Pittsburgh* fired 4.

SSN 691 (*Memphis*) is being used to test new submarine features; however, a projected reconstruction with a single 762-mm torpedo tube (of the type in the *Seawolf* class) that replaced both tubes on one side had to be abandoned. SSN 710 (*Augusta*) became the trials ship for the WAA in July 1987. WAA (designated BQG-5A in this class) was planned for retrofit into earlier boats, but they were too close to their weight limit. A lighter array probably will be developed for this class, particularly if few more advanced submarines are built (see chapter 12).

11

Strategic Submarines

IN 1945, MANY U.S. submariners drew the obvious connection between a submarine, which could survive close to enemy territory, and a nuclear bomb, which was small enough for the submarine to deliver to a vital target ashore. The bomb could be delivered by a ballistic vehicle, such as the V-2, or a winged vehicle, either manned or, like the wartime V-1, unmanned. Obviously, no submarine could carry many vehicles, but only a few atomic bombs would be devastating. Existing nuclear weapons were far too large for either V-1 or V-2 to carry, but within a year or so the potential for smaller ones was well understood.

As submitted in November 1945 (and approved by the CNO on 17 January 1946 and the secretary of the navy that March), the postwar program of the Submarine Officers Conference included two cruise missile conversions and a heavy bombardment submarine, presumably conceived as a super gunboat. The CNO transformed the latter into a platform for an experimental heavy, long-range rocket. A mid-August 1946 OpNav conference on the integration of submarines and missiles accepted that the missiles would have nuclear warheads. Work on compact nuclear weapons began in 1948.[1]

The Germans had designed a special submersible barge for their V-2 ballistic missile; three barges could be towed by a conventional U-boat.[2] If the U.S. Navy could produce an equivalent barge, all of its attack submarines could become potential strategic attackers. Moreover, submarine dimensions would not limit the size (hence the performance) of the missile; even a submarine of reasonable dimensions could launch a big nuclear-armed rocket. Early in November 1946, ComSubPac specifically recommended development of the German submersible missile barge. Scale models were built. Unfortunately, as the missile motor started, its exhaust gas blew the barge apart and threw the missile off course. This program died around 1949 in favor of a lower-priority program for an SSB carrying missiles in canisters with massive exhaust tubes.

Airplanes and cruise missiles needed takeoff ramps or catapults. It seemed obvious that they would require large submarines involving new design problems. Because an aircraft carrier, tentatively designated SSV, would be even larger, it was sketched first to study the new problems.[3]

An SSG would be 400 ft long and carry two missiles in a large pressure tank.[4]

The navy was already developing a primitive cruise missile, Loon (its version of the German V-1). Conversion of two fleet boats, *Carbonero* and *Cusk,* was approved on 5 March 1946; *Cusk* was completed at Mare Island on 6 February 1947.[5] She fired a Loon off the California coast about a week later. The experimental conversions were limited to a 50-ft launching ramp, fueling facilities, checkout equipment, and electrical connections; the submarine had to remain on the surface until the missile was fired. (*Cusk* was later fitted with a small pressure-proof missile hangar.) Loon was command guided and tracked by the submarine's SV-4 air search radar. Range was usually 54 nm, but a submarine could track it out to 80 nm, and a second submarine could extend tracking (hence, effective) range to 135 nm. By 1949, demonstrated CEP (circular error [probable]) was about 6,000 yd, an acceptable distance if the missile were provided with a nuclear warhead.[6]

In 1946, BuAer let contracts for a supersonic (Mach 2.0) ramjet missile, the Grumman Rigel (SSM-N-6), and for a subsonic (initially Mach 0.91) interim turbojet powered missile, the Chance Vought Regulus (SSM-N-8). Each was to carry a 3,000-lb warhead to a range of 500 nm. For the longer term, BuOrd proposed to develop its series of ramjet antiaircraft missiles into Triton, which would achieve Rigel speed but reach a range of 2000 nm. Rigel required a long catapult on deck; it was perceived as too big and too risky. In 1953, it died in an initial round of Eisenhower administration cuts. Chance Vought sold an improved Regulus II, using a turbojet engine, as a simpler alternative to achieve supersonic speed and longer range. It was twice the size of Regulus I and could not fit into the same hangar; the decision to adopt it automatically entailed new Regulus II submarines. Work on Triton continued.[7] In the end, only Regulus I entered service.

Loon proved what a subsonic missile could do. During 1948 fleet exercises, three of these slow (Mach 0.6) missiles were fired at an opposing task fleet. In each case, the fleet knew the missile was coming and knew where the launch submarine was. In one case, the missile even contained a radar beacon for easier tracking. It was never shot down.

Grayback is shown under construction, with her Regulus launcher being assembled.

Cusk shows her launching ramp, her new hangar, and the much enlarged SV radar used for missile tracking (Mare Island, 18 September 1947).

A submarine-borne missile might well evade enemy defenses altogether because of the stealth of its launching platform.

Like Loon, Regulus was command guided; as yet, there was no effective form of inertial guidance. The submarine's TROUNCE (tactical radar omnidirectional underwater navigational control equipment) used a BPQ-1 or -2 radar to track the missile out to the radar horizon at about 250 nm; port and starboard steering commands were superimposed on the tracking radar signal. The missile was sent toward a guidance area near the enemy coast, where a second submarine took over control. She then tracked and guided the missile into position to dive onto the target. The Regulus program included provision for missile guidance in many attack submarines.[8]

A Regulus submarine had to remain on the surface while the missile was unfolded, placed on the ramp, and fired. To guide the missile after launch, she had to remain at periscope depth, with a radar mast raised, for a considerable time (up to $\frac{1}{2}$ hr) after launch. The hangar itself could flood in rough weather.

By 1949, there was some hope that a Regulus conversion of a fleet boat could be included in the FY 51 budget. The budget turned out to be too tight, but the first Korean War program (FY 52) included the conversion of *Tunny* as a prototype SSG (SCB 28). She was recommissioned in

March 1953 and fired her first Regulus missile that July. A repeat *Tunny, Barbero* (SCB 118), was included in the FY 55 program.

Two Regulus I missiles were stowed, with their boosters, in a rotating ring inside a pressure-proof deck cylinder (originally designed for the troop-carrying submarine *Perch*). The lower missile was pulled out onto the launcher and the ring rotated to bring the other missile into position. The missile to be fired was checked out via an access trunk before the submarine surfaced. Like Loon, it was fired from a simple collapsible deck ramp.

The compact warheads that made Regulus attractive also made the submarine carrier more practical. In May 1952, Assistant Secretary of the Navy for Air Dan Kimball suggested that BuShips design a nuclear submarine capable of carrying three fast airplanes. BuAer was then designing the Sea Dart jet seaplane fighter. It would lift two 1,000-lb bombs or an equivalent weight (i.e., one of the new lightweight tactical nuclear weapons). The Design Division sketched a 7,000-ton, 460-ft submarine powered by a (nonexistent) 60,000-SHP reactor. She would achieve 28 kt, and test depth (limited by all the openings required for the airplanes) would be 500 ft. The aircraft would be carried in a hangar, brought up by elevator (this would impose some serious structural problems), and let out through a 16-ft dished door similar to that on a guided

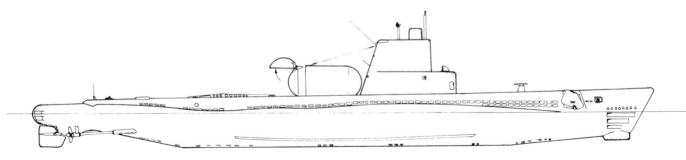

Tunny as a Regulus submarine, with the launcher folded down on deck abaft the pressure tank. (Jim Christley)

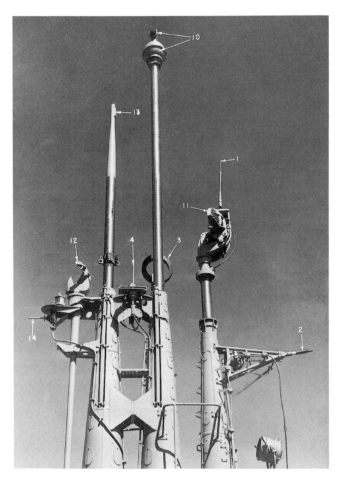

Cusk displays some of her antennas, 8 September 1952. Key: (1) radio whip antenna; (2) MF-HF whip (31-ft); (3) VLF loop (DAQ) on a mast offset to starboard; (4) VHF antenna 1 (66134); (5) UHF antenna (not visible); (6) a IFF Mk 10 antenna (not visible); (7) wing antenna (starboard, not visible); (8) VHF antenna 2, a stub atop the missile hangar (not visible); (9) wing antenna (port, not visible); (10) BPN-1 antenna for missile guidance; (11) SV-1 radar (modified for missile guidance); (12) SS radar; (13) attack periscope with ST radar; (14) ECM stub (RM66F890); and (15) ECM AS-371/S antenna (not visible). Antennas not visible in this photo are listed to indicate *Cusk*'s complete complement.

missile submarine. Sea Darts would be launched from a ramp because they could not take off in rough water. During December 1952–January 1953, the BuShips preliminary design section, with the goal of preparing for a large-scale conversion of fleet boats, studied an SSG conversion to launch Douglas Skyhawk (A-4) attack bombers equipped with hydro-skis. Douglas designed a small jet bomber, its Model 640, which could be handled in much the same way by a Regulus submarine.[9]

By the summer of 1953, the prototype *Nautilus* reactor had run its successful 100-hr test. In September 1953, Assistant Secretary of the Navy for Air James H. Smith proposed a new generation of nuclear Regulus submarines, which he called "underwater aircraft carriers," to carry large numbers of missiles at the expense of such encumbrances as torpedoes. There was as yet no firm interest

in this type of submarine, but OpNav formally requested a design study in December 1953.

The new SAR was the obvious power plant because it alone could drive the SSGN fast enough to evade attack while she was surfaced to fire her missiles. A series of sketch designs executed in January and February 1954 all showed horizontal figure-eight hulls to accommodate a pair of reactors side by side, with eight Regulus missiles in the hull proper. Displacement was 6,500–7,000 tons; length, 322–374 ft; and expected speed, 28 kt. A final undated sketch design, clearly part of the same series, moved the missiles to a long cylindrical hangar above the double-pressure hull. Dimensions were 327×45 ft (6,670 tons submerged); the SSGN was expected to make 27 kt. In addition to missiles, she would have 10 torpedo tubes (6 forward, 4 aft) and the remarkable total of 38 torpedoes. Clearly, she was too expensive; her main virtue was probably the ability to demonstrate that high speed was not yet practical. Moreover, it turned out that the SAR itself was not nearly as light as expected. The navy's attention returned to diesel missile submarines.

The first new-construction SSG (SCB 137) was included in the FY 56 program. Unlike the converted fleet boats, she was to have a large cylindrical hangar forward, built into the hull, that opened forward onto a launch rail fixed in the bow. The bow position was considered the driest, and it allowed the submarine to take the best position for minimum ship motion as she headed into wind and sea. A rejected alternative was placing the hangar in the bow itself, using it as a launcher, and trimming down the submarine to fire. The single hangar would accommodate four Regulus II or eight Regulus I missiles; it had double closure forward. All four torpedo tubes were aft, with 12 torpedoes.[10] Unlike contemporary attack submarines, this SSG was considerably faster on the surface than submerged, presumably because she was in greatest danger while running on the surface as she prepared to fire her missiles.

Early in 1955, a second SCB 137 was included in the tentative FY 57 budget. By June 1955, two more SSGs had been added to the FY 57 program, for a total of three. BuAer's long-term requirement was two SSGs and four SSGNs. In his review of the FY 57 program, CinCLant asked for a total of five SSGNs. CinCPac wanted two SSGs. These programs were small because carrier bombers were by far the preferred means of delivering nuclear weapons; the new *Forrestal*s were designed specifically to support heavy aircraft. That was why they were so expensive.

When Admiral Burke was sworn in as CNO in August 1955, it was clear that the developing technology for strategic strike, air defense, and ASW was extremely expensive. Within a few years, much of the existing fleet would suffer block obsolescence, yet large numbers of ships still would be needed, given the sheer size of the oceans. To build a new fleet in adequate numbers, Burke had to hold down unit costs. The Long Range Objectives Group observed that, if the navy shifted to missiles to deliver strategic weapons, it could drastically cut the size (hence, the cost)

Barbero, the former cargo carrier, shows her Regulus I in the launch position. The ramp folded down when not in use.

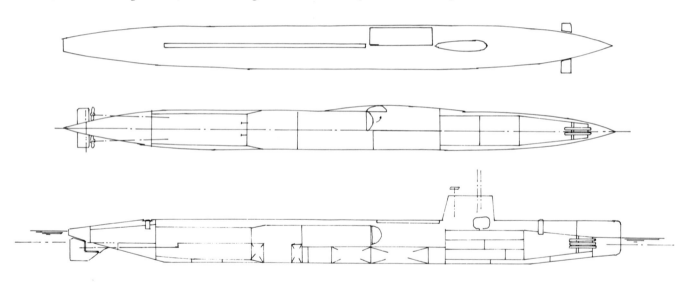

The BuShips Preliminary Design Division produced this sketch of a submarine aircraft carrier on 26 May 1952. A version was included in the January 1955 "dream book." Dimensions: 460 (overall)×38 ft; submerged displacement 9,000 tons (light displacement 6,700 tons). The version described in 1955 had a nonexistent 70,000 SHP power plant (in a single reactor room), to achieve 28 kt submerged, plus 126 Guppy I batteries. She would have carried three Sea Dart (F2Y) sea-based fighters, in three cylindrical hangars (two abreast, plus one to starboard alongside an elevator to port). Aircraft would have been recovered by running up the sloped stern ramp. The upper-deck plan shows the 170-ft launching track, required to launch the airplanes in rough weather. The cross section shows the 15-ft diameter (57-ft long) cylindrical Hangar No. 1 (closed by a dished 16-ft door, as in a missile submarine) above two safety tanks, alongside the free-flooding elevator well. Total hull depth would have been 35 ft.

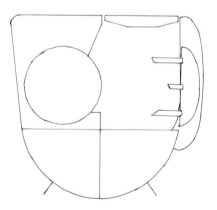

The original feasibility study called for a 60,000 SHP power plant and a test depth of 500 ft (in 1955 it was 700 ft, as in all other contemporary submarine designs). Diameter of the operating compartment (control room, living spaces) was 24 ft; of the reactor room, 26 ft (42 ft long); and of the machinery space, 26 ft (80 ft long).

The big cylindrical hangar in *Tunny* (shown here) and *Barbero* stowed two Regulus I missiles, one atop the other, in a rotating ring.

Newly completed as a missile boat, *Tunny* is shown off Mare Island, 16 April 1953. Her missile ramp has been folded down on deck.

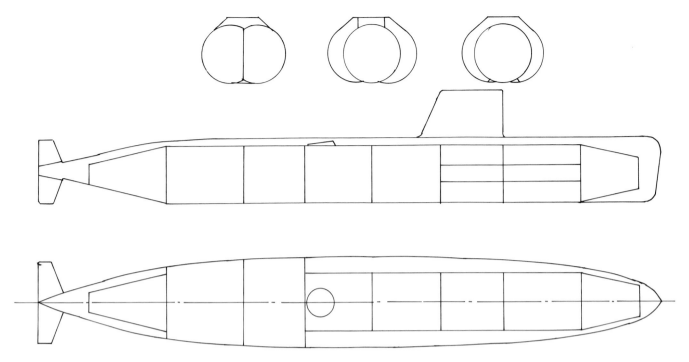

Regulus/SAR feasibility study No. 2, 29 January 1954. At a length of 322 ft, this was the shortest possible submarine that could stow the missiles in tandem, as was then required. Each of two 35-ft compartments abaft the three-deck section (officers' quarters forward of control room) accommodated four Regulus missiles. Abaft them were 32-ft reactor and 40-ft engine rooms, paired abreast (two SAR power trains). Proposed characteristics for the submarine were a displacement of 6,500 to 7,000 tons, a submerged speed of 28 kt, and a complement of 120. All circular-section hull sections (both single and figure eight) had 29-ft diameters. This version did not balance longitudinally, and later versions were longer.

of the next generation of carriers. In its first formal report (December 1955), the group proposed a total of 23 Regulus II submarines (four missiles each) to be in service by 1970 (15 by 1966). Nuclear power would be applied to this fleet as soon as economically feasible; by 1970, there would probably be 11 SSGs and 12 SSGNs. Burke took heed.

As a start, the first new-construction SSG, *Halibut*, was reordered on 27 February 1956 as a nuclear submarine (SCB 137A).[11] To expedite construction, she was powered by an S3W (as in the *Skate* class), which was then the standard attack submarine power plant. The bow launcher position was abandoned in favor of a turntable launcher between the hangar (moved to the bow) and the sail. The turntable could much more easily fire onto a desired heading independent of sea conditions, as well as better dispose of a dud athwartships. In effect, the deep buried hangar, chosen for better surface stability, was a separate

pressure hull (nearly the size of an old S-boat). It could accommodate four Regulus II or five Regulus I missiles stowed one atop another. To maintain overall hull strength, the designers had to provide extra heavy longitudinal-strength members and a thicker than usual outer hull in the area between hangar and main pressure hull. Access between the pressure hull and the hangar was provided by a narrow tube at about the submarine axis.

The submarine carried four long torpedo tubes forward and two short ones aft (for wire-guided Mk 37s); the forward torpedo room was in the forward end of the missile hangar. *Halibut* was the first submarine fitted with SINS, the inertial navigation system already planned for ballistic missile submarines.

Grayback (FY 53) and *Growler* (FY 55), two diesel attack submarines already under construction, were ordered

 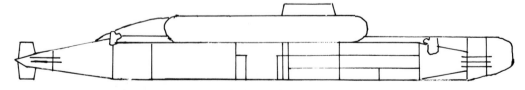

A somewhat different approach to a fast Regulus submarine was sketched later in 1954. By moving the missiles up out of the main pressure hull into a hangar alongside the sail, the designers could drastically shorten the submarine. Dimensions were 327×45 ft (6,670 tons submerged); estimated submerged speed was 27 kt. This submarine would have carried eight missiles plus 10 torpedo tubes (38 torpedoes). A total of 126 Guppy I batteries would have been carried just abaft the forward torpedo room. At this time, with *Nautilus* not yet at sea, the dual-SAR power plant was credited with an endurance of 2,000 hours at full power.

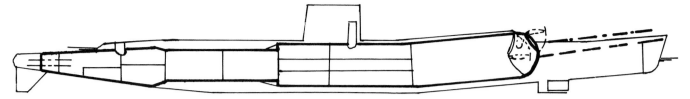

The FY 56 Regulus submarine, SCB 137, as sketched early in 1955 by BuShips. In this version all 12 torpedoes (and their four tubes) were aft; the entire bow was occupied by a big Regulus hangar (four Regulus II or eight Regulus I missiles) firing forward. It would have been relatively easy to swamp; the ships actually built had their hangars facing aft, presenting a blunt watertight bow to the sea. An alternative design eliminated the launching rail altogether; the submarine would have fired missiles directly out of her hangar, trimming down aft to elevate it above sea level. Unlike the two SCB 137As, this design had the new three-level arrangement amidships, with two engine rooms (total 8,000 SHP, for 20 kt) aft. Dimensions: 356×29 ft (2,800 tons light/4,200 tons submerged). Performance: 5,000 SHP = 14 kt submerged, using 378 Sargo II batteries (13 kt snorkeling); endurance 17,000 nm/10 kt surfaced, 10,500 nm/7 kt snorkeling. Estimated cost, in 1956, was $36.5 million.

completed as missile submarines (SCB 161). In effect, this accelerated completion of the 2 planned FY 57 SSGs (SCB 137). They were cut in two on the slip, and a new bow section incorporating two missile hangars (four Regulus I missiles) was added, with a turntable launcher between hangars and sail. *Growler* was 4 ft shorter than *Grayback*. Each had four torpedo tubes for self-defense. Each specially built Regulus submarine carried as many missiles as both of the converted fleet boats.

Initially, one SSG was stationed in each ocean. By late 1958, with 4 SSGs and 4 Regulus cruisers in commission, the navy decided to keep all of the Regulus ships in the Pacific in order to maintain 4 SSG missiles (2 converted fleet boats or 1 newly built submarine) continuously on station. The Regulus submarines formed SubRon 1 at Pearl Harbor and patrolled in the Western Pacific until Regulus was replaced there by Polaris in 1964.

Burke substantially enlarged the Regulus program. As of September 1956, the single FY 56 SSGN and 2 FY 57 SSGs were to have been followed by 5 SSGNs in FY 58 and then 4 per year in FY 59–62, for a total of 20 SSGNs and 2 SSGs. Money was too tight; the FY 58 program was cut to 3 SSGNs. At first the FY 59 budget included only a single SSGN. CinCLant pressed for at least 2 (another was later added). He wanted to build up to a total of 15 SSGNs and keep 5 SSGNs constantly available as a minimum Atlantic deterrent. CinCPac agreed.[12]

By this time, work was beginning on the naval ballistic missile that became Polaris. The planned FY 59 program included the first SSBN prototype. Late in 1956 the Long Range Objectives Group suggested that 2 SSBNs supplement its 23 Regulus submarines. At the end of the year, it shifted 4 of its planned Regulus submarines to SSBNs.

The FY 58 SSGN, SCB 166, was the first one designed from the beginning for the missile mission. Her single large hangar could accommodate the big Triton missile then planned as a Regulus II successor. Like contemporary attack submarines, she was powered by an S5W reactor and could dive to 700 ft. She was armed with four torpedo tubes and eight torpedoes. The big hangar was clearly a liability. If it flooded, the submarine might sink.[13] During 1956, the SSGN was redesigned as SCB 166A. The hangar

was split into four individual cylinders, each large enough for a Regulus II with wing tanks (or two Regulus Is), in fore and aft pairs. Test depth increased to the 1,300 ft adopted for new attack submarines. Separate hangars made for a larger submarine, but they also offered flexibility; the hangars imposed no particular launching sequence, and a dud could be returned quickly to its hangar. In theory, too, the four-hangar arrangement would minimize firing time (vulnerable time, on the surface) for the two ready missiles. The missiles would move only a short distance to the launcher, always on slippers, and with two launch ramps, rather than the usual single ramp, so that a dud would not preclude firing. The limitations of the Regulus system were apparent in the design requirement: the SSGN had to be able to surface, fire a missile, and submerge in no more than 5 min.[14]

Effective missile attack required precise navigation; SCB 166A would have SINS. As in a ballistic missile submarine, alignment between missiles and SINS would be ensured by optics. This was a new departure for the SSGN program. A special stabilized Type 11 periscope, appearing only on board strategic submarines, was developed specifically to take azimuth sights to update SINS. Other backups to SINS were an electromagnetic log, radiometric sextant, NAVDAC computer, ground speed measuring device, and magnetometer. Cruise missiles then lost out to the new Polaris (see below), and SCB 166A was never built.

The underwater aircraft carrier, roughly analogous to an SSGN, was revived twice. In 1955, BuAer patented Magic Carpet, a jet pod that could be fastened under a conventional jet fighter and provide sufficient thrust to launch it vertically. BuAer let Magic Carpet submarine contracts to Boeing and Lockheed in 1958. The idea was to erect several ramps for launching hangar-borne aircraft, but nothing came of it.

A submersible carrier included in the 1956 BuShips sketch book (see chapter 8) was clearly an expensive way to deploy a very few aircraft, but such a ship could avoid detection (and adverse seas) altogether. This version had a more or less conventional flight deck, with the usual arresting gear, but there was a 5-degree ski jump at

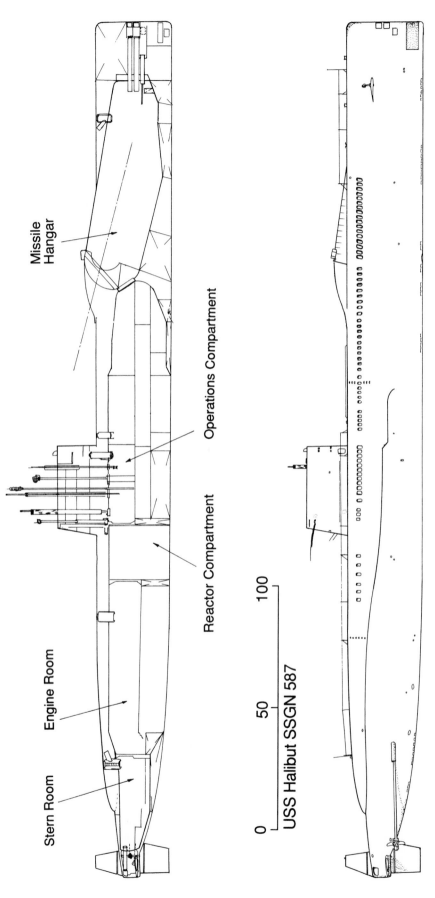

Missile
Hangar

Operations Compartment

Reactor Compartment

Engine Room

Stern Room

0   50   100

USS Halibut SSGN 587

Halibut shows the enormous Regulus hangar that also served as a torpedo room. Abaft it were officers' quarters and then a missile checkout/guidance space forward of the control room. The space under the control room was for an air regenerator. Masts, fore to aft, are: Type 6-A periscope; BPQ-2 (Regulus control); UHF/IFF; radiometric sextant (dome not shown); Type 11 star tracker; and snorkel air induction. The sonars in the forefoot are BQR-2 and BQS-4. The ship carried four torpedo reloads forward for her four long (250-in) tubes (note the reload supports), and two reloads aft for her short (165-in) swim-out tubes. The hangar accommodated four Regulus II or five Regulus I missiles (or four of the abortive Triton missiles). The 126-cell battery is in the single long space forward of the amidships ballast/auxiliary ballast tankage. (Jim Christley)

The purpose-built SSG Growler is shown off Quonset Point, 1 December 1958. Each of the two big doors forward led to a large hangar, missiles from which could be brought back onto the launch ramp in the well forward of the sail. To fire, the ramp trained (its training arc is visible) and elevated slightly. The sheer size of the hangar was a problem because it could flood in a following sea. Growler is now on display in New York as part of the Intrepid Sea-Air-Space Museum.

Grayback enters San Francisco harbor with a Regulus I missile in launch position. The small sonar dome is for an underwater telephone (BQC-1).

Growler hangar framing: note the two separate cylindrical hangars built above the pressure hull.

Growler is shown just before launch. The shutter of one of her two after tubes is visible, as is the framing of her missile hangar forward.

Grayback is shown as an amphibious transport, 7 December 1969, with her missile hangars replaced by special accommodations for SEALs. The original Regulus hangar was adapted from the amphibious hangar developed for the special amphibious operation submarines. In the SSGs, evolution took the opposite path. Note that *Grayback* has been fitted with PUFFS.

During construction, *Halibut*'s hangar and a few of her masts are shown: Type 6-A periscope (with attack periscope, retracted, alongside), ESM(DF) mast, and ECM/UHF/IFF mast (alongside it). The large cutout forward of the ESM(DF) mast was for the BPQ-2 missile guidance radar. Piping visible aft will go into the snorkel induction. One of the two holes atop the sail is for the Type 11 star tracker periscope.

The stern of *Halibut* is shown just before launch. Note how the casing (superstructure) wraps around the pressure hull.

The sheer size of the Regulus hangar in *Halibut* made flooding a major concern throughout the program. A Soviet missile submarine, a Whiskey Twin Cylinder, actually sank after her hangar flooded.

Halibut was the first nuclear Regulus submarine. Unlike the diesel boats, she had a single large hangar (in effect a secondary pressure hull) built into her outer hull forward. It projected up out of the hull, as is evident here. The masts shown carry her Type 6-A periscope, her BPQ-2 missile guidance radar, and her ESM arrays. *Halibut* is shown off Mare Island, 28 November 1959.

In the abortive SSGN 594 class, the hangar flooding problem would have been solved by accepting inefficiency in the form of individual hangars. The big dome shown abaft the missile guidance radar was a radiometric sextant. As in *Halibut*, attack and navigational periscopes would have been mounted alongside each other forward of the missile radar. Abaft the radiometric sextant would have been the MF/HF whip antenna alongside the Type 11 star tracker and the VLF loop, then the BPS-4 search radar and the snorkel induction and exhaust. A somewhat similar scheme for a missile conversion of the big *Triton* was also considered.

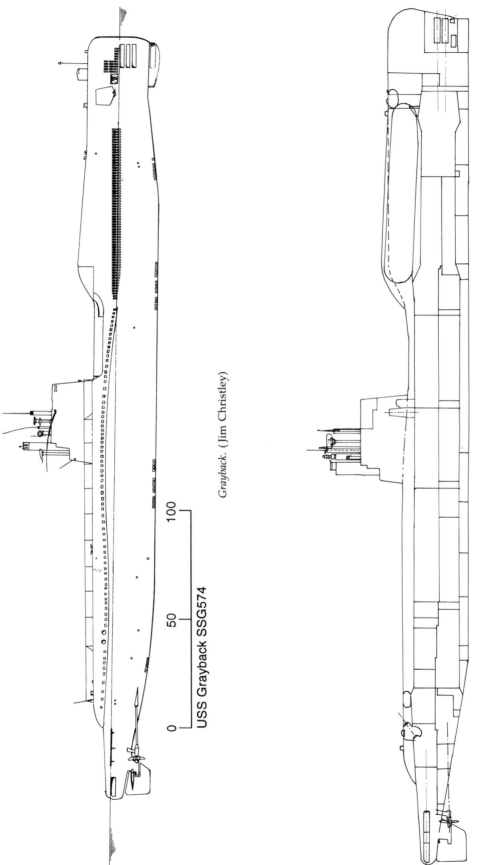

Grayback. (Jim Christley)

USS Grayback SSG574

0   50   100

Growler (SSG 577) inboard profile, showing her big cylindrical hangar forward. Its fore end is above the forward torpedo room. Abaft the torpedo room are living spaces, a missile checkout and control space, then the control room, with the usual living quarters abaft it, followed by the engine and motor rooms. The short oblong under the two torpedo tube shutters is the shutter for the torpedo ejection pump. Masts, fore to aft, are: periscopes side by side (No. 1 [Type 2A] to starboard; No. 2, in a fairing, to port); the BPQ-2 TROUNCE antenna; the UHF-IFF antenna; a retractable whip; the ECM mast with the VLF loop alongside to starboard; and the snorkel induction and exhaust. The SS-2 radar antenna mast is not shown. The forefoot shows BQR-2 and BQS-2 sonars (above it). The ship also had a QXB passive torpedo warner.

the bow. Internal volume was quite limited; the carrier could accommodate only six low-flying attack aircraft (30,000 lb, 500 kt, 1,000-nm radius, takeoff with jet assistance). BuShips suggested that they would be worthwhile only if they could deliver megaton weapons. Submarine size was determined by the length required for landings and takeoffs, which could not be simultaneous because there was no angled deck. Overall dimensions were 500×120 ft (24,000 tons surfaced, 40,000 tons submerged). Speed was estimated at 20 kt surfaced and something over 5 kt submerged, even with 70,000 SHP. The SHP figure did not correspond to any particular reactor or combination of reactors then available but was probably intended to equate to four SARs. This idea was included in at least one 1957 study of the future shape of the navy.

Between 1950 and about 1954, neither the navy nor the air force showed much interest in ballistic missiles. It seemed unlikely that a really long-range ballistic missile could be guided accurately enough to be worth the trouble. A submarine might fire from close in, but liquid fuel would be extremely dangerous, as had been demonstrated in a terrifying experiment at White Sands in 1949. Some ONR and BuAer personnel remained enthusiastic; for example,

there was an unsuccessful proposal to weaponize the navy's Viking research rocket. Sporadic design studies were done, but nothing came of them; cruise missiles seemed a far better proposition.[15]

Between late 1953 and early 1954, the long-range ballistic missile suddenly became a much better proposition than its cruise missile counterpart. The new hydrogen bombs offered far greater explosive power in much less weight than their atomic predecessors. They could be lifted by rockets of reasonable size, and their explosive power would make up for guidance errors. Experience was beginning to show that cruise missile guidance was difficult. Rocket guidance was actually simpler because it was performed during the short period of the missile's thrust up through the atmosphere, rather than during the hours of a cruise missile's flight. Although the air force was the first service much affected by these considerations, they also clearly applied to Regulus and Triton.[16]

The Eisenhower administration had decided to control rising defense costs by relying heavily on nuclear weapons and advancing technology in place of large, expensive conventional forces; the president feared that any further mobilization, as for the Korean War, would break the U.S.

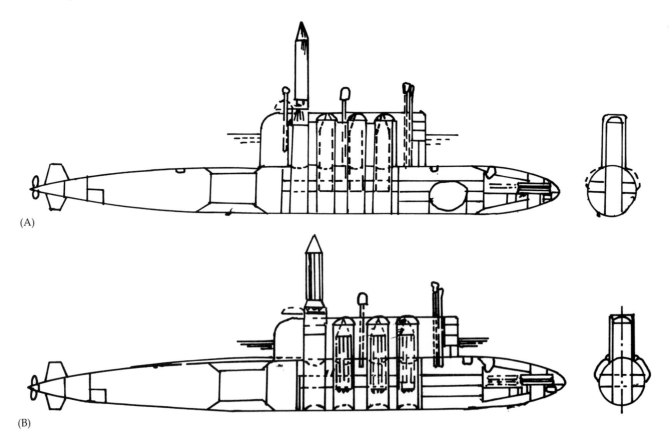

(A)

(B)

The proposed Jupiter ballistic missile submarines all carried their big missiles in their sails, because they were far too long to be accommodated in the hull. (A) is the original version with liquid-fueled rockets, 18 August 1956: 396×39 ft (6,300 tons light, 8,300 tons submerged). (B) is a modified version carrying Jupiters redesigned to use multiple solid-fuel motors, 21 August 1956: 376×40 ft (5,700/7,700 tons). Each was powered by a single S5W reactor (15,000 SHP), and each had 15 officers and 110 enlisted men. The large dome between the pairs of missiles was a radiometric star tracker. Note the elevator on which a missile was elevated before launch. Unlike the roughly contemporary Soviet ballistic missile submarines (Golf and Hotel), these craft would have fired with only their sails above water.

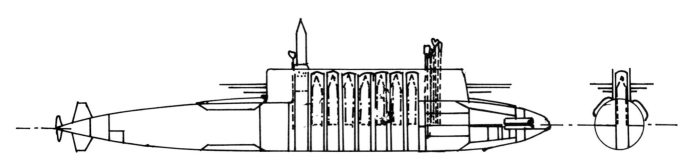

Polaris was so much smaller than the solid-fuel Jupiter that twice as many missiles (eight) could be carried on much the same hull. This sketch is dated 25 October 1956. It still has the elevator. Since the missiles are so small, however, they no longer have to be carried in a sail (the sail was retained to hold them above water at the moment of firing).

economy. There was also a growing fear that once the Soviets had the H-bomb, they could mount a crushing surprise strategic attack on the United States.[17]

In March 1954, President Eisenhower appointed a Technological Capabilities Panel (of the Office of Defense Mobilization) to study the problem of surprise attack. It was chaired by James R. Killian, Jr., of the Massachusetts Institute of Technology (MIT). In February 1955, the Killian Committee reported that the Soviets already had enough bombers and 1-MT H-bombs to cause serious damage to the United States. The United States, however, would retain its strategic superiority for another three to five years, although it still would be vulnerable to surprise attack during that period. There would follow a period of instability and transition (about 1958–60); during this time, the advantage would go to the power that first deployed ballistic missiles, which no air defense could counter. Therefore, Killian urged U.S. concentration on ballistic missiles. His committee pointed out that even a U.S. first strike might well fail to disarm the Soviets. The Soviets tested their first true H-bomb, a 1.6-MT weapon, in November 1955. The following January, the Net Evaluation Subcommittee of the National Security Council reported

that, by 1958, the United States would be unable to blunt a Soviet first strike, even if it had a month's warning.

The Killian Committee saw smaller and, presumably, simpler intermediate-range ballistic missiles (IRBMs) as a way of offsetting the presumed Soviet advantage in longer-range weapons.[18] The air force protested that IRBMs would consume much the same scientific and production resources as ICBMs and thus would dilute the program. Naval officers attached to the Killian Committee convinced it to call for development of a sea-based IRBM. OpNav resisted, fearing that its more mature cruise missiles would be jeopardized. It convinced the Killian Committee to add Triton to the list of essential near-term missile projects. In July 1955, the CNO specifically ordered BuAer not to press a 5- to 7-year IRBM program that it wanted. He failed only because of a peculiarity in the naval bureaucracy: a bureau chief, such as BuAer's Rear Adm. James S. Russell, reported to the secretary of the navy, rather than to the CNO. BuOrd began to compete with BuAer for control of a possible naval IRBM program.

Then, Arleigh Burke became CNO. He saw the IRBM as just the sort of new technology the navy needed; he decided to develop it alongside the cruise missiles. In

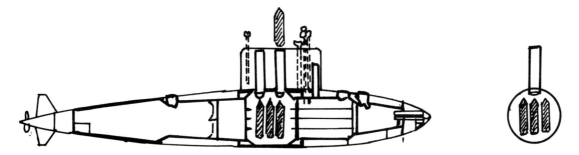

Since Polaris was an extremely small missile, it could be carried within a submarine's hull. This 25 September 1956 sketch shows one possibility for carrying the eight missiles in a magazine and launching them through two tubes. The submarine could be made much smaller: 320×40 ft, 5,200/6,800 tons. In another version, the missiles were carried horizontally. All such schemes failed because no acceptable missile elevator could be devised.

November 1955, Secretary Wilson decided that IRBMs would have priority equal to that of ICBMs. He established a special OSD Ballistic Missile Committee (BMC). To speed development, only two missiles would be developed in each category. The navy had little experience in ballistic missile development; it would have to share the army (Jupiter) or air force (Thor) program. The air force objected that major modifications would be required. The army wanted its missile to be mobile and agreed to collaborate, partly in hopes that the navy would help it win control over IRBMs. The joint program was formally established on 8 November 1955. Admiral Burke solved the problem of competition between BuAer and BuOrd (which felt that it should control missiles) by establishing a new Special Projects Office (SPO) under Rear Adm. W. F. Raborn.

No submarine could carry many huge liquid-fuel missiles. An initial sketch design (23 January 1956) of a nuclear missile submarine showed three 69-ft or 50-ft missiles, all carried in the submarine's sail. Only the sail provided enough depth to carry such large objects and offered space for elevators to lift the missiles to its top before firing (to avoid the fatal exhaust gas problem). SPO's chief submarine designer, Capt. Harry Jackson, and his civilian counterpart from BuShips, Ralph Lacey, found it difficult to provide the necessary elevator. Jackson saw the missiles as not too different from greatly enlarged masts and recalled that air had been used to raise a submarine whip antenna. Calculations showed that it was entirely practicable to raise a missile on a column of air. Suddenly stopping the missile at the top of the sail, however, would impose excessive loads. It occurred to Jackson that there was no particular reason to stop the missile at all; instead, it could be ignited while rising. This was a key to later developments. An alternative scheme, to open the tubes along their length to vent exhaust gas, seems to have been rejected as impractical. The SSBN would have had six torpedo tubes (18 torpedoes), as in an attack submarine, but she would be much slower (18 kt). By August 1956, the

This illustration shows one of several schemes for submarines armed with Jupiter, 1956. At first it seemed that no practicable submarine could accommodate very many ballistic missiles. They would have been fired from the awash position because it was feared that the missile might be tipped over by water resistance as it rose. In this version, the missile rose to the top of the tube by elevator (as in the early Soviet boats), where it was fueled and fired. The illustrated radio signals symbolize navigation by means of the Transit satellite system. Once submarine inertial navigation had been accepted, transit was used to update it rather than for continuous position keeping.

new SSBN, like the SSGN, had been revised to match the deeper operating depth chosen for the new attack submarine; the SSBN also would be built of HY-80 steel. It appeared that a 392×32-ft submarine could accommodate four liquid-fuel missiles. One sketch design showed six missiles in the sail, and at least some versions would have fired with only the tops of their sails above water.

From the beginning, the navy planned to switch from the dangerous liquid fuel to a safer solid fuel as soon as possible. Late in 1955, it asked BMC to approve accelerated research in solid-fuel technology in hopes that a breakthrough might come soon enough to transform the program. BMC refused. A single Jupiter surface ship was planned for each of FY 56, FY 57, and FY 58. The first SSBN was scheduled for FY 59 to allow time for development of a solid-fuel rocket. Triton survived as a backup.

Early in 1956, Aerojet-General and Lockheed informally suggested that a solid-fuel equivalent to Jupiter might be practicable.[19] On 11 February 1956, Secretary Wilson's Scientific Advisory Committee recommended that the navy develop a solid-fuel ballistic missile. BMC agreed to make the solid-fuel IRBM a backup to Jupiter, and Lockheed was awarded a feasibility study contract on 11 April 1956. Because the projected warhead (designed for Jupiter, with a separate ablative heat shield) was so massive (1,500 lb), the rocket had to be big—too big to be lifted by a single solid-fuel motor. Then, it suddenly shrank. The Lawrence Livermore National Laboratory suggested that the bomb casing itself might be used as a heat sink. In 1956, during the Nobska summer study (see chapter 7), Dr. Teller, Livermore's director, had predicted dramatic improvements in warhead yield: "Why use a 1958 warhead in a 1965 weapon?"[20] The SPO staff had done numerous studies of throw weight versus range for various solid-fuel rockets. When Lt. Comdr. (later Rear Adm.) Robert H. Wertheim returned from Livermore with word of the lightweight warhead, the staff knew what it implied. A single rocket could lift such a warhead. Lt. (later Capt.) Charles Allen estimated that a 5-ft diameter rocket could throw a 625-lb warhead 1200 nm. At that late summer meeting in 1956, Admiral Raborn decided to redirect the program toward the small missile.

Raborn moved fast. In August 1956, he formally terminated participation in Jupiter in favor of a small new solid-fuel missile. The new weapon was so attractive that, on 23 October 1956, the Scientific Advisory Committee raised it to the highest priority, equal to that of the air force Thor. A formal development proposal submitted by the secretary of the navy on 9 November 1956 was approved by the secretary of defense a month later. Admiral Burke set his goals on 7 January 1957: interim capability in 1963 and optimum by 1965.

The naval IRBM was initially paid for out of FY 56 OSD emergency funds. In July 1956, however, the DoD comptroller ruled that FY 57 development would have to come out of navy funds (i.e., out of other naval programs). IRBM involved considerable new technology, and its R&D demands escalated rapidly. OSD refused to distinguish

between the missions and characteristics of the cruise and ballistic weapons under development. It wanted the navy to make a definite choice. The FY 58 defense budget request would have to be cut drastically. Early in 1957, Regulus I procurement was stopped and Regulus II cut; Triton was effectively killed. It appeared that the solid-fuel missile would cost a third less to develop than its liquid-fuel ancestor, the naval version of Jupiter. The new missile became Polaris.

For some years, the air force had claimed that an effective strategic attack on the Soviet Union would require thousands of weapons. Because the navy could never deliver more than a few hundred, its strategic role had to be secondary. Only heavy bombers could deliver the sort of attack espoused by the air force. Many outside the air force suspected that the service's targeting requirements were grossly exaggerated and even thought that the fallout from the strike proposed by the air force would destroy U.S. and allied forces. In 1956, President Eisenhower, a skeptic, asked CNO Admiral Burke and Army Chief of Staff Gen. Maxwell Taylor to have their own staffs investigate the sort of damage needed to deter the Soviets. The navy portion of this Project Budapest study was done at China Lake during the summer of 1956 in parallel with Nobska. Its conclusion was startling: a few hundred bombs would suffice. Anything more would add only little to the destruction.[21]

That transformed the situation. Nobska had argued for large numbers of deterrent submarines, each carrying only a few missiles, as a way of focusing Soviet attention. The implication of Project Budapest was that the navy could provide a valuable national deterrent as long as the cost of that deterrent did not wipe out the limited-war programs that the navy also had to pursue. The object now was to carry as many missiles per submarine as possible.

The missiles were now small enough to fit within the pressure hull, and Jackson's air-blast launch eliminated any need for an elevator beneath them. They also could be launched underwater. The single row of missiles, now numbering 8, was moved into the hull abaft the sail. That raised a problem. Missiles were aimed by turning their stable platforms toward the targets. The reference for that setting was a beam of light (the straightest line in nature) extending from the submarine's control center. The control/navigation system had to be under the sail because it needed access to two backup navigational systems, a Type 11 star-tracker periscope and a radiometric sextant aft. Like the missiles, they had to lie along a light path to SINS, the main navigational system. SINS could not be expected to retain its accuracy through a long patrol. It needed periodic updates via backups, which soon included the Transit satellite system. In most nuclear submarines, the reactor, which has the heaviest concentrated weight, is as close as possible to the center of gravity of the submarine in order to minimize the effect of variable weights elsewhere.

One solution to placing the missiles was to distribute them fore and aft of the sail, thus minimizing the distance between the amidships point and the reactor. Jackson's solution was to provide enough missiles, hence enough weight, to balance off the weight of the reactor further aft. He soon concluded that a double row of 16 missiles would be best and convinced Admiral Raborn that it was the optimum number. Each missile required a 6-ft–diameter cut in the pressure hull; this cut was larger than any previously attempted. The more missiles, the greater would be the structural problem. On the other hand, it was clearly preferable to have as many missiles as possible in a single submarine. Jackson recalls drawing two lines to represent additional firepower (rising with the number of missiles) versus structural integrity (falling with the number of missiles) that crossed at 16. Raborn respected Jackson's judgment, and the 16-tube arrangement was adopted in June 1957. Much attention went into flooding arrangements to balance off the weight of each missile as it was fired. Locating the missiles at or near the center of gravity did minimize any pitching that might be associated with suddenly ejecting such heavy weights underwater.

In the summer of 1957, the Atlantic and Pacific fleet commanders both recommended abandoning SSGNs altogether in favor of the new SSBNs. The FY 58 SSGN program was cut from three to one, although the long-range plan continued to include two each year, and the two FY 59 SSGNs survived severe budget cuts.

Timing became urgent. The first Soviet ICBM (SS-6) firing (August 1957) was explained away, at the time, as an unsuccessful satellite shot, but then the Soviets launched the first two Sputniks that fall. There was already considerable fear that Strategic Air Command (SAC) bombers would be caught on the ground by a Soviet surprise attack. In the spring of 1957, the National Security Council asked the Office of Defense Mobilization to set up a Security Resources Panel to study a large-scale civil defense program proposed as a counter to a possible surprise attack. Chaired by H. Rowan Gaither, the panel expanded its charter to consider the entire question of national defense in the ballistic missile era. It reported on 4 November 1957, just as the Soviets launched Sputnik II. The Gaither Committee reported that a 1959 Soviet ballistic missile strike would probably catch SAC bombers on the ground. It was unlikely that a U.S. first strike would cripple Soviet bombers, so the committee concentrated on measures to ensure that U.S. retaliatory forces would survive a Soviet first strike. It strongly supported Polaris, the only inherently invulnerable U.S. strategic system.[22] On 6 November, two days after Sputnik II was launched, Secretary of the Navy Thomas S. Gates asked Admiral Burke whether the Regulus II program could be accelerated.

Burke rejected further SSN conversions on the ground that they would devastate the ASW program. Polaris development was moving so rapidly that new SSBNs might be commissioned as quickly as new SSGNs. The AEC announced that the new warhead could be ready by 1960. In May 1957, SPO had decided to get an interim 1,200-nm surface launch capability by 1 January 1963, with

the full system, 1,500-nm underwater launch, to follow by 1 January 1965. Admiral Burke had approved the plan in June 1957 but ordered the surface ship version of the system deferred. On 22 October 1957, SPO had promised to get two submarines to sea by early 1962, with a third one following 3 mo later and a 1,500-nm missile by 1963.

On 26 November 1957, SPO offered to get the first submarine, armed with an interim A-1 missile, to sea by October 1960. (Later, SPO offered to field the 1,000-nm A1X version by April 1960, if necessary.) The 1,500-nm Model B would appear in June 1963. This schedule was authorized by the secretary of defense on 9 December 1957. The first submarine, USS *George Washington,* was commissioned on 30 December 1959, fired her first missile on 20 July 1960, and departed on her first patrol on 15 November 1960.[23] The air force's Atlas ICBM, the closest rival to Polaris, had only just reached operational status. The planned SSGN vanished from the FY 60 program. Regulus II was canceled in December 1958 to free money for Polaris. Submarines ordered as SSGNs were reordered as *Thresher*-class SSNs.

In February 1959, the Model B version of the missile was renamed A-2 (it entered service in April 1962), and a new-generation Model C (later A-3) was planned for mid-1964.

One navy cruise missile program remained. The navy and air force were working on a nuclear-powered supersonic low-altitude missile (SLAM). In October 1962, the navy proposed that when *Halibut's* Regulus missiles were retired, she should be converted to fire these weapons (FY 66, at a cost of $15 million). She would be followed by two new SLAM-firing SSGNs in FY 68 ($180 million, plus $100 million for long-lead items in FY 67). More submarines may have been planned; the navy submission was for the FY 64–68 five-year plan. OSD rejected the project, and SLAM died. No details of the submarine seem to have survived.[24]

The Gaither Committee recommended that the Polaris force be increased from 6 to 18 submarines. The projected FY 59 nuclear carrier was traded for 1 SSBN and 1 nuclear attack submarine. Early in 1958, enough money was pulled back from the FY 59 budget to buy the first 3 SSBNs in FY 58, and they were not included in FY 59. By August 1958, the secretary of defense wanted 2 more SSBNs in an FY 59 supplemental budget, for an initial total of 5. Congress bought 6 instead, for a total of 9 SSBNs. The Eisenhower administration was reluctant to commit to a strategic weapon not yet demonstrated, so it released funds for only 3 of the FY 59 SSBNs and held back the other 3 to FY 60. The FY 60 budget, submitted to Congress early in 1959, showed long-lead items for 3 more submarines in FY 61. Congress was not pleased. In 1960, the Democrats would charge that the Eisenhower administration had allowed the Soviets to open a "missile gap."

The navy planned to begin with one squadron of 9 SSBNs. Senator Henry M. Jackson publicly called for a force of 100 SSBNs. The VCNO, Adm. Harry D. Felt, talked of 40 to 60 SSBNs. In 1960, the Long Range Objectives Group cited a navy targeting study suggesting that 45 SSBNs could serve as the primary U.S. survivable deterrent force; 37 would deal with Soviet targets and 8 with Chinese targets, and they would cover 80 percent of Soviet industrial targets as then known.[25] Because Soviet industrial targets were so concentrated, this number could be reduced slightly without losing much coverage (e.g., a 25 percent reduction would cut coverage to 70 percent). Creating the 45-submarine fleet on a crash basis would cut the naval modernization program. Instead, it might be possible to think in terms of 45 SSBN loads and build ammunition ships capable of reloading SSBNs after they had fired.[26]

Admiral Burke testified that the navy could build 6 more SSBNs in FY 61, then 1 per month in 1962 and beyond. Eventually Congress voted 5 SSBNs in FY 61, plus long-lead items for 5 more in FY 62. President Kennedy won the 1960 election largely on the missile gap issue. Within 2 weeks of entering office, he ordered immediate construction of the 5 FY 62 SSBNs for which long-lead items had been ordered. His FY 62 budget called for 10 more, for a total of 29 SSBNs. On 22 September 1961, Secretary of Defense McNamara tentatively approved 6 more in FY 63 and 6 in FY 64, for a total of 41 SSBNs. The navy never got five full squadrons, but then again the last few SSBNs were well out on the curve. Nor did the navy win its argument that Polaris might replace land-based nuclear weapons altogether.[27]

The Polaris buildup was much like a wartime mobilization program. Because the force had to operate almost continuously, a new manning concept was developed. Each submarine had two complete crews ("blue" and "gold") that alternated.[28] This concept greatly increased the time a submarine could remain at sea. It also added 82 full submarine crews to the submarine force. Suddenly, the manpower of the overall force was approximately doubled; in fact, the total manpower numbers in SSBNs somewhat exceeded the total numbers in attack submarines. As was usual in such mobilizations, submarines often had to go to sea with a substantial fraction of new crewmen. That there were no accidents testifies to the quality of the officers and also of the training supplied, mainly at New London.

Like the contemporary *Thresher*, SCB 180 would take full advantage of HY-80 steel and the new silencing technology (Electric Boat's first rafted machinery design). She lacked *Thresher*'s spherical active bow sonar because she would rely largely on passive detection with a BQR-7 array, although she did have the less elaborate BQS-4. Thus, her four torpedo tubes could be mounted in the bow and controlled by a version of the Mk 112 used in *Tullibee*, essentially a Mk 101 modified to do bearings-only TMA on distant contacts.

Admiral Rickover had pushed for a twin-screw, twin-reactor submarine (i.e., with a *Triton* power plant) on the ground that it would have to operate under ice and therefore had to be absolutely reliable. This was rejected as far too expensive. Table 11–1 shows alternatives considered in mid-1957. SCB 180 was the single-screw design ultimately selected.

The two rows of missile tubes had to be at least 24 in apart to provide space for optics. Fore and aft spacing was minimized to hold down ship size; it was set mainly by the need to maintain structural strength because the two

Theodore Roosevelt, a new *George Washington*-class SSBN, is shown off Mare Island on 8 January 1961. The device on her bow is for trials; abaft it is her sonar intercept receiver. Compared with later SSBNs, she is not as streamlined because the missile tubes are in a 130-ft section added amidships, rather than faired into an integrated design.

Table 11–1.   SSBN Concepts, 1957

	Single-Screw		Twin-Screw Designs		
	SCB 180	SCB 180A	2 S4G	1 S5W	2 S3W
Surf Displacement	N/A	N/A	7,800	N/A	N/A
Submerged Displacement (tons)	6,700	6,900	10,400	7,400	8,100
Length (ft)	382	373	530	395	420
Beam (ft)	33	33	32	N/A	N/A
SHP	15,000	15,000	34,000	15,000	13,200
Speed (submerged) (nm)	20	20	22	17.5	16
Added costs*					
Lead ship accelerated/normal (millions)	——	——	$57/$50	$6/$5	$19/$17
Follow-on ship accelerated/normal (millions)	——	——	$53/$48	$5/$5	$17/$16

* Compared with SCB 180/180A. As of June 1957, it was estimated that the twin-screw submarine would cost $134 million (lead)/ $108 million (follow-on), compared with $89 million/$70 million for the single-screw submarine.

rows of big tubes cut into the submarine's pressure hull presented some novel structural problems. The missiles had to be accessible at three levels to service the guidance package, transfer optical data, and access the jetavators and their actuators (in the nose) on both sides of the missile.

The submarine was designed to fire while stopped, hovering with the propeller backing. For a time, it appeared that she would be stabilized by a 50-ton gyroscope, which was installed in at least some of the early units,

but it proved unnecessary. Space was reserved in the after part of the sail for a television camera with underwater light to observe the missile tube openings during and after firing and spot malfunctions or possible fouling of the openings.

Each missile was stowed under a diaphragm. When the missile was ready for launch, the space above the diaphragm was flooded while water was pumped *out* of a compensating tank, and the space below was pressurized to match sea pressure. The door then opened. When

Entering the Holy Loch on 18 May 1972 after the thousandth ballistic missile patrol, *John C. Calhoun* displays the faired hull form of most U.S. SSBNs. The small dome in the bow is a sonar intercept receiver. At this time, SSBNs, like SSNs, relied on 3-in decoys fired from standard submarine signal tubes. Beginning about 1975, all SSBNs were fitted with a CSA Mk 1: 6-in external tubes firing horizontally, four on each side. Other deck fittings are temporary, for use only when docking. Polaris and Poseidon required that boats be forward based at Holy Loch, Rota, and Guam. The later Trident missile has sufficient range that no such bases are needed; the entire force now operates out of Kings Bay, Georgia, and Bangor, Washington.

firing air (at 4000 psi) entered the tube, it popped the diaphragm and forced the missile out. The missiles fired their motors well after leaving the tubes in order to avoid damage to the submarine in the event they failed to ignite. In the *Lafayette* (SSBN 616) class, gas generators replaced compressed air.

Each missile had a simple on-board computer in its inertial guidance system that calculated course corrections as it climbed. For any small launch area, the calculations were relatively simple, but the coefficients varied considerably from one area to another. A computer powerful enough to prepare coefficients for all launch areas within a submarine's patrol area was far too massive to go on board. Instead, the first Polaris submarines went to sea with decks of precomputed cards produced ashore at the Naval Weapons Laboratory, Dahlgren, Virginia. They later received computers powerful enough to produce the cards as they patrolled.

The reliable deterrent concept added a new requirement. Submarines on station always had to be ready not only to fire but also to receive the word to fire. In the past, submarine communication had been intermittent. A submarine would periodically expose a mast or come to periscope depth. That was no longer acceptable. The characteristics for the new submarines included a requirement that they be able to receive both VLF and HF/MF at long distances, such as 3000 nm, while proceeding at slow speed below periscope depth. The proposed solution was a long trailing wire terminating either in a streamlined float (carrying a whip antenna) or in a long floating wire. The need for prompt long-range communications, often called connectivity, always would be an important issue; ultimately, numerous alternatives were developed. They now include an ELF transmitter that can reach even a deeply submerged submarine proceeding at high speed.

Had SCB 180 taken a normal course, the first new strategic missile submarines would probably have been ready about 1961 or 1962. By 1957, that schedule was no longer acceptable. Jackson and Lacey began to look for existing or partly built submarines suitable for modification as interim Polaris platforms. They soon fixed on the *Skipjack*s, several of which were being built. Two already on the slip were cut in half so that a new 141 ft 1 in-long midbody, similar to that planned for SCB 180, could be installed. The new midsection had been designed to fit a silenced afterbody (as in *Thresher*); it was beamier than *Skipjack* (33 ft versus 31 ft 7 in) and had to be faired in. This was not a trivial proposition. The control surfaces of the earlier submarine were enlarged, with the new lower rudder extending below the keel. The submarine's hydraulic system was beefed up to handle a considerably greater control load. Internal main ballast tanks to improve reserve buoyancy and obtain satisfactory trim on the surface, in addition to two large hard tanks for missile compensation, were added. The six-tube *Skipjack* bow was retained, but it carried only six reload torpedoes. The characteristics called for a five-man bridge; the four-man bridge of the *Skipjack* had to be enlarged accordingly. It was also widened to

accept additional masts. To allow the SSBN to operate in the Arctic, her entire sail was strengthened to resist ice damage when surfacing. Space in the sail was reserved for two topside sonar transducers for under-ice navigation. Five submarines were completed to this *George Washington* (SSBN 598, SCB 180A) design. They were not as satisfactory as SCB 180, but they were ready much sooner.

The program continued with the original SCB 180 design (SSBN 608, *Ethan Allen* class). The rafted machinery space design was new; probably it was later adapted for the *Sturgeon* class. The design was reengineered in the SSBN 616 (*Lafayette* class, SCB 216) to add more space for maintenance and crew. SSBN 640 (*Benjamin Franklin*, SCB 216A) and later units have quieter machinery and are considered a separate class. Like the *Thresher*, these submarines all had four bow tubes. They had the sonar suite of the earlier SSBNs, but it fed a version of *Thresher*'s Mk 113 fire-control system. Thanks probably to her automatic hovering equipment, SCB 216 could fire missiles far more quickly. Unlike its predecessors, SCB 216 had space for shock absorbers around the missiles. That turned out to provide a margin for future missile growth. Thus, it was obvious quite early that the first 10 submarines would have to be replaced or reduced to nonstrategic roles long before the remainder became obsolete.

With so many submarines under construction, attention turned to possible missile improvements. The 1500-nm range goal was met in the second operational version, Polaris A-2, which fit the same tube and used the same fire-control system. Like all contemporary strategic missiles, each version threw single warheads. By 1960, the United States and the Soviet Union were both working on antiballistic missiles (ABMs).

SPO tried two counters to a Soviet ABM. One was to extend missile range, thus enlarging the possible patrol area. This would frustrate Soviet defenses because the submarine could attack over a much wider azimuth and also be harder to find. It could be argued, for example, that a Polaris submarine firing a 1,200-nm missile would almost have to penetrate the Baltic to hit Moscow. The Soviets erected a simple ABM system near Leningrad, between the Baltic and Moscow. A submarine with a longer-range missile could fire from the White Sea, for example, which was quite outside the arc protected by the Leningrad system.[29] The Polaris operational requirement (SC-16702) was recast in June 1960 to increase maximum range to 2,500 nm and allow for more available sea room.

SPO also split the warhead into three reentry vehicles (RVs). All would be spread over the same target, but an ABM system would find it more difficult to engage them all more or less simultaneously. Although splitting the warhead reduced overall yield for a given weight, it spread overpressure more evenly over a target and thus could result in more destruction. An alternative that would increase warhead yield to deal with hard targets was rejected at this time, probably because Polaris was not yet accurate enough to make it worthwhile.

The Polaris tube, designed so that it could be upgraded

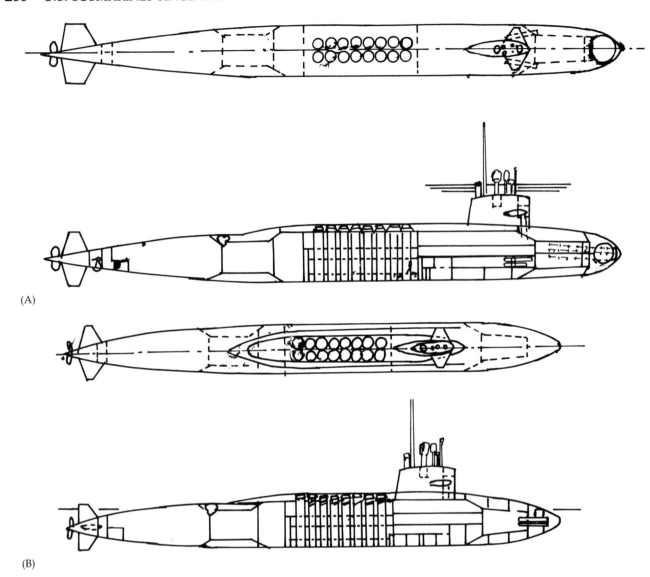

(A)

(B)

SCB 180 was the final and successful approach to designing a Polaris submarine. Two versions were developed in parallel: (A) with *Thresher*-type bow sphere/conformal array sonar and angled torpedo tubes; and (B) a simpler type with only a BQS-4 in the bow. (A) would have been 402 ft long between perpendiculars, carrying 8 long or 16 short torpedoes. It was judged too complex and too expensive. (B) was chosen: 373×33 ft, 5,400 tons light (5,920 surfaced, 6,830 submerged), carrying 10 officers and 90 enlisted men. The masts, fore to aft, are: No. 1 periscope; SS-2A radar plus the VLF loop antenna; ECM/No. 2 periscope/IFF-UHF; the big dome of the radiometric sextant; the tall whip; and the snorkel induction/exhaust. The five-man cockpit was a special feature of this design. Both versions had prominent stabilizing gyros: in (A), on the lower level just forward of the missile compartment; in (B), the double-height space at the fore end of the operations compartment, just abaft the torpedo room. In both versions the missile fire-control center was on the middle level, below the control room and above the crew's quarters.

to A-2, was easily modified to accommodate the A-3 missile. A-3 was first successfully fired by a submarine on 26 October 1963, and A-2 was retired in the fall of 1965. The first eight SCB 216s were completed with A-2 missiles; the rest all began their careers with A-3. Longer range required a new kind of fire control because all of the prepunched card systems applied to only limited patrol areas. A geoballistic computer, in a new Mk 84 fire-control system, continuously computed missile corrections as the submarine moved through the water. A Mk 84 was also the basis for the Mod 5 version of the Mk 113 fire-control system described in chapter 7.

By 1963, the Kennedy administration's program of strategic modernization to close the missile gap was well along, with Polaris submarines and Minuteman ICBMs in hardened silos. Secretary of Defense McNamara began a series of studies of how strategic systems could limit damage to the United States. They included renewed interest in a U.S. ABM system and also discussion of the possibility of attacking hardened Soviet missiles.[30] When a navy contingent joined the studies in 1964, it argued that the best way of limiting damage would be to move more of the U.S. strategic arsenal to sea, where a Soviet strike against it could not damage U.S. cities. A special Strategic Systems

Antennas of the ballistic missile submarine *Thomas Edison* as completed at Electric Boat, 17 March 1962. Key: (1) snorkel exhaust, (2) WRA-2 antenna (housed), (3) BRA-9 radio antenna (with mast retracted), (4) Type 11 periscope, (5) radiometric sextant, (6) AT-693/BLR ESM, (7) AS-1071/BLR ESM, (8) AS-371 B/S ESM, (9) Type 2 attack periscope, (10) BRA-9 radio antenna (whip on top does not show), (11) BPS-9A radar, (12) short whip atop IFF transponder antenna, (13) AS-962/BLR ESM, (14) AS-994/BLR ESM, (15) search periscope (with radar), (16) snorkel intake, and (17) VLF reception loop. The Type 11 periscope was used for star sights, as a backup to radio and inertial navigation. This U.S. Navy photo was declassified when it was retired to the National Archives.

Action Group, later called Great Circle, was formed within OpNav. In 1967, it became Op-97 and was responsible for the earliest approaches to Trident. Great Circle proposed two navy missiles: a Polaris B-3 precision (hard-target killing) weapon that would fill each enlarged Polaris tube (74-in, rather than 54-in, diameter) in the later submarines (*Lafayette* class and beyond) and a small ballistic missile (SBM) that could be widely dispersed. To overcome Soviet ABMs, SBM would have a maneuvering reentry vehicle. Several SBMs could be stuffed into each Polaris missile tube. B-3 was already under development (see below).

Dr. Harold Brown, then DDR&E, rejected the SBM idea altogether.[31] He also rejected any hard-target role for the new full-diameter B-3 missile. Instead, it would embody the new technology of MIRV (maneuvering independently—targetable reentry vehicle), in which each of its warheads could be aimed independently. Such a missile could threaten many targets, albeit with relatively small warheads. A submarine armed with MIRVed B-3s could threaten twice as many targets as the same submarine armed with SBMs.

B-3 began with a 10 October 1963 program change proposal (PCP) to spend $33.2 million on project definition, propulsion development, and continued navy participation in development of a new Mk 12 reentry vehicle. All three items were approved before the end of 1963. President Lyndon B. Johnson revealed B-3 as a "new" missile on 18 January 1965; it was hurriedly renamed Poseidon C-3. At the time, it was credited with twice the accuracy and twice the payload of A-3, but there was no mention of either MIRV or increased range. The manufacturer, Lockheed, credited it with eight times the effectiveness of A-3. BuShips suggested that only the 22 later SSBNs should be converted, to be followed by 11 of a new class (with delivery in FY 73–75).

OSD interest grew as the Soviets built up both their strategic forces and the ABM system around Moscow. Early in 1966, Secretary McNamara decided to accelerate Poseidon development and also to begin work on penetration aids (decoys to overcome ABMs). A Presidential Draft Memorandum of 22 September 1966 ordered all but the first 10 Polaris boats (a total of 31 submarines) converted

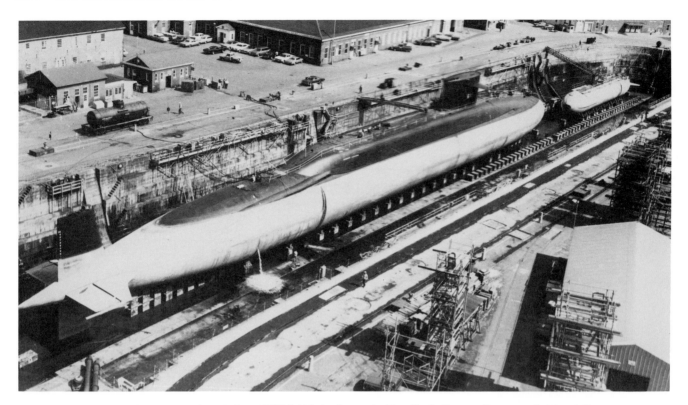

The ballistic missile submarine *Andrew Jackson* (SSBN 619) is shown in Dry Dock Two at Portsmouth Naval Shipyard with the experimental submarine *Dolphin* on 19 April 1971. The bulb on the SSBN's stern horizontal fin is a towed array fitting. The array is stowed externally; its tube, lying mainly under the fairing, covers the heads of the ballistic missile tubes. It emerges and then runs into the after main ballast tank; the array makes a 90-degree turn through the horizontal fin to emerge at its tip. Note that the submarine's propeller has been removed.

to carry the new missile, with the first to be deployed in 1970. The hard-target killing warhead, a Mk 12, was dropped in favor of the smaller Mk 3 of the earlier missiles. Poseidon flight tests began in August 1968. The effect of MIRVing was ultimately to move about half of all U.S. warheads (though hardly half all U.S. megatons) to sea. Electric Boat did the first Poseidon conversion, USS *James Madison*, from 3 February 1969 through 28 June 1970; her first deployment began on 30 March 1971. Conversions were conducted when submarines had their normal refits and refuelings; they took eight years rather than the seven years projected (two in FY 68; two, FY 69; four, FY 70, six each year, FY 71–73, two, FY 74, and the last three, FY 75).

Poseidon required a much more powerful geoballistic computer because the independent warheads on each missile had to be targeted. The Mk 88 fire-control system

supported the Mod 9 version of the basic defensive fire-control system, a Mk 113.

On 1 November 1966, OSD began a new strategic weapon study, STRAT-X, to evaluate the air force proposal for a new strategic missile (WS-120A, which eventually became MX) and the army proposal for the Safeguard ABM system. McNamara's CF/CD rules demanded that all alternatives, including those offered by other services, be taken into account. The criterion was minimum cost per *survivable* RV; about 125 different missiles and basic concepts were compared. The navy offered an SSBN system, the overall cost of which could be reduced by increasing the fraction of the force on station at any one time. Missile range could be increased to the point that the submarine would be on patrol as soon as she left port. That would also greatly increase the water area in which she could patrol and thus improve her security. The sub-

Polaris/Poseidon strategic submarines (*facing page*). The *Lafayette* class was the original SCB 180 design (*George Washington* was an adapted *Skipjack* hull). *Benjamin Franklin* was the improved SCB 216. The rectangle under the sail indicates the countermeasures launchers added in the 1970s. All of these submarines have passive bow arrays and small active sonars. Like the *Skipjack*s, the *George Washington*s had BQR-2B (but they had BQS-4 instead of the attack submarines' SQS-4). Later types had BQR-7 (the triple linear array shown) and BQS-4. Note the auxiliary machinery rooms both fore *and* aft of the reactor in the *Benjamin Franklin* class. The forward space (AMR 1) contained the oxygen generator, CO_2 scrubbers, NO_2 burners, etc. Abaft the control room/attack center (into which the periscopes come) is the navigation center. Forward on the same level are the CO and XO quarters. The level below contains the wardroom (forward) and crew's mess. Below it is crew's berthing. (Jim Christley)

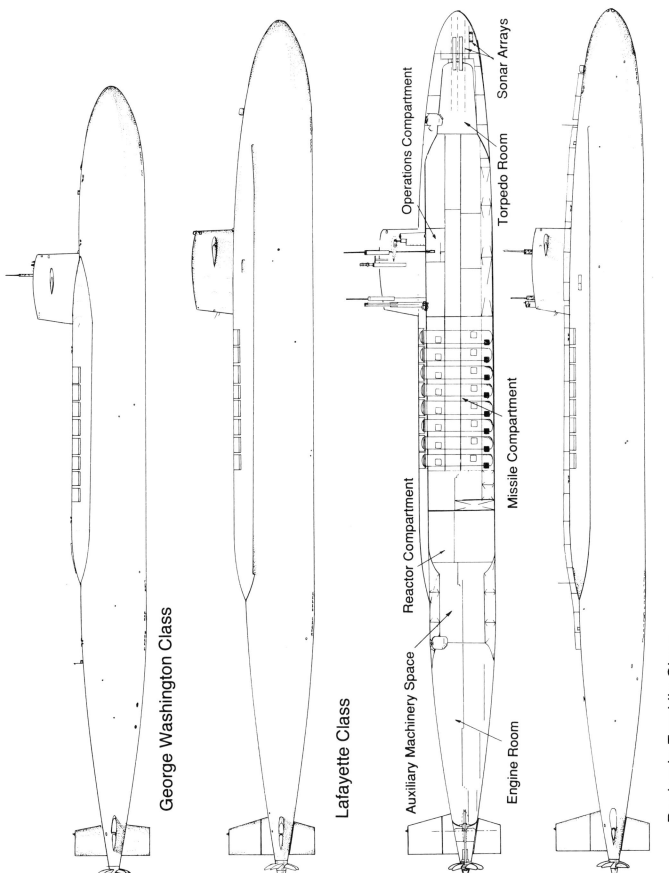

George Washington Class

Lafayette Class

Benjamin Franklin Class

Operations Compartment

Sonar Arrays

Torpedo Room

Reactor Compartment

Missile Compartment

Auxiliary Machinery Space

Engine Room

Ethan Allen is shown off Groton, 15 March 1962. Note the big dome forward for an under-ice sonar.

marine could be designed especially for quick turnaround at a carefully designed facility.[32] She could also be designed for the least expensive type of construction and modernization.

This undersea long-range missile system (ULMS) won the STRAT-X competition, although the August 1967 final report also called for a new land-based ICBM in a hard-rock silo and a new bomber (which became the B-1). The CNO established Advanced Development Objective (ADO) 15-9 for ULMS on 1 February 1968; the FY 70 program included funds for preliminary hull design. The prototype was to go to sea in 1976. The last Polaris submarine had just been completed. Such submarines were credited with a 20-year lifetime, so the first replacements would not be needed until about 1979, still quite far away.

The navy hoped to achieve very long missile range (6,500–9,500 nm) without using new technology; the missiles would have about twice the volume of their Poseidon forebears. Very low submarine speed, which seemed to be necessary for silencing, raised a problem. Interest in limited attacks was increasing. An enemy could locate the launch point by tracing back missile trajectories. To avoid localization, the slow ULMS submarine would carry her missiles externally in capsules and drop them off to float (loiter) in the water before firing while she escaped.[33] This concept was extremely unattractive politically. No administration wanted to leave nuclear weapons entirely unattended, no matter how briefly.

Nor did the quieting associated with low speed preclude accidental detection. The SSBN had to be at least

Daniel Webster was unique in having bow planes, rather than fairwater planes.

Michigan is a typical *Ohio*-class Trident submarine. The four small holes just abaft the sail are for a CSA Mk 1 countermeasures launcher system.

fast enough so that a pursuer could not maintain sonar contact, given current and projected technology. Too, a submarine had to have enough power to "plane up" to the surface to overcome damage. The higher the maximum speed, the more quickly the submarine could attain the much lower speed required to plane up despite flooding. Any unintended dive would be prolonged by the submarine's momentum (i.e., by her sheer size). Considerable power would be needed to overcome that momentum. These points were developed about 1970 by an ad hoc study of the speed of the new submarine.

These considerations led directly back to Polaris-like configurations—large weapons made for a very large submarine. For a time, it seemed likely that Admiral Rickover would insist (as he had tried to in 1957) on two reactors and two screws. To achieve reasonable speed, such a submarine would need considerable power. A 38,000-tonner powered by two S6Gs was sketched in 1970.[34] She would have been fast enough (25–27 kt) but far too large to be practical.[35] Admiral Rickover was persuaded that one reactor was sufficient. He agreed to develop a sufficiently powerful natural circulation reactor, the S8G, that was based on, but produced twice the output of, the S5G of *Narwhal*. Design studies conducted in 1970–71 seem to have incorporated the *Los Angeles* reactor (S6G), which was smaller than the big natural circulation reactor.

SPO was conservative: to avoid using new missile motor technology, it accepted a large missile and therefore a large submarine, about 20,000 tons or larger. The project manager, Rear Adm. R. Y. Kaufman, suspected that SPO could offer something better. He had CNO Admiral Zumwalt sign a letter to SPO calling for a smaller submarine. It turned out that a great deal could be done with an advanced motor. SPO wanted a bit more diameter (80 in) and length (3 or 3.5 ft). Within that tube size, the missile could reach about 6,000 nm, far short of the original requirement of up to 9,000; however, 6,000 nm sufficed for a submarine on the U.S. East Coast or West Coast to hit Moscow. If some RVs were removed, missile range increased to the point at which a submarine transiting to

the Indian Ocean (e.g., passing the Cape of Good Hope) could still hit the Soviet capital. These figures certainly seemed sufficient.

This option, to use the Poseidon volume more efficiently, was called EXPO (expanded Poseidon). If the extra length were not used, EXPO could fit a Poseidon submarine and no new submarine would be needed, at least at first. Thus, for a time, it seemed that a 4,000-nm EXPO competed directly with a bigger missile and a new submarine. DDR&E David Packard liked EXPO, but OSD insisted on a bigger missile (87-in diameter).

In all, about 117 submarine alternatives were considered, ranging between 2 and 32 missiles. Cost-effectiveness curves were flat in the region around 20 tubes. The navy liked a 20-tube variant, displacing about

Kentucky shows the blister of her TB-16 towed array (much of it is under the fairing for her missile tubes). The array emerges from her starboard stern planes. A long thin line array, coiled and stowed inside a main ballast tank, emerges from her port stern planes.

14,000 tons; DDR&E approved it (with the large tubes).[36] Much the same hull would have supported 24 EXPO tubes. A funding profile was drawn up for submission to Congress. Before the Decision Coordinating Paper (DCP) embodying the submarine could be submitted to the secretary of defense, OSD (Systems Analysis) drafted a new memorandum for a 24-tube submarine, this time with the large tubes, and the president approved it. That was embarrassing because some congressmen were well aware that the funding profile they received actually referred to a smaller submarine. The SSBN suddenly grew by 4,700 tons and 5,000 SHP (a shift, most likely, from the S6G to the big natural circulation reactor). The first reactor appeared in the FY 73 budget.

As the baseline Trident design was completed in March 1971, the United States was negotiating the SALT I treaty. President Richard M. Nixon was anxious to find a U.S. strategic system that could be accelerated to enter service within the five-year life of the treaty. Only the EXPO version of the ULMS system fit; it could be installed on board an existing Poseidon submarine. ULMS became both a major bargaining chip and a way of displaying U.S. determination (SALT I would leave the Soviets with a substantial advantage in land-based strategic missiles). A DCP, approved in September 1971, deferred construction of a new submarine until the early 1980s. Effort would be concentrated on EXPO, which would be installed on board existing Poseidon submarines. The EXPO (Trident C-4) missile objective was to double C-3 range without exceeding C-3 ownership costs. Advanced development began in December 1971; the prototype C4X1 missile flew on 18 January 1977.

In October 1971, President Nixon ordered a substantial increase in strategic spending for FY 73. That implied the acceleration of ULMS, formally approved in December by Secretary of Defense Melvin Laird and announced in February 1972. Laird made no reference to SALT; he cited the aging of the Polaris submarines and the fear of sudden and unpredictable improvement in Soviet ASW technology. ULMS was renamed Trident in May 1972, as the SALT treaty was signed.

Opponents of the treaty feared that Trident had been conceived as little more than a bargaining chip. For example, Adm. Thomas Moorer, chairman of JCS, made support of the treaty conditional on continued progress with Trident. Admiral Rickover argued that the program would be abandoned unless it was consummated quickly; he offered to guarantee that the first new-construction Trident submarine would be ready by 1977.[37] EXPO was renamed Trident I. It would initially arm new submarines, but their tubes (unlike those of earlier SSBNs) would be large enough to accommodate the full-size Trident II missile. Full-scale development was approved in December 1972, and submarine contract design was completed in May 1973. The first contract was let in July 1974.

The initial plan, for the 10 Trident submarines to replace the 10 non-Poseidon boats, was to build the first ship under the FY 74 program, then 3 each year (FY 75–77). In fact, only 2 were ordered in FY 75, then 1 in each of FY 76 and FY 77, and 2 in FY 78. None was ordered in FY 79, but then orders resumed at the rate of one per year, except FY 82, when none was ordered because of a contract dispute with General Dynamics. Preliminary plans first called for a total of 20 *Ohio*s, then 24. President George Bush would cap the program at 18 ships (the last ordered in FY 91 for delivery in 1997) as part of his strategic arms reduction program. The D-5 missile, which makes full use of the large tubes, would be introduced in 1990.

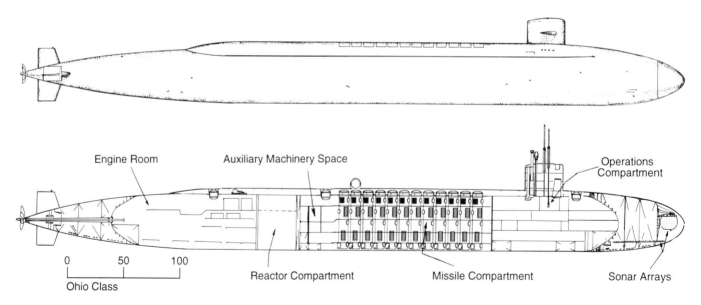

Ohio-class Trident strategic submarine. Note the big logistics hatches ("Yogi hatches," after Rear Adm. R. Y. Kaufman, the project manager). Countermeasures launchers are visible under the sail, and the torpedo-tube shutters are indicated in the outboard profile. Note that, as in a *Los Angeles,* the linear array around the bow is in the chin position, rather than being wrapped around the sonar sphere, as in *Thresher/Permit/Sturgeon.* (Jim Christley)

The big 24-tube submarines were quite expensive. In January 1974, Secretary of Defense James Schlesinger tried to include $16 million for studies of a smaller follow-on, which he called SSBN-X, in the FY 75 program. SSBN-X would have been a 16-tube (EXPO) submarine powered by a *Narwhal* reactor (possibly boosted to 20,000 SHP); she would have entered service in 1984. The Research and Development Subcommittee of the Senate Armed Services Committee denied funds. The senators considered SSBN-X premature because it was widely accepted that the minimum economical Trident run would be 10 submarines.

By about 1970, cruise missile technology again offered interesting possibilities.[38] It had been reviewed periodically since the demise of Regulus. During the late 1960s, for example, cruise missiles were suggested as a means of rearming early Polaris submarines that were not suitable for Poseidon. The STAM program for a tactical cruise missile (see chapter 10) included a strategic variant. A missile design considered in 1971 could fit either a Terrier launcher (1,600-nm range) or a Polaris tube (six 2,600-nm missiles). These weapons became more interesting as the SALT treaty took shape in 1971. Because they comprised a new weapons category, they were not limited in any way. Effective guidance would depend on the sort of microelectronic technology at which the United States excelled. Thus, cruise missiles were initially justified as a bargaining chip for future arms control treaties—an inexpensive form of leverage.

The missile could be launched vertically from SSBN missile tubes or horizontally from submarine torpedo tubes, or from the new SSGN (APHNAS) then under active consideration. Torpedo tube launch was particularly attractive because it could quickly and inexpensively increase the number of U.S. strategic attack submarines. This option was approved on 2 June 1972; on 6 November, the existing STAM program was combined with the new strategic program. General Dynamics and LTV offered competing prototypes, and the former's Tomahawk was chosen after a fly-off. Design, test, and demonstration were funded under the FY 75 program.

One more concept, the diesel Polaris submarine, deserves mention. In the early 1960s, the Kennedy administration offered the European NATO partners participation in a multilateral force of Polaris warships that would include both surface ships (dummy merchantmen) and submarines. Because the U.S. Navy was unwilling to transfer nuclear submarine propulsion technology, the submarines had to be diesel powered. Their design was relatively straightforward, with one interesting exception. The missiles had to be directly adjacent to the control room. In previous diesel submarines, intake and exhaust pipes were led up through the superstructure to the sail; if the missiles were aft (as in the SSBNs), however, the hot exhaust would have run right between the missile tubes, a totally unacceptable arrangement. The solution was to reverse the SSBN configuration and place the missiles *forward* of the sail. In the end, the MLF concept collapsed and no such SSB was ever built.[39]

USS *Ohio* is rolled out of Electric Boat's construction hall at Groton, Connecticut, 7 April 1979. A hull section of another strategic attack submarine is visible at right. This prefabricated construction technique was a major factor in selling the Trident program. The small pipe visible on the right-hand end-plate stabilizer is for a towed array.

12

Seawolf and Beyond

WHEN RONALD REAGAN became president in January 1981, he was determined to reverse what many considered the decline of U.S. defenses. He appointed an aggressive secretary of the navy, John Lehman, whose mandate was to build a more powerful fleet. Lehman often expressed his program in terms of a numerical goal, a 600-ship fleet, but its more important aspect was a definite shift toward a forward Maritime Strategy. For the submariners, that meant going into the bastions, rather than holding back in the barriers.

Although Lehman's goals matched those espoused by Admiral Rickover (including slashes through bureaucratic delays), these two very strong personalities naturally collided. Lehman retired the admiral. He succeeded where many others had failed because, among other reasons, his understanding of congressional politics went deeper. The effect of Rickover's retirement was to remove much of the bitterness that had resulted from the submarine debates of the late 1970s. Quite aside from the merits of fleet attack versus SSNX, many participants who opposed Rickover had suffered badly.

It was now possible to begin again, and the Reagan administration was willing to spend the sort of money needed to start a new program. Too, for the first time in many years, the basis for analysis had changed. The new Maritime Strategy was tested in war games, rather than by static calculation, and would achieve most of its effect by changing Soviet behavior. Ships, including submarines, were evaluated for their ability to execute the strategy.

By this time, a new reactor design, based distantly on the D1W, was finally mature enough to be considered for production. The WAA and the associated standoff ASW missile (to become Sea Lance) were nearly ready. NUSC was working on a new bow sonar that would use separate receiving and transmitting arrays. The receiver could be made much larger than the transmitter for greater gain, and its elements, which would not have to pass high-powered pings, could be made more sensitive. New thin-line towed arrays were nearly ready.

For its part, the submarine force was dissatisfied with *Los Angeles*; many in the submarine community felt that it reflected hidebound NAVSEA thinking. They were sure that the Soviets had done better. Their torpedo guidance wires did not break at the muzzles of the bow tubes. Their sails, carefully blended into their hulls, avoided the horrors of snap roll. Apparently, Soviet designers could pack much more power into more compact plants. The Alfa's titanium hull offered deeper diving without any penalty in weapons or overall size. The Soviets used more torpedo tubes than U.S. submarines, and it appeared that they were packing more weapons into smaller hulls. With Rickover gone, surely the constraints he had embodied could be abandoned.

Hopes of a new, much smaller submarine were soon dashed. A lightweight power plant, such as a nuclear gas turbine, was rejected for fear that it might be so unsafe as to be unacceptable to the public. That decision was probably quite wise; several years later, numerous Soviet officers announced that their more compact reactors had been less than inherently safe. A titanium hull might have reduced overall size, but it would have been too expensive; size and cost do not always go together.

Adm. Nils Thunman was DCNO for Undersea Warfare (Op-02). He demanded that any new submarine be more than a marriage of the new reactor to the *Los Angeles* combat system. To determine the characteristics of the new submarine, he convened a special Group Tango in May 1982. His main objective was more firepower, which ultimately meant twice as many torpedo tubes (and nearly twice as many reloads, 42 instead of 22) as in *Los Angeles*. Clearly, the new submarine would cost far more than its predecessors, but Thunman considered that acceptable if it was better enough. Many of the ideas considered but rejected over the past decade, such as external versus internal weapon stowage, were revived and debated anew. As about a decade earlier, it seemed likely that a new material, this time HY-130, soon would be certified for submarine construction. HY-100, offering 25 percent more strength than the earlier hull material (HY-80), would be a fallback.

The decision was to press ahead with the design but to delay presenting it to Congress, which still considered *Los Angeles* somewhat gold-plated. To hold down size,

Seawolf's bow sonar is a lineal descendant of the spheres of earlier U.S. submarines. The large sphere is the receiver; the smaller hemisphere below it is the transmitter. The external framework supports the conformal passive array, descended directly from the BQR-7 of the earlier BQQ-2.

Op-02 agreed to back off somewhat from the original maximum speed goal (and thus to accept a somewhat smaller, less powerful reactor); high, quiet (tactical) speed was more important. Secretary Lehman approved release of the concept design and looked toward construction of a lead ship in the FY 89 program. He expected the ship to cost $1.6 billion (the fifth ship was to cost $1 billion). The new ship would have larger-diameter (ultimately 30-in) torpedo tubes to allow her to launch existing torpedoes silently by swim-out or, perhaps, ram ejection and also to accommodate a future generation of torpedoes. In December 1983, the CNO approved single-sheet characteristics that reflected the Group Tango deliberations.

NAVSEA listened to the submariners. Its first published sketches showed all eight torpedo tubes in the bow. The sail was much shorter than earlier U.S. types and shaped in Soviet fashion. Planes normally mounted on it were moved to the bow, again to meet criticism of U.S. practice. Aft, the hull showed planes arranged in a nontraditional Y-form, similar in concept to an X-stern. The hull would be about as long as that of *Los Angeles*, but much fatter, for better hydrodynamic performance. Like the *Los Angeles* hull, it would be cylindrical over much of its length, so that the new WAAs could be mounted in the required straight line, fore and aft, on its surface. The reactor, a distant descendant of D1W, was designated S6W.

As in the past, torpedo tubes competed with sonar for valuable bow space. It appeared that the receiving array in this design might be conformal and spread over the surface of the bow (it was called ACSAS, for advanced conformal sonar array system), with holes for the tube muzzles. The beamforming computer would have to contend with a very irregular shape, but that seemed possible. Good sonar performance also depended on cutting self-noise. The new submarine's machinery would be substantially quieter and more compact than earlier attack submarine plants.[1] She would have a propulsor (a pump jet) quieter than any conventional propeller. Comments sometimes indicated that the new submarine would have twice the quiet (tactical) speed of *Los Angeles*.[2] The British were already using such propulsors on board their own attack submarines. Reportedly, they were less efficient than propellers; a speed penalty was paid for quietness.

It turned out that the irregularly shaped conformal array placed far too much burden on even the best computers. It had to be replaced by a spherical receiving array, a direct descendant of BQS-6, plus a linear array wrapped around the bow, a descendant of BQR-7. The eight torpedo tubes were pushed back to the forward bulkhead of the pressure hull. A proposed fully automated torpedo room, akin to surface ship missile magazines, was ultimately rejected in favor of manually controlled power operation. Perhaps most importantly, however, the sonars were part of an integrated BSY-2 system, the developed form of the SUBACS described in chapter 7.

The sail reverted to the usual U.S. pattern, except for a small wedge at its base. Aft, the Y-stern was dropped in favor of the usual cruciform arrangement. A remnant survived, however, in the form of a pair of stubs to carry two towed arrays; a long thin TB-29; and a shorter, fatter TB-16E. The propulsor, the guarantor of high tactical speed, survived.

Some unusual test facilities were built. The large-scale vehicle (LSV) *Kokanee* is a miniature *Seawolf* hull used to test models of the propulsor and to measure flow noise, particularly as the craft maneuvered. Computers were not nearly powerful enough at that time to simulate such complex flows. A submarine shock test vehicle was also built.

Much had been done in the 15 years since APHNAS. The new submarine matched or exceeded the platform characteristics (maximum and quiet speeds, diving depth, silencing, weapons capacity) of the earlier design on about

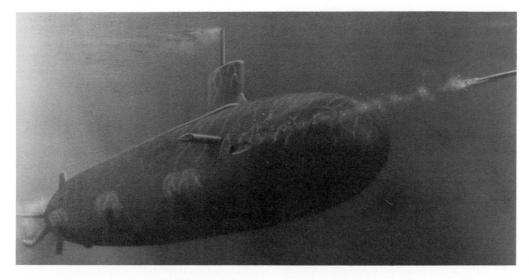

An official U.S. Navy painting shows *Seawolf* operating submerged, with her hull plane extended. The ridge visible above the hull must accommodate a thick-line towed array (TB-16), dispensed through the extra tail plane. Note also the fairing (sail cusp) at the forefoot of the sail, adopted for quieting. The painting does not show the acoustic window, near the top of the sail, for the MIDAS (BQS-24) mine and obstacle-avoidance sonar.

two-thirds displacement. The navy called the new submarine SSN-21—the submarine for the 21st century.

SSN-21 was justified partly by the need to match a new generation of Soviet submarines, Sierra and Akula (the first Sierra was launched in 1983, the first Akula in 1984). If Victor was the beginning of a second generation of Soviet nuclear attack submarines, Sierra and Akula represented a third generation; the quiet Victor III was an intermediate step, foreshadowing the third generation. The introduction of the *Los Angeles* class could be considered a U.S. generational change following the Soviet shift; SSN-21 paralleled the next shift. In particular, although late *Los Angeles*-class submarines were still quieter than the Soviet craft, it was clear that the U.S. acoustic advantage was being lost.[3]

This argument had an ironic twist. SSN-21 would be extremely expensive; many critics preferred not to see that much money spent. They charged that the new submarine still carried the curse of a hidebound NAVSEA bureaucracy. Surely, unspecified new technology could produce something far better. To some extent, this view echoed the feeling within the submarine community that the Soviets were far more innovative than their U.S. rivals. Some of the official arguments favoring the new submarine made the new Soviet craft seem so impressive that critics doubted that the U.S. submarine could cope. To the extent that she could deal with the 1995 threat, she certainly would not match what the Soviets would have a decade or two later. Much more is now known about Soviet submarines, both those built and those planned for later in the 1990s. The Soviets were indeed quite competent, and some of their subsystems were surprisingly good. It seems fair to say that the U.S. submarine developed during the 1980s was the best available counter to the sort of threat the Soviets were developing as the Cold War ended.

Another justification for SSN-21 was the forward Maritime Strategy to which she was particularly well adapted. To tie down Soviet attack submarines in defense of the bastions, in which lay the Soviet SSBNs, the bastion penetrator had to attack Soviet targets periodically. Each such "hot datum" would attract ASW forces, so the attacker had to flee at high but quiet speed. SSN-21 would have to spend as much time as possible in the bastion area. Every pass in and out would be particularly risky as she crossed the barriers erected by the Soviets to protect their bastion. Time in the bastion equated to the number of torpedoes aboard the submarine. That factor favored SSN-21 because vertical tubes suited to carrying only Tomahawks (as in *Los Angeles*) would not count.

The new standoff weapon, Sea Lance, complemented the bastion-attack strategy. The new Soviet submarines were indeed quiet but only at low speed. If they tried to transit at any useful speed, they could be detected, tracked, and hit. Similarly, any attempt on their part to locate a lurking U.S. submarine using active sonar would result in counterattack. Standoff was essential; the bastions were so large that a Soviet commander probably would willingly risk interception by a relatively short-range torpedo. A missile might reach out one or two con-vergence zones, thus giving a single submarine an impressive capacity to block egress. Because the Soviets generally would not know the positions of any lurkers, they would have to limit themselves to slow transits and drastically cut the time available in their patrol zones. Like Subroc, Sea Lance was initially conceived as a nuclear weapon with a possible homing-torpedo derivative. Then, as it became more obvious to the Reagan administration that nuclear war was unlikely, the torpedo version became the only important one. Sea Lance died in the defense cuts of 1990.[4]

Congress included the lead ship, *Seawolf*, in the FY 89 budget and bought two more in FY 91. Then, the Cold War collapsed and defense cuts were necessary. *Seawolf* seemed to be a rather specialized relic of the Cold War. Secretary of Defense Richard Cheney canceled the program in 1992 and asked Congress to agree to rescinding orders for the FY 91 units. Congress demurred, partly because there was a real fear that, without new orders, the U.S. nuclear submarine industry would vanish. Unless peace were forever, that would be a rather heavy sacrifice. In May 1992, the Secretary and Congress agreed to keep the second *Seawolf*. During the 1992 presidential election, Bill Clinton supported building a third *Seawolf* to maintain the submarine industrial base by keeping Electric Boat in business pending the design of a smaller, and presumably less expensive, successor. On 15 March 1993, however, he suggested that it would be better to wait for the next design. Even so, some money appropriated in 1992 to support the submarine industrial base was spent on long-lead items. The decision as of January 1994 was for the third submarine to be bought in FY 96 (it is included in the six-year shipbuilding plan presented in January 1994 and was officially assigned to Electric Boat on 2 September 1993). It remains to be seen whether more will be built.

The projected *Seawolf* price was predicated on series production of two or three per year. The same submarine industrial base would have been building an *Ohio* class ballistic missile submarine, with about twice the tonnage of a *Seawolf*, each year. With the end of the Cold War, the *Ohio* program was terminated at the 18th unit. The attack submarine goal of 100 was dropped. As the defense budget was cut, it became less and less likely that *Seawolf* production would come anywhere near the planned rate. The projected cost per submarine rose; one estimate put the average cost (in a 12-ship program) at $2.8 billion, which included R&D.

Critics argued that no such submarine was affordable, and an inferior design would surely cost less. That might be no longer true. The dominant factor in cost could be the overhead involved in maintaining the specialized shipyards and factories required for submarine production. Overhead is always a cost factor, but it was previously spread over numerous submarines. A slower or louder or smaller submarine does indeed cost less. With a large reduction in the number of submarines built each year, the rise in overhead per submarine wipes out any possible saving. A single *Seawolf* per year would indeed cost more

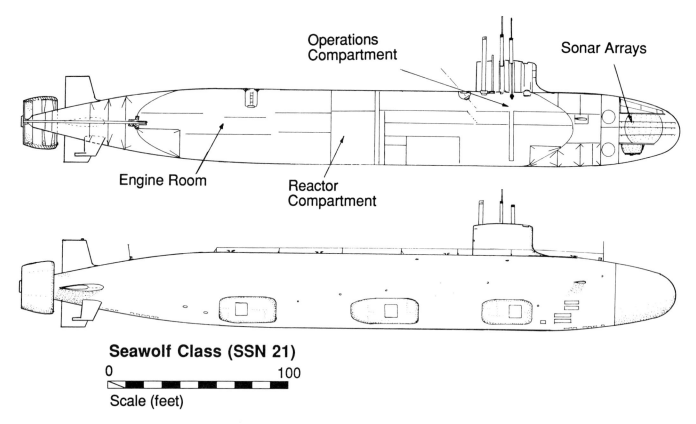

Seawolf (SSN 21), showing her eight torpedo tubes and the WAA passive ranging arrays running down her side. Note the dual bow arrays and the conformal array wrapped around them. The pump-jet configuration is conjectural; details are classified. (Jim Christley)

than a single *Los Angeles* but not nearly as much more as earlier unit costs might suggest. Savings would be apparent only if the overhead (industrial base cost) somehow could be separated from the total price of each submarine. That may happen if the United States adopts an explicit policy of preserving defense industrial assets against future needs, whether or not those plants earn money by current production.

In January 1991, CNO Adm. Frank Kelso ordered the design of an affordable submarine that became known as "Centurion," the submarine for the next century. The secretary of the navy formally authorized design work in February 1991. To some extent, it drew on exploratory studies of a *Seawolf* follow-on, which began at least as early as 1988. Admiral Kelso approved a Mission Need Statement in October 1991; the following January, he issued a list of ranges of required performance levels. The reported Centurion cost goal was half that of *Seawolf*, something closer to the late *Los Angeles* class or about $600 million per follow-on ship in late-1980s terms.

Admiral Kelso explicitly rejected calls to continue production of the existing "improved *Los Angeles*" (688I) design. The weight margin of the design was exhausted; it could not exploit the considerable improvements developed for *Seawolf*. Nor, it was argued, would an improved *Los Angeles* have fared well against the sort of submarines the Soviets were designing at the end of the Cold War. Whatever the fate of U.S. relations with the Russians, it

certainly could be argued that the sort of innovations they were planning might well appear somewhere else through sales of Russian expertise.

Any new U.S. submarine must operate in a world quite different from the one for which her predecessors were designed. Almost certainly, the world will become more, rather than less, unstable. Meanwhile, the United States will lose free access to virtually all of its foreign bases. Submarines were an essential means of gathering electronic intelligence in virtually all crises during the 1970s and 1980s. Their covertness now becomes more important; in many cases, merely deploying an airplane will exacerbate a crisis. Even with stealthy airplanes, it will be virtually impossible to conceal negotiations to gain a base for their operation. Similarly, a submarine should have a better chance of covertly landing special forces than a C-130 flown from a foreign airfield. According to discussions in early 1994, the navy hopes to modify the third *Seawolf* so that its torpedo room can be adapted to transporting up to 50 SEALs. (Figures as high as 200 SEALs have been quoted, but they seem unlikely.) It will also have an enlarged diver lock-out chamber. The others may be modified later. The new SSN design reportedly includes a convertible torpedo room.

Once a carrier force is en route, submarines operating ahead with their ESM sensors can provide invaluable warning of enemy preparations for an attack. For example, *Los Angeles*-class submarines in the Mediterranean during the Gulf War provided "indications and warning" data to the surface force en route to the Persian Gulf. There was a real fear that the Libyans would choose to support Iraq by ambushing ships. Submarines were able to confirm that nothing of the sort was happening. Had there been an attack, the submarines could have struck back with their Tomahawks. No other deep-strike forces suitable for such an operation were in position.

Actual power projection will probably involve Tomahawk missiles, either as the main force of an attack or as support for a carrier air strike. With the decline of the Soviet threat, ASW is less important. It may be possible to revert to the "improved *Los Angeles*" combination of torpedo tubes and vertical missile launch tubes.

These missions define the post–Cold War submarine. She must be fast enough to transit quickly to a crisis area; warning time will be short. Also, she probably will have to work with surface forces. Because she cannot be re-armed at sea, she needs the largest possible weapons capacity for a wide variety of weapons, plus perhaps other equipment occupying weapons slots. She needs the best possible command and control system, one that is adaptable to a wide variety of roles: intelligence gathering, anti-ship and anti-submarine attack, and land missile attack probably the most prominent. When operating in hostile or semihostile coastal waters, she will deal with a dense target environment that must be sorted out.

Silencing will remain essential. This might seem an odd concern in a post–Cold War world; however, as national defense budgets have shrunk or even collapsed, competition for weapons sales has intensified. When governments lose their fear that compromising technology may have devastating consequences (most believe that a major war is now unlikely), they tend to relax export restrictions. Greater sophistication becomes a major selling point for both the Russians and their former enemies in the West. One implication is that very nearly the best current underwater detection technology could be universally available within a decade. Some of the equipment, particularly in sonobuoys and airborne processors, is cheap enough that cost will not be a major barrier to its acquisition by potential enemies.

Admiral Kelso therefore required that the Centurion be as quiet as *Seawolf*. She could be slower but still fast enough to work with surface forces, which implies something like *Los Angeles* speed. The combat system could be simplified, as long as it has an open architecture (like that of BSY-2) to accommodate specialized equipment for particular missions. Weapons load-out and firing rates could be reduced; it might be wise to revert to vertical launchers and simplify the semiautomatic magazine system adopted for *Seawolf*. Test depth could be reduced. Finally, crew size should be minimized to reduce both the size of the submarine and her operating costs.

Initial studies were conducted by the navy's preliminary designers and also by a private yard, probably Electric Boat. To define an acceptable minimum size, the private yard was asked to design a 5,000-ton submarine as quiet as *Seawolf*. The resulting 5,007-tonner was too slow and

could not accommodate a vertical missile launch system; hence, she would have an insufficient missile launch rate. The design failed current standards for shock, fire fighting, and equipment redundancy. Internal bulkheads could not be designed to survive to crush depth. A navy design to current standards (but not to the required speed or launch rate) showed a displacement of 5,800 tons. Similarly, a "long-hull" *Sturgeon* updated to modern silence and shock standards would have displaced 5,768 tons. The conclusion was that 6,000 tons was an effective lower limit on any acceptable new attack submarine. It appeared that no small hull could accommodate sufficiently quiet (double-sound–mounted) shockproofed machinery. The step down from *Seawolf* machinery silencing would be to eliminate an entire level of sound isolation, thus reverting to the design standards of *Los Angeles* and earlier submarines. It might also be possible to eliminate the elaborate propulsor, but then the new submarine, at high speed, might be detectable twice as far away as *Seawolf*. Above 8,500 tons, there was so little to choose between Centurion and *Seawolf* that no new design would have been considered worthwhile.

That left a range of 6,000–8,500 tons. At the lower end, a submarine would carry only the 4 small-diameter (21-in, rather than 30-in as in *Seawolf*) torpedo tubes of *Los Angeles*, with 23 (instead of 22) reloads, and she could not accommodate vertical tubes. Around the middle of this range, vertical tubes and more torpedo reloads could be added. At the upper end, a submarine could carry 16 or more vertical tubes, and 6 or 8 torpedo tubes; she could also work with an unmanned underwater vehicle (UUV) and could support special operations. Any submarine in this size range could accommodate *Seawolf* sonars. On 28 August 1992, Under Secretary of Defense for Acquisition Donald Yockey formally approved Centurion as a DoD program. It was tentatively included in the FY 98 program, with completion in 2003. The navy proposed that long-lead items be included in the FY 96 budget, with R&D funds in FY 94. For example, a new submarine smaller than *Seawolf* would need a new reactor.

As in McNamara's time, the next step was a trade-off study, now called a cost and operational effectiveness analysis (COEA). Six alternatives would be examined: (1) continued *Seawolf* production at one shipyard at the rate of one per year, with the third submarine authorized in FY 96 or FY 98; (2) at least two lower-cost *Seawolf* variants; (3) updated *Los Angeles*, with construction to begin in FY 96 or FY 98; (4) a range of new nuclear submarines, including types with capabilities deleted to meet a tonnage of less than 5,000, with cost less than or equal to that of a 688I and construction to begin in FY 98, FY 2002, or FY 2008; (5) a Trident redesigned for power projection; and (6) a non-nuclear submarine, possibly with an air-independent (closed-cycle) auxiliary power plant or a small reactor for loitering operation.

The COEA would include the effect of oversea basing on the value of the non-nuclear variant. Continued *Seawolf* construction was the baseline against which the variants could be compared. The COEA was completed on 2 August 1993; it was considered at a program decision meeting the following September. Three alternatives seem to have survived: an upgraded *Los Angeles* (which had some congressional support); a repeat or slightly downgraded *Seawolf;* and a new design. The COEA concluded that the upgraded *Los Angeles* could carry out the requisite missions, but that it would be more vulnerable than the alternatives. COEA threat conclusions were not declassified, but apparently it seemed unlikely that this vulnerability was entirely acceptable. Even in the absence of highly capable Soviet SSNs, Third World countries may well be able to field effective acoustic sensors such as Western-type sonobuoys deployed either by aircraft or used as static barriers. By early 1994 the upgraded *Los Angeles* had been rejected altogether on the grounds that the design had no growth margin left and that it could not accommodate the quiet new power plant (see below). That left either *Seawolf* or a wholly new submarine. The COEA concluded that a new design would be worthwhile only if the United States planned on series production (more than 10 units); otherwise, it would be wasteful to spend the requisite $4–5 billion in R&D.

As of early 1994, Centurion had been renamed the New SSN (NSSN; for a time it was the New Attack Submarine, NAS). If it is built, it is to have an open-architecture computer combat system unlike BSY-2, reflecting the navy's current philosophy of buying ruggedized commercial computers. Open combat system architecture would make the submarine more adaptable to alternative missions. Much of the electronics is to be off-the-shelf items. The power plant is to be a new S9G reactor; the designation suggests that it is related to the natural-circulation S8G of the *Ohio* class. If that is true, then reactor characteristics are being used to reduce the degree of structural quieting used and thus to achieve silence in a smaller or less complex hull structure. As of late 1993, the first was planned for the FY 98 program, to enter service in 2003. The FY 94 program included $449 million for development. A 12 January 1994 Defense Acquisition Board ordered a one-year delay, however, which may kill the program in favor of more *Seawolfs.*

Early in 1994 there was talk of a commando version that would have a simplified combat system and would carry up to 200 SEALs, using a reconfigurable torpedo room. There was also interest in a surveillance version carrying a large intercept antenna in a stealthy dome (but it seems more likely that a surveillance submarine would put intercept antennas in place, returning to monitor them periodically). Any new submarine will probably be able to deploy the new unmanned mine-search vehicle. For shallow water, a half-length version of the Mk 48 ADCAP heavy torpedo with a lightweight torpedo seeker has been proposed, to be fired from external tubes.

Reportedly, as of November 1993, the favored alternative displaced 7,000 tons, but the situation remains very fluid. Unfortunately, the economics of buying only one submarine every few years has driven its estimated unit cost up to $2.6 billion (a repeat ship cost of $1.5 billion has also been reported). Cutting quality (in *Seawolf*) has not cut cost: no change in characteristics is likely to do that. This figure makes it much more probable that *Seawolf* will remain in production while yet another next-generation submarine design is developed, to be laid down sometime after the turn of the century.

Late in 1993, a modular version of the post-NSSN submarine (SSXN) was being discussed. Versions would be: SSFN, for special operations (SEAL accommodations, swimmer lock-out); SSCN, for command/control and electronic warfare; SSMN, for mine warfare and mine countermeasures using unmanned vehicles (UUVs); SSLN, for attacking land targets with missiles; SSBN; SSTN, for theater ballistic missiles; and SSKN, for sea control and maritime surveillance. Presumably, different midship sections could be mated with a standard front end and stern (including power plant). Some in the submarine community are arguing that a submarine (like the SSLN) armed with 75 to 100 Tomahawks in vertical tubes will sometimes be a reasonable substitute for an increasingly scarce strike aircraft carrier. *Seawolf* is expected to carry 12 Tomahawks internally; the increasing importance of the SSLN mission is reflected in the 16 tubes associated with the high-end NSSN variants described above (more tubes may be added later).

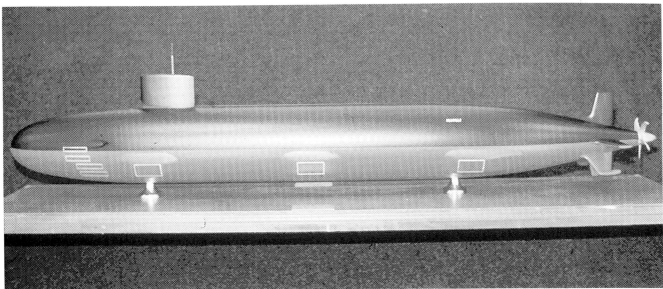

The official *Seawolf* model shows the paired towed-array dispensers and the WAA along the ship's side. It does not, however, show the propulsor (pump-jet), which accounts for much of the submarine's quieting at tactical speed.

Appendix A

Midget Submarines

THROUGHOUT WW II, the British, Germans, Italians, and Japanese all employed midget submarines. Many of them were carried to the scene of action by conventional craft. Midgets could often slip through harbor defenses designed to catch full-scale submarines.[1] They were extremely dangerous to their crews, however, and many midgets succumbed to accidents before reaching their target areas. The wartime U.S. Navy briefly considered building midgets of its own but decided only to monitor the British program. It became vitally interested in the midget threat when it took over responsibility for U.S. harbor defense in 1949.

Two main types of midgets were developed in wartime. One was a true miniature submarine, such as the British X-craft used against the *Tirpitz* and the Japanese cruiser *Takao*, the German Seehund, and the Japanese Type A used at Pearl Harbor, Sydney, and Diego Suarez. This type could achieve considerable range (e.g., to run up the fjord in which *Tirpitz* sat) because the crew rode internally. Except in the case of the Japanese midget, torpedoes or other weapons were carried externally to hold down total size. The postwar U.S. Navy lacked suitable torpedoes (one officer suggested that Seehund failed partly because her external torpedoes were inherently unreliable), so any U.S. equivalent had to be somewhat larger than its wartime inspiration.[2]

The other type of midget was a torpedo enlarged to carry one or more divers. They piloted her into a harbor, then released the warhead under their target. The Italians were the first to develop this "chariot," which was later copied by the British and Germans. She could not run as far as the true midget but was smaller and thus much harder to detect, and her simplicity offered reliability. Chariots sank the British battleships *Queen Elizabeth* and *Valiant* in Alexandria harbor in 1941. A 1949 estimate indicated that enemy chariots had sunk about 150,000 tons of Allied shipping altogether.

Midgets were not just miniature submarines; they represented a quite different point of view. A conventional large submarine is a major capital investment expected to last some years. Midgets were more like contemporary airplanes. They had to be cheap and expendable. In many cases, it was perfectly acceptable for them to be scuttled at the end of a mission.

The Soviets captured numerous German and Italian midgets and manned torpedoes. As in the case of other Axis submarine technology, it was assumed that they would exploit this one. By 1949, midgets were reportedly participating in fleet exercises. Midgets and the swimmers they might carry would threaten the European ends of any future convoy route.[3]

The U.S. Navy and the Royal Navy wanted midgets of their own to test new harbor defense techniques and devices. The same midgets presented an interesting potential for attacking the Soviet submarine fleet in its bases. A wartime British midget (an X-craft) had carried enough explosive to disable a single capital ship. The same weight, five years later, might be put into a nuclear weapon sufficient to knock out an entire base. Such attacks were an attractive form of ASW ("attack at source"), particularly when the type XXI submarine and its ilk seemed to negate more conventional techniques.

In the spring of 1949, ACNO (Undersea Warfare) Rear Adm. C. B. Momsen who chaired the Submarine Officers Conference, appointed an ad hoc working group to study small submarines and sneak craft.[4] ONI produced a classified report on WW II craft. SubLant, in the person of Comdr. R. H. Bass, proposed an "intelligent antisubmarine mine," a U.S. midget that could be placed in a barrier position near a Soviet harbor. She might be either a fast "pursuit" type or a slow "ambush" type. SubLant argued that the U.S. Navy knew far too little about midgets in general to evaluate such ideas. For example, how would limited endurance and armament affect a picket? Certainly, the midget would be a much cheaper alternative to the SSK then under construction and, hence, available in greater numbers.

Although much information was available concerning German midgets, the British would be able to offer even more because of their operational X-craft. The ad hoc working group suggested that two X-craft be borrowed for tests. Comdr. C. H. Varley, RNR, who had developed the X-craft, addressed the group and proposed a new midget that he called a "sea tank."[5]

Midgets were frightening because they were so difficult to see. Even with her spray shield up for surface navigation, *X 1* was quite small. Of course, she was also fairly limited.

Swimmer delivery vehicles (SDVs) (*above and facing*) are the direct successors of the WW II Chariots. Here, one is being loaded into the hangar of the transport submarine *Grayback*, July 1978.

The working group envisaged two types, Commander Bass's attack-type midget (Type I) optimized for high speed and a harbor facility destruction midget, with complete underwater demolition team (UDT) facilities and a submersible boat (Type II). Each was to operate with a minimum crew (the working group suggested four) and was to be as simple as possible to build and operate. The group rejected any U.S. version of the wartime manned torpedo on the ground that any great engineering advances in the human torpedo, such as better breathing apparatus and better performance, would blur the line between it and the midget. It felt that the human torpedo would not be able to do anything that a well-designed midget could not do as well or better.

By this time (1949), David Taylor Model Basin was working on the "Type II target" (SST II) that would become *Albacore*. The working group suggested that her low-resistance hull form be exploited for the highest-priority type, the Bass midget. The hull form's inherent route stability was expected to make one-man control practical, thus reducing crew requirements. The attack midget could have a snorkel and a miniature diesel-electric power plant with a very quiet motor. She could be equipped with sensitive listening gear and armed with homing torpedoes

(a Mk 27 Mod 4). The working group wanted her to keep the sea for at least a week and to operate down to 300 ft. A BuShips design study would be needed to determine submerged speed and endurance. The midget would be designed specifically to be carried on board a tender submarine.

Bass felt that new technology under development could greatly benefit future midgets. This included antisonar and antiradar coverings and closed-cycle power plants for faster and deeper diving. The midgets might be able to anchor in great depths to conserve power. A new mission of missile guidance, either directly or by planting a beacon, was foreseeable. None of this came to pass. Bass correctly predicted, however, that a future midget might be used as a mobile rescue chamber for submarines in deep water. That ultimately became the DSRV.

The working group reported on 27 July. By then, BuShips had produced a preliminary design study that proved the Type I midget to be feasible. This was the first attempt to use the new David Taylor high-speed hull form (the later *Albacore*) in a combatant submarine; it would have become the first U.S. submarine designed for much higher underwater speed than surface speed. The hull form was modified to incorporate two bow tubes loaded

through the muzzles and a small fairwater for a watertight access hatch.

As in the contemporary SSK, using a homing torpedo (in this case, a Mk 27 Mod 4) would considerably simplify fire control and thus the overall design of the submarine. The main sensor would be a low frequency directional passive sonar in the midget's bridge fairwater. "Leading the bearing," the midget could maneuver close to the track of the oncoming target and use her high submerged speed to get close enough to shoot. Simple TMA might even localize the target well enough for a straight gyro shot. The torpedo would be effective against 7–15 kt targets out to about 4,500 yd.

Midgets would have to be made in large numbers by nonspecialist yards. Therefore, BuShips simplified the design and strove to avoid any special fittings or equipment. The hull contained a single central operating compartment, an escape trunk to take two men at a time, interior fuel and ballast tanks, and a WRT (water 'round torpedo) tank high enough so that the torpedo tubes could be flooded by gravity. The diesel generator was commercially available; the main motor generator was not available, but it did not embody any exotic technology. The main storage batteries were commercial items, as were the hydraulic plant and motor. The hull, built in sections for easy production and central assembly, would be relatively thin

($\frac{3}{8}$-in HTS). The snorkel was adapted from one already designed at Portsmouth, and the first few midgets might have used periscopes originally made for German midgets. A one-man cockpit with hydraulic controls would ensure compactness.

Too large to ride a submarine, a midget would be towed to and from her operating station. An operating crew of four to six would then relieve the transit crew for a 10-day mission; it would include swimmers to cut anti-submarine nets.

The completed sketch design showed dimensions of 55 ft×10 ft 8 in×8 ft 6 in (mean draft) for a displacement of 73/84 tons.[6] Designed test depth was 225 ft. The power plant was a 180-BHP 6-71 diesel and a 110/125-SHP motor (64 type MKH 33 truck battery cells, with five-year lifetime) for 7 kt on the surface (8.5 while snorkeling) and 14 kt underwater at the $\frac{1}{2}$-hr rate (12 kt for 1 hr). Expected endurance was 1,900 nm at 6 kt on the surface, 2,000 nm at 7 kt snorkeling, and 100 nm at 3 kt on battery. Berths would be provided for a crew of three.

The working group proposed that characteristics be framed for both Types I and II and that four midgets be included in the new construction program. In November 1949, BuShips proposed that six of each type be built at a total cost of $5.6 million. A formal operational requirement (AS-01402), embodying the Type I design, was issued in

An official model shows *X 1*'s *Albacore* hull form and the shrouded propeller originally planned. As built, she also had a small sail. (Naval Sea Systems Command)

February 1950; by April, it had been abandoned. The only midget in the projected FY 52 program was the 25-ton Type II.

Type II was much closer to the wartime British X-craft, whose designers advised that she had to be far smaller than Type I. She needed only enough sonar to detect and evade enemy ships.[7] Initial draft characteristics called for maximum dimensions of 40×7 ft, rather smaller than the X-craft, and a displacement of about 30 tons. Performance would roughly match that of an X-craft: 6 kt surfaced (radius of 600 nm) and 5 kt submerged (1-hr rate; 60 nm at 2 kt). The midget would have to be controllable while being towed at 15 kt. Test depth would be about 200 ft. Type II would have three berths (crew of two or three), with a one-man air lock. Armament would be a pair of side charges.

The British *XE-7* visited the United States in the summer of 1950. Trials showed that she would be a valuable precursor to an amphibious assault. Approaching a moderately sloping beach, she could remain unseen to within 200 yds. She would carry either two side charges or two swimmer-delivery submersible boats. UDT Team Two estimated that

four X-craft, each carrying a four-man UDT unit, and a total of 2 tons of plastic explosives in streamlined containers would be needed to clear 400 yd of beach.

U.S. designers who visited *XE-7* at Norfolk on 1 September found her design cramped. She had a rudder wheel on a long shaft and a pair of concentric wheels for the planes. Although, in theory, one man could control her, normally both helmsman and planesman were needed. The planesman could also reach the engine throttle and the main motor control. The only really interesting piece of equipment was the joystick used to control trim and compensating tanks. Pushed forward, it started the trim pump to trim by the bow. It trimmed aft in the opposite sense. When pushed to starboard, it pumped from the auxiliary tank to the sea, and to port, from the sea. One man could easily control trim and equilibrium with one hand. The U.S. designs all employed one-man joystick control.

The prototype Type II midget, *X-1*, was included in the FY 52 program as SCB 65. In December 1951, BuShips reported that she could not be completed until June 1953 or beyond. If evaluation of U.S. port defenses was indeed

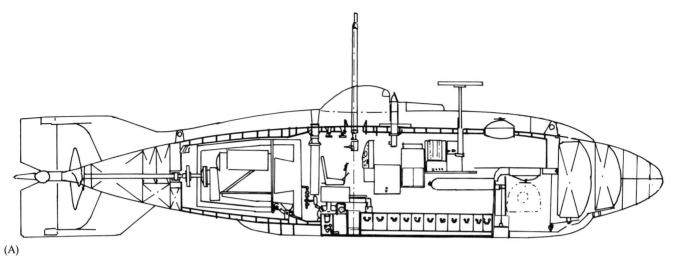

(A)

X-1 was a midget designed for harbor attacks. The two forward tanks are the forward main ballast tank and, abaft it, the 400-gallon hydrogen peroxide tank (containing a rubber bag surrounded by seawater). The diver's air lock doubled as a main ballast tank. Note the two periscopes, with operators' seats abaft them (power-plant instruments to port, ship-control instruments to starboard). Both stations had plane and rudder controls, so the boat could be operated from either. The 33.75 BHP power plant aft was encapsulated, suspended from the after end of the hull section. The main storage battery (60 cells in series) is shown amidships. (B) shows her proposed XT-20A mine. It was installed in an additional (4-ft) forward section, using an adaptation kit. The honeycomb structure abaft the mine is a series of compensating tanks. The mine rests on support arms controlled by a shaft leading to the right, ultimately geared to the door-opening control box (with the wheel on top). It drops away when doors under it open and the arms rotate away. The shaft on top of the mine sets its timer. The 1,700-lb XT-20 could be laid as a magnetic mine or as a demolition charge (for a timed explosion). The mine

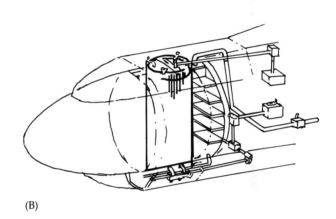

(B)

section was installed at Portsmouth Naval Shipyard during an extended restricted availability (intended partly to correct deficiencies found by the Board of Inspection and Survey) beginning 24 May 1956. X-1 exploded on 20 May 1957, and was then rebuilt with a conventional diesel-electric power plant.

urgent, it might be best to borrow or buy a British X-craft. OpNav was then considering just such a loan; *XE-9* was available for a time in mid-1953. She was then nearly ready for scrapping, so *X-1* was still needed.

Characteristics issued in June 1951 showed $48 \times 6\frac{1}{2} \times 6$ ft (7.5 ft aft). Armament would be a pair of 2,000-lb charges or 14 limpets (5 lb each). Surface endurance was reduced to 500 nm. Formal design work began at Portsmouth in March 1952, somewhat later than originally planned because of uncertainty as to the project's status. By this time, dimensions had grown to 49 ft 3 in $\times$ 6 ft $6\frac{1}{2}$ in (28.7 tons standard, 30.5/35.3 tons, all without armament). Power was 10 SHP surfaced (via a diesel) and 20 SHP submerged (5 and 6 kt, respectively). A proposed torpedo installation was rejected in February 1952 on the ground that it would have added 5–10 ft and 5–10 tons to the midget. Any such revision would have delayed one of the higher-priority full-size submarine designs then under way (the new SSR, the 1953 attack submarine, or the second SSN) by 4–5 mo or the midget herself would have been made a lower priority and the design set back 11 mo.

Compared with the British X-craft then under design, the Type II midget was about a knot slower and somewhat smaller. Test depth was 200, rather than 300, ft. Effective endurance was 4 days (for four men, compared with 21 days for five men). The side charge weighed 2,000 lb versus 3,500 lb.

The characteristics were not particularly exciting. When its design was nearly complete, BuShips let a contract to Fairchild Engine Division of Fairchild Engine and Airplane Corp. to develop an alternative preliminary design. The company suggested a dual-cycle diesel that would function normally on the surface but would burn diesel oil and hydrogen peroxide while submerged. A small motor-generator and battery would provide hotel load power and control when the submarine was towed submerged; it would also provide some limited submerged propulsion. The new study, submitted in October 1952, promised higher submerged speed (7–8 kt) and longer submerged endurance (100 nm at 7–8 kt, 185 nm instead of 6 nm at 6 kt, 300 nm at 3 kt); battery power would be used below 3 kt (endurance 25 nm at 2 kt, compared with 60 nm at 2 kt in the BuShips version). The Fairchild version was selected; X-1 was the only U.S. submarine ever built with a closed-cycle engine. She exploded on 20 May 1957 and was rebuilt with a more conventional diesel-electric power plant.

About 1955, BuOrd had a new weapon especially developed for *X-1:* Mine XT-20A, a vertical cylinder that was carried internally forward of the operator and shot to the surface on release. With a diameter of about 32 in and a height of 70 in, it carried a 1,700-lb charge of HBX-3 and could be laid as a magnetic mine. No documentary evidence of an alternative nuclear payload (as has been reported for the contemporary British X-craft) has emerged.

BuShips built another small submarine. The 250-ton target submarine *T 1* was substituted, under the FY 51 first supplemental program (SCB 68), for the midget that had been initially planned but later deferred to FY 52. Two more target submarines were planned for FY 52, but only one (*T 2*) was built. The design was assigned to Electric Boat. It had a relatively low priority, and completion was delayed from the originally planned mid-1951 date to early 1952.[8]

Like the midget, the SST was intended to explore the possibilities of a type of submarine that neither the United States nor her allies possessed, in this case the Soviet "M" class, which was expected to be particularly effective in coastal and restricted sea areas, such as the Mediterranean. This type of small, fast, maneuverable submarine might negate standard ASW tactics. The SST was particularly wanted to test influence mines, Hedgehog and depth charge patterns, and the new scanning sonar (QHB). In effect, the 25-ton midget (*X-1*) and the 250-tonner were two points on a curve of possible Soviet submarine designs.

A great deal was being asked of a small submarine. In April 1950, the SCB thought that a 140–150-ft submarine (beam 10–12 ft) displacing 200–220 tons could dive to 300 ft, make 12–14 kt at the 1-hr rate, run 100 nm at 3 kt underwater, and make 3,000–4,000 nm at 6 kt on the surface. Because the submarine would be so small, propulsion

The small coastal/target submarine *Marlin* (SST 2) was not quite a midget.

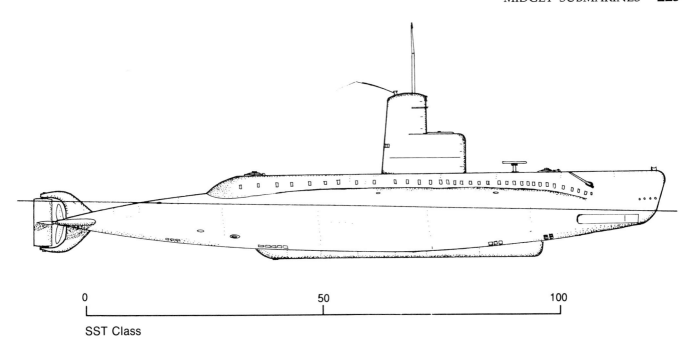

SST Class

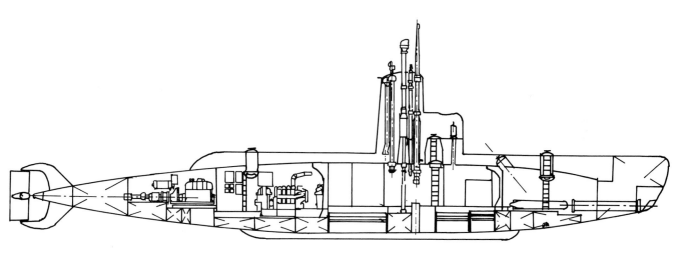

T-2. The sonar transducer in the sail is for BQS-3. Masts, fore to aft, are: the periscope; UHF-IFF mast; snorkel induction; BPS-2 radar; and snorkel exhaust. The battery is split fore and aft, with 69 cells in each. This inboard profile does not show the JT passive array (see the outboard profile), which was offset to port. The single torpedo tube, indicated in both drawings, is on the centerline.

would draw relatively little electric power, only about a third as much as the hotel load (space heating, hot water, and galley). The first BuShips proposal was 140×10-9 ft (177 tons standard, 220 tons surfaced, 260 tons submerged); test depth would be only 225 ft. This boat would make only 11.6 kt at the $\frac{1}{2}$-hr rate, and her best range would be 36 nm at 4.4 kt (extendable to 78 nm at 4 kt if the hotel load were cut to 2.5 instead of three times the propulsion load). Snorkel endurance was satisfactory (4,000 nm at 6 kt). Because submerged performance was the point of the design, surface endurance was cut 30 percent (to 2,800 nm) to buy 100 nm on battery. Surely, the Soviets would do much better with their high-capacity, short-life batteries developed by the Germans during WW II. As the design developed, the single hull was made

shorter and beamier (at the end of preliminary design, 133 ft×13 ft 6 in×11 ft, 250 tons standard, 280/320 tons surfaced/submerged) for maximum underwater maneuverability. Submerged speed was increased to 12.5 kt at the $\frac{1}{2}$-hr rate (11.5 kt at the 1-hr rate) and snorkel endurance increased to 3,000 nm at 8 kt, so that the submarine could operate from a fixed base, such as Key West, and yet reach much of the East and Gulf costs.

Armament was limited to one bow tube (five torpedoes). The torpedo tube was important as a means of exploring the combat potential of small Soviet submarines. For example, it could be used to launch an antiescort torpedo (a Mk 27) as the submarine evaded ASW ships. Complement was only 2 officers and 12 enlisted men, with 20 days' provisions.

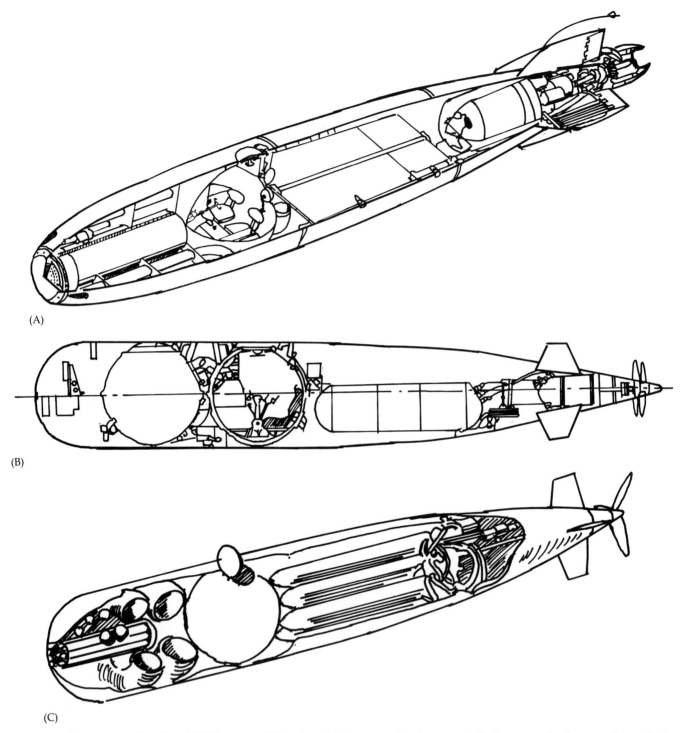

Moray configurations, taken from NOTS reports. (A) is the original proposal, using a torpedo-like pump jet for propulsion. Rocket tubes are wrapped around the bow cylinder that houses electronics. At its fore end is the sonar transducer, and above it is the TV camera. The two pilots are in the sphere, with a hatch on top. Abaft it are the power plant tanks for hydrogen peroxide and, abaft it, diesel oil. The cylinder in the tail is the boiler, with the turbine at its after end connected to the pump jet in the tail by a gearbox. The pump jet is fed by a water scoop under the vertical tail surface. Condenser piping is in the horizontal tail surface. The trailing wire is a radio antenna. (B) is the TV-1A test vehicle, the only form of Moray actually built. The objects in the bow are elements of the sonar (behind an acoustic window, not shown). Abaft it are the spheres for electronics and, further aft, the pilots, with a bottom sounder between them. The cylinder further aft houses the battery. Around it (not shown) is a buoyancy chamber filled with aluminum spheres. Such material is generally provided in deep-diving submersibles, since their hulls are too heavy to be positively buoyant. (C) is a 1962 design concept for a mature Moray powered by a closed-cycle engine, using diesel oil in the toroidal tanks forward (one of them wrapped around the rocket tubes) and gaseous oxygen at 5400 psi in 19 horizontal filament-wound tanks, some of which are shown abaft the control sphere. Note that this version does not show a separate electronics sphere.

The SST and *Albacore* were the first U.S. single-screw submarines since the old B-class. The single screw was justified on the ground that it offered better speed and less resistance; its supposed unreliability was acceptable because the SST was not a combatant.

The midget idea recurred throughout the 1960s and 1970s, usually in the form of an underwater fighter or interceptor launched by a surface ship or submarine. It lay somewhere between Laning's small submarine and wartime manned torpedoes. Moray, a two-man interceptor conceived in 1960 at the Naval Ordnance Test Station (NOTS) at China Lake, was probably the only such device actually built.[9] China Lake hoped that simplicity could be achieved by taking maximum advantage of the decision-making capability of the crew instead of relying on computers. In effect, Moray would supersede both the submarine and the torpedo ends of the submarine weapon system, with no fire-control computer in between.[10] It would loiter quietly to detect a target, then fire itself toward the target at up to 40 kt, slowing to localize and engage using a high-frequency active sonar.[11] The target would actually be attacked by its battery of eight unguided shaped-charge underwater rockets (China Lake was the navy's rocket development center).[12] The crew would visually evaluate the effects of its attacks, using an underwater television camera.[13] Moray would be carried on board a surface ship or submarine, and it would be able to dive as far down as 6,000 ft, not only to search under the layer but also to reach the deep sound channel. China Lake hoped to insure simplicity by using aircraft and missile design practices and by avoiding back-up systems (using fail-safe components instead). Moray lacked any sort of periscope or other means of vision on the surface.

China Lake proposed a 15-ton torpedo-shaped aluminum vehicle (35 ft×64-in diameter). Most of the body would be "soft" (not pressure resistant); the crew would occupy a "hard" 5-ft aluminum sphere. Moray would be powered by a closed-cycle steam plant (using hydrogen peroxide and diesel oil carried abaft the crew sphere), offering an endurance of 1 hour 30 min at 40 kt (1,400 SHP) or 27 hr at 15 kt.

By the fall of 1961 hydrogen peroxide had been abandoned in favor of pure gaseous oxygen, and the vehicle had been rearranged internally, with fuel forward of the crew and oxygen abaft. Because gaseous oxygen is not nearly as dense as hydrogen peroxide, endurance at maximum speed was reduced to 1 hr (10 hr at 15 kt [95 SHP]); estimated minimum speed was 3 kt. By this time, too,

the armament had been reduced to seven 5-in rounds, clustered in the nose instead of arranged around its periphery. Unlike conventional rockets, they expelled their gas from the tips of propeller blades, which actually drove the weapons forward.[14]

NOTS designed an electrically powered test vehicle, TV-1A, of full Moray dimensions, using a motor designed for the Mk 45 (Astor) torpedo. As in the planned ultimate Moray, the crew was in a pressure sphere, with another sphere housing electronics. Sensors were a small sonar and an underwater television. The fiberglass outer hull was free flooding. With a silver-zinc battery, TV-1A made up to 16.4 kt submerged.[15] It had airplane-style controls with a quickened display (apparently similar, but not related, to the contemporary SQUIRE of larger submarines). TV-1A was completed in mid-1962, and by 1963 it had submerged to 900 ft (ultimately it was tested to 2,000 ft). Initial free-manned tests were completed in November 1963. In 1966 a lead-acid battery replaced the silver-zinc unit, reducing speed to 4.5 kt (or 3.2 kt for longer endurance). Together with the television already installed, a new continuous transmission frequency modulated sonar (CTFM, Straza 500) enabled the operators to home and maneuver the vehicle in response to sonar transponder and light beacon signals simulating a "garage" in which Moray would be housed when not in use.

Although TV-1A was tested off the California coast near San Clemente Island, its body is now on the island of Maui, Hawaii; it may have been used as a sonar target. A planned TV-2 with closed-cycle propulsion apparently was never built, although NOTS did produce and test its most critical element, the combustion chamber of its closed-cycle steam plant.

The great problem was that Moray was only part of a weapon system the other elements of which would have been far more complex. An interceptor such as Moray had to be launched in response to initial target detection, and it was probably not fast enough to reach the area of its target quickly enough. Thus, even in 1966, after the vehicle had clearly demonstrated its maneuverability, China Lake had to admit that further development would have to await an operations research study to determine: (i) its roles; (ii) system requirements; (iii) critical technologies requiring further work; and (iv) additional data requirements. In effect, Moray was a manned alternative to a Mk 48 torpedo, and as such, it lost out to the more conventional weapon.

Appendix B

U.S. Post–World War II Submarines

THE FOLLOWING LIST of U.S. submarines includes *Gato* and later class units active after WW II, as well as pierside trainers and boats activated only for transfer abroad. For a complete list of fleet submarines, see the author's forthcoming companion volume on U.S. submarines through WW II.

Building yards: The yard is listed on the second line of each entry. Refer to the following key.

BNY	Boston Navy Yard
CC	Cape Canaveral, Florida (Trident conversion; work done by Norfolk Naval Shipyard; dates are time in hand, so parts were presumably prefabricated)
CR	Cramp Shipbuilding Co., Philadelphia, Pennsylvania
EB	Electric Boat Co. (General Dynamics), Groton, Connecticut
FAIR	Fairchild Engine and Aircraft Co., Farmingdale, New York
FR	Fore River Shipbuilding Co., Quincy, Massachusetts (later Bethlehem Steel, Quincy; later General Dynamics, Quincy)
ING	Ingalls Shipbuilding Corp., Pascagoula, Mississippi
MA	Manitowoc Shipbuilding Co., Manitowoc, Wisconsin
MINY	Mare Island Navy Yard
NN	Newport News Drydock & Shipbuilding Co., Newport News, Virginia
NY	New York Shipbuilding Corp., Camden, New Jersey
PNY	Portsmouth Navy Yard

Other abbreviations: LD, date laid down (appears on first line of each entry); Lch, date of launch (appears on second line of entry; Comm, date of first commissioning on first line with subsequent dates of recommissioning listed below in same column; Decomm, dates of decommissionings, in same order as commissionings; ISIR, in service in reserve.

Fate: This column includes reclassifications and conversions. Use the following key.

AGSS	Auxiliary submarine (e.g., test or at-sea ASW training)
APSS	Transport submarine (replaced by LPSS)
ASSA	Cargo transport submarine (replaced SSA)
BU	Broken up
Deact	Deactivated (part of process to strike an SSN/SSBN)
FS	Fleet Snorkel
G	Guppy (with numeral to indicate type)
ISIR	In service in reserve (pierside trainer)
IXSS	Miscellaneous submarine designation
L	Lost
LPSS	Transport submarine (formerly APSS)
MTS	Moored training submarine
PT	Pierside trainer (with dates)
Ren	Renamed (boats formerly only numbered)
SS	Submarine (reversion to status)
SSA	Cargo submarine (replaced by ASSA)
SSAG	Auxiliary (AGSS retaining combat capability)
SSBN	Ballistic missile submarine
SSG	Missile submarine
SSK	ASW submarine
SSN	Attack submarine (nuclear)
SSO	Oiler submarine
SSP	Transport submarine (replaced by APSS)
SSR	Radar picket submarine
Str	Strike date
L	Loss

No.	Name/Yard	LD/Lch	Comm	Decomm	Fate
212	*George Washington Carver*	5 Oct 40 21 Aug 41	31 Dec 41 1952 (ISIR)	16 Mar 46 1 Mar 60	PT 1952–60, Str 1 Mar 60
213	*Greenling* EB	12 Nov 40 20 Sep 41	21 Jan 42 Dec 46 (ISIR)	16 Oct 46 1 Mar 60	PT 1946–60, Str 1 Mar 60
214	*Grouper* EB	28 Dec 40 27 Oct 41	12 Feb 42	2 Dec 68	SSK Jan 51, AGSS 21 Jun 58, Str 2 Dec 68
217	*Guardfish* EB	1 Apr 41 20 Jan 42	8 May 42 18 Jun 48 (ISIR)	25 May 46 1 Jun 60	PT 1948–60, Str 1 Jun 60
220	*Barb* EB	7 Jun 41 2 Apr 42	8 Jul 42 3 Dec 51 3 Aug 54	12 Feb 47 5 Feb 54 13 Dec 54	G IB 1954 for Italy (*Enrico Tazzoli*)
221	*Blackfish* EB	1 Jul 41 18 Apr 42	22 Jul 42 5 May 49 (ISIR)	11 May 46 19 May 54	PT 1949–54, Str 1 Sep 58
222	*Bluefish* EB	5 Jun 42 21 Feb 53	24 May 43 7 Jan 52	12 Feb 47 20 Nov 53	Str 1 Sep 58
224	*Cod* EB	21 Jul 42 21 Mar 43	21 Jun 43 1 May 60	22 Jun 46 15 Dec 71	PT 1960–71, AGSS 1 Dec 62, IXSS 30 Jun 71, Str 15 Dec 71, memorial at Cleveland
225	*Cero* EB	24 Aug 42 4 Apr 43	4 Jul 43 4 Feb 52	8 Jun 46 23 Dec 53	PT 1959–67, Str 30 Jun 67
228	*Drum* PNY	11 Sep 40 12 May 41	1 Nov 41 18 Mar 47 (ISIR)	16 Feb 46 30 Jun 68	PT 1947–68, AGSS 1 Dec 62, Str 30 Jun 68, memorial at Mobile
229	*Flying Fish* PNY	6 Dec 40 9 Jul 41	10 Dec 41	28 May 54	AGSS 29 Nov 50, sonar tests; Str 1 Aug 58
230	*Finback* PNY	5 Feb 41 25 Aug 41	31 Jan 42	21 Apr 50	Str 1 Sep 58
231	*Haddock* PNY	31 Mar 41 20 Oct 41	14 Mar 42 Aug 48 (ISIR) Jun 56 (ISIR)	12 Feb 47 May 52 1960	PT 1948–52, 1956–60, 1 Jun 60
234	*Kingfish* PNY	29 Aug 41 2 Mar 42	20 May 42 6 Oct 47 (ISIR)	9 Mar 46 1 Mar 60	PT 1947–60, Str 1 Mar 60
235	*Shad* PNY	24 Oct 41 15 Apr 42	12 Jun 42 Oct 47 (ISIR)	1947 1 Apr 60	PT 1948–60, Str 1 Apr 60
236	*Silversides* MINY	4 Nov 40 26 Aug 41	15 Dec 41 15 Oct 47 (ISIR)	17 Apr 46 30 Jun 69	PT 1947–69, AGSS 1 Dec 62, Str 30 Jun 69, memorial at Chicago
239	*Whale* MINY	28 Jun 41 14 Mar 42	1 Jun 42 22 Jan 57 (ISIR)	1 Jun 46 1960	PT 1957–60, Str 1 Mar 60
240	*Angler* EB	9 Nov 42 4 Jul 43	1 Oct 43 2 Apr 51 10 Sep 53 1 Apr 68 (ISIR)	2 Feb 47 10 Nov 52 1 Apr 68 15 Dec 71	SSK 18 Feb 53, SS 15 Aug 59, AGSS 1 Jul 63, IXSS 30 Jun 71, PT 1968–71, Str 15 Dec 71
241	*Bashaw* EB	4 Dec 42 25 Jul 43	25 Oct 43 3 Apr 51 28 Mar 53	29 Jun 49 10 May 52 13 Sep 69	SSK 18 Feb 53, SS 15 Aug 59, AGSS 1 Sep 62, Str 13 Sep 69
242	*Bluegill* EB	7 Dec 42 8 Aug 43	11 Nov 43 3 May 51 2 May 53	1 Mar 46 7 Jul 52 28 Jun 69	SSK 18 Feb 53, SS 15 Aug 59, AGSS 1 Apr 66, Str 28 Jun 69, scuttled for training off Hawaii 3 Dec 70
243	*Bream* EB	5 Feb 43 17 Oct 43	24 Jan 44 5 Jun 51 20 Jun 53	31 Jan 46 10 Sep 52 28 Jun 69	SSK 18 Feb 53, SS 15 Aug 59, AGSS 15 Apr 65, Str 28 Jun 69
244	*Cavalla* EB	4 Mar 43 14 Nov 43	29 Feb 44 10 Apr 51 15 Jul 53 30 Jun 68 (ISIR)	16 Mar 46 3 Sep 52 3 Jun 68 30 Dec 69	SSK 18 Feb 53, SS 15 Aug 59, AGSS 1 Jul 63, PT 1968–69, Str 30 Dec 69, memorial at Galveston
245	*Cobia* EB	17 Mar 43 28 Nov 43	29 Mar 44 6 Jul 51 12 Sep 59 (ISIR)	22 May 46 19 Mar 54 1 Jul 70	PT 1959–70, AGSS 1 Dec 62, Str 1 Jul 70, memorial at Manitowoc

No.	Name/Yard	LD/Lch	Comm	Decomm	Fate
246	*Croaker* EB	1 Apr 43 19 Dec 43	21 Apr 44 7 May 51 11 Dec 53 2 Apr 68 (ISIR)	15 Jun 46 18 Mar 53 2 Apr 68 20 Dec 71	SSK 9 Apr 53, SS 15 Aug 59, AGSS 1 May 67, IXSS 30 Jun 71, PT 1968–71, Str 20 Dec 71, to Groton as memorial, then to Buffalo
247	*Dace* EB	22 Jul 42 25 Apr 43	23 Jul 43 8 Aug 51 22 Oct 54	12 Feb 47 15 Jan 54 31 Jan 55	G IB 1955 for Italy (*Leonardo da Vinci*)
254	*Gurnard* EB	2 Sep 41 1 Jun 42	18 Sep 42 Apr 49 (ISIR)	27 Nov 45 Jun 60	PT 1959–60, Str 1 May 61
256	*Hake* EB	1 Nov 41 17 Jul 42	30 Oct 42 15 Oct 56 (ISIR)	13 Jul 46 19 Apr 68	PT 1956–68, AGSS 1 Dec 62, Str 19 Apr 68
258	*Hoe* EB	2 Jan 42 17 Sep 42	16 Dec 42 Sep 56 (ISIR)	7 Aug 46 15 Apr 60	PT 1956–60, Str 1 May 60
259	*Jack* EB	2 Feb 42 16 Oct 42	6 Jan 43 20 Dec 57	8 Jun 46 21 Apr 58	FS 1958 for Greece (*Amphitriti*)
260	*Lapon* EB	21 Feb 42 27 Oct 42	23 Jan 43 13 Apr 57	25 Jul 46 10 Aug 57	FS 1957 for Greece (*Poseidon*)
261	*Mingo* EB	21 Mar 42 30 Nov 42	12 Feb 43 20 May 55	Jan 47 15 Aug 55	To Japan unmodified 15 Aug 55 (*Kuroshio*)
262	*Muskellunge* EB	7 Apr 42 13 Dec 42	15 Mar 43 31 Aug 56	29 Jan 47 18 Jan 57	To Brazil unmodified 18 Jan 57 (*Humaita*)
263	*Paddle* EB	1 May 42 30 Dec 42	29 Mar 43 31 Aug 56	1 Feb 46 18 Jan 57	To Brazil unmodified 18 Jan 57 (*Riachuelo*)
264	*Pargo* EB	21 May 42 24 Jan 43	26 Apr 43 12 Jun 46 (ISIR)	12 Jun 46 1 Dec 60	PT 1946–60, Str 1 Dec 60
265	*Peto* MA	15 Jun 41 30 Apr 42	21 Nov 42 Jan 43 Nov 56 (ISIR)	25 Dec 42 25 Jun 46 1 Aug 60	PT 1956–60, Str 1 Aug 60 (decomm for barge trip down Mississippi; only she and *Pogy* (266) were decomm this way in wartime)
267	*Pompon* MA	26 Nov 41 15 Aug 42	17 Mar 43 15 Jun 53	11 May 46 1 Apr 60	SSR 11 Dec 51, Str 1 Apr 60
268	*Puffer* MA	16 Feb 42 22 Nov 42	27 Apr 43 46 (ISIR)	28 Jun 46 10 Jun 60	PT 1946–60, Str 1 Jul 60
269	*Rasher* MA	4 May 42 20 Dec 42	8 Jun 43 14 Dec 51 22 Jul 53	22 Jun 46 28 May 52 27 May 67	SSR 11 Dec 51, AGSS 1 Jul 60, IXSS 30 Jun 71, PT 1967–71, Str 20 Dec 71
270	*Raton* MA	29 May 42 24 Jan 43	13 Jul 43 21 Sep 53	11 Mar 49 28 Jun 69	SSR 18 Jul 52, AGSS 1 Jul 60, Str 28 Jun 69
271	*Ray* MA	20 Jul 42 28 Feb 43	27 Jul 43 13 Aug 52	12 Feb 47 30 Sep 58	SSR 2 Jan 51, Str 1 Apr 60
272	*Redfin* MA	3 Sep 42 4 Apr 43	31 Aug 43 9 Jan 53	1 Nov 46 15 May 67	SSR 2 Jan 51, SS 15 Aug 59, AGSS 28 Jun 63, PT 1967–70, Str 1 Jul 70
274	*Rock* MA	23 Dec 42 20 Jun 43	26 Oct 43 12 Oct 53	1 May 46 13 Sep 69	SSR 18 Jul 52, AGSS 31 Dec 59, Str 13 Sep 69
276	*Sawfish* PNY	20 Jan 42 23 Jun 42	26 Aug 42 15 May 47 (ISIR)	20 Jun 46 1 Apr 60	PT 1947–60, Str 1 Apr 60
280	*Steelhead* PNY	1 Jun 42 11 Sep 42	7 Dec 42 12 Nov 47 (ISIR)	29 Jun 46 1 Apr 60	PT 1947–60, Str 1 Apr 60
281	*Sunfish* MINY	25 Sep 41 2 May 42	15 Jul 42 Apr 49 (ISIR)	26 Dec 45 1 May 60	PT 1949–60, Str 1 May 60
282	*Tunny* MINY	10 Nov 41 30 Jun 42	1 Sep 42 25 Feb 52 6 Mar 53	12 Feb 46 30 Apr 52 28 Jun 69	SSG 18 Jul 52, SS 15 May 65, APSS 1 Oct 66, LPSS 1 Jan 69, Str 30 Jun 69
285	*Balao* PNY	26 Jun 42 27 Oct 42	4 Feb 43 4 Mar 52	20 Aug 46 11 Jul 63	AGSS 1 Apr 60, Str 1 Aug 63
286	*Billfish* PNY	23 Jul 42 12 Nov 42	20 Apr 43 1 Jan 60 (ISIR)	1 Nov 46 1 Apr 68	PT 1960–68, AGSS 1 Dec 62, Str 1 Apr 68

No.	Name/Yard	LD/Lch	Comm	Decomm	Fate
287	*Bowfin* PNY	23 Jul 42 7 Dec 42	1 May 43 27 Jul 51 10 Jun 60 (ISIR)	12 Feb 47 22 Apr 54 1 Dec 71	AGSS 1 Dec 62, IXSS 30 Jun 71, PT 1960–71, Str 1 Dec 71, memorial at Pearl Harbor
288	*Cabrilla* PNY	18 Aug 42 24 Dec 42	24 May 43 May 60 (ISIR)	7 Aug 46 30 Jun 68	PT 1960–68, AGSS 1 Dec 62, Str 30 Jun 68, to Galveston as memorial but returned and BU 72
291	*Crevalle* PNY	14 Nov 42 22 Feb 43	24 Jun 43 6 Sep 51 11 Apr 57	29 Jul 46 19 Aug 55 9 Mar 62	AGSS 1 Apr 60, PT 1962–68, Str 15 Apr 68
297	*Ling* CR/BNY	2 Nov 42 15 Aug 43	8 Jun 45 Mar 60 (ISIR)	26 Oct 46 1 Dec 71	PT 1960–71, AGSS 1 Dec 62, IXSS 30 Jun 71, Str 1 Dec 71, memorial at Hackensack
298	*Lionfish* CR/PNY	15 Dec 42 7 Nov 43	1 Nov 44 31 Jan 51 1 Mar 60 (ISIR)	16 Jan 46 15 Dec 53 20 Dec 71	AGSS 1 Dec 62, IXSS 30 Jun 71, PT 1960–71, Str 20 Dec 71, memorial at Fall River
299	*Manta* CR/PNY	15 Jan 43 7 Nov 43	18 Dec 44 2 Aug 49 Apr 60 (ISIR)	10 Jun 46 6 Dec 55 30 Jun 67	AGSS 16 Aug 49, PT 1960–67, Str 30 Jun 67. Was target ship (converted San Francisco) 1949–53
301	*Roncador* CR	21 Apr 43 14 May 44	27 Mar 45 Feb 60 (ISIR)	1 Jun 46 1 Dec 71	PT 1960–71, AGSS 1 Dec 62, IXSS 30 Jun 71, Str 1 Dec 71
302	*Sabalo* CR	5 Jun 43 4 Jun 44	19 Jun 45 Jun 51	7 Aug 46 1 Jul 71	FS 1952, Str 1 Jul 71
303	*Sablefish* CR	5 Jun 43 4 Jun 44	18 Dec 45	1 Nov 69	FS 1951, AGSS 30 Jun 69, Str 1 Nov 69
307	*Tilefish* MINY	10 Mar 43 25 Oct 43	15 Dec 43 30 Jan 60	12 Oct 59 4 May 60	FS 1960 for Venezuela (*Carite*)
309	*Aspro* PNY	27 Dec 42 7 Apr 43	31 Jul 43 23 Sep 51	30 Jan 46 30 Apr 54	AGSS 1 Jul 60, Str 1 Sep 62
310	*Batfish* PNY	27 Dec 42 5 May 43	21 Aug 43 7 Mar 52 Jan 60 (ISIR)	6 Apr 46 Jan 60 1 Nov 69	AGSS 1 Dec 62, PT 1960–69, Str 1 Nov 69, memorial Philadelphia
311	*Archerfish* PNY	22 Jan 43 28 May 43	4 Sep 43 7 Mar 52 1 Aug 57	12 Jun 46 21 Oct 55 1 May 68	AGSS 22 Feb 60, Str 1 May 68
312	*Burrfish* PNY	24 Feb 43 18 Jun 43	13 Sep 43 2 Nov 48 17 Jan 61	10 Oct 46 17 Dec 56 11 May 61	SSR 1 Feb 49, SS 15 Jan 61, to Canada 11 May 61 (*Grilse*)
313	*Perch* EB	5 Jan 43 12 Sep 43	7 Jan 44 20 May 48 11 Nov 61	Jan 47 31 Mar 60 27 May 67	SSP 20 Jan 48, ASSP 31 Jan 50, APSS 24 Oct 56, LPSS 1 Jan 69, IXSS 30 Jun 71, PT 1967–71, Str 1 Dec 71
315	*Sealion* EG	25 Feb 43 31 Oct 43	8 Mar 44 2 Nov 48 20 Oct 61	16 Feb 46 30 Jun 60 20 Feb 70	SSP 5 Apr 48, ASSP 31 Jan 50, APSS 24 Oct 56, LPSS 1 Jan 69, PT 1960–61, Str 15 Mar 77 (test hulk)
317	*Barbero* EB	25 Mar 43 12 Dec 43	29 Apr 44 28 Oct 55	30 Jun 50 30 Jun 64	SSA 5 Apr 48, ASSA 31 Jan 50, SSG 25 Oct 55, Str 1 Jul 64
318	*Baya* EB	8 Apr 43 2 Jan 44	20 May 44 10 Feb 48	14 May 46 30 Oct 72	AGSS 16 Aug 49, sonar tests; Str 30 Oct 72
319	*Becuna* EB	29 Apr 43 30 Jan 44	27 May 44	7 Nov 69	G IA 1951, AGSS 1 Oct 69, SS 30 Jun 71, Str 15 Aug 73, memorial at Philadelphia
320	*Bergall* EB	13 May 43 16 Feb 44	12 Jun 44	18 Oct 58	FS 1952, to Turkey 18 Oct 58 (*Turgut Reis*)
321	*Besugo* EB	27 May 43 27 Feb 44	19 Jun 44	21 Mar 58	AGSS 1 Dec 62; to FS for Italy, transferred 31 May 66 (*Francesco Morosini*)
322	*Blackfin* EB	10 Jun 43 12 Mar 44	4 Jul 44 15 May 51	19 Nov 48 15 Sep 72	G IA 1951, Str 15 Sep 72
323	*Caiman* EB	24 Jun 43 30 Mar 44	17 Jul 44	30 Jun 72	G IA 1951, to Turkey 30 Jun 72 (*Dumlupinar*)
324	*Blenny* EB	8 Jul 43 9 Apr 44	27 Jul 44	7 Nov 69	G IA 1951, AGSS 1 Oct 69, SS 30 Jun 71, Str 15 Aug 73

No.	Name/Yard	LD/Lch	Comm	Decomm	Fate
325	Blower EB	15 Jul 43 23 Apr 44	10 Aug 44	16 Nov 50	FS 1950 for Turkey (Dumlupinar), L 3 Apr 53
326	Blueback EB	29 Jul 43 7 May 44	28 Aug 44	32 May 48	To Turkey 23 May 48 (Ikinci Inonu); FS 1953
327	Boarfish EB	12 Aug 43 21 May 44	23 Sep 44	23 May 48	To Turkey 23 May 48 (Sakarya); FS 1953
328	Charr EB	26 Aug 43 28 May 44	23 Sep 44 28 Jun 69 (ISIR)	28 Jun 69 20 Dec 71	FS 51, AGSS 1 Jul 66, IXSS 30 Jun 71, PT 1969–71, Str 20 Dec 71
329	Chub EB	16 Sep 43 18 Jun 44	21 Oct 44	23 May 48	To Turkey 25 May 48 (Gur); FS 1953
330	Brill EB	23 Sep 43 25 Jun 44	26 Oct 44	23 May 48	To Turkey 25 May 48 (Birinci Inonu); FS 1953
331	Bugara EB	21 Oct 43 2 Jul 44	15 Nov 44	1 Oct 70	FS 1951, AGSS 30 Jun 69, SS 1 Oct 69, Str 1 Oct 70
333	Bumper EB	4 Nov 43 6 Aug 44	9 Dec 44	16 Nov 50	FS 1950 for Turkey (Canakkale)
334	Cabezon EB	18 Nov 43 27 Aug 44	30 Dec 44 Apr 60 (ISIR)	24 Oct 53 15 May 70	AGSS 1 Dec 62, PT 1960–70, Str 15 May 70
335	Dentuda EB	18 Nov 43 10 Sep 44	30 Dec 44 11 Dec 46 (ISIR)	11 Dec 46 30 Jun 67	Bikini target Jul 46, PT 1946–67, AGSS 1 Dec 62, Str 30 Jun 67
336	Capitaine EB	2 Dec 43 1 Oct 44	26 Jan 45 23 Feb 57	10 Feb 50 4 Mar 66	AGSS 1 Jul 60, FS 1966 for Italy (Alfredo Cappellini)
337	Carbonero EB	16 Dec 43 15 Oct 44	7 Feb 45	1 Dec 70	Missile launcher 1949, FS 1952, AGSS 30 Jun 69, SS 1 Oct 69, Str 1 Dec 70
338	Carp EB	23 Dec 43 12 Nov 44	28 Feb 45	18 Mar 68	FS 52, AGSS 1 May 68, IXSS 30 Jun 71, PT 1968–71, Str 20 Dec 71
339	Catfish EB	6 Jan 44 19 Nov 44	19 Mar 45	1 Jul 71	G II 1949, to Argentina 1 Jul 71 (Santa Fe), L 25 Apr 82
340	Entemedor EB	3 Feb 44 17 Dec 44	6 Apr 45 24 Oct 50	10 Dec 48 31 Jul 72	G IIA 1952, to Turkey 31 Jul 72 (Preveze)
341	Chivo EB	21 Feb 44 14 Jan 45	28 Apr 45	1 Jul 71	G IA 1951, to Argentina 1 Jul 71 (Santiago Del Estero)
342	Chopper EB	2 Mar 44 4 Feb 45	25 May 45	27 Aug 69	G IA 1951, AGSS 15 Sep 69, IXSS 30 Jun 71, PT 1969–71, Str 1 Oct 71
343	Clamagore EB	16 Mar 44 25 Feb 45	28 Jun 45	12 Jun 73	G II 1948, G III 1972, Str 12 Jun 75, memorial at Patriots' Point
344	Cobbler EB	3 Apr 44 1 Apr 45	8 Aug 45	21 Nov 73	G II 1949, G III 1962, to Turkey 21 Nov 73 (Canakkale)
345	Cochino EB	13 Apr 44 20 Apr 45	25 Aug 45		G II 1949, L 26 Aug 49
346	Corporal EB	27 Apr 44 10 Jun 45	9 Nov 45	21 Nov 73	G II 1948, G III 1962, to Turkey 21 Nov 73 (Birinci Inonu)
347	Cubera EB	11 May 44 17 Jun 45	19 Dec 45	5 Jan 72	G II 1948, to Venezuela 5 Jan 72 (Tiburon)
348	Cusk EB	25 May 44 28 Jul 45	5 Feb 46	24 Sep 69	SSG 20 Jan 48, FS 1954, SS 1 Jul 54, AGSS 30 Jun 69, Str 24 Sep 69
349	Diodon EB	1 Jun 44 10 Sep 45	18 Mar 46	15 Jan 71	G II 1948, Str 15 Jan 71
350	Dogfish EB	22 Jun 44 27 Oct 45	29 Apr 46	28 Jul 72	G II 1948, to Brazil 28 Jul 72 (Guanabara)
351	Greenfish EB	29 Jun 44 21 Dec 45	7 Jun 46	19 Dec 73	G II 1948, G III 1961, to Brazil 19 Dec 73 (Amazonas)
352	Halfbeak EB	6 Jul 44 19 Feb 46	22 Jul 46	1 Jul 71	G II 1948, Str 1 Jul 71
362	Guavina MA	3 Mar 43 29 Aug 43	23 Dec 43 1 Feb 50 Feb 60 (ISIR)	1946 27 Mar 59 30 Jun 67	SSO 16 Aug 48, AGSS 11 Dec 51, AOSS 22 Jun 57, PT 1960–67, Str 30 Jun 67

No.	Name/Yard	LD/Lch	Comm	Decomm	Fate
363	*Guitarro* MA	7 Apr 43 26 Sep 43	26 Jan 44 6 Feb 52	6 Dec 45 22 Sep 53	FS 1954 for Turkey (*Preveze*)
364	*Hammerhead* MA	5 May 43 24 Oct 43	1 Mar 44 6 Feb 52	9 Feb 46 21 Aug 53	FS 1954 for Turkey (*Cerbe*)
365	*Hardhead* MA	7 Jul 43 12 Dec 43	18 Apr 44 6 Feb 52 24 Mar 53	10 May 46 22 May 52 26 Jul 72	G IIA 1953, to Greece 26 Jul 72 (*Papanikolis*)
366	*Hawkbill* MA	7 Aug 43 9 Jan 44	17 May 44 1953	20 Sep 46 21 Apr 53	G IB 1953 for Netherlands (*Zeeleuw*)
367	*Icefish* MA	4 Sep 43 20 Feb 44	10 Jun 44 5 May 52 10 Dec 52	21 Jun 46 29 Jul 52 21 Feb 53	G IB 1953 for Netherlands (*Walrus*)
368	*Jallao* MA	29 Sep 43 12 Mar 44	8 Jul 44 4 Dec 53	30 Sep 46 26 Jun 74	G IIA 1954, to Spain 26 Jun 74 (*Narciso Monturiol*)
370	*Kraken* MA	13 Dec 43 30 Apr 44	8 Sep 44 1959	4 May 48 24 Oct 59	FS 1959 for Spain (*Almirante Garcia De Los Reyes*)
372	*Lamprey* MA	22 Feb 44 18 Jun 44	17 Nov 44 1960	3 Jun 46 21 Aug 60	To Argentina unmodified 1960 (*Santiago Del Estero*)
373	*Lizardfish* MA	14 Mar 44 16 Jul 44	30 Dec 44 1959	24 Jun 46 9 Jan 60	FS 1959 for Italy (*Evangelista Torricella*)
374	*Loggerhead* MA	1 Apr 44 13 Aug 44	9 Feb 45 1 Jun 60 (ISIR)	1946 30 Jun 67	PT 1960–67, AGSS 1 Dec 62, Str 30 Jun 67
375	*Macabi* MA	1 May 44 19 Sep 44	29 Mar 45 6 May 60	16 Jun 46 11 Aug 60	To Argentina unmodified 1960 (*Santa Fe*)
376	*Mapiro* MA	30 May 44 9 Nov 44	30 Apr 45 1960	16 Mar 46 18 Mar 60	FS 1960 for Turkey (*Piri Reis*)
377	*Menhaden* MA	21 Jun 44 20 Dec 44	22 Jun 45 7 Aug 51 6 Mar 53	31 May 46 13 Aug 52 13 Aug 71	G IIA 1953, Str 15 Aug 73
378	*Mero* MA	22 Jul 44 17 Jan 45	17 Aug 45 1960	15 Jun 46 20 Apr 60	FS 1960 for Turkey (*Hizir Reis*)
381	*Sand Lance* PNY	12 Mar 43 25 Jun 43	9 Oct 43 6 Apr 63	14 Feb 46 7 Sep 63	To Brazil unmodified 1963 (*Rio Grande do Sul*)
382	*Picuda* PNY	15 Mar 43 12 Jul 43	16 Oct 43 19 Jun 53	25 Sep 46 1 Oct 72	G IIA 1953, to Spain 1 Oct 72 (*Cosme Garcia*); had been chosen for abortive minelayer conversion, FY 52, canceled 1 Oct 52
383	*Pampanito* PNY	15 Mar 43 12 Jul 43	6 Nov 43 Apr 60 (ISIR)	15 Dec 45 20 Dec 71	PT 1960–71, AGSS 1 Dec 62, IXSS 30 Jun 71, Str 20 Dec 71
384	*Parche* PNY	9 Apr 43 24 Jul 43	20 Nov 43 10 Feb 48 (ISIR)	11 Dec 46 8 Nov 69	Bikini target 46, PT 1948–69, AGSS 1 Dec 62, Str 8 Nov 69
385	*Bang* PNY	30 Apr 43 30 Aug 43	4 Dec 43 1 Feb 51 4 Oct 52	12 Feb 47 15 May 52 1 Oct 72	G IIA 1952, to Spain 1 Oct 72 (*Cosme Garcia*)
390	*Plaice* PNY	28 Jun 43 15 Nov 43	12 Feb 44 18 May 63	Nov 47 7 Sep 63	To Brazil unmodified 1963 (*Bahia*)
391	*Pomfret* PNY	14 Jul 43 27 Oct 43	19 Feb 44 5 Dec 52	Apr 52 1 Jul 71	G IIA 1953, to Turkey 1 Jul 71 (*Oruc Reis*)
392	*Sterlet* PNY	14 Jul 43 27 Oct 43	4 Mar 44 26 Aug 50	18 Sep 48 30 Sep 68	FS 1952, Str 1 Oct 68; BQR-4 fitted 1955
393	*Queenfish* PNY	27 Jul 43 30 Nov 43	11 Mar 44	1 Mar 63	AGSS 1 Jul 60, Str 1 Mar 63
394	*Razorback* PNY	9 Sep 43 27 Jan 44	3 Apr 44 1954	Aug 52 30 Nov 70	G IIA 1954, to Turkey 30 Nov 70 (*Murat Reis*)
395	*Redfish* PNY	9 Sep 43 27 Jan 44	12 Apr 44	27 Jun 68	AGSS 1 Jul 60, Str 30 Jun 68
396	*Ronquil* PNY	9 Sep 43 27 Jan 44	22 Apr 44 16 Jan 53	May 52 1 Jul 71	G IIA 1953, to Spain 1 Jul 71 (*Isaac Peral*)

No.	Name/Yard	LD/Lch	Comm	Decomm	Fate
397	*Scabbardfish* PNY	27 Sep 43 27 Jan 44	29 Apr 44 24 Oct 64	5 Jan 48 26 Feb 65	FS 1965 for Greece (*Triaina*)
398	*Segundo* PNY	14 Oct 43 5 Feb 44	9 May 44	1 Aug 70	FS 1951, Str 8 Aug 70
399	*Sea Cat* PNY	30 Oct 43 21 Feb 44	16 May 44	2 Dec 68	AGSS 30 Sep 49, SS 11 Dec 51, FS 1952, AGSS 29 Jun 68, Str 2 Dec 68
400	*Sea Devil* PNY	18 Nov 43 28 Feb 44	24 May 44 3 Mar 51 17 Aug 57	9 Sep 48 19 Feb 54 17 Feb 64	AGSS 1 Jul 60, Str 1 Apr 64
401	*Sea Dog* PNY	1 Nov 43 28 Mar 44	3 Jun 44	27 Jun 56	AGSS 1 Dec 62, PT 1960–68, Str 2 Dec 68
402	*Sea Fox* PNY	2 Nov 43 28 Mar 44	13 Jun 44 5 Jun 53	15 Oct 52 14 Dec 70	G IIA 1953, to Turkey 14 Dec 70 (*Burak Reis*)
403	*Atule* PNY	2 Dec 43 6 Mar 44	21 Jun 44 8 Mar 51	8 Sep 47 6 Apr 70	G IA 1951, AGSS 1 Oct 69, SS 30 Jun 71, Str 15 Aug 73, to Peru 31 Jul 74 (*Pacocha*)
404	*Spikefish* PNY	29 Jan 44 26 Apr 44	30 Jun 44	2 Apr 63	AGSS 1 Jul 62, Str 1 May 63
405	*Sea Owl* PNY	7 Feb 44 7 May 44	17 Jul 44	15 Nov 69	FS 1951, AGSS 30 Jun 69, Str 15 Nov 69; BQR-4 fitted 1955
406	*Sea Poacher* PNY	23 Feb 44 20 May 44	31 Jul 44	15 Nov 69	G IA 1952, AGSS 1 Nov 69, SS 30 Jun 71, Str 15 Aug 73, to Peru 1 Jul 74 (*La Pedrera*)
407	*Sea Robin* PNY	1 Mar 44 25 May 44	7 Aug 44	1 Oct 70	G IA 1951, Str 1 Oct 70
408	*Sennet* PNY	8 Mar 44 6 Jun 44	22 Aug 44	2 Dec 68	FS 1952, Str 2 Dec 68
409	*Piper* PNY	15 Mar 44 26 Jun 44	23 Aug 44	16 Jun 67	FS 1951, AGSS 15 Jun 67, PT 1967–70, Str 1 Jul 70; BQR-4 fitted 1955
410	*Threadfin* PNY	18 Mar 44 26 Jun 44	30 Aug 44 7 Aug 53	10 Dec 52 18 Aug 72	G IIA 1953, to Turkey 18 Aug 72 (*Birinci Inonu*)
412	*Trepang* MINY	25 Jun 43 23 Mar 44	22 May 44 Feb 60 (ISIR)	27 Jun 46 30 Jun 67	PT 60-67, AGSS 1 Dec 62, Str 30 Jun 67
413	*Spot* MINY	24 Aug 43 19 May 44	3 Aug 44 19 Aug 61	19 Jun 46 12 Jan 62	To Chile unmodified (*Simpson*)
414	*Springer* MINY	30 Oct 43 3 Aug 44	18 Oct 44 24 Sep 60	Jan 47 23 Jan 61	To Chile unmodified (*Thomson*)
415	*Stickleback* MINY	1 Mar 44 1 Jan 45	29 Mar 45 6 Sep 51 26 Jun 53	26 Jun 46 14 Nov 52	G IIA 1953, L 29 May 58
416	*Tiru* MINY	17 Apr 44 16 Sep 47	1 Sep 48	1 Jul 75	Completed as G II; G III 1959, Str 1 Jul 75; last U.S. fleet submarine in service
417	*Tench* PNY	1 Apr 44 7 Jul 44	6 Oct 44 Oct 50	Jan 47 8 May 70	G IA 1951, AGSS 1 Oct 69, SS 30 Jun 71, Str 15 Aug 73 (to Peru for spares 16 Sep 76)
418	*Thornback* PNY	5 Apr 44 7 Jul 44	13 Oct 44 2 Oct 53	6 Apr 46 1 Jul 71	G IIA 1953, to Turkey 1 Jul 71 (*Uluc Ali Reis*)
419	*Tigrone* PNY	8 May 44 20 Jul 44	25 Oct 44 Jul 48 10 Mar 62	Jan 47 Oct 57 27 Jun 75	SSR 5 Apr 48, SS 1 Mar 61, AGSS 1 Dec 63, Str 27 Jun 75
420	*Tirante* PNY	28 Apr 44 9 Aug 44	6 Nov 44 26 Nov 52	20 Jul 46 1 Oct 73	G IIA 1953, Str 1 Oct 73
421	*Trutta* PNY	22 May 44 18 Aug 44	16 Nov 44 1 Mar 51 2 Jan 53	1947 14 May 52 1 Jul 72	G IIA 1953, to Turkey 1 Jul 72 (*Cerbe*)
422	*Toro* PNY	27 May 44 23 Aug 44	8 Dec 44 13 May 47	2 Feb 46 11 Mar 63	AGSS 1 Jul 62, Str 1 Apr 63
423	*Torsk* PNY	7 Jun 44 6 Sep 44	16 Dec 44	4 Mar 68	FS 1952, AGSS 1 May 68, IXSS 30 Jun 71, PT 1968–71, Str 15 Dec 71, memorial at Baltimore
424	*Quillback* PNY	27 Jun 44 1 Oct 44	29 Dec 44 27 Feb 53	Apr 52 23 Mar 73	G IIA 1953, Str 23 Mar 73

No.	Name/Yard	LD/Lch	Comm	Decomm	Fate
425	*Trumpetfish* CR	23 Aug 43 13 May 45	29 Jan 46	15 Oct 73	G II 1948, G III 1962, to Brazil 15 Oct 73 (*Goias*)
426	*Tusk* CR	23 Aug 43 8 Jul 45	11 Apr 46	18 Oct 73	G II 1948, to Taiwan 18 Oct 73 (*Hai Pao*)
435	*Corsair* EB	1 Mar 45 3 May 46	8 Nov 46	1 Feb 63	AGSS 1 Apr 60, Str 1 Feb 63
475	*Argonaut* PNY	28 Jun 44 1 Oct 44	15 Jan 45	2 Dec 68	FS 1952, to Canada 2 Dec 68 (*Rainbow*)
476	*Runner* PNY	10 Jul 45 17 Oct 44	6 Feb 45	29 Jun 70	FS 1952, AGSS 1 Feb 69, IXSS 30 Jun 71, PT 1970–71, Str 15 Dec 71
477	*Conger* PNY	11 Jul 44 17 Oct 44	14 Feb 45	29 Jul 63	AGSS 9 Mar 62, Str 1 Aug 63
478	*Cutlass* PNY	22 Jul 44 5 Nov 44	17 Mar 45	12 Apr 75	G II 1948, to Taiwan 12 Apr 73 (*Hai Shih*)
479	*Diablo* PNY	11 Aug 44 1 Dec 44	31 Mar 45	1 Jun 64	AGSS 1 Jul 62, FS for Pakistan, transferred 1 Jun 64 (*Ghazi*)
480	*Medregal* PNY	21 Aug 44 15 Dec 44	14 Apr 45	1 Aug 70	FS 1952, AGSS 1 May 67, SS 1 Oct 69, Str 1 Aug 70
481	*Requin* PNY	24 Aug 44 1 Jan 45	28 Apr 45	2 Dec 68	Picket 1946 (SSR 20 Jan 48), SS 15 Aug 59, AGSS 29 Jun 68, IXSS 30 Jun 71, PT 1969–71, Str 20 Dec 71, memorial at Pittsburgh
482	*Irex* PNY	2 Oct 44 26 Jan 45	14 May 45	17 Nov 69	FS 1947, AGSS 30 Jun 69, Str 17 Nov 69; had prototype U.S. snorkel
483	*Sea Leopard* PNY	7 Nov 44 2 Mar 45	11 Jun 45	27 Mar 73	G II 1949, to Brazil 27 Mar 73 (*Bahia*)
484	*Odax* PNY	4 Dec 44 10 Apr 45	11 Jul 45	8 Jul 72	G I 1947, G II 1951, to Brazil 8 Jul 72 (*Rio de Janiero*)
485	*Sirago* PNY	3 Jan 45 11 May 45	13 Aug 45	1 Jun 72	G II 1949, Str 1 Jun 72
486	*Pomodon* PNY	29 Jan 45 12 Jun 45	11 Sep 45 2 Jul 55	1 Apr 55 1 Aug 70	G I 1947, G II 1951, Str 1 Aug 70
487	*Remora* PNY	5 Mar 45 12 Jul 45	3 Jan 46	29 Oct 73	G II 1947, G III 1962, to Greece 29 Oct 73 (*Katsonis*)
488	*Sarda* PNY	12 Apr 45 24 Aug 45	19 Apr 46	1 Jun 64	AGSS 1 Jul 62, Str 1 Jun 64
489	*Spinax* PNY	14 May 45 20 Nov 45	20 Sep 46	11 Oct 69	Completed as picket (SSR 20 Jan 48), SS 15 Aug 59, AGSS 30 Jun 69, Str 11 Oct 69
490	*Volador* PNY	15 Jun 45 21 May 48	1 Oct 48	18 Aug 72	G II as completed; G III 1963, to Italy 18 Aug 72 (*Gianfranco Gazzana Priaroggia*)
522	*Amberjack* BNY	8 Feb 44 15 Dec 44	4 Mar 46	17 Oct 73	G II 1947, to Brazil 17 Oct 73 (*Ceara*)
523	*Grampus* BNY	8 Feb 44 15 Dec 44	26 Oct 49	13 May 72	G II as completed; to Brazil 15 May 72
524	*Pickerel* BNY	8 Feb 44 15 Dec 44	4 Apr 49	18 Aug 72	G II as completed; G III 1962, to Italy 18 Aug 72 (*Primo Longobardo*)
525	*Grenadier* BNY	8 Feb 44 15 Dec 44	10 Feb 51	15 May 73	G II as completed; to Venezuela 15 May 73 (*Picua*)

Note: Although hulls 548–562 were canceled in 1945, 551–556 were reused. SS 553 and SS 554 were offshore purchases for the Norwegian and Danish navies under the FY 60 program (554 was the Danish *Springeren*); SS 556 was an FY 61 offshore purchase for Norway. Both Norwegian contracts were canceled in August 1961, with the United States contributing half the cost of the entire 15-submarine *Kobben* class.

551	Number later used for *Bass* (K-2); see SSK 2 below				
552	Number later used for *Bonita* (K-3); see SSK 3 below				
555	*Dolphin* PNY	9 Nov 62 8 Jun 68	17 Aug 68		AGSS

No.	Name/Yard	LD/Lch	Comm	Decomm	Fate
563	*Tang* PNY	16 Apr 49 19 Jun 51	25 Oct 51	8 Feb 80	AGSS 30 Jun 76; sale to Iran as *Dolfin* canceled 3 Feb 79; to Turkey 8 Feb 80 (*Piri Reis*)
564	*Trigger* EB	24 Feb 49 14 May 71	31 Mar 52	20 Feb 74	To Italy 10 Jul 74 (*Livio Piomarta*)
565	*Wahoo* PNY	24 Oct 49 16 Oct 51	30 May 52	27 Jun 80	In overhaul for sale to Iran as *Nahang;* sale was canceled because of revolution, 31 Mar 79; Str 15 Jul 83
566	*Trout* EB	1 Dec 49 21 Aug 51	27 Jun 52	19 Dec 78	Str 19 Dec 78 for sale to Iran as *Kousseh,* but Iranian crew abandoned her Mar 79 because of revolution; retained at Philadelphia while finances were resolved (to United States 1992)
567	*Gudgeon* PNY	20 May 50 11 Jun 52	21 Nov 52	30 Sep 83	AGSS 1 Apr 78 (replaced 565 as acoustic test ship); SSAG 1 Nov 79
568	*Harder* EB	30 Jun 50	10 Aug 52	10 Jul 73	To Italy 20 Feb 74 (*Romeo Romei*)
569	*Albacore* PNY	15 Mar 52 1 Aug 53	5 Dec 53	1 Sep 72	AGSS, Str 1 May 80, memorial at Portsmouth
570	Redesignated SST 1 (see below)				
571	*Nautilus* EB	14 Jun 52 21 Jan 54	30 Sep 54	30 Mar 80	SSN, memorial at Groton 1985
572	*Sailfish* PNY	8 Dec 53 7 Sep 55	14 Apr 56	29 Sep 78	SSR, SS 1 Mar 61, Str 30 Sep 78 to be memorial at Quincy
573	*Salmon* PNY	10 Mar 54 25 Feb 56	14 Apr 56	1 Oct 77	SSR; SS 1 Mar 61, AGSS (for DSRV) 29 Jun 68 but SS 30 Jun 69, Str 1 Oct 77
574	*Grayback* MINY	1 Jul 54 2 Jul 57	7 Mar 58 9 May 69	25 May 64	SSG; LPSS converted 7 Nov 67–21 Aug 69 (reclassified 30 Aug 69); Str 16 Jan 84
575	*Seawolf* EB	15 Sep 53 21 Jul 55	30 Mar 57	30 Mar 87	SSN, Str 10 Jul 87
576	*Darter* EB	10 Nov 54 28 May 56	20 Oct 56	1 Dec 89	Str 17 Jan 90
577	*Growler* PNY	16 Feb 55 5 Apr 57	30 Aug 58	25 May 64	SSG, Str 1 Aug 80, museum ship in New York
578	*Skate* EB	21 Jul 55 16 May 57	23 Dec 57	12 Sep 86	SSN, Str 12 Sep 86
579	*Swordfish* PNY	25 Jan 56 27 Aug 57	15 Sep 58	15 May 88	SSN, Str 2 Jun 89
580	*Barbel* PNY	18 May 56 19 Jul 58	17 Jan 59	4 Dec 89	Str 17 Jan 90, memorial at Portland, Oregon
581	*Blueback* ING	15 Apr 57 16 May 59	15 Oct 59	30 Jun 90	Str 30 Oct 90, last U.S. diesel attack submarine
582	*Bonefish* NY	3 Jun 57 22 Nov 58	9 Jul 59	28 Sep 88	Str 28 Sep 88 after fire 24 Mar 88

Note: All submarines from 583 on were nuclear powered (SSN, SSGN, SSRN, or SSBN). Some decommissioning dates, as listed, are deactivation dates.

No.	Name/Yard	LD/Lch	Comm	Decomm	Fate
583	*Sargo* MINY	21 Feb 56 10 Oct 57	1 Oct 58	6 May 87	Str 21 Apr 88
584	*Seadragon* PNY	20 Jun 56 16 Aug 58	5 Dec 59	12 Jun 84	Str 30 Apr 86
585	*Skipjack* EB	29 May 56 25 May 58	15 Apr 59	19 Apr 90	Str 19 Apr 90
586	*Triton* EB	29 May 56 19 Aug 58	10 Nov 59	3 May 69	SSRN; SSN 1 Mar 61, Str 30 Apr 86
587	*Halibut* MINY	11 Apr 57 9 Jan 59	4 Jan 60	30 Jun 76	SSGN; SSN 15 Aug 65, DSRV test ship, Str 30 Apr 86
588	*Scamp* MINY	23 Jan 59 8 Oct 60	5 Jun 61	26 Apr 88	Str 28 Apr 88

No.	Name/Yard	LD/Lch	Comm	Decomm	Fate
589	*Scorpion* EB	20 Aug 58 29 Dec 59	29 Jul 60		L 22 May 68
590	*Sculpin* ING	3 Feb 58 31 Mar 60	1 Jun 61	3 Aug 90	Str 3 Aug 90
591	*Shark* NN	24 Feb 58 16 Mar 60	9 Feb 61	11 Oct 89	Str 30 Sep 90
592	*Snook* ING	7 Apr 58 31 Oct 60	24 Oct 61	15 May 86	Str 8 Oct 86
593	*Thresher* PNY	28 May 58 9 Jul 60	3 Aug 61		L 10 Apr 63
594	*Permit* MINY	16 Jul 59 1 Jul 61	29 May 62	23 Feb 91	Str 23 Feb 91
595	*Plunger* MINY	2 Mar 60 9 Dec 61	21 Nov 62	10 Feb 89	Str 31 Jan 90
596	*Barb* ING	9 Nov 59 12 Feb 62	24 Aug 63	20 Dec 89	Str 31 Aug 90
597	*Tullibee* EB	26 May 58 27 Apr 60	9 Sep 60	1 Dec 87	Inactive since 1986, Str 18 Jun 88
598	*George Washington* EB	1 Nov 57 9 Jun 59	30 Dec 59	24 Jan 85	SSBN; SSN 20 Nov 81, Str 30 Apr 85
599	*Patrick Henry* EB	27 May 58 22 Sep 59	9 Apr 69	25 May 84	SSBN; SSN 24 Oct 81, Str 25 May 85
600	*Theodore Roosevelt* MINY	30 May 58 3 Oct 59	13 Feb 61	28 Feb 81	SSBN, Str 28 Feb 81
601	*Robert E. Lee* NN	25 Aug 58 18 Dec 59	16 Sep 60	1 Dec 83	SSBN; SSN 1 Mar 82, completed final Polaris patrol 1 Oct 82, Str 30 Apr 86
602	*Abraham Lincoln* PNY	1 Nov 58 14 May 60	11 Mar 61	28 Feb 81	SSBN, Str 28 Feb 81
603	*Pollack* NY	14 Mar 60 17 Mar 62	26 May 64	30 Jan 89	Str 1 Apr 89
604	*Haddo* NY	9 Sep 60 18 Aug 62	16 Dec 64	12 Jun 91	Str 12 Jun 91
605	*Jack* PNY	16 Sep 60 24 Apr 63	31 Mar 64	11 Jul 90	Str 29 Jun 90
606	*Tinosa* PNY	24 Nov 59 9 Dec 61	17 Oct 64	15 Jan 92	Deact 15 Jul 91, Str
607	*Dace* ING	6 Jun 60 18 Aug 62	4 Apr 64	2 Dec 88	Str 30 Mar 89
608	*Ethan Allen* EB	14 Sep 59 22 Nov 60	22 Nov 60	31 Mar 83	SSBN; SSN 1 Sep 80, Str 30 Apr 86
609	*Sam Houston* NN	28 Dec 59 2 Feb 61	6 Mar 62	12 Aug 91	SSBN; SSN 10 Nov 80, SEAL transport, Str 6 Sep 91
610	*Thomas A. Edison* EB	15 Mar 60 15 Jun 61	10 Mar 62	1 Dec 83	SSBN; SSN 6 Oct 80, Str 30 Apr 86
611	*John Marshall* NN	4 Apr 60 15 Jul 61	21 May 62	23 Nov 91	SSBN; SSN Feb 81, SEAL transport, Deact 14 Feb 92
612	*Guardfish* NY	13 Feb 61 15 May 65	20 Dec 66	4 Feb 92	Deact 14 May 91
613	*Flasher* FR	14 Apr 61 22 Jun 63	22 Jul 66	1992	Deact 18 Jun 91
614	*Greenling* EB	15 Aug 61 4 Apr 64	3 Nov 67		Deact 31 Oct 93
615	*Gato* EB	15 Dec 61 14 May 64	25 Jan 68	1994	
616	*Lafayette* EB	17 Jan 61 8 May 62	23 Apr 63	12 Aug 91	SSBN

No.	Name/Yard	LD/Lch	Comm	Decomm	Fate
617	*Alexander Hamilton* EB	26 Jun 61 18 Aug 62	27 Jun 63	FY 93	SSBN; deact 1 Oct 92
618	*Thomas Jefferson* NN	3 Feb 61 24 Feb 62	4 Jan 63	24 Jan 85	SSBN; SSN Apr 81, Str 30 Apr 86
619	*Andrew Jackson* MINY	26 Apr 61 15 Sep 62	3 Jul 63	6 Sep 89	SSBN; Str 31 Aug 89 for conversion to ARTB (moored training barge)
620	*John Adams* MINY	19 May 61 12 Jan 63	12 May 64	14 Sep 88	SSBN, Str 30 Sep 89
621	*Haddock* ING	24 Apr 61 21 May 66	22 Dec 67		Deact 3 Feb 92
622	*James Monroe* NN	31 Jul 61 4 Aug 62	7 Dec 63	23 Jun 90	SSBN, Str 25 Sep 90
623	*Nathan Hale* EB	2 Oct 61 12 Jan 63	23 Nov 63	3 Nov 86	SSBN, Str 31 Jan 87
624	*Woodrow Wilson* MINY	13 Sep 61 22 Feb 63	27 Dec 63	FY 93	SSBN, deact Nov 93
625	*Henry Clay* NN	23 Oct 61 30 Nov 62	20 Feb 64	6 Nov 90	SSBN, Deact 12 Mar 90, Str 5 Nov 90
626	*Daniel Webster* EB	28 Dec 61 27 Apr 63	9 Apr 64	30 Aug 90	SSBN, to MTS 626
627	*James Madison* NN	5 Mar 62 15 Mar 63	28 Jul 64	17 Feb 92	SSBN, first Trident conversion to deactivate; Trident converted 3 Aug 79–9 Feb 82 NN (FY 79)
628	*Tecumseh* EB	1 Jun 62 22 Jun 63	29 May 64	FY 93	SSBN, missile system deactivated FY 92; deact 15 Feb 93
629	*Daniel Boone* MINY	6 Feb 62 22 Jun 63	23 Apr 64		SSBN; Trident conversion 3 Apr 80–30 May 80, CC (FY 80); deact Oct 93
630	*John C. Calhoun* NN	4 Jun 62 22 Jun 63	15 Sep 64		SSBN; Trident conversion 30 Jun 80–26 Aug 80, CC (FY 80)
631	*Ulysses S. Grant* EB	18 Aug 62 2 Nov 63	17 Jul 64	14 Feb 92	SSBN
632	*Von Steuben* NN	4 Sep 62 18 Oct 63	30 Sep 64	FY 93	SSBN; Trident conversion 13 Jan 80–28 May 82, NN (FY 80); deact 7 Jul 93
633	*Casimir Pulaski* EB	12 Jan 63 1 Feb 64	14 Aug 64		SSBN; Trident conversion 1 Jul 80–10 Dec 82, NN (FY 80); deact Oct 93
634	*Stonewall Jackson* MINY	4 Jul 62 30 Nov 63	26 Aug 64		SSBN; Trident conversion 8 Sep 81–6 Nov 81, CC (FY 82); deact Sep 94
635	*Sam Rayburn* NN	3 Dec 62 20 Dec 63	2 Dec 64		SSBN; began Deact Sep 85 for conversion to nonpropelled nuclear training platform (ARTB) but Str instead, unconverted, 28 Aug 89
636	*Nathanael Greene* MINY	21 May 62 12 May 64	19 Dec 64	12 Dec 86	SSBN, Str 31 Jan 87
637	*Sturgeon* EB	10 Aug 63 26 Feb 66	3 Mar 67		Deact Apr 94
638	*Whale* FR	27 May 64 14 Oct 66	12 Oct 68		Deact FY 95
639	*Tautog* ING	27 Jan 64 15 Apr 67	17 Aug 68		
640	*Benjamin Franklin* EB	25 May 63 5 Dec 64	22 Oct 65		SSBN; Trident conversion 12 Nov 79–18 Sep 81, PNY (FY 80); deact 1 Apr 93
641	*Simon Bolivar* NN	17 Apr 63 22 Aug 64	29 Oct 65		SSBN; Trident conversion 2 Mar 79–28 Dec 80, PNY (FY 79)
642	*Kamehameha* MINY	2 May 63 16 Jan 65	10 Dec 65		SSBN; became SSN (SEAL transport), work began Aug 92, MINY
643	*George Bancroft* EB	24 Aug 63 20 Mar 65	22 Jan 66		SSBN; Trident conversion, 1 Jun 80–5 Mar 82, PNY (FY 80); deact 1 Mar 93
644	*Lewis and Clark* NN	29 Jul 63 21 Nov 64	22 Dec 65	27 Jun 92	SSBN; Deact 1 Oct 91

No.	Name/Yard	LD/Lch	Comm	Decomm	Fate
645	*James K. Polk* EB	23 Nov 63 22 May 65	16 Apr 66		SSBN; to SSN (as SEAL transport)
646	*Grayling* PNY	12 May 64 22 Jun 67	11 Oct 69		
647	*Pogy* NY	5 May 64 3 Jun 67	15 May 71		
648	*Aspro* ING	23 Nov 63 29 Nov 67	20 Feb 69		Deact Sep 94
649	*Sunfish* FR	15 Jan 65 14 Oct 66	15 Mar 69		
650	*Pargo* EB	3 Jun 64 17 Sep 66	5 Jan 68		Deact FY 95
651	*Queenfish* NN	11 May 64 25 Feb 66	6 Dec 66	8 Nov 91	Deact 27 Sep 90; Str 8 Nov 91
652	*Puffer* ING	8 Feb 65 30 Mar 68	9 Aug 69		
653	*Ray* NN	4 Jan 65 21 Jun 66	12 Apr 67	FY 93	Began Deact Jul 92
654	*George C. Marshall* NN	2 Mar 64 21 May 65	29 Apr 66	FY 92	SSBN
655	*Henry L. Stimson* EB	4 Apr 64 13 Nov 65	20 Aug 66	FY 93	SSBN; Trident conversion 4 Dec 79–7 Feb 80, CC (FY 80); deact 2 Nov 92
656	*George Washington Carver* NN	24 Aug 64 14 Aug 65	15 Jun 66	FY 93	SSBN; deact 2 Nov 92
657	*Francis Scott Key* EB	5 Dec 64 23 Apr 66	3 Dec 66		SSBN; Trident conversion 24 Sep 78–4 Dec 78, CC (FY 79); deact 1 Feb 93
658	*Mariano C. Vallejo* MINY	7 Jul 64 23 Oct 65	16 Dec 66		Deact FY 95; Last first-generation SSBN; Trident conversion 3 Sep 79–5 Nov 79, CC (FY 79)
659	*Will Rogers* EB	20 Mar 65 21 Jul 66	1 Apr 67	FY 93	SSBN; deact 2 Nov 92
660	*Sand Lance* PNY	15 Jan 65 11 Nov 69	25 Sep 71		
661	*Lapon* NN	26 Jul 65 16 Dec 66	14 Dec 67	25 Jun 92	Deact 1 Oct 91
662	*Gurnard* MINY	22 Dec 64 20 May 67	6 Dec 68		Deact FY 95
663	*Hammerhead* NN	29 Nov 65 14 Apr 67	28 Jun 68		Deact FY 95
664	*Sea Devil* NN	12 Apr 66 5 Oct 67	30 Jan 69	16 Oct 91	Deact 25 Feb 91, Str 16 Oct 91
665	*Guitarro* MINY	9 Dec 65 27 Jul 68	9 Sep 72	29 May 92	Deact 1 Oct 91; delivered late because of flooding in dock
666	*Hawkbill* MINY	12 Sep 66 12 Apr 69	4 Feb 71		
667	*Bergall* EB	16 Apr 66 17 Feb 68	13 Jun 69		
668	*Spadefish* NN	21 Dec 66 15 May 68	14 Aug 69		
669	*Seahorse* EB	13 Aug 66 15 Jun 68	19 Sep 69		Deact FY 95
670	*Finback* NN	26 Jun 67 7 Dec 68	4 Feb 70		
671	*Narwhal* EB	17 Jan 66 9 Sep 67	12 Jul 69		
672	*Pintado* MINY	27 Oct 67 16 Aug 69	11 Sep 71		

No.	Name/Yard	LD/Lch	Comm	Decomm	Fate
673	*Flying Fish* EB	30 Jun 67 17 May 69	29 Apr 70		
674	*Trepang* EB	28 Oct 67 27 Sep 69	14 Aug 70		
675	*Bluefish* EB	13 Mar 68 10 Jan 70	8 Jan 71		
676	*Billfish* EB	20 Sep 68 1 May 70	12 Mar 71		
677	*Drum* MINY	20 Aug 68 23 May 70	15 Apr 72		Deact FY 95
678	*Archerfish* EB	19 Jun 69 16 Jan 71	17 Dec 71		
679	*Silversides* EB	28 Nov 69 4 Jun 71	5 May 72		Deact Feb 94
680	*William H. Bates* ING	24 Nov 69 11 Dec 71	5 May 73		
681	*Batfish* EB	9 Feb 70 9 Oct 71	1 Sep 72		
682	*Tunny* ING	22 May 70 10 Jun 72	26 Jan 74		
683	*Parche* ING	10 Dec 70 13 Jan 73	17 Aug 74		
684	*Cavalla* EB	4 Jun 70 19 Feb 72	9 Feb 73		
685	*Glenard P. Lipscomb* EB	5 Jun 71 4 Aug 73	21 Dec 74	11 Jul 90	Str 11 Jul 90
686	*L. Mendel Rivers* NN	26 Jun 71 2 Jun 73	1 Feb 75		
687	*Richard B. Russell* NN	19 Oct 71 12 Jan 74	16 Aug 75	FY 93	Deact 1 Jul 93
688	*Los Angeles* NN	8 Jan 72 6 Apr 74	13 Nov 76	FY 94	
689	*Baton Rouge* NN	18 Nov 72 26 Apr 75	25 Jun 77	Nov 93	First *Los Angeles* decommissioned
690	*Philadelphia* EB	12 Aug 72 19 Oct 74	25 Jun 77		
691	*Memphis* NN	23 Jun 73 3 Apr 76	17 Dec 77		
692	*Omaha* EB	27 Jan 73 21 Feb 76	11 Mar 78		Deact FY 95
693	*Cincinnati* NN	6 Apr 74 19 Feb 77	10 Jun 78		Deact FY 95
694	*Groton* NN	3 Aug 73 9 Oct 76	8 Jul 78		
695	*Birmingham* NN	26 Apr 75 29 Oct 77	20 Dec 78		
696	*New York City* EB	15 Dec 73 18 Jun 77	10 Mar 79		
697	*Indianapolis* EB	19 Oct 74 30 Jul 77	5 Jan 80		
698	*Bremerton* EB	8 May 76 22 Jul 78	28 Mar 81		
699	*Jacksonville* EB	21 Feb 76 18 Nov 78	16 May 81		
700	*Dallas* EB	9 Oct 76 28 Apr 79	18 Jul 81		

No.	Name/Yard	LD/Lch	Comm	Decomm	Fate
701	*La Jolla* EB	16 Oct 76 11 Aug 79	24 Oct 81		
702	*Phoenix* EB	30 Jul 77 8 Dec 79	19 Dec 81		
703	*Boston* EB	11 Aug 78 19 Apr 80	30 Jan 82		
704	*Baltimore* EB	21 May 79 13 Dec 80	24 Jul 82		
705	*City of Corpus Christi* EB	4 Sep 79 25 Apr 81	14 Dec 82		
706	*Albuquerque* EB	27 Dec 79 13 Mar 82	21 May 83		
707	*Portsmouth* EB	8 May 80 18 Sep 82	1 Oct 83		
708	*Minneapolis-St. Paul* EB	20 Jan 81 18 Dec 82	10 Mar 84		
709	*Hyman G. Rickover* EB	24 Jul 81 27 Aug 83	21 Jul 84		
710	*Augusta* EB	1 Apr 82 21 Jan 84	19 Jan 85		
711	*San Francisco* NN	26 May 77 27 Oct 79	24 Apr 81		
712	*Atlanta* NN	17 Aug 78 16 Aug 80	6 Mar 82		
713	*Houston* NN	29 Jan 79 21 Mar 81	25 Sep 82		
714	*Norfolk* NN	1 Aug 79 21 Oct 81	21 May 83		
715	*Buffalo* NN	25 Jan 80 8 May 82	5 Nov 83		
716	*Salt Lake City* NN	26 Aug 80 16 Oct 82	12 May 84		
717	*Olympia* NN	31 Mar 81 30 Apr 83	17 Nov 84		
718	*Honolulu* NN	10 Nov 81 24 Sep 83	6 Jul 85		
719	*Providence* EB	9 Oct 82 4 Aug 84	27 Jul 85		
720	*Pittsburgh* EB	15 Apr 83 8 Dec 84	23 Nov 85		
721	*Chicago* NN	5 Jan 83 13 Oct 84	27 Sep 86		
722	*Key West* NN	6 Jul 83 20 Jul 85	12 Sep 87		
723	*Oklahoma City* NN	4 Jan 84 2 Nov 85	9 Jul 88		
724	*Louisville* EB	16 Sep 84 14 Dec 85	8 Nov 86		
725	*Helena* EB	28 Mar 85 28 Jun 86	11 Jul 87		
726	*Ohio* EB	10 Apr 76 7 Apr 79	11 Nov 81		SSBN
727	*Michigan* EB	4 Apr 77 26 Apr 80	11 Sep 82		SSBN
728	*Florida* EB	9 Jun 77 14 Nov 81	18 Jun 83		SSBN

No.	Name/Yard	LD/Lch	Comm	Decomm	Fate
729	*Georgia* EB	7 Apr 79 6 Nov 82	11 Feb 84		SSBN
730	*Henry M. Jackson* EB	9 Jan 81 15 Oct 83	6 Oct 84		SSBN
731	*Alabama* EB	27 Aug 81 19 May 84	25 May 85		SSBN
732	*Alaska* EB	9 Mar 83 12 Jan 85	25 Jan 86		SSBN
733	*Nevada* EB	8 Aug 83 14 Sep 85	16 Aug 86		SSBN
734	*Tennessee* EB	9 Jun 86 13 Dec 87	17 Dec 88		SSBN
735	*Pennsylvania* EB	2 Mar 87 23 Apr 88	9 Sep 89		SSBN
736	*West Virginia* EB	18 Dec 87 14 Oct 89	20 Oct 90		SSBN
737	*Kentucky* EB	18 Dec 87 8 Aug 90	13 Jul 91		SSBN
738	*Maryland* EB	18 Dec 87 10 Aug 91	13 Jun 92		SSBN
739	*Nebraska* EB	18 Dec 87 15 Aug 92	Aug 93		SSBN
740	*Rhode Island* EB	Jul 93	Aug 94		SSBN
741	*Maine* EB	Jul 94	Aug 95		SSBN
742	*Wyoming* EB	Oct 94	Aug 96		SSBN
743	*Louisiana* EB		Aug 97		SSBN

Note: 744–749 were reserved for *Ohio*-class SSBNs, but they will not be used for that purpose in view of agreed arms limitations.

No.	Name/Yard	LD/Lch	Comm	Decomm	Fate
750	*Newport News* NN	3 Mar 84 15 Mar 86	3 Jun 89		
751	*San Juan* EB	16 Aug 85 6 Dec 86	6 Aug 88		
752	*Pasadena* EB	20 May 85 12 Sep 87	11 Feb 89		
753	*Albany* NN	22 Apr 85 13 Jun 87	7 Apr 90		
754	*Topeka* EB	13 May 86 23 Jan 88	21 Oct 88		
755	*Miami* EB	24 Oct 86 12 Nov 88	30 Jun 90		
756	*Scranton* NN	29 Jun 86 3 Jul 89	26 Jan 91		
757	*Alexandria* EB	19 Jun 87 23 Jun 90	29 Jul 91		
758	*Asheville* NN	1 Jan 87 24 Feb 90	28 Sep 91		
759	*Jefferson City* NN	21 Sep 87 16 Aug 90	28 Sep 92		
760	*Annapolis* EB	15 Jun 88 2 Feb 91	11 Apr 92		
761	*Springfield* EB	29 Jan 90 9 Nov 91	Jul 93		

No.	Name/Yard	LD/Lch	Comm	Decomm	Fate
762	*Columbus* EB	7 Jan 91 20 Jun 92	Jun 93		
763	*Santa Fe* EB	9 Jul 91 12 Dec 92	Jan 94		
764	*Boise* NN	25 Aug 88 23 Mar 91	7 Nov 92		
765	*Montpelier* NN	19 May 89 23 Aug 91	Mar 93		
766	*Charlotte* NN	31 Jul 90 3 Oct 92	Jan 94		
767	*Hampton* NN	2 Mar 90 28 Sep 91	Sep 93		
768	*Hartford* EB	24 Apr 92 Aug 93	Sep 94		
769	*Toledo* NN	26 Apr 91 Dec 92	Jun 94		
770	*Tucson* NN	20 Sep 91 May 93	Nov 94		
771	*Columbia* EB	Aug 92 Feb 94	1996		
772	*Greenville* NN	Jan 92 Oct 93	1996		
773	*Cheyenne* NN	Aug 92	1996		
21	*Seawolf* EB	1995	1996		Hull number may change to fit usual sequence
22	*Connecticut* EB				
	SSK 1 (K 1) EB	1 Jul 49 2 Mar 51	10 Nov 51	1 Oct 73	Ren *Barracuda*; SST 3 Jul 59, Str 1 Oct 73
	SSK 2 (K 2) MINY	23 Feb 50 2 May 51	16 Nov 52	20 Dec 57	Ren *Bass*; SS Dec 55, Str 1 Apr 65
	SSK 3 (K 3) MINY	19 May 50 21 Jun 51	11 Jan 52	7 Nov 58	Ren *Bonita*; SS Dec 55, Str 1 Apr 65
	SST 1 (T 1) EB	1 Apr 52 17 Jul 53	9 Oct 53	31 Jan 73	Ren *Mackerel*; Str 31 Jan 73, target
	SST 2 (T 2) EB	1 May 52 14 Oct 53	20 Nov 53	31 Jan 73	Ren *Marlin*; Str 31 Jan 73, memorial at Omaha
	X-1 FAIR	8 Jun 54 7 Sep 55	7 Oct 55	2 Dec 57 16 Feb 73	Str 9 Jul 74, memorial at Annapolis

Appendix C

Submarine Data

THE TABLES BELOW list the main characteristics of 10 diesel-electric attack submarines, 12 nuclear attack submarines, 6 missile submarines, and 3 special types of submarines.

In the battery listings, the first number refers to the number of batteries and the second number to the number of cells in each battery (e.g., 2×126 means two 126-cell batteries). G indicates a Guppy-type battery and S a *Sargo*-type (in each case, with suffix). The numbers given for torpedoes include those in tubes. N/A means the information was not available, generally for security reasons.

Table 1.   Diesel-Electric Attack Submarines

	Fleet Submarine SS 285	Guppy IA SS 417	Guppy II SS 350	Guppy III SS 343	*Tang* SS 563	*Darter* SS 576	*Barbel* SS 580	*Sailfish* SSR 572	K-1 SS 551	T-1 SST 1
LOA (ft)	311-9	307-7	307-0	321-0	269-2	268-7	219-2	350-6	196-1	131-3
Beam (extreme) (ft)	27-3	27-4	27-4	27-4	27-2	27-2.25	29-0	29-1	24-7	13-7
Draft (ft)	15-3	17-0	17-0	17-0	18-0		29-0	16-4	14-5	12-2
Pressure hull diameter (ft)	16-0	16-0	16-0	16-0	17-0	16-8.625	20-7.3125			
Surfaced displacement (tons)	1,525	1,800	2,040 (NOR)	1,975 (NOR)	1,821	1,871.7	2,145.7	1,990 (STD)	765 (STD)	303 (STD)
Submerged displacement (tons)	2,415	2,400	2,400	2,870	2,260	2,372	2,639.2	3,168	1,160	347
Complement	10/70–71	10/5/64–69	9–10/5/70	8–10/5/70–80	8/75	8/5/70	8/9/60	10/85	4/33	2/12
Surface plant	5,400 SHP	5,400 SHP	5,400 SHP	5,400 SHP	3,400 BHP	3,100 BHP	3,150 BHP	6,000 BHP	1,125 BHP	250 BHP
Submerged plant	2,740 SHP	4,610 SHP	4,610 SHP	4,610 SHP	4,700 BHP	4,700 SHP	4,700 SHP	8,200 BHP	1,050 SHP	380 SHP
Battery	2×126	2×126	4×126	4×126	4×126 G	4×126 G IA	4×126 G IA	2×126 S II	——	——
Surface speed (kt)	20.25	17–18	18	17	15.5	15.5	14.0	20.5	13	10
Surface endurance (nm/kt)	11,000/10	17,000/11	15,000/11	15,900/8.5	11,500/10	13,500/10	14,000/10	16,000/10	——	2,000/10
Submerged speed (nm)	8.75	15	17.5 (½ hr)	16 (½ hr)	18.3	16.0	18.5	10.0	8.5	10.5
Submerged endurance	48 hr/2 kt	36 hr/3 kt	48 hr/4 kt	36 hr/3 kt	43 hr/3 kt	48 hr/3 kt	102 hr/3 kt	120/3 (60 hr)	——	——
Test depth	400	400	400	400	700	700	700	——	400	225
Tubes: bow	6 Mk 34	6 Mk 34	6 Mk 34	6 Mk 34	6 Mk 43	6 Mk 54	6 Mk 58	6 Mk 49	4 Mk 47	1 Mk 48
Tubes: stern	4 Mk 35	4 Mk 35	4 Mk 35	4 Mk 35	2 Mk 44	2 Mk 55	0	0	0	0
Torpedoes	24-28	22	24–28	24–28	22/4	22/4	22	18	8	
Active search sonar	WFA	WFA	WFA	BQS-4	BQS-4	BQS-4	BQS-4	BQS-2	——	——
Active attack sonar	——	——	——							
Passive search sonar	——	——	——	BQR-2B	BQR-2	BQR-2	BQR-2	BQR-2B	BQR-4	——
Passive attack sonar	JT	JT	JT	BQG-4	——	——	——	——	BQR-3	JP, JT
TFCS	TDC Mk 4	Mk 106	Mk 106	Mk 106	Mk 101	Mk 101	Mk 101	Mk 106-10	Mk 101-4	Mk 109

Notes: Guppy IIIs were all converted Guppy IIs, but the program was stopped at 9 conversions before the other 15 could be done. Dimensions: Guppy IIA LOA was 306–307 ft long; Guppy III SS 416, 319 ft.

Power plants: Guppy IIA surface power was reduced to 3,430 SHP. Guppy III SS 416 retained only three main engines (3,430 SHP surfaced). When batteries required replacement, Sargo II superseded the original fleet boat type. In *Barbel*, the motor (rated at 6,440 SHP) has greater capacity than the battery; it had been designed for a silver-zinc battery. The 4,700-SHP rating above is the 1-hr rate.

Torpedo tubes: Some fleet submarines had a Mk 32 and a Mk 33 tubes. Mks 32 and 34 are about 250 in long; Mks 33 and 35 are about 273.8 in long. All tubes were pneumatic. Guppy IA conversions from the SS 475 class had 16 reload torpedoes (total of 26 torpedoes). By 1953, the Guppy II CIP called for stowage for 12 reloads (total of 22) in SS 313 (SS 339, 343, 344, 346, 347, 349–52) and SS 381 (SS 416, 425, 426) classes, and 15 reloads (total of 25) in SS 475 class (SS 478, 483–87, 490, 522–25); the SS 313/381 classes originally carried 24 torpedoes, and the SS 475 class carried 28. SS 566 and 568 had a Mk 45 and a Mk 46 torpedo tubes. Mks 43, 45, 54, and 58 were hydraulic tubes, 249.8 in long. Mks 44, 46, and 55 were swim-out (countermeasure) tubes, 139.8 in long, for a Mk 27, and later a Mk 37, torpedoes. *Barbel* had power loading. She carried 12 long torpedoes (plus 6 in the tubes) and also had space for 4 short ones. A Mk 47 was a long (249.8 in) pneumatic tube. A Mk 48 was a swim-out tube. A Mk 49 was a long (249.8 in) hydraulic tube, with power-operated weapons handling but not power loading (there was one centerline dolly in the torpedo room).

Missiles: In 1964, at least some U.S. submarines carried Redeye hand-held infrared missiles for self-defense if they were caught on the surface. These missiles were listed on board the diesel-electric attack units of SubRon (Submarine Squadron) 4: SS 341, 408, 418, 425, 484, 522, 564, 566, 568, and 576; contemporary records do not indicate whether other squadrons carried similar weapons.

Sonar: The 1952 CIP called for installation of BQR-3 passive sonar (in place of JT) on all but SS 324 and SS 407. All submarines had BQS-2 active scanning sonar. In Guppy II, the modified Mk 106 FCS (fire control system) provided electric setting for 2 tubes in each nest, fore and aft. WFA was replaced by BQS-2 and JT by BQR-3. By 1964, a typical Guppy II had BQR-2B, BQR-3, and BQS-4, plus Prairie-Masker silencing (one to reduce self-noise from machinery and propellers and one to quiet propellers).

Table 2. Nuclear Attack Submarines

	Nautilus SSN 571	Seawolf SSN 575	Skate SSN 578	Skipjack SSN 585	Triton SSN 586	Tullibee SSN 597	Thresher SSN 593	Sturgeon SSN 637	Narwhal SSN 671	Glenard P. Lipscomb SSN 685	Los Angeles SSN 688	Seawolf SSN 21
LOA (ft)	323-8.5	337-6	267-8	251-9	447-6	272-9.5	278-6	292-3.125	314-8	364-9	362-0	326-0
Beam (extreme) (ft)	27-8	27-8	25-0	31-7.75	36-11	23-4	31-8	31-8.125	37-7	31-7	33-0	40-0
Draft (ft)	21-9.3125	22-0	20-6.625	25-2.5	23-6	19-4	25-1.75	24-5.125	29-0	---	32-0	35-11
Surfaced displacement (tons)	3,533	3,741	2,550.1	3,070	5,963	2,316	3,705	4,229	4,450	5,813	6,080	7,460
Submerged displacement (tons)	4,092	4,287	2,848	3,500	7,773	2,607	4,311	4,762	5,350	6,480	6,927	9,150
Complement	13/12/80	12/13/80	8/10/66	9/11/65	16/19/145	6/9/41	9/12/73	12/12/83	12/108	12/109	12/115	12/121
Power plant	S2W	S2G	S3W	S5W	S4G	S2C	S5W	S5W	S5G	S5W (TED)	S6G	S6W
Battery	1×126 G I	1×126 G I	1×126 G IA	1×126	1×126 GI	1×126	1×126	1×126	---	---	N/A	N/A
Surface speed (kt)	22	19	15.5	15	27	12.9	15	15	20	18	N/A	N/A
Submerged speed (kt)	23.3	20 plus	18.0	29	---	14.8	28	25.0	25	23	+30	35
Test depth (ft)	700	700	700	700	700	700	1,300	1,300	1,300	1,300	N/A	N/A
Tubes: bow	6 Mk 50	6 Mk 51	6 Mk 56	6 Mk 59	4 Mk 60	4 Mk 64	4 Mk 63	4 Mk 63	4 Mk 63	4 Mk 63	4 Mk 67	8
Tubes: stern	0	0	2 Mk 57	0	2 Mk 60	0	0	0	0	0	0	0
Torpedoes	22	22	18/4	24	10/5	12	23	23	26	23	26	50
Active search sonar	SQS-4	SQS-4	SQS-4	SQS-4	BQS-4	BQQ-2	BQQ-2	BQQ-2	BQQ-2	BQQ-2	BQQ-5	BSY-2
Passive search sonar	BQR-4A	BQR-4A	BQR-2	BQR-2B	BQR-2	BQR-7	BQR-7	BQR-7	BQR-7	BQR-7	---	---
TFCS	Mk 101	Mk 101	Mk 101	Mk 101	Mk 101	Mk 112	Mk 113	Mk 113	Mk 113	Mk 113	Mk 117	BSY-2

Notes:

Dimensions: *Triton* was unique among nuclear attack submarines in having a pressure hull of smaller maximum diameter (29 ft) than her beam. *Jack* (SSN 605) was 299 ft 8 in long (lengthened to accommodate her special machinery). SSN 613, 614, and 615 all have longer hulls (292 ft). Similarly, SSN 678–684, 686, and 687 all have longer hulls (302 ft 3 in). As refitted at Mare Island between January 1987 and 1991, *Parche* (SSN 683) has an overall length of 393 ft (6,140/7,140 tons). The extension is all forward of her sail.

Torpedo tubes: a Mk 50, a hydraulic tube that was later fitted with power loading, was 249.8 in long. A Mk 51 (also hydraulic, 249.8 in) also later had power loading. Mks 56 and 59 were similar hydraulic tubes; a Mk 57 was a long (214.6 in) swim-out tube. Only the forward tubes had power loading (from cradles). *Triton* did not have power loading (a Mk 60 was a long hydraulic tube, 249.8 in long).

Speed: The figure for *Thresher* is the author's rough estimate, based on the 25-kt speed given for *Sturgeon* by Patrick E. Tyler in *Running Critical* (New York: Harper & Row, 1986), allowing for reduced drag (because of less displacement, i.e., hull volume, and about half the appendage resistance, resulting from a much smaller sail and no end plates on the tail planes). The speed given for *Narwhal* is that usually published; it is consistent with a simple calculation based on *Sturgeon* (greater SHP roughly balances off the increased displacement). The speed given for *Lipscomb* is the author's estimate based on the widely published report that losses associated with her turboelectric drive reduced her SHP to 12,500. The 30-kt figure used for *Los Angeles* in 1968 (as reported in Tyler, *Running Critical*) was almost certainly the minimum acceptable, an estimate based on very conservative figures; the ship probably did a knot or two better in service. A crude estimate suggests that APHNAS would have been about 11 to 12 percent faster than *Los Angeles*, say 33–35 kt. The *Seawolf* figure is the speed cited in the Preface.

Sonar: By 1964, *Nautilus* had BQR-4A, BQR-3A, and SQS-4 Mod 4 sonars. *Seawolf* had BQR-4A and BQR-2B (incorporating BQS-4), plus SQS-4 Mod 3. At this time, *Skate* had BQR-2B (with BQS-4) and SQS-4, plus a new mine detection sonar, BQS-8, the predecessor of the later BQS-10 and -14. *Tullibee* had PUFFS (BQG-1).

Table 3.   Missile Submarines

	Grayback SSG 574	Halibut SSGN 587	George Washington SSBN 598	Ethan Allen SSBN 608	Lafayette SSBN 616	Ohio SSBN 726
LOA (ft)	322-4	350-0	381-8	410-5	425-0	560-0
Beam (extreme) (ft)	30-0	29-6.125	33-0	33-0	33-0	42-0
Draft (ft)	19-0 (max)	20-9	26-8	27-6.825	27-9.5	36-3
Pressure hull diameter (ft)	N/A	25-0	33-0	33-0	33-0	42-0
Surfaced displacement (tons)	2,670	3,845.5	5,959	6,946	7,325	16,764
Submerged displacement (tons)	3,650	4,894.9	6,709	7,884	8,251	18,750
Complement	9/75	12/12/87	12/12/88	10/12/88	14/15/111	14/136
Power plant (surface)	4,200 SHP	S3W	S5W	S5W	S5W	S8G
Submerged plant	3,060 SHP	——	——	——	——	--
Battery	4×126 Guppy IA	N/A	N/A	N/A	N/A	N/A
Surface speed (kt)	12.0	15.0	16	16	16	18
Submerged speed (kt)	15.0	14.0	22	21	21	Approx. 25
Test depth (ft)	700	700	700	1,300	1,300	N/A
Tubes: bow	6 Mk 52	4 Mk 61	6 Mk 59	4 Mk 65	4 Mk 65	4 Mk 68
Tubes: stern	2 Mk 53	2 Mk 62	0	0	0	0
Torpedoes	N/A	8/4	12	12	12	
Active search sonar	BQS-4	BQS-4	BQS-4	BQS-4	BQS-4	——
Active attack sonar	——	——	——	——	——	
Passive search sonar	BQR-2	BQR-2	BQR-2	BQR-7	BQR-7	BQQ-6
Passive attack sonar	——	——	——	——	——	
TFCS	Mk 101	MK 101	Mk 112	Mk 112	Mk 113	Mk 118

Notes: SSBN 598, 608, and 616 speed and depth data are from Hudson Institute Report HI-67-209 (Visit to Polaris Facility, Charleston, 8–9 May 1967, dated 15 May 1967, declassified 1979).

Dimensions: Grayback was lengthened to 334 ft during her LPSS (amphibious support) conversion at Mare Island, 1967–69.

Torpedo tubes: Unlike Grayback, Growler (SSG 577) had a Mk 54 hydraulic tubes forward and a Mk 55 swim-out tubes aft. Mks 52 and 61 are hydraulic; Mks 53 and 62 are swim-out tubes. Halibut did not have power loading. SSBN 640 class is similar to 616 class, but it was reengineered and had slightly greater torpedo stowage (total 13 full-length or 14 short [161-in a Mk 37] or 23 half-length [a Mk 27] weapons).

Missiles: SSG/SSGNs could check out only two Regulus missiles while submerged. SSBN 598 and 608 classes could launch missiles at the rate of one per minute; SSBN 616 could launch four per minute. These figures apply to Polaris, not necessarily to later missiles.

Table 4.   Special Types

	Dolphin AGSS 555	Albacore AGSS 569	X-1
LOA (ft)	152-0	203-10	49-7
Beam (extreme) (ft)	19-4	27-4	7-0
Draft (ft)	18-1	18-7	6-2
Pressure hull diameter (ft)	N/A	21-0	7-0
Surfaced displacement (tons)	860	1,242	29
Submerged displacement (tons)	930	1,847	36
Complement	4/33	4/36	1/3
Surface plant	1,650 SHP	2,000 BHP	30 SHP
Submerged plant	1,650 SHP	7,500 SHP	N/A
Surface speed (kt)	7.5	15	15
Surfaced endurance	N/A	N/A	+500
Submerged speed (kt)	10	25	12
Submerged endurance (hr)	12	8–9	N/A
Test depth (ft)	N/A	600	N/A
Tubes	1 Mk 66	0	0
Torpedoes	1	0	0

Notes: A Mk 66 was a 30-in external ram-catapult tube usable at great depth. It was only temporarily installed.

Dolphin has 2×165-cell lead-acid batteries; she reaches 15 kt when silver-zinc batteries are substituted.

Notes

Preface

1. A postwar Pacific Fleet analysis of wartime Japanese ASW, (anti-submarine warfare) probably written in 1945, concluded that this was not the case. This report is in the files of the OpNav Submarine Division, Naval Historical Center. It is undated and does not give the author's name.

2. Diving depth: the shift to 700 ft in the SS 563 (*Tang*) class is discussed in detail in several issues of *FTP 225*, a postwar OpNav (Office of the Chief of Naval Operations) magazine on undersea warfare. It ceased publication in 1949 and was declassified in 1975. *Nautilus* and *Albacore* diving depths (and, incidentally, speed, horsepower, and turning characteristics) were included in the Operational Development Force's *First Interim Letter Report on Project Op/S395/A16-8, "Evaluate Current Antisubmarine Tactics Against the Modern High Speed Submarine"* (29 March 1957), declassified in 1982. The 1955 declassified document cited in chapter 8 (referring to a possible extension to 1,600 ft) makes it obvious that the 700-ft standard survived through the *Skipjack* class. No 700-ft submarine survives in the U.S. Navy. The shift to 1,300 ft in the *Thresher* class has been widely publicized. An official declassified reference is R. F. Cross Assoc. Ltd., *Sea-Based Anti-Submarine Warfare 1940–1977*, 2:11 (report prepared for Op-95; originally Secret but declassified 31 December 1990). Figures for the *Los Angeles* and *Ohio* classes have not been released.

I have relied on Patrick E. Tyler, *Running Critical* (New York: Harper & Row, 1986), for the 30-kt requirement in the *Los Angeles* class, for the 29 kt achieved by *Skipjack*, and for the 25 kt of the *Sturgeons*, as well as for the significance of the 5-kt speed advantage. It is clear from his text that Tyler obtained these figures from official papers written at the time. The *Los Angeles* speed would have been a design figure, and past evidence suggests that designers typically keep a knot or two in hand to ensure success on trials. The speeds given for *Ohio* and other SSBNs are taken from the 1975 government publication on the Trident program (see below). Submarine speeds change considerably when different propellers are used, so official figures are likely to vary by several knots from one source to another. No tactical speeds (maximum quiet speeds, for example) are given. They are not releasable. For *Seawolf*, I have used the 35-kt figure given by Norman Polmar in various editions of *Ships and Aircraft of the U.S. Fleet* (Annapolis, Md.: Naval Institute Press). In the 14th edition (1987, p. 49), Polmar claims that this figure and a statement that tactical speed would exceed 20 kt were revealed by then CNO (Chief of Naval Operations) James Watkins in March 1985.

The horsepower figures for *all* current power plants except that planned for *Seawolf* (SSN 21) were revealed in a remarkable document, *Adequacy of Current Organization: Defense and Arms Control* (Washington, D.C.: Government Printing Office, June 1975), Appendix K (vol. 4 of appendices). Chapter 6 of part 2 ("Acquiring Weapons," ed. Frederick A. Norris), an account of the Trident program, is based on a case study by Barry E. Carter and John D. Steinbruner. It uses figures clearly supplied by the Defense Department: p. 179 includes a list of alternatives, with their horsepowers and speeds; p. 177 gives the horsepower of the *Narwhal* reactor and p. 178 the horsepower of the *Los Angeles* reactor. The 60,000-SHP figure for the big abortive missile submarine (see chapter 10) is consistent with published official figures (ca 1960) for the output of the destroyer power plant (D2G) and with the incorrect account of Trident in Adm. Elmo Zumwalt's memoirs, *On Watch* (New York: Quadrangle, 1976), 152. It seems quite likely that he confused the big cruise missile submarine, which he killed, with Trident. Given the 1975 government publication, the significance of the 60,000-SHP figure is quite obvious. The output of the *Seawolf* (SSN 21) reactor has not been given officially. The output of the *Skate* and *Skipjack* power plants (S3W and S5W) are given in a 1958 British report, now declassified, in the Public Record Office (ADM 205/178, M.618/8/57 of January 1958) that was written in connection with the planned purchase of a U.S. submarine reactor. For earlier plants, no longer in service, I have used the remarkably consistent figures in standard unofficial sources, such as *Jane's Fighting Ships*. It appears that *Jane's* data were officially supplied. Reportedly, nuclear horsepower data were closely guarded only after the appearance of an informative Russian book on nuclear submarine design, purportedly based on U.S. sources, in 1964.

For torpedo loadouts of current attack submarines, both of the standard unclassified references, *Jane's Fighting Ships 1991–92* (London: Jane's Information Group, 1991) and *Combat Fleets 1993* (Annapolis, Md.: Naval Institute Press, 1993) credit the *Los Angeles* with 22 reloads weapons (a total of 26 if all four tubes are occupied) and the *Sturgeon* class with 19. The *Los Angeles* figure is credible because it was first published (1984 by *Jane's Defence Weekly*) in connection with a shipyard visit to the commissioning of a *Los Angeles*-class submarine. The author of the article could actually count the spaces in the torpedo room.

Two references deserve special mention: J. D. Alden, *The Fleet Submarine in the U.S. Navy* (Annapolis, Md.: Naval Institute Press, 1979), and B. D. Bruins, "U.S. Naval Bombardment Missiles" (Ph.D. diss., Columbia University, 1981).

Chapter 2

1. Many navies, including the U.S., British, and Dutch, had rejected such devices on the ground that the exhaust tube would

raise a visible plume of water and exhaust. At night, when the plume was invisible, the submarine could safely surface to charge her batteries. Night surfacing became dangerous when Allied patrol planes were equipped with radar. The plume sometimes did reveal the submarine, but the snorkel had a far smaller radar signature than the entire U-boat.

2. At the May 1952 ASW symposium, Capt. E. T. Hydeman of SubDevGru 2 credited JT with an average range of 8,000 yd. An experimental unit installed on a bottomside shaft in *Toro* did about 50 percent better. JT could detect a target at 40,000 yd under ideal conditions but at only 3,000 yd under really bad conditions.

3. WCA and WFA were both high-frequency searchlight sets; QHB, the first U.S. scanning sonar, also operated at high frequency (about 25 kHz).

4. A 1927 German acoustic handbook captured in 1945 showed two groups of six hydrophones each, sensitive in the 600- to 1200-Hz range. Arranged in a straight line, they were attached to a compensator network so that they could be trained electrically. A complete account of wartime German equipment is found in Lee E. Holt, ''German Use of Sonic Listening,'' *Journal of the Acoustical Society of America* 19, no. 4 (July 1947) 678–681. GHG used much the same concept as the U.S. WW I MV, which had been installed on board some destroyers and submarines.

5. BQS-2, first installed in 1954 and not widely used, operated at 31 kHz, the high end of the WW II range. With 60 staves (12–13-degree beams), it was somewhat larger than QHB.

6. In May 1951, Capt. W. B. Sieglaff of SubDevGru 2 reported that average submarine passive sonar search range, presumably using BQR-2, was 8,000 yd (best range, 20,000–30,000 yd; worst range, 2,000–4,000 yd). Active sonars varied similarly. Sieglaff expected Lofar (see chapter 4) to do far better because the sound of a submarine cruising on her diesels or snorkeling was concentrated in particularly narrow low-frequency bands. He planned to use low frequency for initial detection and approach, then passive high frequency (JT) to complete the approach and attack.

7. Notes on BQR-2, -4, and -7 are largely based on A. D. Little, Inc., *The Submarine as a Surveillance Platform*, Project Trident technical report, December 1960 (held in DTIC as AD 366434; formerly Confidential, now declassified). There was also a BQR-2D. BQS-4B, -4D, -4E, and -4F were all adaptable to BQR-21, the DIMUS (digital multi-beam steering) version of BQR-2. BQS-4B was also adaptable to BQR-2C, and BQS-4D to BQR-2D. Like later versions of the spherical bow sonar, later BQS-4s had solid-state transmitters. There was never an operational DIMUS version of BQR-7, although later versions (at least BQR-7E) had electronically, rather than mechanically, scanned beams (one scanning continuously, one steered).

8. DIMUS was invented about 1951 by Dr. Victor C. Anderson of the Marine Physical Laboratory in San Diego. Sponsored by the Office of Naval Research (ONR), he built an analog version during a sabbatical at the Harvard Acoustics Laboratory; ONR later pushed the DIMUS concept, despite a lack of enthusiasm from BuShips. C. B. Bishop, in ''Applied Research—the RDT&E Orphan?'' *Submarine Review*, April 1987, claims that DIMUS was tested on the destroyer *Brown* and on the submarines *Baya* and *Blackfin*, after which a three-dimensional array was installed on board *Albacore*. Other sources suggest that *Albacore* had the first DIMUS version of the two-dimensional BQR-2. Bishop credits Anderson with inventing the delay-line time compressor (Deltic) frequency analyzer (for Lofar) at about the same time.

9. Comdr. D. G. Irvine, ''Trends in the Sonar Approach and Attack,'' presentation before the Submarine Officers Conference, January 1951. Irvine, chief staff officer of SubDevGru 2, pointed out that submarines could be heard only on snorkel. Like their U.S. counterparts, Soviet boats would probably snorkel at 8–12 kt. Therefore, TMA could begin on the basis of an 8-kt target speed, which could be checked by how well the solution corresponded with further observations (or against a turn count). Considerable errors can be tolerated because a snorkeling submarine is so much slower than a torpedo. According to Irvine, ''Everyone has the same reaction to this thing when he first digs into it. At first one is somewhat overwhelmed by the difficulty of the solution—probably from looking too hard at the theoretical side of it—then when one goes out and tries it, everyone has the reaction of pleasant surprise—he finds it much easier than expected and probably for the reasons just outlined.'' A typical TMA solution requires that four bearings be taken in sequence. For each, the submarine has to run in a straight line until the target bearing changes appreciably (the rule of thumb was 1 min/1,000 yd of range, or over 1 hr *per bearing* at convergence zone range). Devices like PUFFS (passive underwater fire control feasibility study) and WAA (wide aperture array) are attractive partly because they quickly measure bearings very accurately, even if the target is far beyond triangulation range. The text account of techniques is based largely on D. H. Wagner, ''Target Motion Analysis Innovations by Naval Officers,'' *Submarine Review*, July 1991.

10. In all, 54 PUFFS were made from 1960 through 1966 for nine Guppy III, four *Tangs*, *Darter*, *Grayback*, *Tullibee*, 2 *Salmons*, and some *Threshers* and SSBNs. PUFFS almost certainly inspired the contemporary French passive ranger, DUUX-2, which was widely exported. Raytheon developed Micropuffs, which uses hull patches rather than line hydrophones, for the Royal Australian Navy (''micro'' refers to the use of a microprocessor). It was also adopted by the Royal Navy (as Type 2041) and the Canadian Navy (as BQG-501). The U.S. Navy tested Micropuffs on board *Barb* in 1980 and a modified version, PASRAN (passive ranging), on board *Haddock* in 1979; it used larger arrays and presumably was conceived as an alternative to WAA.

11. Within the Mk 101, the Mk 7 analyzer operator entered a series of three target bearings taken at intervals, plus range, target course (target angle), or target speed. Target range also could be fed back from the position keeper. The analyzer fitted a straight-line constant speed track across the bearings. This technique differed from most bearings-only solutions in that the submarine could maneuver during the analysis period. Maximum analysis time after the first bearing was 20 min. The second or third bearing could be discarded during analysis and a new bearing substituted. Alternatively, a pair of endpoints (bearing and range) could determine target course and speed. Solutions could be passed automatically to the position keeper.

12. BuOrd thought that the ultimate propeller-driven torpedo would burn gasoline in a helium-oxygen mixture. A 750-HP engine could drive a full-length torpedo to 10,000 yd at 60 kt; 1,500 HP would give 75 kt. Higher speeds would probably require jet propulsion; in 1946 BuOrd began work on a jet-propelled air-dropped torpedo, a Mk 40.

13. A Mk 36 Mod 0 was an electric (seawater battery) weapon intended to reach 7,000 yd at 47 kt. It was the only version ever built. (It was canceled in 1950 in favor of a Mk 42, which was also aborted.) By 1947, work was proceeding on three schemes for a 60-kt internal combustion version: turbines (General Electric and Naval Torpedo Station Newport), internal combustion (Ranger and NOL), and underwater jet engines (Aerojet and China Lake). None materialized.

14. A Mk 35, conceived in October 1944 as a fast successor to the Mk 27 ASW homing torpedo, was to be launched by aircraft,

surface ships, and submarines. Because the August 1945 OpNav requirement omitted submarines, the standard air-launched torpedo caliber, 22.4 in, was adopted. Then submarines became prime ASW platforms; 21-in caliber was adopted in June 1946 (in 1948, air drop was abandoned because aircraft were assigned their own lightweight weapons). By 1947, maximum depth was 1,000 ft. Enabling range could be set at 300 to 10,000 yd. A Mk 35 could be set to attack surface/snorkel targets only (floor 50 ft), submerged targets only (ceiling 50 ft), or targets anywhere in the whole depth of the water. A Mk 35 was intended to home on a 175 × 20-ft target, with at least 100 ft between keel and sea bottom. Formal evaluation of the Mk 2 production version began in March 1953. The fleet submarine *Manta* was reactivated at Mare Island specially as a live Mk 35 target. Two main engines were removed, she was strengthened in way of her single hull, hatches were tightened, and floodable space was reduced by filling torpedo rooms with wood.

15. A censored version of the court's conclusions was released in December 1993 in connection with questions about radioactivity, which might have been released. Initially, the main evidence was a series of 15 acoustic pulses detected by the SOSUS system but only discovered when SOSUS records were reviewed. These records were used to find the sunken submarine, and their details were used to reconstruct her loss. The initial pulse was clearly an explosion (a second pulse was from the same explosion, transmitted along a different acoustic path). It was clear that the submarine was turning as she was struck. Other pulses described the breakup of the submarine as her compartments gave way, beginning with the operating compartment. Apparently power was not lost, since there was evidence that the crew tried to accelerate and plane up to the surface (they also blew all main ballast tanks). That proved impossible: too much buoyancy had already been lost. The engine room bulkhead collapsed, and (except for the engine room) the ship flooded before reaching collapse depth. The court concluded that one torpedo warhead had exploded; it considered ejection and homing most likely. The next possibility was a fire in the torpedo room (the turn might be ascribed to hydraulic damage causing the stern planes to induce both a rising and a turning moment, or to a rupture on one side causing drag, which slewed the ship around; or to the tumbling of a gyro that would cause the helmsman to follow the swing of the repeater). An even less likely possibility was the accidental explosion of a torpedo detonator while torpedoes were being disarmed prior to arrival home. Sabotage and collision were both considered and ruled out. Nor was it likely that *Scorpion* had been lost to a jammed stern plane (the court examined her ability to recover, given her running depth and capabilities). When the wreckage was found, the sail had been blown away from the pressure hull, and much of the hull around the control room was missing (roughly Frames 34-38 port and 29-38 starboard: the operations compartment extended between Frames 26 and 44). Debris around the ship seemed to have come from the operations compartment rather than the torpedo room. Visible structural damage was more likely due to explosion than implosion, supporting the self-torpedoing theory. However, the court pointed out that "the identifiable debris does not lead to a determination of the cause for the loss of *Scorpion*." At the time of her loss *Scorpion* carried 2 Mk 45 ASTOR nuclear torpedoes, 4 Mk 37-0, 10 Mk 37-1, and 7 Mk 14-5 torpedoes. Mk 37 batteries had been accidentally activated; standard procedure was to pull the torpedo from the tube to remove the exploder (if the fin velocity switch was activated, the exploder could go off). *Scorpion* had had a Mk 37-1 run hot in a 5 December 1967 exercise: the torpedo refused to start properly, but shortly after another tor-

pedo was successfully fired, it began a hot run in the tube. It was allowed to swim out.

16. The strength of the torpedo afterbody also limited firing depth. A Mk 14, for example, could not be fired below a depth of about 180 ft.

17. QXB-3, however, was initially planned for the *Skate* class; in September 1957, the characteristics were changed to show that it would be replaced by WLR-2 as soon as the latter was service approved.

18. BLQ-2 was intended both to break sonar contact and to decoy homing torpedoes. The feasibility study was completed in June 1954. The first five were successfully tested in 1956, but BLQ-2 failed its operational evaluation, which began in December 1961. With dimensions of 10 × 80 in and weight of 250 lb), six could be stowed in a single torpedo tube. BLQ-2 could be launched at depths to 1,000 ft; set before launching to run for 30 to 60 sec at 12 kt, then for 19 min at 6–9 kt on a preprogrammed course at a depth of 50–300 ft; and repeat or jam signals at 10–70 kHz. The on-board beacon electronically simulated submarine sounds, such as propeller beat, gear whine, and machinery noise. It could create a false wake by running seawater over lithium hydride. The successor BLQ-9 had similar dimensions, was rated at 8–10 kt at 50–400 ft, and probably handled a wider frequency range. The current self-propelled contact breaker, a MOSS Mk 57, can be carried four to a torpedo tube. Attack submarines and Poseidon-firing SSBNs each carry one catapult launcher and four MOSSs; *Trident* submarines carry two launchers and six MOSSs.

19. It is not altogether clear when various pieces of the puzzle became available to the U.S. submarine community. According to the official history, F. H. Hinsley, *British Intelligence in the Second World War*, vol. 3, part 1 (London: Her Majesty's Stationery Office, 1984) 49–50, 238–245, 519–526, the British Admiralty, which shared intelligence with the U.S. Navy, first became aware in November 1943 that the Germans were experimenting with new types of fast U-boats. The first snorkel boats ran sea trials in December 1943; the British knew about them by February 1944. By April, aerial photos showed the new types under construction. In May, the British decrypted a full account of the "revolution in U-boat design and construction" radioed home by the Japanese ambassador to Berlin.

20. According to the unpublished British Department of Naval Construction official history of wartime naval construction, a copy of which is in the National Maritime Museum (Greenwich, London), early 1944 reports of fast German submarines (16 kt submerged, 20 kt on the surface) caused the British to convert HMS *Seraph* into a "high-speed target" at Devonport between July and August 1944. *Seraph* made 12.52 kt at periscope depth, compared with 8.82 kt before conversion (her resistance was estimated at 55 percent of that of an unconverted craft). The other two wartime conversions were *Satyr* and *Sceptre*, followed after the war by *Selene, Sleuth, Solent, Statesman*, and the higher-powered *Scotsman*. Large numbers were needed to train both the deployed fleets (Home and Mediterranean) while conducting tactical trials in home waters.

21. Based on a SubLant report on U-2513 performance of 18 February 1946 and on W. E. Schevill and A. C. Vine, *Submerged Performance Tests of Type XXI*, Woods Hole, 17 March 47 (Submarine Warfare Division papers, Operational Archives). In December 1946, Andrew McKee, a senior BuShips submarine designer, commented that Type XXI would have been devastating except that, "as they have done so often," the Germans committed the fatal error of overcomplicating its hydraulic system (paper on German hydrogen peroxide submarines delivered to the American Society of Mechanical Engineers).

22. It was suggested that a Guppy could not quite duplicate Type XXI as (1) an echo target, (2) a listening target, and (3) in performance, particularly maneuverability. Precise duplication seemed important because the U.S. Navy assumed that the Soviets would soon mass produce this exact design. These arguments kept the two Type XXIs in service for one refit longer than might otherwise have been the case. With the advent of Lofar, the second argument returned. German (and, presumably, Soviet) submarines had 4-cycle diesels, whose line (narrowband) spectra, which Lofar detected, would differ significantly from those of U.S. 2-cycle diesels. On 2 April 1951, SubLant asked OpNav for permission to operate one of the engines of the laid-up U-2513 for low-frequency detection tests, inspired by tests of a British submarine also powered by 4-cycle engines.

23. U-3008 was laid up to provide spares to keep U-2513 in service a bit longer. A September 1947 materiel study showed that the two boats could operate for about 15 mo between overhauls. U-2513 was overhauled 24 March–23 September 1947; her battery was replaced and new hydraulic piping installed. The next overhaul was then scheduled for 1 January 1949. U-3008 was scheduled for a similar overhaul 3 December 1947–March 1948. Prior to that time, she developed a leak on the starboard side of the lower after battery tank in a position corresponding to a leak (resulting from faulty welding) that had just been repaired at Charleston. Operations were canceled. A 2-mo hull survey, which was impractical, would have been required to ensure that she was safe to operate. U-2513 had shown no hull welding problems, so she remained in service.

24. The same letter released U-505, which became a museum in Chicago.

25. U-2513 was sunk in 200 ft of water on 8 October 1951 by three rounds of Weapon Alfa. The first was detonated by influence at a depth of about 50 ft. The second and third, fired in rapid succession, went off at or near the bottom as the submarine sank. The explosions made two large holes in her pressure hull on its port side, one just forward of the conning tower, the other just forward of the after escape hatch, and both centered at about the designed waterline (about 15-ft diameter). The superstructure around the forward hole was completely demolished for 35 ft, and the second hole was about 30 ft long. Any holes on the starboard side were hidden, as the submarine rolled over to starboard. For years, underwater photographs of the sunken U-2513 were shown to weapons officers of ships armed with Weapon Alfa to convince them that their weapons would work.

In November 1950, U-3008 was ordered preserved for deep explosive tests, possibly a planned nuclear test. On 29 June 1951, she was released for full-scale tests of the new (now standard) underwater explosive, HBX-3. British tests had just shown that bubble energy, rather than the shock wave, did the most underwater damage. HBX-3 had more aluminum content (35 percent) than its predecessor, HBX-1 (17 percent) to gain 40 percent more bubble energy. Such explosions could not be tested with scale models because a bubble does not scale like a shock wave. A bubble is affected by gravity; shock is not. It was particularly critical to test the HBX-3 warhead of the new aircraft torpedo, a Mk 43, whose weight had to be minimized. Information on the hull-splitting range of charges less than 100 lb was scanty. A Mk 43 had been designed by extrapolating from larger charges, and BuOrd wanted reassurance that it could defeat the toughest existing target. The first shots (22 May 1952 and 19 September 1953) were Weapon A projectiles loaded with HBX-1 and then with HBX-3. A Mk 43 Mod 1 was then tested. In June 1954, the last of five test series left U-3008 so badly damaged that she could

not move on her own bottom without extensive repairs. She had to be broken up. U-3008 was used for these tests because the two incomplete fleet boats were not immediately available. The SS 427 hull was being used for noise tests and SS 428 for structural damage and shock/vibration studies.

26. A 27–28 August 1945 conference at Guam suggested that a liquid oxygen closed-cycle diesel plant (21 kt surfaced, 15 kt submerged) be installed at once in an old B-class submarine.

27. The list of submarine preliminary designs for this period shows only three between SS 198 (*Tambor*, the basic fleet submarine) and the 1944–45 enlarged fleet submarine: two 800-ton coastal submarines (*Marlin* and 1940) and a 6,000-ton cargo submarine (undated).

28. Nuclear weapons seem to have been intended here, but they were not explicitly mentioned.

29. At the request of Buships Electrical Section, General Electric and Electric Storage Battery Company estimated the maximum power output of a battery with one fourth of the usual 6-yr lifetime. On 1 November 1945, they reported that two 126-cell groups in parallel, 2 ft longer and 34 percent heavier than the usual battery, could provide 5,000 SHP (10.75 kt). Another 2,000 SHP would have added 1.25 kt. Eventually, it was discovered that careful peacetime operation of this special Guppy battery could extend cell life from 18 to about 30 mo.

30. In April 1951, Capt. L. R. Daspit, the SCB submarine expert, asked what could be done on 800 tons, with a submerged speed of 16–18 kt, a snorkel, and two diesels. Preliminary Design submitted a rough sketch based on the prewar *Marlin*. The submarine would have six tubes and would carry 12 long torpedoes. Operating depth was 350 ft, half the depth of *Tang*, and slightly less than that of a Guppy. The surface power plant was a pair of GM 12-278A engines (about 2,000 BHP), and the submarine would have had half a Guppy battery. Quick estimates showed a speed of 14 kt submerged (1-hr rate), 10 kt on snorkel (two diesels), or 14.5 kt surfaced on trial. Endurance (in time) would be 80 percent of Guppy (90 percent of distance): 3,500 nm at 10 kt snorkeling, 6,000 nm surfaced at 7.5 kt (one engine), or 7,000 nm at 10 kt surfaced. These figures were based on two alternative sets of dimensions, derived from Guppy (243 × 21.7 ft, 870/1,200 tons) or from the new *Albacore* (168.5 × 24.0 ft, 870/1,200 tons). The submarine would not have a conning tower, and she would rely on a modest sonar array. These figures were so attractive that the senior submarine designer, Capt. Armand Morgan, refused to pass them on without further calculation. The design book shows no further work; presumably, the idea soon died.

31. A list of preliminary design drawings shows an attempt to increase *Tang* periscope depth as early as July 1948, presumably in connection with a possible FY 50 program.

32. Capt. H. A. Jackson, USN (Ret.), "The Influence of USS *Albacore* on Submarine Design," paper presented at the Submarine Symposium of the Royal Institution of Naval Architects, London, 1993. Jackson designed the *Albacore*, and he gave the 1959 lecture.

33. Motor (hence propeller) speed was set by voltage. The power transmitted depended on both voltage and current (amperage). The fleet boat made 280 RPM at 415 volts and 2,700 amperes. Tests showed that the motors could carry 3,000 amperes continuously. In parallel, Guppy cells put out high amperage at limited voltage. When motor current reached 3,000 amperes, the cells were switched to series (up to 500 volts at limited amperage). The propellers were designed for 300 RPM, the motor rate at 460 volts, and the switch-over point between parallel and series

operations. It turned out that they could operate at even higher voltages, with all batteries in series for the 1/2-hr rate of discharge (6,500 SHP or more, compared with 4,700 at the 1-hr rate).

Chapter 3

1. U-1406 arrived in the United States as deck cargo, stripped after having been gutted by fire and flooded twice. Portsmouth Navy Yard considered putting her into service (at an estimated cost of $1 million over a period of 15 mo) on the ground that nothing short of a Walter boat would provide a target that was fast enough. This plan was rejected because peroxide seemed to present an unacceptable fire risk and was too costly ($100,000 for each 6-hr run at full power). Too, U-1406 was unlikely to exceed a speed of 20 kt and that only at shallow depth. In March 1946, OpNav formally decided to retain the hulk but not to place U-1406 in service. At about the same time, the British were working to recommission her sister, U-1407. Disposal was authorized in February 1948.

2. Model basin tests in 1947 showed that at 17 kt, for example, Type XXI (figure eight) required about 2,400 EHP, compared with about 1,900 EHP for *Tang*'s current design. It is not clear to what extent the difference was due to the better bridge fairwater of the U.S. design.

3. BuShips stated its targets on 11 May 1948, but no formal characteristics had been set. Maximum underwater power, 15,000 SHP at 375 RPM, would drive the submarine at 28.4 kt. Maximum snorkel power was set at 3,215 SHP (a keel depth of 52 ft 5 in) at 210 RPM, for 14.9 kt (when not charging batteries). A surface power of 5,000 SHP at 246 RPM would suffice for 18 kt while charging at 1,500 kw. When not charging, the plant would produce 7,250 SHP (298 RPM) for 20.1 kt. Maximum continuous electric motor power would be 3,500 SHP (17.5 kt submerged, 16 kt surfaced). There would also be a silent creep motor (190 SHP, 6 kt). The submarine would have 252 Sargo battery cells. These figures were probably calculated on the basis of the 286-ft hull form of Table 3–1. A 279 × 31-0 × 17-6 (2,305.6 ton) hull was tried earlier. These figures are taken from a BuShips memorandum in the SSX design file. The 15,000-SHP requirement had been set much earlier.

4. The faster the turbine, the smaller it is. Hence, there was a need to gear a small, fast turbine to a relatively slow-turning propeller.

5. This judgment is based on the notes to the 1946–50 Submarine Conferences.

6. BuOrd had already set up a peroxide plant for its new fast torpedoes (Mks 16 and 17), but its product was only 70 percent pure; submarine power plants needed 90 percent. BuShips obtained 1,000 tons of wartime German peroxide, 82 percent pure and heavily laced with stabilizers, and traded it to a commercial manufacturer for 750 tons of 90 percent peroxide.

7. The pressure tanks could not be used for compensation. On the other hand, peroxide could be stowed in plastic bags between the inner and outer hulls of the submarine. As the peroxide was used, seawater flooded the empty space, thus automatically compensating for the change in weight and volume.

8. As of November 1953, dimensions would have been 345 ft overall by 31 ft 9 in molded by 26 ft 9 in depth to main deck amidships on centerline; displacement, submerged, 3,611 tons; surfaced (Condition M) 2,960 tons; surfaced (Condition N) 2,672 tons. The submarine was expected to achieve 24.75 kt on the surface (on trial) and 12.25 kt submerged (snorkel speed 10.3 kt), with an endurance of 16,000 nm at 10 kt with 625 tons of oil.

Other characteristics would approximately duplicate those of the new diesel-electric *Salmon* class.

9. On 9 January 1951, three schemes were proposed: scheme A, two main engines replaced by 58,000 lb of oxygen tanks; scheme B, one main engine removed from one engine room and 7,000 lb of oxygen stowed in the after torpedo room; scheme C, two main engines removed and replaced by two four-cycle diesel generator-compressors, with liquid oxygen tanks installed in one of the battery compartments (50,000 lb), in the after torpedo room (65,000 lb), or in both. Maximum submerged speed would be 12 kt in A and B, 15 in C; endurance at maximum speed would be 9 hr in A, 1 hr in B, and 9.5 hr in C (combined stowage). Operation on one engine (8.5 or 9 kt) would extend endurance to 18, 2, and 44 hr, respectively. Scheme A was most attractive but too slow; scheme B was considered the worst (too slow, too little underwater endurance, and too few weapons); scheme C seemed best in terms of underwater speed and endurance, but the speed was still considered insufficient, and the weapons and tubes in the after torpedo room had to be given up. All were considered too noisy and too slow to evade homing weapons or depth charges. The closed-cycle conversion was not worthwhile.

10. The British also worked briefly on a free-piston diesel (using a Deltic engine, which was too massive), a gas turbine (similar to Wolverine, but operating only submerged), and Kreislauf (using oxygen or hydrogen peroxide to top off the recirculated gas). They abandoned the latter because 280 cylinders would have been required to achieve the desired 10,000 SHP. A British delegation, visiting BuShips in April 1951, suggested that Kreislauf was a waste of time, talent, and money. At this time, the British were building a 7,500-SHP Walter turbine and were working on a 10,000-SHP version (Walter cycle, but with liquid oxygen rather than hydrogen peroxide). Officially, the shift to oxygen was to simplify supply, but BuShips developers suspected that the British were finding hydrogen peroxide too dangerous. The British did not require their closed-cycle plants to operate during snorkeling or surface runs, nor did they require the substantial backing power desired by the U.S. Navy. They argued that the effect of hull resistance on a diving submarine would far outweigh any effect of the propellers.

11. A speaker at the Fifth Underwater Symposium (1950) suggested using a primary battery (*not* a storage battery; presumably a fuel cell), but the idea was not pursued at this time.

12. The BuShips High Submerged Speed Submarine Program began in the spring of 1946. In his oral history, John C. Niedermair, a senior navy designer, claimed credit for basing the fast submarine on an airship form. It was not an entirely new idea. Probably unknown to Niedermair, the British modeled their fast R-class boats in WW I on airship forms. Airship data could not be used directly because existing data were inconsistent. The same model experienced different resistance in different tunnels as a result of turbulence. There were laminar flow problems, and results varied too much with Reynolds number. A literature search proved futile. BuShips agreed to tank tests. Although the forms involved might not be practical for submarine hulls, test results would guide future designers. On 8 July 1946, BuShips officially requested that the David Taylor Model Basin conduct the Series 58 tests. It was already known that, for a given displacement and sectional area distribution, a circular section minimizes wetted area, hence frictional drag. The problem was to select a distribution of sectional areas that gave both a small wetted area for a given volume and a small form or residual drag. For example, very blunt ends reduce wetted area but cause flow separation and, thus, enormously increase residual drag. Length-to-

diameter ratio, prismatic coefficient (fatness), nose and tail radius, and the position of the maximum section were all varied. Twenty-four 9-ft models were used. The series demonstrated that prismatic coefficient and length-to-diameter ratio are the major factors in overall drag.

13. The earliest design for what would become *Albacore*, dated February 1949, showed a 150×30 ft hull. Additional versions had lengths of 170, 185, and 191 ft. By April 1950, the design had a 27-ft diameter and a length of 190–200 ft.

14. Jackson, "The Influence of *Albacore.*"

15. In April 1950, however, Capt. Armand Morgan, a senior submarine designer representing BuShips before the General Board, estimated a speed of 23 kt at the 1-hr rate (27.4 kt at the 1/2-hr rate). He therefore rejected BuOrd's proposal to add a torpedo tube, which would have added so much length that speed might have been reduced to roughly that of *Tang*. By October 1951, the estimated 1-hr speed was 20.9 kt (23.8 kt at the 1/2-hr rate, only marginally better than that expected for the new nuclear submarine). From a control point of view, these speeds were equivalent to much higher speeds as applied to a 300-ft submarine. *Albacore* could maneuver faster, and the effect would give much the same response as in a longer ship at higher speed. Time factors in maneuvering were considered particularly important because they affected human responses and, thus, the degree of automatic or semiautomatic control required.

16. The Soviet Alfa was conceived about 1956; her designers may have been inspired partly by U.S. official speculation about the possibility of attaining very high speeds. According to one recent account, she was designed to exceed the expected performance of foreign submarines over the next 10 to 15 years. ("J.M.," "Okrety podwodue typu 'Alfa,'" *Okrety wojenne* 4–6/92, pp 57–60.) This article appears to give the tactical-technical requirement (TTZ) to which Alfa (Project 705) was designed, but it does not give the 1956 date.

17. Evidence includes statements at General Board hearings on the design in 1950 and descriptions given by senior BuShips officers before the Submarine Officers Conference and at annual lectures.

18. Notes from R. P. Largess and H. S. Horwitz, "Albacore—The Shape of the Future," in R. Gardiner, *Warship 1991* (Annapolis, Md.: Naval Institute Press, and London: Conway Maritime Press, 1991), 179–198. The article was based on recollections of former crew members.

19. According to her designers, Capt. Harry Jackson and Professor Eugene Allmendinger, *Albacore* incorporated numerous details based on aircraft practice, as quoted in Largess and Horwitz, "Albacore."

20. Jackson, "The Influence of *Albacore.*" Jackson suggests that the earlier attempts failed because the fins were so short that they lay within the boundary layer; water may have flowed *forward* across these planes. The stern control surfaces in the Phase I *Albacore* were supported by large arms that experienced very high bending and twisting stresses during high-speed turns.

21. Largess and Horwitz, "Albacore," 187. Hull vibration was caused by water flow over the thin plating; the plastic was a form of hull damping. Hull damping was also applied to many U.S. destroyers at this time as part of the FRAM program.

22. Jackson, "The Influence of *Albacore*," Figure 7. Jackson points out that turning diameter is independent of speed at the start of a turn because all forces (both helping and resisting the turn) are proportional to the square of the speed.

23. The rejection of computer control is generally blamed on a reactionary Admiral Rickover. A recent experience suggests just how embarrassing computer control can be. The electric motor of the new British *Upholder* is computer-controlled. The program was designed to cut out the motor if it overloaded. On trial, the commander ordered a crash reverse from full ahead to full astern. The motor promptly cut out, almost sinking the submarine. The problem, unsuspected by the programmer, was inertia: because the propeller kept moving ahead for a time after the field in the motor had been reversed, the motor briefly overloaded. The solution was to program in a time delay. This type of subtle, yet simple, error is not uncommon. A future integrated combat/control system might have to order sudden evasive maneuvers to deal with short-range threats, in which case computer maneuvering would be inescapable.

24. The contraprops were initially 10 ft apart; they were later moved to 5 ft apart. The silver-zinc battery had twice the capacity of the previous battery.

25. *Jane's Fighting Ships 1967–68* (London: Sampson and Low, Marston & Co., Ltd., 1967), 365. These are probably official figures. To achieve such high underwater power, *Albacore* had to be virtually filled with batteries, even though each silver-zinc cell had much greater energy density than a Guppy cell.

26. Largess and Horwitz, "Albacore," 197. Some years later, there was speculation that the Soviet Alfa-class submarines achieved their very high speeds by polymer ejection, the theory being that they could not possibly achieve sufficient power from their reactors. It turned out that Alfa indeed achieved much higher power densities than U.S. submarines by adopting a less reliable liquid metal reactor and eliminating at-sea access to the power plant, which made her even less reliable.

Chapter 4

1. According to SubPac, *Submarine Bulletin*, June 1945, the Japanese submarine threat increased considerably about May/June 1944. U.S. submarines made more enemy submarine contacts on patrol and also experienced more torpedo attacks per patrol. Most attacks occurred at night, with twice as many on moonlit nights as on dark nights. The submarines' SJ radar provided very little warning; inside 3,000–4,000 yd, the small echo of the attacker's periscope was drowned in sea returns. SJ had to be modified for automatic reduction of receiver gain at short range. A special Arma course clock was introduced to steer the submarine on a programmed irregular zigzag specifically to avoid such attacks.

2. Contemporary General Board hearings, which included Office of Naval Intelligence (ONI) material, do not refer to this figure. ONI believed that the Soviets might approach German building rates (25/mo) in 5 yr and surpass them in 10, so that they might begin a war with five to ten times the number Hitler had had (i.e., 280 to 570 submarines) but with only two to three times the overall effectiveness. The 2,000-boat figure was a worst case projection. For the present, ONI correctly doubted that the Soviets had been able to complete the partially built Type XXIs they had obtained. It was by no means universally agreed that the mass Soviet threat was a future, rather than an immediate, problem.

3. One of the earliest descriptions of Lofar must have been a presentation by Lt. Comdr. C. B. Bishop before the Submarine Officers Conference, 18 January 1951. Woods Hole had just tested a vibrating reed meter (a form of narrow-band filter). Submarine diesel noise consisted mainly of harmonics of the engine rotational speed, the strongest being engine explosion frequency that was identifiable above other noise produced by a submarine. Early tests, using an omnidirectional (i.e., low-gain) hydrophone, were spectacular: *Halfbeak* was held to a range of

12 nm in a Force 4 sea and *Tusk* to 24 nm in Force 3. Because Lofar so improved the signal-to-noise ratio, it appeared that three small (3-in diameter) hydrophones could detect a target at long range. These experiments also revealed that most of the noise coming from the bow of a submarine was at propeller frequencies, whereas noise heard astern was from the engine. Propeller vibration traveled up the shaft into the ship and excited the hull itself; the mass of the hull blocked the stronger diesel vibrations from the direction of the bow. Such propeller noise only became a serious problem with the advent of single-screw nuclear submarines. In 1951, the main concern was that the two noise sources operated at different frequencies, so no single-frequency filter could suffice.

Lofar was a carefully guarded secret for many years. During the 1980s, however, numerous sonar manufacturers were permitted to show simulated Lofar displays. Recently declassified British papers on passive acoustics, written in the 1950s and now in the Public Record Office, particularly ADM 204/1041, a 1952 visit to the prototype SOSUS site, and ADM 204/2547, E. J. Risness, *Some Thoughts on the Recent History, Present Status, and Future Prospects of Passive Acoustic Submarine Detection* (Teddington: Admiralty Research Laboratory, May 1961), discuss Lofar in detail, including Lofar frequency ranges. However, they do not give the main frequencies at which modern Soviet submarines are detected, nor do they give the resolution of modern Lofar systems (which would make it possible to estimate their detection range). That information remains classified.

Risness credits Bell Telephone Laboratories with applying a narrow-band frequency analyzer, originally intended for speech analysis, to the submarine problem about 1950. He argues that the U.S. Navy found Lofar particularly attractive because, as it happened, Guppies had a strong and stable line structure at 80–100 Hz (their diesel-electric arrangement allowed the diesels to run at nearly constant speed). Direct-drive submarines, like those used by the British and the Soviets, would have much less stable signatures. Because SOSUS uses Lofar technology, it was originally described as a chain of Lofar stations. See, for example, R. J. Watson, *The History of the Joint Chiefs of Staff*, vol. 5 (Washington, D.C.: Government Printing Office, 1986), in connection with Lofar as a contribution to continental defense. M. D. Fagan, ed., *A History of Engineering & Science in the Bell System: National Service in War and Peace* (Bell Telephone Laboratories, 1978) includes a section (474–477) on spectral analysis but does not identify it with Lofar. Fagan also illustrates a Lofargram (475). It is not clear when the Soviets obtained Lofar; during the 1970s, they began to deploy Lofar sonobuoys, and their submarine towed array uses Lofar (and DEMON) processing.

4. One counter to silencing was a high-powered active sonar, Lorad. Another was explosive echo-ranging (E2R, later EER). A practice depth charge produced a ping in a pattern of the existing broadband sonobuoys that functioned as the receivers of this kind of bistatic sonar. A submarine version, SEER (with a directional varient, DEER) was proposed to support the new Mk 45 nuclear torpedo. SEER would have used a 1.8-lb charge fired from the standard submarine signal tube. DEER used a spark-gap or blasting cap in a parabolic reflector on the submarine's deck. In each case, the submarine's passive sonar acted as receiver. Range would have been 20,000 yd. The feasibility study was completed in March 1957, and an operational requirement (AS-02101) issued in June 1958. DEER was tested on board *Hardhead*, but PUFFS was chosen instead. The sonobuoy version of EER died because airborne Lofar proved so successful.

5. Largess and Horwitz, "Albacore," 190. Capt. Frank Andrews, submarine project officer at David Taylor Model Basin in 1953–1954, attributed the towed array concept to Marvin Lasski, who had suggested many aspects of *Albacore*.

6. SOSUS collected its own signature intelligence, which was relatively easy against snorkelers. The Lofar sonobuoy program began in the late 1950s and was first actually tested against snorkelers during the 1962 Cuban missile crisis. The U.S. Navy did not decide until about 1962–63 that first-generation Soviet nuclear submarines were operational. The urgency to collect their acoustic data accounted for the intense interest in acoustic surveillance (to support Lofar, particularly for sonobuoys) in 1964–65. The alternative to submarines was to drop wideband calibrated sonobuoys among Soviet submarines on exercises, but this could not be done to submarines remaining in home waters under the protection of Soviet air defenses.

7. TB-16 was a dual-purpose array, for both Tuba and tactical roles. At least the first 12 were clip-ons. TB-16A appeared around 1982, with better self-noise, standard hydrophones (the same type as SQR-19), and smaller components. TB-16B was further refined, with a foam-filled interior. TB-16D was the digital version, each channel having its own A/D (analog-to-digital) converter (the channels were sampled in sequence). This version uses multiple hydrophones per channel, with flow noise averaged over them. The current TB-16E is a refined TB-16D. The new TB-16 ( ) (to be TB-16F) adds some nonacoustic capability to detect array shape, depth, heading, and elevation angle (which earlier versions did not measure). In the past, the ship heading was used as the array heading.

8. The first 10 *Ohios* (SSBN 726–735) have Rockwell BQQ-9 broadband stand-alone processors for their long TB-16s; they also tow short TB-16s, which are part of their BQQ-5 integrated systems. The next 5 *Ohios* have less expensive BQR-23 narrowband processors instead; as of 1992, Rockwell hoped to sell the navy a BQQ-9 replacement for these and later *Ohios*. It appears that the interim thin-line TB-23 array entered service, about 1986–87, only on board some *Los Angeles*-class submarines.

9. The TB-29 engineering development model (EDM) was tested at sea in the fall of 1993.

10. In a few locations, such as the Arctic, the surface is so cold that the ocean is very nearly at a constant temperature and complex refraction phenomena are more or less irrelevant.

11. *Baya* was first recommended as a laboratory ship in 1948. For Naval Electronic Laboratory Center (NELC)/SubDevGru 1 Lorad experiments, she was fitted in 1956 with three experimental transducers: (1) 14×14 element active/passive billboard (0.5–1.2 kHz, abaft the conning tower, facing to starboard), (2) 50-element line hydrophone array (2.5-ft separation) on the starboard side at deck level, and (3) omnidirectional hydrophone in her bow. She was converted again in 1958–59: 23 ft added amidships and blunt sonar bow installed; all forward torpedo tubes were removed, but aft four tubes retained. She was fitted with a mushroom anchor and quarters for 12 scientists. In this form, her dimensions were 334.8×27×17 ft (1,900/2,625 tons) and she was capable of 10.5/8 kt. The three transducers in this version were (1) 1.5-kHz forward-facing billboard projector near bow, (2) two 40-ft linear receivers in extendable booms at bow, and (3) 4.3-kHz active/passive transducer forward of the conning tower. *Grouper* was similarly fitted. *Rock* was used in Lorad experiments in 1960. BRASS submarines were *Conger* (1961–63), *Grouper*, and *Tigrone* (1963). BRASS II consisted of a bow-mounted 144-dB transducer (4.5 kHz) and a portside 85-ft line array receiver (two 25-degree preformed beams). BRASS III employed a more powerful lower-frequency parabolic bow transducer (2.15 kHz, 150 dB). These experiments led to work on active

DIMUS and narrowband reception to reduce interference from reverberation.

12. Sphere size was proportional to wavelength. The original NUSC proposal corresponded roughly to the contemporary SQS-23 surface ship sonar; the more massive BQS-6 sphere was more closely comparable to the much larger SQS-26.

13. BQS-6 data from Little, *Submarine as a Surveillance Platform.*

14. A CW pulse is transmitted at a fixed frequency; it is detected because its energy rises above that of the surrounding noise. There is no way to distinguish the beginning of an echoed pulse from the beginning of an overlapping pulse following some other path. Because FM pulse changes frequency over its length, the sonar, in theory, can distinguish different parts of the pulse. This technique is similar to the use of pulse compression in radar.

15. The BQQ-5 feasibility study was conducted in 1969–71, followed by pre-production tests in *Guitarro* and *Pintado* in 1972 and a production model test aboard *Bergall* in December 1972; production was authorized in February 1973. It equipped the last three *Sturgeon*s. Later that year (1973), incorporation of a towed array was approved and competitive contracts for six arrays were awarded. In all variants through BQQ-5D, the (V)1 version is for the *Los Angeles* class, (V)2 is for *Sturgeon*, and (V)3 is for *Permit*. The original BQQ-5 used three beam formers: one active and one passive for the sphere, and one passive for either the chin or the towed array (25 port and 25 starboard beams and 2 noise-nulling beams for the chin array). The active beamformer forms a total of 600 beams (10 elevation/depression beams between +19 and −53 degrees for each of 60 6-degree aximuth beams). BQQ-5A added another UYK-7 computer and a towed-array broadband processor. BQQ-5B added a separate steerable hull array beamformer (SHAB) for the chin array and an improved control display console (ICDC). BQQ-5C, which passed operational evaluation in June 1984 (the upgrade program began in FY 80), expands DIFAR (directional Lofar) reception and is the current version. BQQ-5D, certified for service in May 1989, has a multiarray signal beamformer and a new expanded DIFAR analyzer (using three UYK-44 computers) in place of the earlier multiple interface unit/digital spectrum analyzer. It adds the thin-line TB-23 array; there is no (V)3 version because *Permit*s are being retired. BQQ-5E, the newest version, uses the long TB-29 array with its TARP passive ranger. The (V)3 version equips *Los Angeles*-class submarines; (V)4, in *Ohio*-class submarines, supersedes BQQ-6 and is integrated with combat control system (CCS) a Mk 2. The next version will be able to operate TB-16 and TB-29 simultaneously. About 75 percent of BQQ-6 components are taken from BQQ-5. This sonar has a 944-element sphere and a 100-element hull array. It supports two towed arrays but processes only one at a time.

16. The operational requirement was declassified in 1982.

17. As early as November 1948, Capt. P. R. Heineman, then attached to DCNO (Operations), had suggested that SSKs be part of combined surface-air-submarine killer teams.

18. An initial feasibility study for general-purpose underwater voice communications (GPVC) and secure communications was done in June 1953; an operational requirement followed in October 1955. GPVC was a single-sideband replacement for the existing UQC-1. Around 1960, the two main projects were SESCO (SEcure Submarine COmmunications [BQA-2]) and SPUME (Short PUlse MEssage), the latter imagined as a sort of underwater TACAN. Neither went anywhere. SESCO pointed the relatively narrow beam of a big spherical sonar at the receiver. The transmitter and receiver had to be precisely synchronized, but the clock in the system tended to wander. SPUME derived its supposed security from its short pulses and promised a high data rate, but multipath could scramble its pulses. The Soviets were often credited with effective long-range underwater communication, but that was apparently achieved by drastically limiting the number of alternative messages and using stereotyped tactics.

Chapter 5

1. In a 1939 U.S. exercise, *Argonaut* tended PBY flying boats. In September 1940, CNO Adm. Harold R. Stark ordered three large submarines (*Narwhal, Nautilus,* and *Argonaut*) modified to carry 19,000 gallons of aviation gas each. *Nautilus* was completed first; by October she had made a successful 300-ft dive with the fuel on board. Admiral Stark then recommended that two squadrons of the new fleet submarines (24 boats) be modified to carry 9,000 to 15,000 gallons of aviation gas each. The secretary of the navy approved the idea on 9 October; each would carry 9,500 gallons. SS 217–227 and 240–252 were selected (possibly only SS 222–225 and 227 were converted) to have their No. 6 tanks fitted. On 2 September 1944, Commander in Chief, Pacific (CinCPac) Admiral Nimitz endorsed a proposal to modify a few fleet submarines to fuel seaplanes, but it is unlikely that anything was done before the end of the war.

2. In February 1942, Capt. E. W. Burrough of the Plans Division asked BuShips to evaluate a submarine cargo carrier. A quick study showed that stripping a big prewar boat (*Argonaut*) would provide only 198.6 tons of cargo capacity (a fleet submarine would have carried 138.6 tons). Even these quantities probably could not have been realized. Interest revived in August, partly because of Lake's congressional testimony. President Franklin D. Roosevelt asked for a study of a 5,000-ton cargo carrier to supply beleagured ports, such as Murmansk in Russia and Tulagi in the Solomons. BuShips now estimated that removing half the engines and all the armament of a fleet boat would buy a 500-ton capacity (later cut to 370 tons). The old *Barracuda*s were more attractive, perhaps because they were such awful combatant submarines. Removing their main engines (leaving auxiliary engines for battery charging) would provide space for 447 tons of cargo (later increased to 600 or 700 tons). Admiral King's office disagreed: "Much opinion holds that [they] should be moored in some nice corn field and scrapped." The *Barracuda*s leaked oil so badly that they could hardly survive in the face of serious enemy ASW efforts.

BuShips sketched a 6,000-ton cargo submarine (375× 45×20 ft), capable of 12 kt surfaced but only 2 kt submerged to minimize battery weight, that could carry 1,500 to 2,000 tons of dense cargo. She would lack any cargo-handling capabilities. Because no comparable design existed, this one would require model basin tests. Design would take 6 mo, construction another 12 mo. Her cost was estimated at about $6 million. A 2,200- to 2,400-ton boat could probably carry 600 tons of dense cargo.

3. The full program consisted of six parts: (1) develop contract plans and specifications for a cargo-troop carrier conversion; (2) continue development and installation of snorkels; (3) continue research on improved submarine maneuverability; (4) convert at least two submarines into cruise missile launchers ("pilotless aircraft carriers"); (5) convert at least one submarine into an experimental long-range heavy-rocket bombardment ship (SSB); and (6) continue development of a fighter-director submarine (SSR). In addition to SSK, SSP, SSO, and SSE, the other new submarine categories were SSV (piloted or unpiloted airbreather) and SSRecce. SSRecce was soon dropped on the ground that a conventional attack submarine could perform the mission quite well. SSE, later SS(AE), was assigned an SCB project num-

ber (SCB 40), but characteristics were not formulated; apparently, no design work was done. On 10 January 1947, Admiral Nimitz approved a program, formulated in Navy Department conferences between 11 September 1946 and 8 January 1947, calling for immediate conversions for SSR, SSB (heavy bombardment, i.e., ballistic missile) SSP, and SSK. SS-A/S (ASW submarine), SS-R (super picket), SSV (submarine aircraft carrier), and SSB would be designed. Another special type, SSS (combination service type for supplying relief crews, supplies, and services to submarines on station), was proposed by the Submarine Planning Group as a means of extending patrols up to 12 mo. By mid-1947, the SSE designation had been applied to a proposed electronics experimental ship, later denoted AGSS.

4. The 12 submarines actually carried slightly more than a battalion because each carried a full company.

5. In 1950, the Submarine Officers Conference considered a proposal for a larger SSP and similar boats to deliver a regimental assault force, a third of a division. Existing submarines were too small; this operation would have required 59 SSPs, 127 SSAs, and 10 SSOs.

6. Under the FY 65 program, *Grayback* was lengthened 6 ft, the hangar doors were altered, the launcher ramp was removed, new electronics were installed, and she was re-engined with more powerful Fairbanks-Morse diesels (total 5,500 BHP, instead of 4,000 BHP). A similar conversion of *Growler* was deferred in 1968 because of rising costs; she eventually became a museum ship in New York.

7. *Combat Fleets 1993*, 814, states that the SEALs have 15 SDVs, ranging in size from converted Mk 37 torpedoes to the six-man vehicle carried in a dry deck shelter (DDS). In December 1990, 3 EX-8 Mod 1 SDVs were ordered from Unisys; 10 SDVs are to be delivered in 1998–2003.

8. Because the navy was nominally limited to attacks on naval targets, BuAer described the P6M as a heavy minelayer for closing off Soviet submarine bases.

9. Two additional pickets, *Threadfin* (SS 410) and *Remora* (SS 487), were completed after the war; neither saw picket duty.

10. At first, crush depth was set at 795 ft (versus 880 ft for a fleet submarine), mainly to cut hull weight. The designers wanted the ends to survive, however, even if the submarine took on a steep down-angle, in this case 30 degrees, so they were strengthened to crush at 845 ft.

11. Canceled in 1960, BPS-10 was a submarine equivalent of the surface ship SPS-26 radar. *Triton* probably never carried one. The evidence on SPS-26 is somewhat ambiguous. Although Largess and Horwitz (see below) say *Triton* was completed with this radar, Largess ("USS *Triton:* The Ultimate Submersible," *The Submarine Review,* January 1994, pp 101–7) says (p 105) that according to Capt. Bob Bulmer, her first operations officer, she never carried SPS-26 (her CO, Capt. Edward L. Beach, recalls SPS-26, however.) Unfortunately, none of the BuShips photographs transferred to the U.S. National Archives shows the ship with antennas raised.

12. Carrier-based airborne early-warning aircraft appeared as early as 1945, but they were merely radars transmitting to carriers below; they had to remain within line of sight of the carrier. Because she had her own CIC, an SSR could operate well beyond the carrier's horizon. The E-1B was the first carrier-based airplane to incorporate a CIC and thus control fighters. Before the E-1B entered service, the only airborne alternative was a large land-based warning aircraft (typically an EC-121) with limited endurance above a distant naval force.

13. *Triton* was apparently used experimentally about 1963–64 to control air strikes. A two-dimensional BPS-2 apparently re-placed her original 3-D SPS-26 during a 1962 overhaul. The big CIC was adapted to other undisclosed missions. She was also tested as a possible wartime Atlantic submarine force command ship (but that proved impractical due to a lack of means of underwater communications). R. P. Largess and H. S. Horwitz, "USS *Triton,* the Ultimate Submersible," in *Warship 1993* (Annapolis: Naval Institute Press and London: Conway Maritime Press), pp 167–187. They speculate that *Triton* was used to collect electronic intelligence. Presumably the big CIC was valuable before *Sturgeon*s, with their enlarged spaces, became available. Alternatively, *Triton* may have been used to test electronic intelligence-gathering equipment planned for other submarines (surely she was too noisy to acquire acoustic intelligence).

14. *Salmon* was redesignated AGSS in 1969 as a deep-submergence rescue vehicle (DSRV) mothership. The program was delayed, and she reverted to attack submarine status. *Seawolf* may have been converted in her place.

15. The information about these modifications appears in a series of six articles on U.S. submarines in the Cold War, *Chicago Tribune,* beginning 6 January 1991. The authors claim that the articles are based on interviews with numerous crewmen who participated in the incidents and on declassified documents. Most of the articles deal with penetrations of Soviet waters by otherwise unmodified attack submarines in order to evaluate Soviet ASW (a vital consideration if war had occurred) and to gather information on Soviet submarines. According to the *Tribune* series, U.S. submarines have conducted continuous 30-day intelligence-gathering patrols off the major Soviet bases since the mid-1950s. This would explain why *Seawolf* lasted as long as she did; she was decommissioned in March 1987. Presumably, *Halibut* was withdrawn as soon as long-hull *Sturgeon*s, capable of operating submersibles, became available. *Halibut* was the first of a series of submarines specially adapted to retrieve or examine objects in the very deep sea, using remotely controlled submersibles. In February 1994, Dr. John P. Craven, former head of the Navy Deep Submergence Systems Project, stated that the program was conceived after USS *Thresher* was lost in April 1963; it became clear that the Soviets too might leave valuable information on the ocean floor if they lost modern submarines accidentally. *Halibut* was refitted in 1965 with reconnaissance gear, cable spools for a tethered submersible, and thrusters to keep her in position below the surface. In the summer of 1968 she investigated a Soviet Golf-class missile submarine lost off Hawaii the previous March. Reportedly, her submersible photographed the wreck; it may have retrieved some equipment (the 1974 attempt to salvage the submarine was mounted from the surface ship *Glomar Explorer*). For his efforts, Dr. Craven received the Defense Department Distinguished Civilian Service Award. Later claims that *Halibut* was mother ship for the DSRV were apparently false, intended to camouflage her true role. Dr. Craven's statement was included in written testimony for a subcommittee of the Senate Energy and Natural Resources Committee, which was interested in underwater mining (which would use much the same technology as the underwater salvage submarines). This information was in W. J. Broad, "Navy Has Long Had Secret Subs For Deep-Sea Spying, Experts Say," in the *New York Times* of 7 February 1994 (pp A 1 and B 7). According to the article, an anonymous navy expert confirmed Dr. Craven's account.

16. In May 1992, Rear Adm. Anatoly Shtyrov, formerly of the Soviet Pacific Fleet, said that *Grayback* had recovered two nuclear bombs from the wreckage of a Soviet bomber in the North Pacific near Sakhalin in 1976. Shtyrov said that he began his investigation after medals were awarded to virtually the entire crew of the *Grayback.* His reported words were, "If you take into account

that the Yankees are miserly about handing out military awards . . . then the question immediately arose: what impressive thing had been done?" This account is from *Newsday*, 15 May 1992.

17. The *Chicago Tribune* series (see note 15) quotes Rear Adm. (Ret.) Walter Dietzen as describing "show and tell" sessions at both the White House and in Congressional committees following unusually successful trips. After such briefings, "You could get a couple of more subs in the budget." In the past, accounts of budget fights over the number of submarines have generally credited the sheer size of the program to Admiral Rickover's political power exerted through the Joint Committee on Atomic Energy (JCAE). Admiral Dietzen's comment suggests that the reality was far more complex.

Chapter 6

1. It is unlikely that Admiral Rickover rammed nuclear down the throats of entirely unwilling colleagues. By 1948, nuclear power seemed far preferable to the frustrating closed-cycle plants. Rickover might have dramatized his own role in order to maintain support for the quasi-independent organization that he considered necessary. The semiofficial historians of the program, R. G. Hewlett and F. Duncan, *Nuclear Navy 1946–1962* (Chicago: University of Chicago Press, 1974), suggest that Rickover tended to be almost obsessive about his program. Such heat, however, might have been essential in a period of budgetary austerity and sharply conflicting priorities. Hewlett and Duncan were, respectively, chief historian and assistant historian of the AEC; the book is based on AEC and Naval Reactors Division records.

2. Ibid., 44.

3. According to *Combat Fleets 1993*, 813, the later S5W, as installed in the *Sturgeon* class, "has two primary steam loops and two steam generators to supply steam to the two turbines." The two turbines, alongside each other, are geared together to the single shaft.

4. At a 1950 General Board hearing, Admiral Momsen, the senior submariner, argued that not to arm the SSN would be a tacit agreement that the United States had no future requirement for offensive (i.e., torpedo) submarines. Rickover is said to have rejected suggestions that the nuclear prototypes carry the weapon of the future, the cruise missile. He probably wanted to limit risk; the nuclear plant would be innovation enough for one hull. Missiles could be added once nuclear power had proved itself. In January 1954, in much the same vein, the Submarine Officers Conference called for a change to nuclear propulsion in missile and radar picket submarines of the FY 56 building program in the event that the *Nautilus* was successful. It is often suggested that *Seawolf* was redesigned for better surface seakeeping specifically because it was hoped eventually to install a large-diameter vertical launch tube in her forward torpedo room. No documentary evidence of such a plan has emerged.

5. The weight of the reactor and shielding is classified. Declassified notes of the 18 May 1949 Submarine Officers Conference show that the weight, as then estimated, was 800 tons, about three fourths of that shielding.

6. This version was 275×27 ft, 2,570 tons (standard), and about 3,100 tons submerged. This was probably the version that introduced the three-deck configuration forward of the reactor, which saved considerable length. Presumably, later growth back to (and beyond) 293 ft was due to power plant expansion.

7. The double-hull design called for an overall length of 315 ft, inner hull diameter of 24 ft, and outer hull diameter of 30 ft, with single-hull construction only in the stern room. Compared with *Nautilus*, *Seawolf* had a better distribution of tankage and improved structural features.

8. W. D. Roseborough, Jr., "Evolution of Modern U.S. Submarines from End of World War II to 1964," *Submarine Review*, December 1989, 52. Model tests showed that *Nautilus* would push her bow under as she approached full power. Captain Roseborough, who had the submarine desk in BuShips, ordered model basin tests of a redesigned bow that was expected to add 3 kt in surfaced speed at the cost of $\frac{1}{10}$ kt submerged and give a more efficient sonar location. In 1957, a spare SIR core had been available. Both SSNs were badly needed for ASW trials and training, and using the core instead of replacing the reactor would have cut refit time from 21 to 3 mo. Roseborough learned that Admiral Rickover had already ordered GE to cut up the spare core.

Chapter 7

1. The rattle was soon fixed; it was not a fundamental problem.

2. This account is based on notes prepared for the British Admiralty in October 1957 when *Nautilus* visited England (file DEFE 13/182 in the Public Record Office, Kew, England). The British concluded that, unless there was some unsuspected technical development, only an SSN (in the barrier or escort role) could defeat another SSN.

3. Early experiments were: April 1957, *Seawolf* versus *Blenny* using SQS-4; May 1957, *Seawolf* maintained contact on *Halfbeak* for 35 of 41 hours, 13–15 May; and August 1957, *Seawolf* versus *Halfbeak*, with torpedo detection at 400 to 1,000 yd. In another exercise, *Nautilus* and *Swordfish* held *Darter* even though sonar range was only 1,000 yd. Although *Darter* could hear the boats' turbine whine and their chatter over the UQC-1 underwater telephone, she was unable to evade them. SSNs needed not only long-range but also high-resolution sonar (UQS-1, the standard mine detector of the time).

4. About 1957, *Seawolf* demonstrated that she could easily dive in or out of the beam of the standard surface ship SQS-4 medium-range sonar. At long range, the beam may extend all the way down to the maximum operating depth of the submarine.

5. *Skate*s actually suffered Mk 37 hits. An officer riding *Seadragon* described the "awesome sight" on the sonar intercept gear as the torpedo pinged, shifted to its terminal homing mode (with a faster ping rate), and then hit aft, with a slight tremor. Evasion was impossible.

6. Summer studies were intended to attract senior academic experts who were free from university duties during the summer recess. The first study may have been Project Hartwell on the security of North Atlantic Treaty Organization (NATO) sea communications, which was conducted by the Massachusetts Institute of Technology (MIT) in the summer of 1950 (see chapter 4). According to Ivan A. Getting, a CUW member from 1954 until it was disbanded in 1972, CUW was a direct outgrowth of Division Six of the WW II Office of Scientific Research and Development, which had managed the mobilization of academic scientists and engineers. Getting served as associate director of the Nobska project. See Getting, *All in a Lifetime: Science in the Defense of Democracy* (New York: Vantage Press, 1989).

7. Getting, *All in a Lifetime*, recalls, in particular, that Columbus Iselin of Woods Hole remarked that "a true submarine, operating in an evasive mode, could hide forever in the vast oceans." Getting knew that the navy was already working on a version of the army's Jupiter, but he felt that the navy did not realize the full potential of strategic missiles carried by such submarines. The CUW wanted to include all defensive and offensive aspects of nuclear weapons and nuclear propulsion. Admiral

Burke reluctantly agreed at a meeting at the National Research Council on 2 December 1955.

8. Getting, *All in a Lifetime,* recalls that it helped considerably that the aide to the AEC director was Comdr. William Rowan, his former Ph.D. student at MIT. Also, the director of the AEC was a former naval man, Adm. Lewis Strauss. Among the AEC participants were Dr. Edward Teller (group leader), Dr. Harold Agnew (later director of the Los Alamos National Laboratory), and Dr. John E. Foster (Lawrence Livermore National Laboratory); the latter two were the senior weapon designers of their laboratories.

9. Stinger was adapted from a missile conceived to attack surface targets. Early in May 1955, Comdr. J. D. Miller, former commander of Submarine Division (SubDiv) 51 (Regulus submarines), proposed a new short-range solid-fuel rocket to be fired at surface ships from a torpedo tube. *Tunny's* missile officer, Lt. M. E. Phares, submitted a more detailed proposal late in December. ComSubPac transformed this missile into a shore-bombardment weapon, which would make every submarine an SSG. The Pacific Fleet staff strongly agreed, and an operational requirement for the new weapon (AS-08701) was published in April 1956. Range would be at least 5 nm, and guidance would be inertial. At BuOrd, Comdr. (later Rear Adm.) E. B. Hooper transformed the short-range ballistic missile into an ASW weapon. As assistant for nuclear applications under the BuOrd assistant for R&D in 1950–51, Hooper had helped to start development of the Betty nuclear depth bomb. He began a follow-on study, ALIEX, which envisaged a nuclear ASW missile to be launched from a torpedo tube. Hooper returned to BuOrd in 1955 and revived ALIEX, so the Pacific Fleet idea fell on fertile ground. Stinger was developed by NOL at White Oak. China Lake (NOTS) designed its own torpedo tube missile, Marlin, more in line with the original bombardment or anti-ship concept. It found that a 4,000-lb missile with a 600-lb warhead could reach 25 to 100 nm, carrying a 300-kT (1961 technology) or 0.5- to 1-MT (1963 technology) warhead.

10. BuOrd chose to develop a new torpedo rather than follow Nobska's recommendation to fit 100 or 200 existing torpedoes with Lulu (W34) warheads.

11. The standard joke was that Astor had a kill probability (PK) of two: the target and the launcher. From 1973 on, Northrop marketed the wake-following conventional Mk 45F ''Freedom Torpedo'' that used an Astor body. A sale to Turkey was pending when Turkey invaded Cyprus in 1974, and the U.S. government imposed an arms embargo. Some Mk 45 bodies ended up as Mk 30 targets.

12. In 1962, it was estimated that four shots would kill the target. The weapon was to be adaptable to the Mk 46 successor (now designated a Mk 50). Requirement W23-20 was formally canceled on 18 March 1969.

13. Subroc technology was reportedly compromised in 1964–65. The Soviet missile was SS-N-15. (A larger SS-N-16 was later developed.) The associated BQQ-1 sonar was compromised at the same time. The Soviet version, Barracuda, probably first equipped Victor II class submarines. Its sonar sphere is smaller than the U.S. type, with about 1,000 hydrophones, but it operates at much the same frequencies (3.5 kHz active, 0.5–5 kHz passive). The purely passive array is wrapped directly around the sphere, rather than around the hull of the submarine. It is smaller than BQR-7 and, reportedly, tuned to 3.5 kHz, the primary active frequency of modern U.S. and British submarine sonars. Unlike Subroc, SS-N-15 can be fired from surface-ship torpedo tubes; also, there is now a torpedo-carrying version.

14. A Mk 130 had a 4k-word memory; access time was

20 microsec, add time was 40 microsec, and maximum multiply time was 424 microsec. It cycled (time-shared) among inputs from the analyzers, reading an input control signal at least every 1.2 sec and at most every 2.0 sec. If the input data did not indicate that a new analysis of range, bearing, course, or speed should be carried out, the data were averaged with previous data; the solution from the previous analysis was position-kept (projected ahead) and output twice a second. Alternatively, a new analysis was available about 2 sec after new data were read. A Mk 130 found the four target coordinates (two position, two velocity) by forming a 4×4 matrix to solve four simultaneous linear equations. Because analysis of the matrix indicated the quality of the solution, the computer could determine when no sufficiently good solution was available. A much more powerful Mk 130 Mod 1 used in the Mod 8 version of a Mk 113 corrected sonar inputs by estimating sonar acoustic path. The earlier Mk 112 fire-control system was a Mk 101 with an analyzer suited to bearings-only solutions (mechanized analog TMA, rather than the digital four-target TMA of a Mk 113). Although it could certainly match Subroc range (the limit was 70,000 yd, the first convergence zone), a Mk 112 was never fitted to handle the missile. A Mk 112 equipped *Tullibee* and the early ballistic missile submarines (SSBN 598 and 608 classes).

15. SUBIC was administered by ONR, mainly through Electric Boat. IBM and Librascope were also important early contractors. This account of SUBIC is based largely on three annual progress reports on submarine system integration: 1962–63 (AD 349906, originally Confidential, declassified 1976), 1963–64 (AD 361641, 1 February 1965, originally Confidential, declassified 1977), and 1964–65 (AD 377749, 18 April 1966, originally Confidential, declassified 1978). In addition to SUBIC, these papers reported work by the Naval Underwater Ordnance Station on EX-10/ Mk 48, by the Bureau of Naval Weapons (formerly BuOrd) SDAP (Systems Development Analysis Program), and work by SubDevGru 2. Related SubDevGru 2 reports on TMA tactics began with ''The Performance of the Plot Coordinator and Time/ Bearing Plotter,'' 29 June 1956.

16. The 1962–63 SUBIC report argued that sonar no longer should be separated from the control room and fire control. COs already wanted to be in the sonar room, particularly during the preconfirmation, preclassification phase of an attack on a single contact. A CO in the control room could not get sonar data quickly enough for maneuvering; he had to wait for data processed by the sonar team. Using the TMA range estimate being developed by the Mk 113 system, the sonar operator could minimize the power of the single ranging ping and thus also minimize the chance that the target would detect it. The fire control coordinator, who supervised sonar during an attack, needed sonar displays. The report argued that a control room sonar repeater would be too expensive, nor did it seem possible to move part (but not all) of the sonar system into the control room.

17. The broadband noise is modulated by lower-frequency components; for example, flow noise is modulated by blade rate. DEMON extracts that Lofar signature. It is often associated with sonobuoy processors.

18. The computer system could turn its ray trace into an image of the way sonar coverage varied with range and bearing, including minor shadow zones (gaps) that were partly due to multipath. An operator could estimate target range from the way in which the target signal faded in and out as it crossed gaps. In experiments, bottom-bounce pinging showed that such solutions were always accurate to within 2,000 yd. This technique is analogous to the use of fades to estimate the height of a radar target.

19. There were four main target parameters: range, bearing

rate, speed, and speed across the line of sight. SubDevGru 2 developed a family of deflection (lead) angle curves corresponding to target range and bearing rate or speed and aspect (course). Then it dealt with a more realistic case, in which two of the four parameters were only approximately known. The curves were designed to position the torpedo's acoustic cone over the range of possible target positions. Sets were produced for a Mk 37 running at high or low speed.

20. Normal plane maneuvering (NPM) with sail and stern planes was effective at any pitch angle at or above 6 kt. Below 6 kt, the effects of the stern planes could reverse at some pitch angles. Depth was best changed on an even keel by using the planes, referred to as even keel planes maneuvering (EKPM). Below about 3 kt, the submarine had to rely on ballast water, referred to as even keel ballast maneuvering (EKBM). Work was also done on control near the surface in rough weather (e.g., for surveillance work).

21. ADSCS had a follow-the-pointer display (a point of light on the edge of the rudder and diving plane angle displays), which gave the system its name. The display was driven through the UYK-20 computer that controlled the submarine. ADSCS underwent a formal technical evaluation between 23 April and 7 May 1977. See A. J. Giddings, "USS *Los Angeles* and the Aided Display Control System (ADSCS)," *Submarine Review,* January 1989, 89–91; and K. Hart, "Submarine Automation," *Submarine Review,* July 1988, 49. Autonetics was disappointed in its expectation that the navy did not buy ADSCS for the *Los Angeles* class after its successful test; Giddings blames a mentality in the submarine force that rejects automated control.

22. Vice Adm. D. L. Cooper, "SSN-21 Status: Combat Systems History" in *NSL Fact Book 1991* (Annandale, Virginia: Naval Submarine League), 43–45. Cooper was then DCNO for submarine warfare.

23. A briefing on the 1959 study listed the following post–WW II projects for small submarines:

1949: Capt. Bass's ASW midget (see Appendix A)

1955: X-1 (see Appendix A); this was a classic midget

1955: Studies leading to *Tullibee*

1957: BuShips medium submarine study (1,300 tons); Fairchild study of machinery for a 60-kt submarine

1958: Aeroject small submarine; that year, CNO asked for small submarine studies, presumably in response to Nobska

1959: Naval Ordnance Test Station (China Lake) design of a two-man torpedo (Moray; see Appendix A); Capt. Bass recommended design of a small submarine

24. In 1963, Admiral Rickover discussed these examples in detail for JCAE. The boiling water reactor was rejected because radioactive impurities might well contaminate the turbine, as well as the reactor vessel; thus, the turbine could not be repaired at sea. Steam generation was difficult to control. Too, added shielding would be needed because the steam generators would not help shield the reactor. A liquid metal reactor had just been developed for the abortive nuclear jet aircraft. Gas cooling would have used helium, which is very difficult to contain but cannot be made radioactive.

Chapter 8

1. Hewlett and Duncan, *Nuclear Navy.*

2. *Nautilus* carried her boilers (heat exchangers) low, abaft her reactor; both were covered by a thick deck. In 1955, Milton Shaw

and Robert Panoff of Code 1500 proposed a more vertical arrangement extending through the whole height of the hull. A shielded tunnel provided access through the reactor compartment to the after end of the ship. The short tunnel weighed far less than the long heavy deck; in both cases, the end bulkheads of the reactor compartment were about the same and the sides were shielded mainly by the sea. Although the keel of *Skate* had already been laid, the tunnel design (S3W) was immediately applied to her and to *Sargo.* The other two ships used the earlier horizontal arrangement (S4W). The tunnel was adopted for all later nuclear submarines. See T. Rockwell, *The Rickover Effect* (Annapolis, Md.: Naval Institute Press, 1992), 223–224.

3. This sequence is given in a brief history of naval nuclear propulsion appended to unclassified JCAE hearings, 1963.

4. According to Hewlett and Duncan, *Nuclear Navy,* 274, specifications for SAR were fixed in 1955. In August 1955, its consequences (the size of the radar picket submarine that it was to power) so horrified the SCB that some members favored a shift to a single reactor plant or to two lower-powered reactors. Some argued that $25 million could be saved by the sacrifice of 2 kt. Neither Code 1500 nor the Knolls laboratory could meet the specific weight requirements, and the result was little superior to the original STR. SAR was kept alive primarily to maintain GE as a viable competitor of Westinghouse, so that the Navy could be sure of having two sources of design advice and reactor production. Hewlett and Duncan also state that Rickover wanted to keep SAR alive as a possible missile submarine power plant; it certainly figured in many contemporary missile submarine designs. SAR was also proposed as an alternative to the newer S5W. About 1957, a single-SAR submarine and a two-SAR "high speed submarine" were both sketched. The latter was associated with a study of more reloads in the *Thresher* class. No details are available.

5. This version of the planned reactor outputs is taken from a Soviet book based on published U.S. and other Western material. See V. M. Bulakov et al., *Atomic-Powered Submarine Design* (Leningrad: Sudostroyeniy, 1964), translated by the U.S. government and published by the National Technical Information Service in 1967 as AD 664961; the list of reactor projects is on page 237. Some versions of the "family of five" omitted the abortive 1,500-SHP plant altogether and distinguished the HPR and LSR plants. The small plant appeared in a sketch proposal for a FY 56 submarine.

6. F. Duncan, *Rickover and the Nuclear Navy: The Discipline of Technology* (Annapolis, Md.: Naval Institute Press, 1990). Preliminary calculations were completed by September 1956, but many of the figures were based on forced circulation experience. Only in September 1958 did the Department of Defense (presumably Rickover, wearing his Code 1500 hat) formally request an NCR for submarine propulsion. AEC was skeptical and ordered a review panel to decide whether the technology was sufficiently mature. The prototype reactor was included in the FY 60 budget. Design work was shifted from Bettis (Westinghouse) to Knolls (GE) in the summer of 1959 after Westinghouse reassigned some of its personnel to space projects. Construction began in May 1961, with completion scheduled for 1963; it was delayed to the fall of 1965, going critical on 13 September. The prototype made a successful simulated trans-Atlantic voyage (equivalent to the test of the *Nautilus* reactor) in June 1966. It moved to simulate the motion of a ship because there was some concern that water circulation within the reactor would be affected when the submarine pitched, rolled, and maneuvered.

7. Many of the British papers on the acquisition of the S5W are collected in the 1958 First Sea Lord papers, vol. I, ADM

205/178, Public Record Office, Kew. This file includes a Royal Netherlands Navy letter stating that agreement with the U.S. Navy was imminent.

8. In August 1953, the cost of the new SSN was estimated at $50 million, including $20 million for the reactor and an estimated $5 million to develop the reactor and its controls. The 1954 navy figure probably did not include the AEC-financed reactor.

9. The new picket would cost the navy less than a nuclear attack submarine ($32 million versus $41 million) because the AEC would pay for its SAR reactor. A diesel submarine would cost $28 million.

10. An SSN cost $45 million and a diesel submarine, $33 million. These figures and the note on performance are found in DCNO (Logistics), memorandum to Chairman, Standing Committee on the Long Range Shipbuilding and Conversion Program, 18 July 1955, declassified by Op-09BH, 24 April 1976.

11. The BuShips preliminary designers had already sketched out an *Albacore*-hull *Skate*. Then they compared a single-screw *Nautilus* to an *Albacore*-hull submarine with a similar power plant. On 3 August 1955 Preliminary Design formally adopted Model 4176 (one of the Series 58 forms, the model for which was built in 1949) as the basis of a four-deck attack submarine with 31ft 6in hull diameter. (Identification of the model was by William G. Day of DTNSRDC, who is in charge of the basin's towing-model collection). The main difference between *Skipjack*s and a pure Series 58 hull was the spine for the snorkel piping: Rickover's nuclear group refused to allow any snorkel piping to pass through the reactor compartment, and there was no double-hull section around that compartment. The 3 August date is from G. E. Weir, *Forged in War: The Naval-Industrial Complex and American Submarine Construction, 1940–1961* (Washington: Naval Historical Center, 1993), pp 201–202.

Electric Boat's chart certainly parallels Preliminary Design's choice, but its significance is probably different. The company was not responsible for overall submarine design but for the preliminary and later design of power plant arrangement (BuEng and its successor portion of BuShips never developed power plant arrangements; designs offered to contractors left machinery spaces blank). In 1989, Electric Boat's former nuclear engineer, J. S. Leonard, recalled that the company tried five or six twin-screw designs for a submarine powered by an AFSR (S5W). They were unimpressive; Electric Boat decided to use its own money to try a single-screw *Albacore* configuration. Leonard recalls a 5 August 1955 presentation (probably giving the details listed below), which greatly impressed Rickover. Given Rickover's role, it seems likely that Electric Boat was designing machinery spaces, not a complete submarine. At that time Rickover much favored twin-screw power plants for reliability, so he would not have financed a single-screw machinery design. That Electric Boat had a single-screw configuration ready (in preliminary form) just as the preliminary designers in Washington came to favor it would have made a tremendous difference in the speed with which the new submarine could be developed. Machinery configuration depended critically on outside hull dimensions, so for each arrangement, the company had to develop an overall hull form, including appropriate compartment lengths and weights. The speed consequences of alternative arrangements depended, of course, on how the machinery drove overall submarine size and shape. The Electric Boat designs may have been more a move in a larger fight to convince Rickover to approve a single-screw design than a contribution to the Preliminary Design decision to go for an *Albacore* hull. Leonard recalled that an Electric Boat engineer, Harlan Turner, had proposed moving the bow planes to the sail (some of the preliminary designers of the time disagree;

they think the idea arose in Washington). Certainly, the sail planes were an important element of the design the Ship Characteristics Board saw on 6 September 1955. (Leonard interview cited by Weir, pp 202–7.)

Electric Boat offered two versions of AFSR, producing 12,000 and 15,000 SHP; it arranged them in hulls of varying diameter. Its summary sheet showed 9 alternatives: (1) *Skate,* (2) through (6) with 12,000 SHP power plants, and (7) through (9) with 15,000 SHP.

1. *Skate* (257×25 ft, 2367/2711 tons).
2. A conventional twin-screw 12,000 SHP submarine with *Skate*'s 6 bow and 2 stern tubes (271×25 ft, 2565/2910 tons). Speed roughly matched that of the larger *Nautilus*, which was about 10 percent more powerful. Nearly doubling *Skate* SHP added 14 ft to engine room length (and, remarkably, nothing to reactor room length). This design was unacceptable because its operations compartment was too short to provide Regulus missile guidance and control equipment (4 ft would have been added; length would have grown to 280 ft).
3. A *Skate* with 12 ft added to its engine room, and with its stern extended to take a single screw; there were no tubes aft (278×25, 2540/2885 tons), 0.8 kts faster than (2). Like (2), it was too short to provide Regulus guidance and control.
4. A conventional twin-screw submarine without stern tubes (258×28 ft, 2750/3250 tons), 0.6 kts slower than (2). This version and (5) had shorter reactor rooms; (6) and (8) had slightly longer rooms; except for (9), the others all had reactor rooms the same length as *Skate*'s.
5. A somewhat longer fat single-screw conventional submarine saving some engine room length compared to (4) (258×28 ft, 2660/3770 tons), 0.5 kts faster than (2).
6. An *Albacore*-form single screw submarine with a very short engine room (259×29-4ft, 2780/3160 tons), 3.2 kts faster than (2).
7. A conventional twin-screw 15,000 SHP submarine (275× 25 ft, 2620/2960 tons), 2 kts faster than (2). It had the longest single engine room in the series.
8. A single-screw *Albacore*-hull submarine with 4 bow tubes and the same machinery lengths as (6) (259×29-4 ft, 2780/ 3160 tons), 5.4 kts faster than (2).
9. *Nautilus* with the 15,000 SHP plant (319-6×27-8 ft, 3539/ 4101 tons), 0.9 kts faster than (2), i.e., slightly faster than the original lower-powered *Nautilus*. Machinery lengths were very long. Unlike any of the others, this design lacked a tunnel over its reactor, so its reactor room was nearly twice the length of the very short ones in designs such as (4) or (8). It had two engine rooms, whose total length was about twice that of the short engine spaces in (6) and (8).

Compared to *Skate*, specific machinery weight (lbs/SHP) was also drastically reduced (roughly halved in one case). The main problem in the *Albacore*-hull forms was to locate the required pair of sonars (SQS-4 or -5 and BQR-2) within the streamlined bow. The Electric Boat designers dispensed with one of the usual three tiers (two tubes each), providing only 4 bow tubes with 6 reloads. Apparently, Preliminary Design realized that each tier could accommodate three rather than two tubes, to maintain the six-tube standard; presumably, that was one advantage of its greater-diameter design. The Electric Boat series was designated EB design 269 (EB designated *Skipjack* design 269A; the later ships of the class were EB-274A).

The *Skipjack* design can also be placed in the series of consecutively numbered *navy* preliminary submarine design studies. The SCB 154 (*Skipjack*) project was S-109, immediately after *Barbel* (S-108, the three-level attack submarine, which was descended from Portsmouth's 1954 S-98 project). S-110 was the study of increased test depth that fed into the *Thresher* design. To give a sense of what was happening in 1955–57, S-111 was a modified *Barbel* with a sodium amalgam battery and a fuel cell. S-112 was the SSG 574 conversion (to apply to SS 574-6 and 577), S-113 was the Jupiter missile submarine, S-114 was Mare Island's nuclear *Halibut*, S-115 was the big SCB 166A Regulus submarine, and S-116 was *Thresher*. S-118 was a deep-diving rescue submarine or sonar drone; S-119 was the abortive *Triton* conversion to a Regulus submarine; S-120 was the LORAD conversion of the fleet submarine *Baya*; and S-121 was a proposed nuclear submarine transport (ASSPN). No S-117 has been found. S-122 was Mare Island's abortive Regulus II SSGN. S-123 was a study of batteries for SSNs, S-124 an SSN with a single SAR reactor, S-125, a positive buoyancy submarine, S-126 a detachable escape chamber, S-127 *Dolphin* (and studies of deeper-diving submarines), S-128 a study of silver-zinc batteries for *Barbel* and a Guppy II, S-129 Project Flying Carpet (see chapter 11), S-130 contraprops, S-131 an escort submarine (1959) for a major BuShips convoy escort study, S-132 an SSN using the paired SAR reactors and a single screw (and a *Thresher* with more reloads, and S-133 a small SSBN for construction in 1965–70 (presumably for the 1959 Long Range Objectives study of the 1965–70 fleet). S-134 was the Guppy FRAM project, S-135 a modified *Barbel* with a *Thresher* bow and silver-zinc batteries, S-136 a small submarine (presumably inspired by Nobska), S-137 the FY 65 attack submarine (November 1957 advanced concept, presumably the Laning project), and S-138 a communications drone (PICES). Other interesting projects of this period were S-140, PUFFS; S-146, a Lithium Fluoride Stirling engine; S-144, a single-screw SSN using the *Skate* reactor; S-150, the 1960/64 SSBN; S-152, a submarine convoy escort; S-155, Lockheed's Project EMPIRE small submarine (for Laning); S-156, an Electric Boat optimum submarine study; S-158, a fleet submarine conversion to carry two Polaris missiles (project 43-60, hence circa 1960); S-159, the SSCN submarine command center (the abortive *Triton* conversion); S-160, a proposed FBM experimental submarine; S-164, nonnuclear studies; S-170, advanced attack submarine studies; S-171, Wetback, a FY 65 ASW SSN study; S-174, the FY 63 submarine redesign (*Sturgeon*); and S-175, a sailless submarine. The series also included design reviews of foreign submarines (BuShips had to review all designs whose construction the United States financed) and of a variety of design features.

To put these designations in context, S-32 was the last World War II design; the first postwar fast design was S-34 (Guppy was S-35; other early fast diesel boats were S-36 [261 ft version], S-38 [243 ft version with figure-8 hull], S-43 [271 ft], S-47 [SCB 2, *Tang*], S-50 [262 ft SS 563], S-77 [SCB 2A: effect of wraparound tanks in a 295×19.5 ft attack boat, SS 574], and S-96 [Electric Boat proposals for SS 576]). There were several *Albacore* designs: S-56 (fast training submarine); S-60 (185 ft); S-61 (miscellaneous SST studies); S-65 (191 ft); S-67 (200 ft); S-68 (185 ft); and S-69 (170 ft). The SSKs were S-45 (newly built units), S-58 (SSK 214), and S-73 (SSK II series); SSX was S-48 and S-84 (the closed-cycle SSR was S-91); the small coastal submarine (T-1 type) was S-63; the X-1 midget was S-82 and S-83 (outside design). Early missile submarines: S-40 (SS[GW]), S-41 (120 ft barge for V-2 missile), S-71 (Rigel submarine conversion), S-94 (SSA 317 converted to fire Regulus). *Nautilus* began as S-57 (293 ft version), evolving into S-70 (302 ft 6 in and then 319 ft 6 in); *Seawolf* (SSN II) was

S-79. The abortive 1953 fast attack submarine was S-87 (the 1952 nuclear submarine carrier came earlier, but no S-number has been found for it). *Skate* was S-88. The next nuclear submarine design in the series was S-99, *Triton*. S-101 was probably the series of fast SSGNs, initially to have been built as SSGN 587. S-102 was SSO-N, the 1955 fantasy (S-105 was the accompanying submarine LST). S-103 was *Tullibee*. S-107 was an abortive twin-screw *Barbel*. No S-100, S-104, or S-106 has been identified, but one of them was surely the small 1955 submarine (SSK/SSKN); another was probably the small SSN depicted in the BuShips "dream book," and yet another was probably the diesel SSG that became *Halibut*. The series from S-70 on is complete enough to make it unlikely that a major project was missed. Not all the preliminary design projects were particularly serious, but the list as a whole gives a good idea of what was being considered.

12. Chairman, SCB, memorandum to files of SCB, Serial 0012P43 of 14 September 1955, declassified by Op-09BH, 24 April 1976.

13. *Skipjack* probably exceeded 30 kt on trials, but her maximum speed was somewhat reduced when she was refitted with quieter but less efficient propellers.

14. Capt. J. Patton, "Stealth is a Zero-Sum Game," *Submarine Review*, April 1992. The ability to shift between stealthy and very visible operating modes was suddenly attractive. According to the Chicago *Tribune* series cited in Note 14, Chapter 5, Capt. Norman "Buzz" Bessac, *Scorpion's* CO, had reason to appreciate his submarine's agility and high-speed endurance. Cornered by Soviet ASW ships off Vladivostok in August 1957, he was held down for more than 30 hours. Peppered with practice depth charges, Bessac was finally forced to surface; he was allowed to leave. *Scorpion's* exploit was typical of what a nuclear submarine could do to a surface force that imagined it had cornered her.

15. SCB, memorandum 160-56, 19 July 1956, declassified by Op-09BH, 23 May 1975.

16. Because she was delayed, *Thresher* became R&D ship for the greater test depth chosen in 1956. In July 1956, SCB proposed adoption of an intermediate depth (between 700 ft and the new standard) for the FY 58 missile ships; in September, CNO decided that the extra cost and delay were not worthwhile. Similar considerations applied a few months later to *Tullibee*.

17. As of 30 April 1957, the estimated cost of the new SSN was $47 million, compared with $89 million for the prototype of the SSBN and $70 million for follow-ons, a ratio of about 3 : 2. A new SSGN would cost about $58 million, and a *Skipjack* about $42 million. It was inevitable that the SSGNs would be reordered to *Thresher* characteristics, rather than *Tullibee*; both the *Thresher* and the abortive SSGNs used the same reactor, and long-lead elements already had been ordered. The reorder date cannot be precisely established, but BuShips still carried FY 59 SSGNs in its program as of April 1957 and still referred to their FY 58 prototypes. The FY 59 SSN was described as a repeat FY 57 *Thresher*.

Chapter 9

1. In May 1957, contraprops were estimated to buy about 1.5 kt, or about equal to eliminating the sail.

2. Smoothness had been improving for some time. *Albacore* was rated as twice as smooth as *Tang* or *Nautilus*. Another 40 percent of smoothing might have bought as much as 2 or 3 kt but was considered impractical.

3. Had the generator been kept aft, an external spine would have been necessary because intake and exhaust piping could not run through the reactor compartment. The generator was

insulated from the living compartments above it by a heavy steel deck.

4. A twin-screw installation limited propeller diameter: the shafts could not emerge at very large angles, but the screws still had to clear the hull. They could not be angled down to meet the hull at a narrower point. Running *Skipjack* over a sound range, the British found that, unlike a twin-screw submarine, her propeller could be heard even below cavitation depth; that was blade rate. ADM 204/1359 (*Skipjack,* July 1960), ADM 204/1360 (*Scorpion,* February 1961), and ADM 204/1361 (*Scorpion,* November 1961), all in the Public Record Office, Kew.

Skipjack operating modes were battery creep (reactor off), reactor creep (running on battery but with the reactor operating and one of two turbogenerators running), and full speed (both turbogenerators running). The ship had a 15-ft, five-blade propeller (approximately 7 RPM/kt). At battery creep speed, the only prominent line was generated by the main lubricating oil pump. At reactor creep, the turbogenerator lines appeared. At 20 kt, blade rate dominated. Compared with *Skipjack, Scorpion* had quieter main reduction gearing and direct-drive, rather than geared-drive, turbogenerators and some hull damping. Turbogenerator lines at 60 and 120 Hz were still quite evident. For her second trial, *Skipjack* had dynamic absorbers and flexible couplings fitted to her turbogenerators; several auxiliary machines had been sound-isolated.

5. K. M. Heggestad, "Submarine Propellers," *Maritime Defence,* June 1981, 179–182, probably one of the first published unclassified descriptions of blade rate.

6. This account is based partly on Capt. W. D. Roseborrough, Jr., "Evolution of Modern U.S. Submarines from End of World War II to 1964," *Submarine Review,* December 1989, 52. Roseborrough had the submarine desk in BuShips.

7. In 1975, *The New York Times* reported (and the U.S. government confirmed) that for some time U.S. nuclear attack submarines, particularly the *Sturgeon* class, had gathered intelligence in Soviet home waters. S. Hersh, "Submarines of U.S. Stage Spy Missions Inside Soviet Waters," 25 May 1975.

8. In July 1962, the last three *Threshers* (SSN 613–615) were lengthened to 292 ft (3,600 tons instead of 3,450 tons surfaced, 4,650 tons instead of 4,300 tons submerged). They were not rearranged internally, nor did they get larger sails. By August 1963, the submarine was becoming marginal in volume and weight.

9. This account is based on International Maritime Associates Inc., *A Study of Ship Acquisition Cost Estimating in the Naval Sea Systems Command,* unclassified report, October 1977 (AD-A 046978). SSN 678 is one of the ships whose cost and development history are described.

10. The main new electronic systems were BRD-7 and, probably, WLR-6. The periscope program developed new electro-optical technology that probably was fed back into the submarine fleet. The new periscopes were Types 16, 17, and 18; the program included a new electro-optical sensor, BXQ-4 (the earlier Pereviz was BXQ-3). The first experimental U.S. electro-optical periscope sensor, a television installed by Kollmorgen in the upper part of a Type 8, proved unreliable. Work on Pereviz began in 1964; Lear Sigler's television could be attached to the Type 8 or 15 eyepiece. Eventually, 26 improved BXQ-3s were made. Type 16 was a special mission periscope with improved optics and a universal mounting collar on top. Type 17 was an abortive attack periscope (to replace Type 2) carrying an electro-optical sensor for better night capability. Type 18 was envisaged as a reconnaissance periscope optimized for photography (with a 70-mm objective lens) and low-light–level viewing; it used a

combined television and image intensifier as a secondary optical system. This designation was later taken over for the new standard search periscope introduced in the *Los Angeles* class.

On 17 December 1969, OpNav approved a next-generation electro-optical system (not formally a periscope), preferably for use on a nonpenetrating mast. It had a hemispherical high–scan-rate (15 RPM) head, using seven cameras (six each covering a 60-degree sector, plus one for the zenith). This system was never tested at sea, although work was done on a new mast configuration for reduced wake and water disturbance. Around 1972–73, interest shifted to infrared sensors; FLIRs (forward-looking infrared [sensors]) were coming into service on board aircraft. The electro-optical mast was canceled in favor of a new IR program, Dark Eyes, which began in November 1973. The optics was gyro-stabilized, with two fields of view (8 and 32 degrees). Dark Eyes first went to sea on board the submarine *Sand Lance* in December 1978. Installed on the nuclear submarine *Hammerhead* in 1982, Dark Eyes passed its operational evaluation, but the program was killed in 1983 as too expensive. Meanwhile, the naval intelligence community developed its own IR surveillance periscopes. About 1972, Texas Instruments adapted a B-52 FLIR to a submarine periscope (Sundance); it was the first test of an IR sensor at low level over the sea. Six were made. Cluster Nessie, a projected replacement, was begun in 1984 and tested in February and March 1988. Periscope-type numbers were used alongside a more complex designator that consisted of a sequence number, a series of letters indicating manufacturer (typically K for Kollmorgen) and function (A for altiscope, F for fixed eyepiece, H for high-power altiperiscope, N for night, P for photographic), and a number indicating length in feet. Periscope Types 1 through 4 were used in World War II. The Type 2 attack periscope survived; it was redesigned in 1959 as Type 2D (123KA43.3/HA and 123KA43T/HA with treated optics) with new optics. Its edge illumination, important for photography, was four times as good as that of the World War II Type 2A. Later versions are Types 2E (124KA36/HA) and 2F (129KA40T/HA). The photoreconnaissance Type 5 was 96KAP40/HA; Type 7 was 97KN36.

Type 6 (105KAF40/HA; 6B was 105KAF/HA; 6A was 108KAF/HA; 6C was 115KAF/HA; 6D was 120KAF/HA) was a fixed-eyepiece, any-height periscope in which optical length was constant while the barrel moved up and down (so that a submarine could come closer to the surface without putting the tube too far above it). It was based on German concepts dating back to World War I. The optical path included a mirror at the bottom of the periscope, and, as in early U.S. submarines, the eyepiece was fixed while the barrel rotated. Type 8 (1951: 98KN/36) was a modernized World War II Type 4 (i.e., with an ST range-only radar), introducing a tilting-head prism with synchro signals of elevation to act as one element of a sextant. Types 9 (113KNC36) and 10 (114KNC36) realized this potential, with celestial navigation capability. Type 9 was the first periscope with elements stabilized in line-of-sight and with an altitude-setting unit. Type 10 was a Type 8 with a photoelectric sextant on top for continuous automatic star tracking. Both types were superseded by Type 8B. In 1957, three Type 8s were converted to Type 8A (118KN36) (with added communications capability). The combination of communications and navigation (Type 3 sextant) produced Type 8B (first delivered in 1959: 121KN36, 125KN36; there are also 8C, 122KN28.5, 8D, 130KN41, and 8L, 127KN46). It incorporated broadband microwave communications and ESM and completely new optics, similar to those in 2D; it also added an E&E (Electric and Electronic) adapter, a 14-in cylinder at the base of the eyepiece box.

Type 11 (116KNC36; 11A was 126KNC36) was a special star

tracker for Polaris submarines, for automatic star sights to correct the submarine's SINS. No Type 12 or 13 periscopes appear to have been built. Type 14 (128KA28/HA) was a special periscope for *Dolphin,* essentially a short Type 2 modified for deep diving (presumably Type 8C was a companion instrument). Type 15 (131KN36; 15A was 132KN36, 15B was 134KN36T, and 15D was 135KN41T) is the current general-purpose (search) periscope. Type 18 (137KN36T) adds $12 \times$ and $24 \times$ modes to the $1.5 \times$ and $6 \times$ of the past, plus a 70-mm photographic mode. It has visual, TV, and low-light channels. Type 22 is a Sperry Electronic Systems (Sperry Marine) periscope that temporarily replaces a Type 2 to test specific electro-optical systems. Kollmorgen also built two short periscopes, 111KA10 and 112KN3/HA, probably for X-1. They did not receive type numbers and came between Types 8 and 9, i.e., about 1951. (Data mainly from the Kollmorgen Corp. Electro-Optical Division pamphlet *The Submarine Periscope 1916–1991,* and from a Kollmorgen Corp. design designation list dated 14 October 1965, kindly provided to the author by Paul J. Lepinski, the company's field service manager. No details of Types 19, 20, or 21 have appeared.)

11. SUPRAD meant, literally, supplementary radio; it was an ESM system that probably used WLR-6.

12. Rickover also disliked rafting because it required untested flexible steam lines; the reactor and steam generator were fixed to the hull, whereas the turbines were all on the movable raft. They might be less reliable than conventional rigid piping. Capt. E. P. Wilkinson (first CO of *Nautilus*) raised the flexible steam line issue at a special SCB meeting on 2 March 1959 (quoted in G. E. Weir, op. cit., p 223). Numerous submarine power plants were being rafted in advance of any sea trials by the prototype ship.

13. Characteristics issued in July 1967 described *Lipscomb* as a minimum-cost modification of the basic *Sturgeon* design to incorporate the new propulsion system; at that time, length was 365 ft. Diameter did not change because the reactor, the main factor in determining diameter, was the same S5W. Estimated displacement was 5,813/6,480 tons, about a third larger than a *Sturgeon.* The design did include space and weight for a future AIGS (towed array) installation. There was some hope that the towed array could replace the standard BQR-7 hull array.

14. *Scorpion* had a mocked-up horizontal fin mounted vertically just forward of her sail, which greatly enlarged its area. It increased snap roll enormously so that, in a tight turn, she could dive quite suddenly.

15. This perception was not limited to the U.S. Navy. In 1990, a Soviet naval officer publicly complained that Soviet double-hull submarines were inherently very noisy for exactly this reason.

16. Such high-level games should be distinguished from the tactical trials OSD encouraged as a way of obtaining the data needed for the mathematical models. On this level, tactics certainly counted because the real commanders taking part would do their best, for example, to penetrate ASW screens. OASD(SA) was responsible for the continuing SHAREM and Vassel series of trials.

17. In many cases (e.g., amphibious fire support), the two levels of analysis merged. In the case of submarines, the trade-off of submarine versus nonsubmarine solutions to the open ocean ASW problem was at the DPM level; CF/CD compared different types of submarines.

18. The requirement for about 100 attack submarines was first formally stated in NSC-68, the pre–Korean War mobilization document. The previous force level target of 90 had been justified on the ground that any force that was much smaller would not provide enough command billets to keep tactical innovation alive

in the submarine force (even so, the force fell to 69 fleet submarines in 1951). Like the usual figure for aircraft carrier strength, the submarine force level is an affordability number and is not based on the much larger number of submarines often required to best execute a particular war plan. In 1960, for example, Admiral Burke published a statement of long-range objectives for 1970–75 that listed the forces the navy would have liked had it not been fiscally constrained. For the Cold War, it wanted 178 submarines (40 of them SSNs); for some other cases, the requisite number of SSNs rose to 82. SSNs were to be used in forward antitransit operations and against Soviet surface ships. The 1975 force-level study showed requirements ranging from 88 to 173, depending on circumstances. About 1984, the deputy chief of naval operations (Op-02) stated that the Atlantic Fleet war plan required about 150 SSNs.

19. The 45-boat figure, to the author's knowledge, was never stated explicitly. The navy's statement strongly implies, however, that the 8 SSN annual program would modernize the attack submarine force by FY 66. In 1961, there were 48 Guppies (2 had been lost): 10 Guppy IAs, 23 Guppy IIs (including the original pair of Guppy Is), and 15 Guppy IIAs. Presumably, the intention was to retire all Guppy IIAs to secondary roles in order to simplify logistics.

20. The 105-submarine force level survived in internal OSD documents, but it was never publicly stated. It is not clear why McNamara used a 100-submarine figure in his unclassified defense statement.

21. The April 1965 version of the medium-range objective (MRO-76) called for a wartime force of 101 forward ASW attack submarines—46 for the Barents Sea, 53 for the Northwest Pacific, and 2 for the Arctic (to counter possible SSBN operations). Another 10 would directly support the Atlantic Fleet and 12 the Pacific Fleet at any one time; this would require totals of 17 and 27, respectively. Contingency support would require another 6 on station (8 in all). Another 8 would be needed for surveillance, with a total of 28 to support this number because a surveillance submarine has to leave her post to bring information home. The MRO added 10 for ASW training and 5 for R&D support (totals of 18 and 6 SSN, respectively). These figures could not be met; the MRO called for a total of 98 SSNs plus 7 post–1947 SSs, 6 AGSSs (4 post–1947 boats plus 2 new ones), and 16 less capable AGSSs (13 WW II submarines plus 3 modern ones).

Chapter 10

1. The 5-kt speed advantage appears again and again in Tyler, *Running Critical.*

2. Direct support was emphasized in the staff requirement for HMS *Dreadnought.* For the first time, the British had a submarine that could keep up with a surface formation. The Type 2001 DIMUS bow sonar array could simultaneously track an enemy submarine and friendly surface ships; it could also filter out the noise of surface ships. In addition, the British developed an underwater data link to transmit submarine sonar data to the surface ships, which were expected to prosecute the contact. U.S. experiments are mentioned in a contemporary official letter describing nuclear power developments. Remarkably, only the *Dreadnought* experiments were cited about 1965 as the inspiration for a U.S. direct-support role, despite these experiments and Task Group ALFA work just a few years earlier.

3. The evidence is ambiguous. The Naval Reactors Division file on *Los Angeles* is marked "Fast Escort Submarine" (F. Duncan, *Rickover and the Nuclear Navy,* 315, n. 31), but that designation was later commonly used and may have been applied retroactively. A

retired Naval Reactors engineer recalls much more concern over the loss of speed in the *Sturgeon* class. Rickover and many others had assumed that the Soviet November (Project 627) class was a relatively slow submarine, like *Nautilus,* with a speed of no more than 20–22 kt. That might have made it a threat to conventional, but not to nuclear, carriers. Thus, the successful interception of the nuclear carrier *Enterprise* by a Soviet November-class nuclear submarine was quite shocking.

4. Many have suggested that, by the 1960s, Rickover was most interested in developing a spectrum of proven reactors; he therefore had to put several prototypes to sea. Hence, his insistence on the D1G submarine. Against that, the D1G itself was already on its way to sea on board surface ships, and the submarine version cannot have been very different. The prototype designation was critical to the survival of the fast submarine program because it evaded McNamara's CF/CD requirement and thus bypassed CONFORM.

5. This transfer seems to have been intended to develop an alternative to Electric Boat; the previous alternative, Portsmouth Navy Yard, was being eliminated by Secretary McNamara's decision to close the naval shipyards as design and construction yards. Newport News was the obvious choice because of its experience in building nuclear surface ships. At this time, too, the navy was having disputes with Electric Boat over delays in the new attack submarine construction program. The demand for parallel competing suppliers was so ingrained in classic BuEng thinking (as in the case of the prewar submarine diesels) that this decision would have been second nature for Admiral Rickover.

6. About half the extra length was due to two extra turbogenerators, specifically to feed the active sonar. There was some fear that a sudden drain on the ship's service power (for each ping) would affect the reactor. Because that was not the case, the new sonar cost far less than had been imagined, and it could be backfitted in *Permit*- and *Sturgeon*-class submarines.

7. The big buoy would be supplemented by a floating wire (LF and VLF) and an emergency expendable buoy, neither of which was usable above very low speed. Ironically, the submarine, as built, lacked both the buoy and the towed wire (abandoned as too draggy).

8. Contemporary surface ship installations planned for U.S. frigates and missile cruisers fired aft, through the transom, specifically to avoid this problem.

9. Figures are from the memory of a CONFORM participant; only the diameter, set by the size of the reactor, is certain. CONFORM would have been shorter than *Narwhal,* thanks to her far more compact geared turbine. A contemporary official document lists CONFORM displacement as 5,880 tons, but that may refer to a later, larger version. Note that *Narwhal* had a considerably larger diameter than the remembered CONFORM hull.

10. The first Soviet November-class submarine appeared as early as 1958, but it was subject to serious teething problems. At first, there was apparently some disagreement within the intelligence community as to whether these new craft were nuclear powered, but the NATO-assigned reporting name, the phonetic code for "N," suggests otherwise. Evidence of nuclear propulsion included the streamlined shape of their sails, which lacked the prominent exhausts of contemporary Soviet diesel craft. The observed maximum speed of the Soviet nuclear attack submarine (November class) increased by 2 kt between 1966 and 1967 to match *Sturgeon* performance. The speed trends of U.S. and Soviet submarines had crossed; there seemed to be no possibility of increasing the speed of a U.S. submarine powered by the S5W reactor. The recent Soviet account (in *Morskoi Sbornik*

1993 No. 8, pp 59–62) of the liquid-metal reactor version of November (Project 645) suggests that design speed was 30.2 kts, on 35,000 SHP.

11. Victor really was fast; Charlie turned out to be a lot slower, about 24 kt. Neither proved to be as quiet as was then imagined. It is sometimes suggested that *Los Angeles* was inspired by reports of the Alfa class. Well into the mid-1970s, however, it was credited with no more speed than a Victor, even though the prototype may have been completed as early as 1967.

12. The trip was made in early June 1968; the submarines were *Dace* (SSN 607; Comdr. Kinnaird R. McKee, who later succeeded Rickover) and *Shark* (SSN 591). *Sturgeons* were slower than *Threshers,* so they would have been at a greater disadvantage. After this trip, Foster decided officially to advance the fast submarine into FY 69 and to build her as a large class. See Duncan, *Rickover and the Nuclear Navy,* 39–40.

13. The FY 70–74 five-year defense plan (late 1969) showed three submarines in FY 70, then four each from FY 71 through FY 74. In his memoirs (see *On Watch* 105–106), Admiral Zumwalt (then the CNO) recalls a planned program of three per year. In November 1970, he offered Admiral Rickover a revised plan in which the class would be bought out early (at the rate of five per year for three years, then two per year thereafter) to free funds for new low-mix ships, such as the sea control ship (SCS). Zumwalt also hoped that increased *Los Angeles* production would preclude construction of the much larger SSGN (advanced performance high-speed nuclear attack submarine [APHNAS]) that Rickover favored. If the four submarines for FY 71 represented a compromise between Zumwalt and OSD, the purchase of six in FY 73 would have bought back the submarine lost in FY 71.

14. An attempt to prune back size even further (to 314 or perhaps 308 ft and about 5,200 tons) failed, partly because so short a hull could not accommodate sufficient gearing for a slow-turning (hence, quiet) propeller. Nor did a short hull allow sufficient space forward of the machinery, but abaft the sail, for a DSRV to mate. No position forward of the sail was acceptable.

15. Because stocks of old anti-ship torpedoes were running out, the Mk 48 program was restructured in 1967 to provide the torpedo with true anti-ship capability. The all-digital decision also precluded the new submarine from carrying mines; all of them dated from the 1950s and, hence, were analog weapons.

16. Pereviz was later applied to existing Type 8 and Type 15 periscopes. It was a major departure in submarine operation because, in the past, only the CO could actually see what was happening; no one else could second-guess his decisions.

17. The tubes would fire beneath the bow sphere, rather than to either side (as in U.S. submarines). Torpedoes would have been loaded from above. This configuration was adopted by the Royal Navy.

18. The encapsulated Harpoon, which could be fired from existing torpedo tubes, was chosen in 1971 as the interim standoff weapon. NUSC had already done capsule launch studies. McDonnell-Douglas, the manufacturer, became interested when it was told informally that the market for such weapons might be quite large, perhaps a thousand. At this time, too, PMS 393 (the future submarine development office) was aware of air force interest in the SCAD (subsonic cruise armed decoy), which eventually led to the modern cruise missiles. PMS 393 found that such a weapon could be packaged in a 21-in torpedo tube. Again, the idea was rejected at the time, but it resurfaced (see chapter 11).

19. On 4 August 1970, Admiral Rickover wrote Representative Mendel Rivers, chairman of the Joint Committee on Atomic Energy, to urge development of the new, fast cruise missile subma-

rine; on 10 March 1971, the committee formally recommended development. Rickover's letter preceded CNO action.

20. In theory, the noise strobe generated by a fast torpedo points back to the firing submarine. The target can "snap shoot" a torpedo back along the strobe. At the very least, the attacker will have to evade and thus probably break any guidance wire. On the other hand, wire guidance also allows a torpedo to be doglegged toward the target, in which case the strobe will point away from the launching submarine. After the collapse of the Soviet Union, former Soviet naval officers said that their standard countermeasure to an approaching torpedo was to snap-fire a pair of straight-running nuclear torpedoes in the direction of the noise strobe. They even designated these weapons as large evasion torpedoes (BGTs). The Soviets also had smaller-diameter decoys more comparable to Western ones.

21. The notional diesel submarine, a modified *Barbel*, would have been slightly noisier than a *Sturgeon*. Characteristics: 3,985 tons submerged; length, 271 ft; test depth, 700 ft; 10 officers and 75 crew; maximum (1-hr) speed, 17.2 kt; snorkel endurance, 10,000 nm at 7 kt; armament, 4 torpedo tubes and 19 weapons (probably 19 reloads). Sonar: BQR-7, BQR-21 (probably with BQS-4), BQS-15 (mine evasion), and a towed array. In 1974, estimated R&D cost (assuming a start in FY 80) was $40–$55 million, and unit cost was $95 million ($178 million for the lead ship). Life-cycle cost would have been 69 percent of that for Type A; acquisition cost, 67 percent of that for Type A. Diesels were nominally more cost-effective in a barrier against surface ships, but the result was rejected as artificial.

22. The central problem in evaluating the importance of speed was how to weight different submarine roles. In each role, high speed had a different value. The 1975 study broke up submarine utilization into:

Barrier ASW	46.4%
Carrier protection/area clearance	29.9%
Distant ASW	8.7%
Distant anti-surface warfare (ASUW)/coast interdict	5.8%
Barrier ASUW	5.2%
Vector intercept	4.0%

These figures entirely neglect such important areas as intelligence gathering and special warfare support.

23. Vice Adm. Daniel Cooper, statement at hearing of Subcommittee on Seapower and Strategic and Critical Materials of the House Armed Services Committee, 1989, 283. The class started with a margin of 250 tons. SSN 700 added a Mk 117 and the BQQ-5B sonar, which reduced the margin to 200 tons. SSN 716 added BQQ-5C (margin, 165 tons). SSN 719 had the vertical launching system and special hull treatment (anechoic coating); the margin fell to 75 tons. SSN 751, the first "improved 688" or 688I, had BSY-1 and was capable of operating under ice; her margin was only 30 tons. The margin vanished altogether when ships were fitted with the improved propulsion plant (e.g., SSN 771, FY 89). (Later in the same hearing, Cooper asserted that the two FY 90 ships, with the improved performance machinery plant, exhausted the margin.)

24. As of mid-1980, vertical launchers for Tomahawk were already planned for the *Ticonderoga* (FY 82) and *Spruance* classes (FY 85). An underway test with a former SSBN was proposed (3 mo to install and 3 mo to test) but not carried out. The first formal requirements document was issued in November 1980, the capsule launcher contract came in January 1981, and the first ship contract was modified in December 1981.

Chapter 11

1. B. D. Bruins, "U.S. Naval Bombardment Missiles" (Ph.D. diss., Columbia University, 1981), 157. The bombs dropped on Japan in 1945 weighed about 10,000 lb. Only after the production a Mk 4 bomb had been test fired in April and May 1948 could the AEC begin work on a smaller (3,000-lb) Mk 5. The AEC did not formally discuss missile warheads until April 1949; the navy formally requested a missile warhead for Regulus in June 1949. In September, shortly after the explosion of the first Soviet A-bomb, an ad hoc committee of the AEC Military Liaison Committee formally recommended that four missiles be developed with nuclear warheads, one being Regulus (which got a warhead version of the 100-kT Mk 5 bomb). In 1958, this W-5 was superseded by the W-27 thermonuclear warhead. BuOrd knew lighter bombs were coming because it was responsible for a series of gun-type uranium weapons, beginning with a Mk 8. A ballistic missile armed with the smaller bomb would be small enough to fire directly from a submarine, rather than from the much larger barge towed by the submarine; hence, the barge project could be canceled.

2. The Germans proposed the barge in 1944, as Allied advances in Europe endangered the launch sites. It would have been derived from a 19 × 120-ft container (on a towline up to 80 ft long) that was used for carrying food, fuel, and ammunition to German bases in Norway. These barges had 2 percent buoyancy and were submerged under tow by the pull of the towline acting on eccentric stabilizer surfaces. As soon as the U-boat stopped, the barge floated to the surface. U-boat personnel would then have boarded it, pumped and ballasted it to an upright position, and fueled the missile. A small motor-driven propeller, controlled by the submarine gyro compass through a connecting cable, would turn the barge into the appropriate bearing for launch. No tests, either scale- or full-size, were conducted. As in the case of the Type XXVI U-boat, the U.S. Navy assumed that anything this elaborate had been thoroughly thought through. Failures of scale-model tests killed the project: in 1948 a planned FY 50 budget request for $1 million for work on the barge was replaced by $90,000 for a ballistic missile submarine. The Soviets built as many as 300 missile barges in numerous series, none of which ever worked; they had only about 20 intact units at any one time. Deciding to launch the same missiles from atop a submarine's sail (to avoid the exhaust gas problem), the Soviets fired their first missile in September 1955. Before April 1944, the Germans had experimented with small rockets that a submarine could fire at ASW craft at 100–200 ft. Fired at an elevation of up to 55 degrees, the rockets flew at about 100 ft/sec and reached about 300 yd.

3. The SSV study for the FY 48 program was assigned on 6 November 1946; the study is dated 21 November. The SSV was expected to have a collapse depth of 500 ft and to make 15 kt surfaced or submerged. She could accommodate either two 60,000-lb bombers (ADR-45A, later North American A2J) carrying a single 8,000-lb atomic bomb or four Banshee (F2H) jet fighters. Each ADR-45A was 94 × 73 ft (44-ft folded span), with a height of 25 ft, so the hangar had to be 50 ft in diameter. Two ADR-45As would require a 160-ft hangar, and each would need a 150-ft catapult and a total take-off run of 400 ft. The first approach was to place the hangar between a 400-ft runway and a 140-ft landing deck, for a total length of 700 ft. Atomic power would have been required. The hangar would have been too close to the stern, thus making the ship trim by the stern. Placing the hangar amidships (with 420 ft on either side), however, made for an absurdly long submarine. The solution was to break the

hangar into two 75-ft sections separated by a well, in which an elevator would run. That would cut overall length to 600 ft (with a 50-ft pressure hull); the flight deck would be 400 × 68 ft (displacement 25,000/34,000 tons; 35 percent reserve buoyancy would have kept the flight deck dry). The depth from hangar floor to flight deck would be 58 ft. The entire submarine would be built of 1⅛-in HTS steel (42,000-lb yield strength). A 40,000-SHP atomic or closed-cycle plant would drive the SSV at 18 kt surfaced and 15 kt submerged. This monster could not be built in existing U.S. yards. The designers observed that it would be more cost-effective to double aircraft capacity with a 300-ft hangar; the resulting 750-ft ship would displace 34,000 tons surfaced. Any SSV would suffer from serious underwater control problems, partly because the big flat flight deck would act as a diving plane. It might have been slotted to limit this effect.

4. For some 1948 studies, the missiles and boosters were expected to weigh 76,000 lb and to occupy a tank 21 ft in diameter and 124 ft long. The first sketch design (May 1948) was based on a *Gato*-class submarine stretched to 395 ft, with an 18-ft pressure hull diameter (displacement 3,050/4,700 tons). That size was insufficient, so a second design was developed. It included a 20-ft pressure hull (beam 37 ft) and a submerged displacement of 7,100 tons (21 ft gave 7,600 tons). The hangar itself had a displacement of 1,158 tons.

5. Initially only *Cusk* was fitted to launch missiles; *Carbonero* had only the radio control device. Later, she was fitted with a lightweight launcher.

6. The 3 × 8-ft SV-4 antenna could not be raised very high, and the guidance transmitter antennas on the periscope shears could not be used at periscope depth. In 1949, an antenna replaced *Cusk*'s No. 2 periscope, and she was fitted with a lighter SV-1 antenna topped by a vertically polarized control antenna. To automate control, the new tracking radar fed an Arma automatic plot and a Sperry Gyro azimuth-control signal computer. The plot automatically lined up on the true course to the target, so deviation showed clearly. In May 1950, submariners in the missile program suggested that Loon be armed with a lightweight nuclear warhead as an emergency weapon. OpNav was unenthusiastic, possibly because in some circumstances it might have to be launched as close as 8 nm from the target. After war broke out in Korea, a 25-missile war reserve requirement was established. The last Loon was test fired in 1953.

7. The FY 50 budget was particularly tight. The Joint Chiefs of Staff (JCS) demanded that short-term projects take priority over long-term projects. In effect, this resulted in favoring cruise missiles over ballistic missiles. Regulus was nearly killed in favor of the air force's comparable Matador, whose airframe was about a year ahead in development. BuAer argued successfully that guidance, rather than airframe, was the crucial technology. Regulus needed two guidance stations; Matador needed three. It later turned out that Matador was quite jammable, even by civilian communications in West Germany. As an outgrowth of BuOrd's Bumblebee antiaircraft project (which produced Talos, Tartar, and Terrier, the ancestors of the current SM-2), Triton was not part of the BuAer program.

8. *Trounce* encountered development problems; in December 1955, an alternative, Shoran (a short-range version of Loran), was dropped to provide extra money to solve them. Like Loran, Shoran used a master and two slave stations (in this case, on submarines near the target) to set up a grid of hyperbolas that the navigator in the missile could use to find its position. It would pitch over when it reached the appropriate coordinates. Regulus II had inertial guidance plus some form of terminal guidance,

ultimately the terrain-comparison technique (using a side-looking radar) developed by BuOrd for Triton.

9. This design is shown in T. C. Treadwell, *Submarines with Wings* (London: Conway Maritime Press, 1985), 50, 53–55. Treadwell dates the design from late 1955.

10. Dimensions were 356 × 29 ft (2,800 tons light, 4,200 tons submerged). Performance: 8,000 SHP: 20 kt surfaced; 5,000 SHP (378 Sargo II cells) submerged: 14 kt (13 kt snorkeling). Test depth would have been the usual 700 ft of this period. Estimated cost was $36.5 million.

11. Although an S3W-powered missile submarine had already been proposed (in 1954), Mare Island seems to have been responsible for the decision that *Halibut* be nuclear. Apparently, the design history turned over to the yard when it was assigned the *Halibut* project included an account of the 1954 SSGN studies (using SAR reactors); diesel power had been selected in hopes of speeding construction. G. E. Weir (p 239) quotes a 27 January 1956 letter from the yard's commandant, Rear Adm. M. J. Lawrence, to BuShips. His yard was already building *Sargo*, a *Skate*-class SSN. Studies made at the yard (on its own initiative) showed that the planned *Halibut* bow section could be combined with the *Sargo* reactor and stern, providing not only the benefits of nuclear power but also saving as much as two months because no new power plant design would be required (the 8,100 SHP diesel *Halibut* would have been a new design, not an adaptation of an existing type). Admiral Burke formally approved the change on 4 April 1956, well *after* the reorder date. A 16 March 1954 BuShips memorandum (by Capt. J. M. Farrin of Code 410) gives the background of the earlier proposal; it describes a 15 March meeting of the Long-Range Shipbuilding Committee. Rear Admiral Rickover "reviewed the present status of the SAR power plant and indicated the desirability of an early decision on the submarine in which it will be installed." Farrin described BuShips studies of SAR-powered SSGN and SSRN and an SFR (S3W/ S4W) powered eight-missile SSGN. A 2-SAR 28 kt submarine would displace about 6,900 tons, a 1-SAR 23.5 kt submarine about 5,000 tons. Farrin thought the committee wanted to hold down cost by holding displacement (submerged) to about 5,000 tons; the FY 56 program might comprise a 23 kt SAR-powered SSRN and a slower SFR-powered SSGN. Other documents of this period show that the fleet badly wanted an SSR capable of at least 25 kts. SSG speed was not nearly as critical. Early estimates of power plant length and weight suggested that the SSR could be 400 ft long, displacing 4,650 tons light (*not* submerged). Thus, the choice fell on the 2-SAR *Triton* and a diesel SSG. Then drastic changes in the design of the SAR (and seaworthiness tests with models) slowed the *Triton* preliminary design by about four months. Early in June 1955, estimated reactor plant weight increased by about 20 percent, length by about 18 percent, and other machinery weight by about 50 tons, pushing the SSRN to 430 ft (5,200 tons). Ultimately, *Triton* grew another 17 ft 6 in longer, but she did not gain more light displacement, so the crisis in SAR design was probably limited to 1954–1955. These increases presumably precluded further interest in SAR-powered SSGs. Mare Island continued its involvement in the SSGN program. Sometime in 1957 it developed the S-122 design for a Regulus II submarine based on the SSBN (SCB 180), using a new single hangar, presumably in place of the vertical-tube section.

12. Even after Polaris appeared, CinCLant continued to want SSGNs; in September 1958, he recommended that one be built in each of FY 61–63 (for a total of three during FY 61–66).

13. The Soviets lost a modified Whiskey-class submarine to exactly this type of accident.

14. Dimensions of the SCB 166 design of October 1956–May 1957 were 360×31.5 ft (4,500 tons surfaced, 6,000 tons submerged); speed would be 16/19 kt. SCB 166A dimensions were 370×36.25 ft (4,470 tons light, 4,800 tons surfaced, 6,770 tons submerged); speed would be 17.5/16.0 kt. Complement would be 10 officers and 88 enlisted.

15. The earliest surviving study of a V-2 conversion of a fleet submarine is dated December 1948. Plans called for four vertical launch cylinders, each 14 ft in diameter and 70.5 ft long, paired in a blistered section of the submarine hull (by January 1949, the beam in this section was 43 ft, with the cylinders 5 ft apart). Between early 1949 and 9 June 1950, BuAer completed 56 test runs, firing 1,000-lb thrust JATO (jet [actually rocket]–assisted take-off) boosters in tubes to check how well rocket exhaust could be vented through a U-tube. Each missile cylinder would have had two uptakes. A V-2 SSG study plan was issued on 24 October 1951, but details are not available. The V-2 was credited with the ability to throw a 1-ton warhead 180 mi in 5 min, by using a vertical gyro for roll and yaw control and a horizontal gyro for pitch in flight. Dimensions were (5 ft 5 in × 46 ft 1 in (11 ft 8 in across the fins). The rocket, including its warhead, weighed 4 tons unloaded and 12.46 tons with its fuel (10,930 lb of liquid oxygen, 8,150 lb of alcohol, and 370 lb of hydrogen peroxide to drive pumps).

16. The air force initially resisted the shift to ballistic missiles. Its Convair Atlas received far less funding than the contemporary North American Aviation Navaho and Northrop Snark cruise missiles (the army was far more interested in ballistic missile technology). In 1953, however, the Eisenhower administration brought with it Trevor Gardner, who became special assistant for R&D to Secretary of the Air Force Harold E. Talbott. Convair convinced Gardner that the intercontinental ballistic missile (ICBM) was both feasible and desirable. At the same time, the army and air force were arguing fiercely over responsibility for long-range surface-to-surface missiles; in January 1953, the army asked for permission to buy some Regulus missiles to gain operational experience, but the air force resisted the request. In hopes of reducing duplication, Secretary of Defense Charles Wilson asked Talbott to organize a study of the national missile program; it was delegated to Gardner. Rather than use the existing air force's Scientific Advisory Board, which would have favored cruise missiles, Gardner had Dr. John E. Neumann head a special Strategic Missiles Evaluation Committee (Teapot Committee). With his connections to the AEC, Neumann was well placed to appreciate the potential of the ICBM. In February 1954, he recommended that Atlas be greatly accelerated at the cost of the cruise missiles and that its development be conducted by a special centralized group (which would become the Air Force Western Division). At just about the same time, RAND, the air force's internal think tank, reported that an ICBM would be the ideal delivery vehicle for lightweight hydrogen bombs, which did not yet exist. The Gardner report of 24 January 1954 allowed the army to keep its medium-range missile program, which became Jupiter. See D. Mackenzie, *Inventing Accuracy* (Cambridge: MIT Press, 1990), especially 98–123; and Watson, *History of Joint Chiefs of Staff,* 177–186. The abortive Navaho was important to the later navy program because its inertial navigator, designed to function during several hours of flight, was the basis for SINS. The official air force history, J. Neufeld, *Ballistic Missiles in the United States Air Force 1945–1960* (Washington, D.C.: Office of Air Force History, 1990), reports that the Air Research and Development Command (ARDC) strongly favored Atlas over the cruise missiles as early as April 1953. The powerful Air Materiel Command favored bombers over both.

17. D. A. Rosenberg, "The Origins of Overkill," *International Security* (Spring 1983), 3–71.

18. In a November 1954 directive issued in the wake of the Gardner report, the army was allowed to develop missiles to attack tactical targets within the zone of combat operations; the air force was assigned intercontinental attack. The army thought in terms of a 500-nm range development of its 150-nm Redstone. The air force was already developing a 500-nm air-breathing missile, Matador. No one seriously considered an IRBM. In June 1954, however, the secretary of defense agreed with British Minister of Supply Duncan Sandys to extend cooperation to missiles. The British were to develop an IRBM (1,500-nm missile, Blue Streak) to complement the longer- and shorter-range U.S. weapons. The air force was assigned liaison with the British. In January 1955, its Scientific Advisory Board suggested developing a ballistic replacement for Matador, which it called the tactical ballistic missile (TBM). Both the TBM and the long-range Redstone soon grew into IRBMs, Thor and Jupiter. Blue Streak could not be readied nearly as quickly, and the British finally bought Thors (they first requested TBM information in February 1955). See Watson, *History of Joint Chiefs of Staff,* 185–186; and Neufeld, *Ballistic Missiles,* 143.

19. Jupiter began as a 95-in missile about 90 ft long. The navy wanted a short fat missile (120 in × 50 ft); Secretary Wilson ordered a compromise (105 in × 58 ft). Quite aside from the inherent danger of liquid-fuel rockets, the SPO disliked them because they accelerated slowly after firing and might fall over if the launching ship rolled too violently. On the other hand, as of Spring 1956, no one had demonstrated solid-fuel thrust termination (for velocity control) or thrust vectoring. The solid-fuel Jupiter-S, which used multiple motors (in an inefficient staging ratio, 6:1), was 120 in × 41 ft 3 in and weighed 162,000 lb. This weapon was expected to throw 3,000 lb to a distance of 1500 nm. The 1,200-nm Polaris A1 missile was 54 in × 28 ft and weighed 28,000 lb. Data from R. A. Fuhrman, "Fleet Ballistic Missile System: Polaris to Trident," paper delivered at the 14th Annual Meeting of the American Institute of Aeronautics and Astronautics, February 1978.

20. Nobska suggested 2000-ton submarines, each carrying two or three missiles (by 1965, 800 tons might suffice). A 25,000–30,000-lb missile using existing liquid-fuel technology would probably throw a 300–350-kT warhead 800–1,200 nm; by 1965, a 20,000–25,000-lb missile would probably throw a 350–650-kT (perhaps even 1-MT) warhead 1,000–1,500 nm (optimistically, 1,200–1,600 nm). The 1965 missile would be a two-stage solid-fuel or a one-stage liquid-fuel missile.

21. Rosenberg, "Origins of Overkill." The JCS found the demands of the Strategic Air Command (SAC) for more weapons excessive. President Eisenhower did approve increased production for FY 56–59 (on 29 February 1956) but only in the expectation that the stockpile would not be expanded much thereafter. To buttress his position on the future limit, Eisenhower asked the JCS to review the targeting plans to reduce the use of H-bombs, which were "inappropriate against industrial targets of too little industrial importance, and to avoid overlapping of large numbers of high-yield weapons on specific targets." The resulting Burke-Taylor study (Project Budapest) was presented to the JCS on 28 August 1957. It concluded that SAC had consistently underestimated weapons effects, hence, as Eisenhower suspected, it had grossly inflated weapons requirements.

22. Rosenberg, "Origins of Overkill," sees the Gaither report as a symptom of changing U.S. perceptions, rather than as a moving force. He reports that President Eisenhower was skeptical of claims of Soviet advances in ballistic missile technology.

He suggested (correctly, as it turned out) that for the next five years aircraft would remain the primary means of strategic attack, during which period the United States would still enjoy strategic superiority.

23. There were numerous proposals to deploy Polaris on board surface ships, such as U.S. and, later, NATO cruisers. For example, launching tubes were actually installed on board the Italian *Giusseppe Garibaldi*; the U.S. cruiser *Long Beach* had foundations for Polaris tubes amidships, but the concept died before the tubes could be installed. In 1958–59, SPO considered conversion of a fleet submarine with two Polaris tubes abaft the sail.

24. See G. Herken, "The Flying Crowbar," *Air and Space,* April/May 1990, 28–34, for an account of SLAM development. The 500 MW nuclear reactor was called Pluto (the name later referred to the missile as well). SLAM would have carried several H-bombs to drop along its route, and it also would have caused damage with its radioactive exhaust. SLAM was originally an air force project; on 1 January 1957, Lawrence Livermore National Laboratory was chosen to develop it. The nuclear ramjet was first fired on 14 May 1961; the project was canceled on 1 July 1964. The estimated unit cost of the Mach 3 missile was $50 million. Herken gives no missile dimensions. The TERCOM terrain-matching guidance system used by the current Tomahawk was developed by LTV (and patented in 1958) specifically for SLAM. Also see K. P. Werrell, *The Evolution of the Cruise Missile* (Maxwell Air Force Base, Alabama: Air University Press, 1985), 136.

25. In 1957, the projected 1965 force was 6 submarines (2 or 3 always on station), each carrying 3 to 10 missiles. By 1959, the criterion had changed from the number of submarines that could fit within a larger naval force to the number of targets that the deterrent force had to keep constantly within range: 200 (i.e., 400 missiles, or 25 submarine loads). Admiral Burke wanted to maintain 30 submarines on station (total force, 45 to 50).

26. The Long Range Objectives Group suggested that 12 SSBN loads be maintained aboard six survivable ammunition ships (AEB) "so located that their chance of surviving surprise attack will approximate that of the SSBN, and so maintained that they can be promptly loaded, ready for firing, on SSBNs exhausting initial loads." This was a throwback to earlier war-fighting concepts. Much later, the Soviets were sometimes credited with similar ideas, particularly for use with their big Typhoon submarines.

27. Eisenhower seems to have been the last Cold War president to question the need for really large numbers of strategic weapons. The sheer size of the U.S. force took on symbolic, rather than operational, significance. Presidents who sought to control the number of nuclear weapons had to contend with the fact that the Soviets had more missiles, even though there was always a real question of whether the numbers were terribly significant. The air force tried to gain control of Polaris by forming a unified strategic command on the ground that it would eliminate duplication of effort. Eisenhower ordered a compromise, in which both navy and air force strategic weapons would fall under a joint single integrated operational plan (SIOP) developed by the Joint Strategic Target Planning System (JSTPS) at SAC headquarters in Omaha. In 1992, the unified Strategic Air Command was finally formed, but now the naval component is so large that it sometimes will be commanded by an admiral. (Originally, SAC had imagined that its commander would command the entire strategic force.)

Early in the career of JSTPS (around 1961) Gen. Thomas Powers, then SAC commander, ordered a war game to disprove the claimed survivability of Polaris. (See J. Miller et al., "The Battle

for Polaris Survival," *Submarine Review,* April 1986, 5.) Despite extraordinary assumptions—the Soviets were credited with sonar and submarine performance equivalent to that of the U.S. Navy, with 9 surface action groups, 40 diesel submarines, 9 nuclear submarines, 1,000 trawlers, and 50 Badgers (10 of them armed with nuclear depth bombs and all capable of attacking as soon as a missile cleared the surface) to oppose 3 U.S. SSBNs—the SSBNs survived long enough to launch 36 of their 48 missiles. Disappointed, General Powers decided that the result was inconclusive. It was too laborious to play multiple games and thus test alternative circumstances; this game took 6 wk.

28. The two-crew idea was inspired by the Royal Navy practice of alternating crews for warships on the China Station.

29. The Leningrad system may have been abandoned precisely because Polaris range increased so quickly.

30. A hard-target killer could reduce damage to the United States by destroying Soviet weapons that were not fired in the first salvo. It was also possible that the United States could have early warning of a planned Soviet attack. Much later, there would be great interest in credibly threatening attacks on the hard command centers in which Soviet leaders planned to shelter in wartime, on the theory that no other threat would be really meaningful to them.

31. The SBM did survive in a series of studies of ballistic missiles, with roughly 1,500-nm range, launched from torpedo tubes. The earliest formal study of such a weapon seems to have been conducted by China Lake in 1964; about 1967, some of the major missile companies carried out feasibility studies. SBM was strongly advocated by Project Seabed, a 1964 summer study review of the navy's Advanced Sea-Based Deterrence program begun in July 1960 to develop follow-ons to Polaris for the 1970s and beyond. Seabed wanted an SBM program defined about 1970, with the SBM ready to enter service in 1975 on board an existing SSBN. Its version of SBM was slightly larger than a torpedo tube: about 30×336 in; three SBMs could be stuffed into one Polaris tube. The increased size would have bought considerably more yield and range. Project Seabed also supported the MIRVed Polaris that became Poseidon.

32. Quick turnaround would be achieved partly by providing a hatch so large that entire components could be removed for testing and servicing ashore.

33. Using external capsules would minimize submarine displacement for a given weapon load. The capsules (8 × 64 ft) would be stowed horizontally. The STRAT-X ULMS submarine would carry 24 missiles; dimensions would be 443×59×32 ft (8,240 tons), powered by a derated S3W for longer core life. By early 1970, the dimensions had grown to 500×55×38 ft (12,000 tons). By way of contrast, a Trident submarine, carrying 24 smaller missiles internally, is 560×42×35.5 ft (18,700 tons).

34. This was the first attempt in many years to revert to twin screws. It would turn out that a twin-screw beaver-tail stern was significantly better than a conventional twin-screw stern, although significantly worse than a single screw. The Soviet Typhoon had a beaver-tail stern.

35. SPO originally wanted an 18,000-ton submarine powered by the S5W reactor, but it would have been too slow—19–20 kt, rather than the 20–25 kt of earlier submarines. See *Adequacy of Current Organization,* 175–182, with table of design alternatives, 179 (Note 2, Preface).

36. The 14,000-tonner may have been one version of the "Super 640," a variant of the SCB 216A submarine. As proposed in January 1971, it would have carried 74-in × 37-ft missiles. Speed would have been 25 kt. The bigger submarine design offered in September 1971, and finally selected, displaced 18,700 tons; its

35,000-SHP natural circulation reactor was expected to drive it at 25 kt.

37. Other emergency options were considered. Polaris submarines could be cut amidships and new 8-missile sections added (to meet the new goal of 24), *Los Angeles*-class attack submarines could be gutted (to add 24 tubes, in analogy to the earlier *Skipjack*s), or new submarines could be built to modified Polaris plans. There was even some consideration of moving Minuteman missiles to sea aboard merchant ships. The new Trident submarines would initially replace the 10 non-Poseidon units, so such alternatives were compared on the basis of a 10-submarine program (240 missiles). That figure was never a goal but merely a way of comparing options. Admiral Rickover stated that he could build new submarines as quickly as existing ones could be modified, and the new construction option was chosen. In fact, the program was slowed by strikes and welding problems.

38. The current generation of U.S. cruise missiles apparently stems from a series of air force studies. During 1966 and 1967, the Institute for Defense Analysis (IDA), RAND, and a Defense Science Board task force each proposed a new subsonic decoy (SCUD, for subsonic cruise unarmed decoy, and an armed version, SCAM) to replace the existing short-range Quail carried by air force strategic bombers. Gen. Glenn Kent of Air Force Systems Command proposed SCAD, a SCUD with a warhead and a 20-lb ECM package. All of these missiles were limited in size to fit the standard B-52 rotary launcher. Three contractors (Beech, Boeing, and Lockheed) studied SCAM. They concluded that it should use TERCOM guidance and that any range beyond 1,500 nm would require a missile so large that it would have to be carried externally. Because one major virtue of the missile was that it would multiply the effect of any one bomber, it had to be carried internally; hence, it had to be limited in range. An air force SCAD project office was set up in October 1968. The program divided into (1) a low-cost, low-risk B-52 decoy with a warhead option and (2) a modular missile for the follow-on B-1, to be decoy, armed decoy, or attack missile. There was apparently some fear that a successful cruise weapon would undermine the rationale for the B-1. SCAD died in May 1973, but its technology was kept alive. Moreover, work on SCAD seems to have convinced OSD that a cruise missile was viable. Like Trident, it offered the sort of strategic initiative required during and after SALT.

In January 1972, the secretary of defense had asked DDR&E to begin a strategic cruise missile (SCM) with FY 72 supplemental funds. Reportedly, the navy convinced Secretary Laird that the cruise option offered a low-cost combination of tactical and strategic firepower. In mid-1972, the navy had five missile options: three for vertical launch, ranging from 19-in to 36-in diameter and from 1,850 to 8,350 lb, and two 19-in encapsulated weapons. By the end of the year, there were five proposals for vertically launched missiles. Three of the missiles would fit a Polaris tube: Convair, 31 in×28 ft, 7,775 lb; Lockheed, 32 in×26.5 ft, 8,316 lb; and LTV: 32.7 in×29.3 ft, 10,631 lb. The navy received five proposals for encapsulated vertical-launched missiles (3 to 6 per tube). They ranged from McDonnell-Douglas's 23-in, 2,890-lb missile to Convair's 35-in wedge at 9,610 lb. The navy cut the choices down in favor of a torpedo tube–launched encapsulated missile using existing technology, such as a Subroc booster and SCAD engine. Five development contracts were awarded in December 1972. The following year, Secretary of State Henry Kissinger decided that cruise missiles would be useful SALT II bargaining chips. That revived the air force program, and the air force and navy programs were merged under a single Joint Cruise Missile Program Office. The Soviets did not include cruise missiles in the SALT negotiations because they did not want to give up their own tactical anti-ship cruise missiles, hence the loophole. See Werrell, *Evolution of the Cruise Missile*, 144–169.

39. The preliminary design was completed in May 1963. Dimensions were 376×33×27.5 ft (5,650 light/6,685 surfaced/7,615 submerged tons); the power plant would consist of three 12-cylinder Fairbanks-Morse 38ND-1/8 engines for diesel-electric drive, with 504 silver-zinc battery cells (5,760 SHP surfaced, 13.5 kt; 6,000 SHP submerged for 4 hr, 16 kt). Operating on a 60-day cycle, the SSB would transit 250 nm to its European patrol area at maximum snorkel speed (11.5 kt, 4,760 SHP) and patrol at 5 kt. Armament would match a U.S. SSBN of that period: 16 A-3 missiles and four torpedo tubes, with four reloads of a Mk 37 Mod 1 torpedoes. The sonars would be BQS-4 and BQR-7, as in the SSBNs. No estimated cost figure has survived.

Chapter 12

1. Neither *Seawolf* power output nor plant weight has been disclosed officially. Stan Zimmerman, *Submarine Technology for the 21st Century* (Arlington, Virginia: Pasha Publications, 1990), claims that the navy has stated that output is 45,000 SHP. He also quotes Adm. Bruce DeMars, in testimony at a hearing of the House Armed Services Committee on the naval nuclear propulsion program, 20 March 1990. DeMars stated that this 50 percent improvement had been achieved on only 10 percent more weight than the earlier submarine's S6G plant. Zimmerman is editor of *Navy News and Undersea Technology*, an industry newsletter, so he well might be quoting reliable sources. No figures appear in the published testimony of the 20 March hearing, but oral comments are censored before they reach print. Ron O'Rourke of the Congressional Research Service quotes the same power output in "Seawolf or SSN-21 Nuclear Powered Attack Submarine," CRS Issue Brief IB85169, but he might be quoting Zimmerman. *Jane's Fighting Ships 1993–94* lists *Seawolf* power as 52,000 SHP; *Combat Fleets 1993* says 60,000 SHP, but that is unlikely given the account in the text. A rough estimate shows that the claimed official figure of 35-kt maximum speed given in Polmar, *Ships and Aircraft* (it is also described as only a few knots faster than *Los Angeles*), is generally consistent with 45,000 SHP and a *Los Angeles* speed somewhat below 33 kt; 52,000 SHP seems to give too high a maximum speed for *Seawolf* (60,000 SHP would give something closer to 39 kt).

2. Admiral DeMars, Rickover's successor, in testimony at 20 March 1990 hearing on naval nuclear propulsion, said that *Seawolf* under way at quiet speed was as quiet as *Los Angeles* at the pier. At an earlier hearing of the Seapower and Strategic Materials Subcommittee of the House Armed Services Committee (1989, 283), Representative R. K. Machtley had stated that the *Seawolf* quiet speed was at least 40 percent greater than that of *Los Angeles*. Polmar, *Ships and Aircraft,* claimed that then-CNO James Watkins disclosed that *Seawolf* would have a quiet speed greater than 20 kt.

3. It now seems that the Soviets were always well aware of what would have been required to silence their submarines. The impetus to silencing seems to have been the shock, presented by the Walker spy ring during the 1970s, that SOSUS and similar systems could easily track the Soviet undersea fleet. By this time, the Soviets were aware of the extent to which Western navies depended on narrowband detectors and were about to deploy their own narrowband systems. In Victor III, they rafted the power plant to the extent possible within the existing hull envelope. Meanwhile, the fully rafted Akula and Sierra plants were being designed. These submarines have fatter hulls to accommo-

date silenced power plants. Other, more exotic silencing measures were also adopted. This project probably included the quiet propeller program, in which computer milling machinery was bought. One comforting thought was that, whatever their platform characteristics, the Soviets would always suffer from poor electronics, particularly combat systems. Unfortunately, it turned out that they had been quite effective in industrial espionage. In the early 1990s, Victor III submarines were being refitted with data-bus combat direction systems using stolen software developed by the Norwegians for the MSI-90U systems on board their *Ula*-class submarines. The sonar suites of the Victor III class included devices based on U.S. (BQQ-2 and TB-16 towed array), British (Type 186/2007), and French (passive ranger [DUUX-2/5] and sonar intercept receiver [DUUG-2/Type 2019]) equipment. It was not clear, of course, to what extent Russian technology could reproduce the Western prototypes. For example, the Russian data bus apparently is significantly less capable than the Budos bus of the Norwegian MSI-90U.

4. Ironically, Sea Lance seems to have been canceled in the erroneous belief that it was a nuclear weapon and therefore irrelevant. The official reason, that it could not be targeted on quiet new submarines, ignored the important tactical deterrent role for which it had been developed.

Appendix A

1. According to the 1949 report of an ad hoc panel of the Submarine Officers Conference, these devices presented a quite small radar target; hence, they were difficult to detect when awash. They were virtually invisible to standard sonar and far too quiet to be detected by any but the most alert hydrophone operator at very short range. Standard harbor magnetic loops could not detect even the largest midget submarines beyond about 20 ft. Swimmers were an even more difficult proposition.

2. The X-craft were conceived in 1940. Characteristics of the final production version were: 53 ft 1½ in×5 ft 9½ in without side charges (30.3/33.6 tons). Beam, including side charges, was about 8 ft; the ¼-in pressure hull was 5 ft in diameter. The power plant was one 42-BHP Gardner diesel and one 35-HP electric motor. Maximum surface speed, not very accurately tested, was about 6.6 kt (range 1,000 nm at 6.6 kt or 1,150 nm at 6 kt on 1.1 tons of oil fuel). Submerged maximum speed was 6 kt; the boat could maintain 1.5 kt for 78 hr. Armament was a pair of side charges (their weight had been reduced from 2 to 1.5 tons by 1949) that could be dropped on the seabed. Test depth was originally 300 ft but was reduced to 150 ft by 1949–50 because of age. Accommodations were very poor; the one bunk originally provided had been removed.

Seehund was a much smaller (39 ft×5 ft 5 in, 15 tons) two-man midget carrying a pair of T IIIc torpedoes. The power plant was a six-cylinder 85-BHP truck diesel and a 70-HP electric motor (8 kt on the surface, range 120 nm at 8 kt and 250 nm at 5 kt); submerged endurance was 20 nm at 5 kt or 60 nm at 3 kt. Diving depth was 5 m (about 165 ft); the pressure hull was 5 mm (about 0.2 in) thick. The U.S. submariners considered Seehund a superior midget with a large fuel capacity. A May 1948 intelligence report described it as "the only midget submarine type that was seriously built by the German Navy." In all, 285 were delivered between September 1944 and April 1945.

At the end of the war, the Germans were working on a closed-cycle version. The Soviets overran Schichau, one of the two building yards, when they took Prussia. They captured 18 completed or nearly complete boats, 38 partly built boats, and parts for others. As of May 1948, the Soviets had reportedly set up a training base at Kronstadt. Our present knowledge of Soviet naval developments under Stalin does not confirm the midget submarine reports, but such a design probably would have originated in a secret design bureau and might not have been used by the navy itself. It seems likely that the closest Soviet approach to midgets at this time was the small conventional M-type submarine. In the 1980s, the Swedes reported Soviet midgets in their waters. The Soviet navy later denied having any such submersibles (two under construction were never successful), but they could have been built for Soviet special forces.

3. In 1949, it was assumed that midgets of the Black Sea fleet would be used against Turkey and that they might also penetrate the Mediterranean. Because midgets could be carried on a submarine's deck, they also might be used against U.S. Atlantic ports.

4. A midget (SCB 24) had been included in early lists of potential submarine types. In December 1946, the Submarine Officers Conference wanted to determine definitely whether it was to be a small submarine or an underwater guided missile. Nothing came of this idea. Likely midget submarine missions suggested in 1949 were: operation in barrier or picket lines with homing or controlled weapons; destruction of ships at sea or in port and destruction of port facilities; reconnaissance and weather observation; landing of saboteurs and spies; tender for UDTs; use as beacons for missile attacks or planting of beacons; hydrodynamic or sonar test vehicles; rescue and salvage operations; and training of harbor defense and other ASW forces.

5. The "sea tank" was an enlarged X-craft, 56 ft 6 in×8 ft (over side charges)×6 ft 9 in (36.5/46.5 tons, 30.5 tons without externally carried armament), with a double X-craft power plant (two Gardner diesels and two 35-HP motors). Fuel capacity would have been 5 tons (radius 3,000 nm at 7.5 kt, 4,000 at 7 kt, 6,700 at 6 kt). The main improvement, compared with the original X-craft, was greater reliability, thanks to the paired engines (one would have sufficed for the 6 kt of the original X-craft). Armament was a pair of 21-in torpedoes, a pair of side charges (1,500 lb of explosive each), and eight limpet charges (150 lb of explosive each). Varley was responsible for the submariners' choice of a four-man crew: CO, sonar/acoustics/tactical officer, diver to reload tubes and stores on relief, and engine/mechanical rating. He argued that four was a minimum, so they could stand three watches while the CO concentrated on some particular plan of campaign. He also emphasized the need for sufficient endurance to bring the midget back after its attack in the event that it could not rejoin the mother ship. Commander Varley strongly advocated a boat of much higher underwater speed, and the first Type II characteristics (August 1949) seem to have been drafted with his ideas in mind.

6. The dimensions were shaved down from an earlier (August–September 1949) estimate of 60×12 ft (120 tons). The planned power plant was 150 BHP for surface operation (75 for propulsion, 75 to charge the battery). Draft characteristics, as of 24 August, showed 9 kt on the surface and 12 kt submerged, with neither snorkel nor sonar. The midget would carry four torpedoes, with two in tubes. Operating depth was set at 350 ft. The final Type I design was dated 23 September 1949.

7. In May 1950, the new British X-craft sonar could detect harbor defense craft, under way at 5–6 kt, at not less than 3,000 yd while the X-craft was making 4 kt. Bearing accuracy would be 5 degrees, and the sonar would discriminate between targets 15 degrees apart.

8. Early versions of the FY 51 program listed the new submarine as SS (250 tons) to avoid confusing it with the SST *Albacore*. The latter was put back into the FY 50 program; for a short time in April 1950, the 250-tonner had the third priority in the

FY 51 program. It was then dropped because, given the load of other work, very little could be spent on it during 1951. The project was revised when the first supplemental budget was prepared in June/July 1950 on the outbreak of the war in Korea.

9. The first configuration model was tested in 1961, and the design finalized in 1962. This account of Moray is based on several Moray documents: an undated proposal; the NOTS Moray Data Book dated 10 May 1960 (but incorporating Change 2, 1 March 1961); a NOTS report ("Moray: The Attack Phase") dated 1 June 1960; and Moray progress reports (produced by NOTS) for 1962–66. I am grateful to Mark Wertheimer of the Naval Historical Center and to the Naval Weapons Center (formerly NOTS) at China Lake for providing this material. The June 1960 paper describes the "universally" understood elements of the Moray concept and then examines the problems of fire control and closing with the target. By 1960 NOTS had been involved in torpedo propulsion and hydrodynamics for some years, at least since beginning RETORC work about 1954. It also developed the REVEL (REVerberation ELimination) sonar processing panel used in Mk 46 lightweight torpedoes. Moray was, in effect, a manned torpedo.

10. Moray would still need a computer to navigate, however, to keep track of its position relative to the launch point and/or the expected rendezvous with the mother ship.

11. According to the May 1960 report, Moray was practical only because of recent dramatic advances in active sonar performance, resolution, and presentation (the latter made it possible for the crew to steer Moray into position). Even so, "unfortunately, active sonar has a low repetition rate, depending on range to the target; its angular resolution is very limited; and range rate information is not available in anything but an intuitive form." ("Moray: The Attack Phase," May 1960 report referenced above, p. 9.) This report assumed that Moray's 15 kHz sonar (range 4,000 to 6,000 yd) would cover a total sweep angle of 45 deg to either side, with a resolution of 3 or 4 deg at center and 10 or 15 deg at the edge. It seemed likely that the sonar picture would become confusing at short range, partly because the target would cover so large an angle. Expected passive sonar range on a cavitating target would be 10,000 to 15,000 yd (the

1960 report showed no interest in convergence zone or bottom-bounce sonar operation).

12. These weapons were apparently selected on the basis of the May 1960 report. The alternative, a homing torpedo effective at 1,000 to 2,000 ft, would be too large to carry internally. The best simpler weapon would be a 5- or 6-in underwater rocket fired at less than 1,000-ft range. To be effective, it would have to make a direct hit with a shaped charge. NOTS had already done some work on underwater rockets. The effective limit on speed was the onset of cavitation at a shallow depth, which would make control surfaces ineffective. Thus, it appeared that a 5-in rocket could run at 70 kt at a depth of 100 ft or more, to a range of 1,600 ft; a deeper-running rocket could run faster.

13. It was assumed that TV range in deep water (using a powerful searchlight) would be no more than about 100 ft, too little for final fire control. Possibilities explored in 1960 were to use rockets for shadow illumination or to use pulse gating to reduce backscattering of the light. The latter was rejected as too remote to be relevant to Moray.

14. According to a 1963 Moray status report, the two-blade supercavitating propeller would have been driven, pinwheel fashion, at 30,000 RPM. The design speed goal was 80 kt. The round was 5×50 in; it could carry either a shaped-charge warhead or an underwater flare to illuminate the target for Moray's underwater television. The hub of the propeller moved 2.7 times as fast as the vehicle, so nozzle-to-gas velocity ratio was 2.7 times that of a conventional rocket, with correspondingly improved propulsive efficiency. Tests run in 1964 were moderately successful (the hub turbines cracked and the hot-gas passageways and gas-lubricated bearing surfaces suffered pitting, melting, and deformation, but the vehicles did manage their full 8.5-second runs).

15. According to the 1 March 1961 version of the Moray Data Book, planned TV-1A maximum speed was 15 kt, with an endurance of 1 hour (full power for 15 min, half for 15 min, and 1/4 power for 30 min). Planned operating depth was 2,000 ft (design [presumably collapse] depth was 6,000 ft). The control sphere was designed for the ultimate Moray, however, so it had to be able to operate at 6,000 ft (maximum allowable working depth was 7,840 ft).

INDEX

NOTE: *Entries for ships' class names are identical to entries for the name ship of the class.*